Advanced Physics in Creation

by Dr. Jay L. Wile

Advanced Physics in Creation

Published by
Apologia Educational Ministries, Inc.
1106 Meridian Plaza, Suite 220
Anderson, IN 46016
www.apologia.com

Manufactured in the United States of America
Second Printing 2006

ISBN: 1-932012-18-4

Printed by CJK, Cincinnati, OH

Cover Illustration ©Fullerton Technology Co., LTD./SuperStock, Inc.

Need Help?

Apologia Educational Ministries, Inc. Curriculum Support

If you have any questions while using Apologia curriculum, feel free to contact us in any of the following ways.

By Mail:

Dr. Jay L. Wile
Apologia Educational Ministries, Inc.
1106 Meridian Plaza, Suite 220
Anderson, IN 46016

By E-MAIL:

help@highschoolscience.com

On The Web:

http://www.highschoolscience.com

By FAX:

(765) 608 - 3290

By Phone:

(765) 608 - 3280

"Let's get down to the nuts and bolts." Have you ever heard that phrase before? Usually, it means that the speaker is going to tell you the fundamentals of how something works. In a way, you might consider this a "nuts and bolts" class on Creation. Why? Well, physics is the fundamental science. It attempts to describe how Creation works in very precise terms. Although biology might teach you about the plasma membrane of a cell and what it does, physics actually describes how the plasma membrane works. In the same way, although chemistry might tell you about a chemical reaction and what it makes, physics describes how and why the reaction takes place. In principle, then, all of the sciences are based on physics. If you really want to understand science, you need to understand physics.

Well, then, let's get down to the nuts and bolts, shall we?

Pedagogy of the Text

This text contains 16 modules. Each module should take you about 2 weeks to complete, as long as you devote 45 minutes to one hour of every school day to studying physics. At this pace, you will complete the course in 32 weeks. Since most people have school years which are longer than 32 weeks, there is some built-in "flex time." You should not rush through a module just to make sure that you complete it in 2 weeks. Set that as a goal, but be flexible. Some of the modules might come harder to you than others. On those modules, take more time on the subject matter.

To help you guide your study, there are several student exercises which you should complete.

- The "**on your own**" problems should be solved as you read the text. The act of working out these problems will cement in your mind the concepts you are trying to learn. Complete solutions to these problems appear at the end of the module. Once you have solved an "on your own" problem, turn to the back of the module and check your work. If you did not get the correct answer, study the solution to learn why.

- The **review questions** are conceptual in nature and should be answered after you have completed the entire module. They will help you recall the important concepts from the reading.

- The **practice problems** should also be solved after the module has been completed, allowing you to review the important quantitative skills from the module.

Your teacher/parent has the solutions to the review questions and practice problems in the solutions and test manual.

Any information that you must memorize is centered in the text and put in boldface type. In addition, all definitions presented in the text need to be memorized. Words that appear in bold-face type (centered or not) in the text are important terms that you should know. Finally, if any student exercise requires the use of a formula or skill, you must have that memorized for the test.

Experiments

The experiments in this course are designed to be done as you are reading the text. I recommend that you keep a notebook of these experiments. This notebook serves two purposes. First, as you write about the experiment in the notebook, you will be forced to think through all of the concepts that were explored in the experiment. This will help you cement them into your mind. Second, certain colleges might actually ask for some evidence that you did, indeed, have a laboratory component to your physics course. The notebook will not only provide such evidence but will also show the college administrator the quality of your physics instruction. I recommend that you perform your experiments in the following way:

- When you get to the experiment during the reading, read through the experiment in its entirety. This will allow you to gain a quick understanding of what you are to do.

- Once you have read the experiment, start a new page in your laboratory notebook. The first page should be used to write down all of the data taken during the experiment and perform any calculation explained in the experiment.

- When you have finished the experiment, write a brief report in your notebook, right after the page where the data and calculations were written. The report should be a brief discussion of what was done and what was learned. You should not write a step-by-step procedure. Instead, write a brief summary that will allow someone who has never read the text to understand what you did and what you learned.

> **PLEASE OBSERVE COMMON SENSE SAFETY PRECAUTIONS. The experiments are no more dangerous than most normal, household activity. Remember, however, that the vast majority of accidents do happen in the home. Chemicals should never be ingested; hot beakers and flames should be regarded with care; and OSHA recommends that all experiments be performed while wearing some sort of eye protection such as safety glasses or goggles.**

Advanced Physics in Creation
Table of Contents

Module #5: Rotational Motion

Module #6: Oscillations and Waves

Module #7: Sound and Light

Module #8: Gravity and Relativity

Module #9: Heat

Module #10: Thermodynamics

Module #11: Electrostatics

Module #12: Electrical Potential Energy and Electric Potential

Module #13: DC Electric Circuits

Module #14: Magnetism and Electromagnetic Induction

Module #15: Atomic Physics

Module #16: Nuclear Physics

Module #1: Units and Vectors Revisited

Introduction

There are probably no concepts more important in physics than the two listed in the title of this module. In your first-year physics course, I am sure that you learned quite a lot about both of these concepts. You certainly did not learn everything, however. Whether we are talking about units or vectors, there is simply too much information to possibly learn in just one year. As a result, we will take another look at both of these concepts in this first module. This will help you "warm up" to the task of recalling all of the things you learned in your first-year physics course, and it will help you to learn both of these valuable concepts at a much deeper level.

Units Revisited

Almost regardless of the physics course, units should be covered first, because a great deal of physics is based on properly analyzing units. In your first-year course, you were taught how to solve problems such as the one in the following example:

EXAMPLE 1.1

A sample of iron has a mass of 254.1 mg. How many kg is that?

In this problem, we are asked to convert from milligrams to kilograms. We cannot do this directly, because we have no relationship between mg and kg. However, we do know that a milligram is the same thing as 0.001 grams and that a kilogram is the same thing as 1,000 grams. Thus, we can convert mg into g, and then convert g into kilograms. To save space, we can do that all on one line:

$$\frac{254.1 \text{ mg}}{1} \times \frac{0.001 \text{ g}}{1 \text{ mg}} \times \frac{1 \text{ kg}}{1,000 \text{ g}} = 0.0002541 \text{ kg} = 2.541 \times 10^{-4} \text{ kg}$$

The sample of iron has a mass of 2.541 x 10^{-4} kg.

Did this example help dust the cobwebs out of your mind when it comes to units? It should all be review for you. I converted the units using the factor-label method. Because this is a conversion, I had to have the same number of significant figures as I had in the beginning, and even though it was not necessary, I reported the answer in scientific notation. If you are having trouble remembering these techniques, then go back to your first-year physics book and review them.

There are a couple of additional things I want you to learn about units. I am not going to show you any new techniques; I am just going to show you new ways of applying the techniques that you should already know. Consider, for example, the unit for speed. The standard unit for speed is $\dfrac{m}{sec}$. However, *any* distance unit over *any* time unit is a legitimate unit for speed. Since that is the case, we should be able to convert from one unit for speed to any other unit for speed. Study the following example to see what I mean.

EXAMPLE 1.2

As of 2001, the record for the fastest lap at the Indianapolis 500 ("The greatest Spectacle in Racing") was held by Arie Luyendyk. He averaged a speed of 225.2 miles per hour over the entire 2.5-mile stretch of the Indianapolis speedway. What is that speed in meters per second?

This problem requires us to make two conversions. To get from miles per hour to meters per second, we must convert miles to meters. Then, we must convert hours to seconds. This is actually easy to do. Remember, in miles per hour, the unit "miles" is in the numerator of the fraction and the unit "hours" is in the denominator. Also remember that there are 1609 meters in a mile and that 1 hour is the same as 3600 seconds.

$$\frac{225.2 \ \cancel{\text{miles}}}{1 \ \cancel{\text{hr}}} \times \frac{1609 \ \text{meters}}{1 \ \cancel{\text{mile}}} \times \frac{1 \ \cancel{\text{hr}}}{3600 \ \text{sec}} = 100.7 \ \frac{\text{meters}}{\text{sec}}$$

Although there is nothing new here, you probably haven't seen a conversion done in this way. Despite the fact that the unit for speed is a derived unit, I can still do conversions on it. I could have just converted miles to meters and gotten the unit meters/hour. I also could have just converted hours to seconds and gotten miles/second. In this case, however, I did both. That way, I ended up with meters/second. When working with derived units, remember that you can convert any or all units that make up the derived unit. Thus, 225.2 miles per hour is the same thing as <u>100.7 meters per second</u>. Please note that although 3600 has only 2 significant figures, the number is actually infinitely precise, because there are *exactly* 3600 seconds in an hour. Thus, it really has an infinite number of significant figures. This is why I say that the best rule of thumb is to always end your conversion with the same number of significant figures as that with which you started your conversion.

Okay, we are almost done reviewing units. There is just one more thing that you need to remember. Sometimes, units have exponents in them. You were probably taught how to deal with this fact in your first-year physics course, but we need to review it so that you *really* know how to deal with it.

EXAMPLE 1.3

One commonly used unit for volume is the cubic meter. After all, length is measured in meters, and volume is length times width times height. The more familiar unit, however, is

cubic centimeters (cc) which is often used in medicine. If a doctor administers 512 cc of medicine to a patient, how many cubic meters is that?

Once again, this is a simple conversion. If, however, you do not think as you go through it, you can mess yourself up. We need to convert cubic centimeters to cubic meters. Now remember, a cubic centimeter is just a cm^3 and a cubic meter is just a m^3. We have no relationship between these units, but we do know that 1 cm = 0.01 m. That's all we need to know, as long as we think about it. Right now, I have the following relationship:

$$1 \text{ cm} = 0.01 \text{ m}$$

This is an equation. I am allowed to do something to one side of the equation as long as I do the exact same thing to the other side of the equation. Okay, then, let's cube both sides of the equation:

$$\left(1 \text{ cm}\right)^3 = \left(0.01 \text{ m}\right)^3$$

$$1 \text{ cm}^3 = 0.000001 \text{ m}^3$$

Now look what we have. We have a relationship between cm^3 and m^3, exactly what we need to do our conversion!

$$\frac{512 \text{ cm}^3}{1} \times \frac{0.000001 \text{ m}^3}{1 \text{ cm}^3} = 5.12 \times 10^{-4} \text{ m}^3$$

So 512 cc's is the same as $\underline{5.12 \times 10^{-4} \text{ m}^3}$.

When most students do a conversion like the one in the example without thinking, they simply use the relationship between cm and m to do the conversion. That, of course does not work, because the cm^3 unit does not cancel out, and you certainly don't get the m^3 unit in the end:

$$\frac{512 \text{ cm}^3}{1} \times \frac{0.01 \text{ m}}{1 \text{ cm}} = 5.12 \text{ m} \cdot \text{cm}^2$$

Do you see what happened? The cm unit canceled one of the cm out of cm^3, but that still left cm^2. Also, since m is the unit that survives from the conversion relationship, you get the weird unit of $m \cdot cm^2$! When you are working with units that have exponents in them, you need to be very careful about how you convert them. At the risk of "beating this to death," I want to combine the previous two examples into one more example.

EXAMPLE 1.4

The maximum acceleration of a certain car is 21,600 miles per hour². What is the acceleration in feet per second²?

Once again, this is a derived unit, but that should not bother you. All we have to do is convert miles into feet and hours² into seconds². There are 5280 feet in a mile, so that conversion will be easy. We do not know a conversion between hours² and seconds², but we do know that:

$$1 \text{ hour} = 3600 \text{ seconds}$$

To get the conversion relationship between hours² and seconds², then, we just square both sides:

$$(1 \text{ hour})^2 = (3600 \text{ seconds})^2$$

$$1 \text{ hour}^2 = 1.296 \times 10^7 \text{ seconds}^2$$

Once again, please note that the conversion relationship between hours and seconds is exact. Thus, both numbers have an infinite number of significant figures. That's why I reported all digits when I squared 3600 seconds.

Now that I have the conversion relationships that I need, the conversion is a snap:

$$\frac{21,600 \text{ miles}}{1 \text{ hr}^2} \times \frac{5280 \text{ ft}}{1 \text{ mile}} \times \frac{1 \text{ hr}^2}{1.296 \times 10^7 \text{ sec}^2} = \underline{8.80} \, \frac{\text{ft}}{\text{sec}^2}$$

Notice once again that had I not squared the conversion relationship between hours and seconds, the units would not have worked out. In order for hr² to cancel, the unit hr² had to be in the problem. That's why it is important to watch the units and make sure they cancel properly.

Make sure that you understand how to manipulate units this way by performing the following "on your own" problems.

ON YOUR OWN

1.1 The speed limit on many highways in the United States is 65 miles per hour. What is the speed limit in centimeters per second? (There are 1609 meters in a mile.)

1.2 The size of a house is 1600 square feet. What is the square yardage of the house?

1.3 The standard energy unit is the Joule ($\frac{kg \cdot m^2}{sec^2}$). An alternative energy unit is the erg ($\frac{g \cdot cm^2}{sec^2}$). I am serious. It is called the erg! Convert 151 Joules into ergs.

A Review of Vectors

In your first-year physics course, you learned about **vectors**. A quantity is called a vector if it contains information about both magnitude and direction. A quantity is called a **scalar** if it contains only information about magnitude and no information about direction. For example, if I tell you that my car is moving at 55 miles per hour, I am giving you a scalar quantity. The speed of the car tells you "how much" (magnitude), but it does not tell you in what direction the car is moving. If I tell you that my car is moving at 55 miles per hour *due west*, then I am giving you a vector quantity. Not only do you know how fast I am traveling (the magnitude), but you also know which way I am heading (the direction). You should have already learned that we call the scalar quantity in this case **speed**, and we call the vector quantity **velocity**.

Since vectors contain information about both magnitude and direction, we use arrows to represent them. The length of the arrow represents the magnitude, while the direction in which the arrow points represents the direction. When I refer to vectors, I will emphasize that they are vectors by placing them in boldface type. For example, if you see "**A**" in an equation, you will know that it is a vector quantity because it is in boldface type. If you see "A" in an equation, you will know that it is a scalar quantity because it is not in boldface type.

Now although vectors and scalars are quite different, they can interact mathematically. For example, I can multiply a vector by a scalar. What happens if I do that? Well, a vector contains information about magnitude and direction, while a scalar contains information only about magnitude. If I multiply a vector by a scalar, then, the multiplication will affect the *magnitude* of the vector. If the scalar happens to be negative, it does affect the direction of the vector as well. Study the following figure to see what I mean.

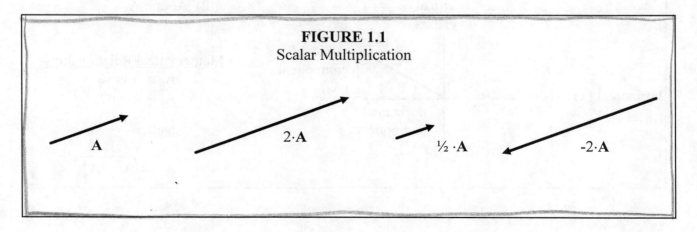

FIGURE 1.1
Scalar Multiplication

Notice in the figure that I start with an arrow which represents vector **A**. It has a magnitude (the length of the arrow) and a direction (the direction in which the arrow points). When I multiply by 2 (a scalar), what happens? The arrow points in the same direction, but it is twice as long. That's because when I multiply a vector by a positive scalar, I multiply its magnitude by the scalar, but I leave the direction alone. Thus, the length of the arrow (the magnitude) changes, but the direction does not. In the same way, when I multiply **A** by ½, the length of the arrow changes (it gets cut in half), but the direction does not.

Now look at the last arrow in the figure. This arrow represents what happens to the vector **A** when I multiply by a negative scalar. When you multiply a vector by a *positive* scalar, the direction of the vector does not change. However, when you multiply by a *negative* scalar, the direction of the vector becomes *opposite* of what it once was. Thus, when I multiply **A** by negative 2, the length of the vector increases by a factor of 2, but the vector also points in the opposite direction. Vector **A** points towards the upper right hand corner of the figure, while the vector -2·**A** is twice as long and points to the lower left-hand corner of the figure.

When vectors are multiplied by scalars, then, the result is another vector. As you already learned in your first-year physics course, vectors can not only be multiplied by scalars, but they can also be added to other vectors. The result in that case is a vector as well. To review how vectors are added to one another, however, we must first review the way that vectors can be mathematically represented.

A two-dimensional vector can be mathematically represented in one of two ways. It can be represented by its magnitude and an angle, or it can be written in terms of two perpendicular **components**. Although *any* two perpendicular components can be used to define a two-dimensional vector, we typically use *horizontal* and *vertical* components. These two ways of mathematically representing a vector, as well as the relationships between them, are summarized in Figure 1.2.

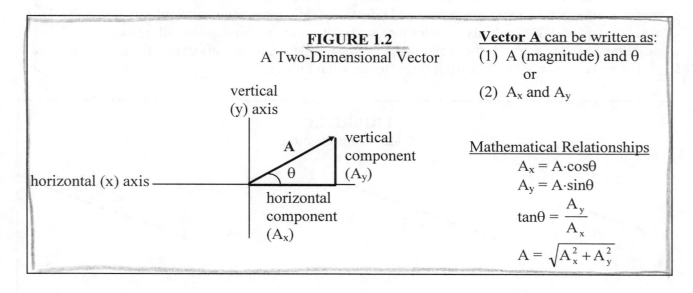

FIGURE 1.2
A Two-Dimensional Vector

Vector **A** can be written as:
(1) A (magnitude) and θ
or
(2) A_x and A_y

Mathematical Relationships
$$A_x = A \cdot \cos\theta$$
$$A_y = A \cdot \sin\theta$$
$$\tan\theta = \frac{A_y}{A_x}$$
$$A = \sqrt{A_x^2 + A_y^2}$$

vertical (y) axis

horizontal (x) axis

A

θ

vertical component (A_y)

horizontal component (A_x)

Notice, then, that the vector **A** can be represented with a magnitude (A) and a direction (θ). For example, if I told you that there was buried treasure 10.5 miles away from your current location at an angle of 50.4°, I would be giving you a vector to describe the location of the treasure. I would be giving you that vector in terms of its magnitude and angle. Alternatively, I could tell you that to get to the treasure, you need to walk straight for 6.5 miles then turn left and walk another 8.1 miles. That is also a vector which represents the location of the treasure, but the vector is given in terms of two components rather than a magnitude and direction. Of course, since both methods represent the same vector, they should be related to one another. The figure summarizes the various means by which the components of a vector relate to the vector's magnitude and direction.

Now we can move on to adding vectors. In order to graphically add vectors, we simply put the tail of the second vector at the head of the first vector, and then we draw an arrow from the tail of the first to the head of the second. The new arrow is the graphical representation of the final vector, which is the sum of the two original vectors. Alternatively we can mathematically add vectors. To do this, we simply add their x-components to get the final vector's x-component, and we add their y-components to get the final vector's y-component. These processes are summarized in Figure 1.3.

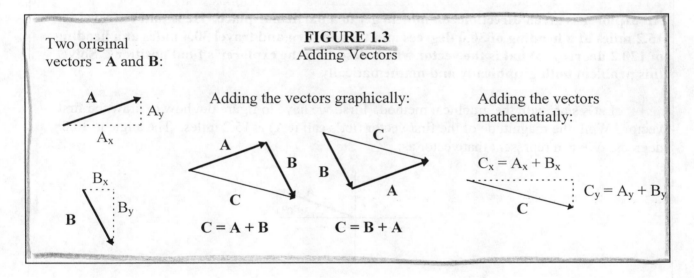

FIGURE 1.3
Adding Vectors

On the left-hand side of the figure, two vectors (**A** and **B**) are drawn. Their horizontal (x) components (A_x and B_x) as well as their vertical (y) components (A_y and B_y) are shown. In the middle of the figure, the graphical method for adding vectors is shown. To add vectors **A** and **B**, we put the tail of **B** on the head of **A**. Then, we draw an arrow from the tail of **A** to the head of **B**. The resulting arrow is the sum of **A** + **B**. Notice that the figure also shows the graphical representation of **B** + **A**. At first glance, you might think that the result of **A** + **B** is different than the result of **B** + **A**. That's not true. Remember, a vector is determined by its magnitude and direction. Both the result of **A** + **B** and the result of **B** + **A** have the same magnitude (length) and direction (they both point in the same direction). Thus, they each represent the same vector. They are simply shifted relative to one another.

That brings up an important thing to remember about vectors. They can be moved around without affecting their value. As long as you do not change the length of the arrow or the direction in which the arrow points, you can move it all over the place without changing the meaning of the vector at all.

Since physics is inherently a problem-solving science, the graphical approach to adding vectors is not enough. It gives us a visual picture of the sum of vectors, but it does not give us any numbers with which to work. Thus, we will mostly use the mathematical method for adding vectors, which is shown in the right hand portion of the figure. To add two vectors mathematically, we simply add the horizontal components together. This gives us the horizontal component of the final vector. We then add the vertical components together, and that gives us the vertical component of the vector. In the figure, then, the x-component of the final vector is simply $A_x + B_x$, while the y-component is simply $A_y + B_y$. Let me go through a quick example problem to jog your memory on all of this.

EXAMPLE 1.5

An explorer is given directions on how to get to a particular place. He is told to travel for 15.2 miles at a heading of 30.0 degrees and then to turn and travel 30.4 miles at a heading of 170.2 degrees. What is the vector which describes the explorer's final position? Solve this problem both graphically and mathematically.

Let's start with the graphical method. First, we have to figure out how to draw the first vector. Well, the magnitude of the first vector (let's call it **A**) is 15.2 miles. The angle is 30.0 degrees. We can represent that vector as:

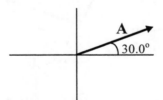

Please realize that the drawing simply approximates the values of the vector to give us a visual idea of what it looks like. We know that if the arrow pointed straight along the horizontal axis to the right, the angle would be 0 degrees. If it pointed up along the vertical axis, the angle would be 90.0 degrees. If it bisected those two, it would be pointing at 45 degrees. An angle of 30.0 degrees, then, is close to bisecting the two axes, but not quite.

Next, we put the tail of the second vector at the head of the first. The second vector has a magnitude of 30.4 miles and an angle of 170.2 degrees. Putting it on the head of the first vector gives us the following drawing:

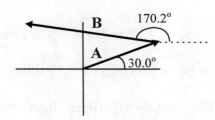

Remember, if the vector pointed straight up, its angle would be 90.0 degrees. If it pointed directly to the left, its angle would be 180.0 degrees. Thus, an angle of 170.2 degrees points almost directly to the left, but just a little up. In addition, the magnitude is twice that of the first vector, so the arrow is twice as long as the first.

Adding the vectors is now a snap. We just draw an arrow from the tail of the first to the head of the second.

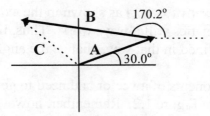

The arrow labeled **C** represents the sum of the two vectors.

Now, although that gives us a picture of the vector which represents the explorer's final position, it is only a picture. To get numbers which describe this vector, we must add the two vectors mathematically. To do that, we must get the horizontal and vertical components of each vector and add them together. Figure 1.2 gives the relationships between the components of a vector and its magnitude and direction, so that's not too bad:

$$A_x = (15.2 \text{ miles}) \cdot \cos(30.0) = 13.2 \text{ miles}$$

$$A_y = (15.2 \text{ miles}) \cdot \sin(30.0) = 7.60 \text{ miles}$$

$$B_x = (30.4 \text{ miles}) \cdot \cos(170.2) = -30.0 \text{ miles}$$

$$B_y = (30.4 \text{ miles}) \cdot \sin(170.2) = 5.17 \text{ miles}$$

Notice that I used the rules of significant figures here. If you have forgotten those rules, go back to your first-year physics course (or chemistry if you took that course) and review significant figures so that you understand why I rounded the answers where I did.

To get the x-component of the sum (vector **C**), we just add the two x-components together, and to get the y-component of the sum, we just add the two y-components together.

$$C_x = A_x + B_x = 13.2 \text{ miles} + -30.0 \text{ miles} = -16.8 \text{ miles}$$

$$C_y = A_y + B_y = 7.60 \text{ miles} + 5.17 \text{ miles} = 12.77 \text{ miles}$$

In this case, I had to add numbers, and the significant figure rules are different for addition and subtraction as compared to multiplication and division. Make sure you remember the difference!

The answer, then, is that the explorer's position has an x-component of -16.8 miles and a y-component of 12.77 miles. This means the explorer is 16.8 miles left (west) of his starting position and 12.77 miles up (north) from his starting position.

Before I leave this review, there is one more important thing of which I must remind you. When dealing with the angle associated with a vector, you need to define the angle *counterclockwise from the positive x-axis*, as shown in the example above. If you define the angle in that way, the mathematics will always work. Thus, if you find yourself working with a vector whose angle is *not* defined in that way, change the angle so that it is defined properly.

If you have the components of a vector and need to get its magnitude and its angle, you can use the equations given in Figure 1.2. Remember, however, that the angle needs to be defined counterclockwise from the positive x-axis. How can you be sure it is defined properly when working with those equations? Well, remember from algebra that you can divide the Cartesian coordinate plane into four regions:

When taking the inverse tangent of a number, the definition of the angle that your calculator gives you depends on which of these regions the vector is in. If the vector is in region I, the angle that your calculator gives you is defined relative to the positive x-axis, just as it should be defined. Thus, if your vector is region I, the angle that your calculator gives you for the inverse tangent function will be defined properly.

However, if the vector is in region II of the Cartesian coordinate plane, then the angle that your calculator gives you is defined relative to the negative x-axis and is negative. In the Cartesian coordinate system, negative angles mean clockwise rotation while positive angles mean counterclockwise rotation. So, when a vector is in region II, your calculator gives you the number of degrees clockwise from the negative x-axis. Thus, if your vector is in region II and your calculator gives you a direction of -60 °, this is what it means:

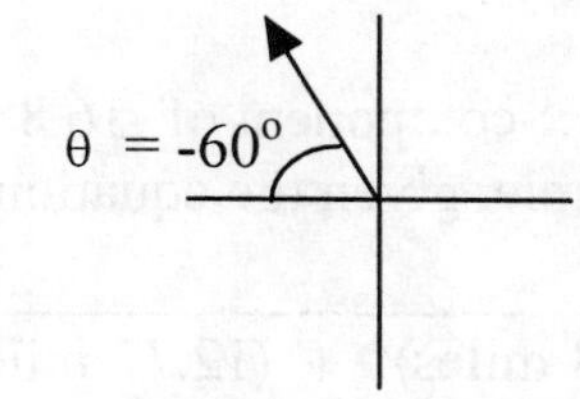

$$\theta = -60°$$

This definition of angle is not proper for our purposes. As a result, we must convert it to the proper definition. It turns out that in both regions II and III of the Cartesian coordinate plane, if you simply add 180 to the angle that your calculator gives you, you will have converted your calculator's answer to an answer in which the angle is defined properly. If the vector is in region IV, then you must add 360 to the calculator's answer in order to get the properly defined angle.

In summary, Figure 1.4 tells you what you must do in order to change your calculator's answer into a properly defined vector angle, based on the region of the Cartesian coordinate system:

FIGURE 1.4

Converting reference angle to vector angle

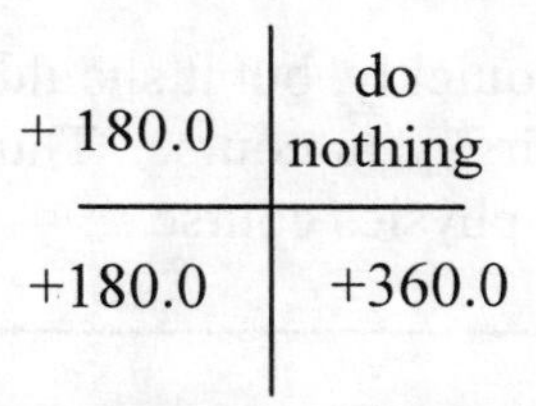

+ 180.0	do nothing
+180.0	+360.0

This figure, of course, does you no good if you can't tell what region of the Cartesian coordinate plane your vector is in. Luckily, however, this is not a difficult task. All you have to do is look at the signs on the vector components. If the x-component and y-component are both positive, then the vector must be in region I. After all, a positive x-component indicates that you are to the right of the origin, while a positive y-component means you are above the origin. The region that is both to the right and above the origin is region I. On the other hand, suppose that both components are negative. Since a negative x-component means left of the origin and a negative y-component means down, you must be in region III, since that is the only region that is to the left and below the origin. See how you do this? Following the same logic, if the x-component is negative and the y-component is positive, you must be in region II. If the x-component is positive and the y-component is negative, however, you must be in region IV.

I want to make sure you understand this by showing you a quick example.

EXAMPLE 1.6

What are the magnitude and direction of vector C in the previous example?

In the previous example, **C** had an x-component of -16.8 miles and a y-component of 12.77 miles. Getting the magnitude is simple, given the equation in Figure 1.2.

$$C = \sqrt{C_x^2 + C_y^2} = \sqrt{(-16.8 \text{ miles})^2 + (12.77 \text{ miles})^2} = 21.1 \text{ miles}$$

Getting the angle is a bit more difficult, because it must be defined properly. When we use the equation in Figure 1.2, we get:

$$\theta = \tan^{-1}\left(\frac{12.77 \text{ miles}}{-16.8 \text{ miles}}\right) = -37.2°$$

Now that we have an answer, we must figure out the region of the vector. It has a negative x-component (and is therefore left of the origin) and a positive y-component (and is therefore above the x-axis). Thus, it is in region II. According to Figure 1.4, then, we must add 180.0 to it. The properly-defined angle, then, is 142.8°. Thus vector **C** can also be represented as 21.1 miles at an angle of 142.8°.

I went through all of this rather quickly, but it should be review for you. You really should have learned all of this in your first-year course. Thus, if all of this seems a bit "fuzzy" to you, go back and review your first-year physics course.

ON YOUR OWN

1.4 The velocity vector of a car has an x-component of 23 m/sec and a y-component of 11 m/sec. What are the magnitude and direction of the velocity vector?

1.5 Vector **A** has a magnitude of 3.1 m/sec at an angle of 60.0 degrees, and vector **B** has a magnitude of 1.4 m/sec at an angle of 290.0 degrees. What is the sum of these two vectors? Give your answer both graphically and in terms of magnitude and direction.

Unit Vectors

Everything in the previous section should be review for you, and that's why I went through it so quickly. However, I now want to introduce some notation that may be new for you. Since a two-dimensional vector can be represented in terms of its horizontal and vertical components, it is nice to actually define two **unit vectors** – one in the horizontal direction and one in the vertical direction. A unit vector, as shown in the figure below, has a magnitude of 1 and a direction along either the horizontal (x) or vertical (y) axis.

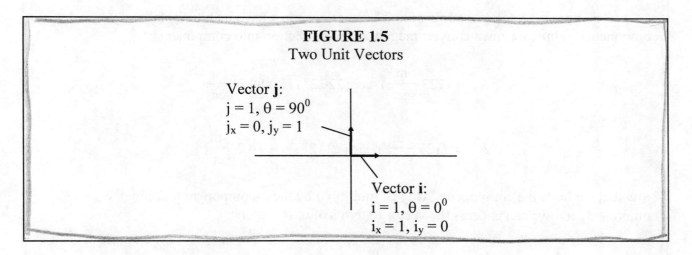

FIGURE 1.5
Two Unit Vectors

Vector **j**:
$j = 1, \theta = 90^0$
$j_x = 0, j_y = 1$

Vector **i**:
$i = 1, \theta = 0^0$
$i_x = 1, i_y = 0$

Why do I bother to define these vectors? Think about it. I can define any vector in terms of a horizontal component and a vertical component. Well, suppose I multiply vector **i** by a scalar. What will happen to the magnitude of the vector? Well, since the original magnitude is 1, the new magnitude will be equal to the value of the scalar. What about the direction? Well, unless the scalar is negative, the direction will not change. If the scalar is negative, the direction will simply be reversed. The vector 3·**i**, for example, has a magnitude of 3 and points horizontally to the right. The vector -5·**j**, on the other hand, has a magnitude of 5 and points vertically down.

So what? Think about the fact that we can define a vector by its horizontal and vertical components. Suppose velocity vector **A** has a horizontal component of 5 m/sec (A_x = 5 m/sec) and a vertical component of -4 m/sec (A_y = -4 m/sec). We could write that in terms of adding unit vectors:

$$A = (5 \text{ m/sec}) \cdot i + (-4 \text{ m/sec}) \cdot j$$

After all, if the x-component is 5 m/sec, then the x-component points to the right and has a magnitude of 5. That's what 5·**i** is. If the y-component is -4 m/sec, then the y-component points down with a magnitude of 4 m/sec. That's what -4·**j** means. In the end, then, we can also note any vector in terms of unit vectors:

$$\text{For any vector } A, \quad A = A_x \cdot i + A_y \cdot j \tag{1.1}$$

This is one of the standard ways in which vectors are expressed, so it is important that you understand it.

EXAMPLE 1.7

The acceleration vector of an airplane is **123 m/sec^2 at $\theta = 223.2^0$. Express the vector in terms of unit vectors. Draw a graph of the vector.**

To express a vector in terms of unit vectors, we must have its horizontal and vertical components. Thus, we must convert magnitude and direction into components:

$$A_x = (123\ \frac{m}{sec^2}) \cdot \cos(223.2°) = -89.7\ \frac{m}{sec^2}$$

$$A_y = (123\ \frac{m}{sec^2}) \cdot \sin(223.2°) = -84.2\ \frac{m}{sec^2}$$

Now that we have the components, we just multiply **i** by the x-component and **j** by the y-component, and we can express the vector in terms of unit vectors:

$$\mathbf{A} = -89.7\ \frac{m}{sec^2} \cdot \mathbf{i} + (-84.2\ \frac{m}{sec^2}) \cdot \mathbf{j}$$

Usually, if the vector **j** is multiplied by a negative, we just replace the plus sign with a minus sign, so the more standard answer is:

$$\mathbf{A} = -89.7\ \frac{m}{sec^2} \cdot \mathbf{i} - 84.2\ \frac{m}{sec^2} \cdot \mathbf{j}$$

Now remember, the numbers multiplying **i** and **j** are simply the components of the vector. Thus, drawing the vector is a snap:

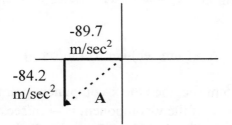

Now remember that to add any two vectors, you simply add the x-components together and the y-components together. Similarly, to subtract vectors, you simply subtract the x-components and the y-components. In this notation, then, vector addition and subtraction is as follows:

$$\mathbf{A} + \mathbf{B} = (A_x + B_x) \cdot \mathbf{i} + (A_y + B_y) \cdot \mathbf{j} \qquad (1.2)$$

$$\mathbf{A} - \mathbf{B} = (A_x - B_x) \cdot \mathbf{i} + (A_y - B_y) \cdot \mathbf{j} \qquad (1.3)$$

We can also express scalar multiplication in this notation. When I multiply a vector by a scalar, I can simply multiply each component by the scalar. Thus, in this notation, scalar multiplication becomes:

$$k \cdot \mathbf{A} = (k \cdot A_x) \cdot \mathbf{i} + (k \cdot A_y) \cdot \mathbf{j} \qquad \text{(where k is a scalar)} \qquad (1.4)$$

Make sure you understand this new notation by solving the following problems.

ON YOUR OWN

1.6 Draw the vector $\mathbf{A} = (5.0 \text{ m}) \cdot \mathbf{i} - (11 \text{ m}) \cdot \mathbf{j}$. Give its magnitude and direction.

1.7 What is the sum of vector $\mathbf{A}$ above with vector $\mathbf{B} = (-11 \text{ m}) \cdot \mathbf{i} + (22 \text{ m}) \cdot \mathbf{j}$? What is the difference $\mathbf{A} - \mathbf{B}$? Answer using the notation you learned in this section of the module.

1.8 Write (in unit vector notation) the vector which corresponds to 6 times the vector $\mathbf{C} = (2.0 \text{ m/sec}) \cdot \mathbf{i} + (3.0 \text{ m/sec}) \cdot \mathbf{j}$.

The Dot Product

When we add or subtract two vectors, the result is a vector. When we multiply a vector by a scalar, the result is also a vector. Thus, you might think that when you mathematically manipulate vectors, the result is always a vector. That's not true. One mathematical manipulation is called the **dot product**, and it is important in physics. When you compute the dot product of two vectors, the result is a scalar.

How can two vectors produce a scalar? Well, first let's look at the mechanics of taking the dot product of two vectors, and then I will tell you what the dot product really *means*.

$$\mathbf{A} \bullet \mathbf{B} = A_x \cdot B_x + A_y \cdot B_y \qquad (1.5)$$

In order to compute the dot product of two vectors, I multiply their x-components together and add that result to the product of their y-components. Notice that there are no vectors on the right hand side of the equation, so the result is, indeed, a scalar.

EXAMPLE 1.8

Given the following vectors:

$\mathbf{A} = 14 \cdot \mathbf{i} + 11 \cdot \mathbf{j}$
$\mathbf{B} = -2.0 \cdot \mathbf{i} + 3.0 \cdot \mathbf{j}$

Compute the dot product $\mathbf{A} \bullet \mathbf{B}$.

Using Equation (1.5):

$$\mathbf{A} \bullet \mathbf{B} = A_x \cdot B_x + A_y \cdot B_y$$

$$\mathbf{A} \bullet \mathbf{B} = 14 \cdot (-2.0) + 11 \cdot 3.0 = -28 + 33 = 5$$

The dot product, then, equals 5.

Computing the dot product between two vectors isn't too bad, is it? Of course, being able to perform a mathematical operation is not the same as understanding what that mathematical operation means. Thus, you also need to know the *meaning* behind the dot product. When you take the dot product of two vectors, you are really multiplying the magnitude of the first vector by the component of the second vector which is *parallel* to the first vector. Now I know that sentence is confusing, so I want to try and explain it with a figure.

FIGURE 1.6
The Meaning of the Dot Product

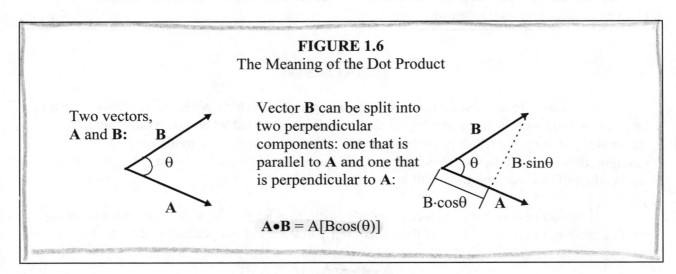

Two vectors, A and B:

Vector **B** can be split into two perpendicular components: one that is parallel to **A** and one that is perpendicular to **A**:

$$\mathbf{A} \bullet \mathbf{B} = A[B\cos(\theta)]$$

Start by looking at the drawing on the left-hand side of the figure. I have two vectors there, our old friends **A** and **B**. If you put their tails together (remember, moving vectors around is okay as long as you don't change length or direction), you can define θ, the angle between them. Now we already know that any two-dimensional vector can be expressed in terms of two perpendicular components. We usually use the horizontal and vertical components, but that's not necessary. We can really use *any two perpendicular components*. For the purpose of this discussion, then, let's define **B** in terms of a component that is parallel to **A** and one that is perpendicular to **A**. That's what is shown on the right hand side of the figure.

Now look what happens when you split up **B** into those two components. One component lies right on vector **A**. That's the parallel component of vector **B**, and it is calculated by taking the magnitude of the vector (B) and multiplying by the cosine of the angle (θ). Thus, that little section labeled $B\cdot\cos\theta$ is the component of vector **B** that lies parallel to vector **A**.

When you take the dot product, you are calculating the value of the magnitude of vector **A** multiplied by the length of the *component* of vector **B** which lies parallel to **A**. That's why the last line of text in the figure says that the dot product is A (the magnitude of vector **A**) times Bcosθ (the length of the component of **B** which is parallel to **A**). This is actually another way of expressing the dot product:

$$\mathbf{A} \bullet \mathbf{B} \ = \ A \cdot B \cdot \cos\theta \tag{1.6}$$

The dot product of two vectors, then, can be found one of two ways. If you know the components of the vector, you use Equation (1.5). If you know the magnitudes of each vector and the angle between them, use Equation (1.6). Alternatively, if you know the dot product and magnitudes of the vectors, you can determine the angle between them. See what I mean by studying the following example.

EXAMPLE 1.9

Given the following vectors:

A = 12**i** + 6.0**j**
B = -3.0**i** + 9.0**j**

Determine the angle between the vectors.

To get an idea of just what we are solving for, let's draw the two vectors with each tail at the origin. This is not a necessary step for solving the problem. It simply gives us a visual of the angle.

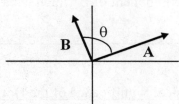

How do we determine the angle? Well notice that we have the components of each vector. Thus, we can determine the magnitude of each. Also, we can determine the dot product using Equation (1.5). Once we have that, then we can solve for the angle using Equation (1.6).

Let's start with the magnitudes of each vector. That's not too hard:

$$A = \sqrt{12^2 + 6.0^2} = 13$$

$$B = \sqrt{-3.0^2 + 9.0^2} = 9.5$$

Now let's figure out the dot product. Since we have the components, we use Equation (1.5):

$$\mathbf{A \bullet B} = 12 \cdot (-3.0) + 6.0 \cdot 9.0 = 18$$

At this point, we have all of the information in Equation (1.6) except the angle, so we can solve for it:

$$\mathbf{A \bullet B} = A \cdot B \cdot \cos\theta$$

$$18 = 13 \cdot 9.5 \cdot \cos\theta$$

$$\theta = \cos^{-1}\left(\frac{18}{13 \cdot 9.5}\right) = \cos^{-1}(0.15) = 82°$$

The angle, then, is 82°. Look back at the drawing of the two vectors. Notice that the angle looks very close to a right angle. Thus, the answer we have makes sense based on the drawing.

ON YOUR OWN

1.9 Compute the dot product of the following vectors: $\mathbf{A} = (-2.3 \text{ m}) \cdot \mathbf{i} - (1.2\text{m}) \cdot \mathbf{j}$, $\mathbf{B} = (1.2 \text{ m}) \cdot \mathbf{i} + (4.3 \text{ m}) \cdot \mathbf{j}$.

1.10 Two vectors, $\mathbf{A}$ and $\mathbf{B}$, are defined. The angle between them is 61.0°. Vector $\mathbf{A}$ has a magnitude of 15.1 meters, and the component of $\mathbf{B}$ which is parallel to $\mathbf{A}$ is 1.2 meters long. What is the magnitude of vector $\mathbf{B}$?

The Physical Significance of the Dot Product

In the last section, you learned how to compute the dot product of two vectors and what that means mathematically. However, this is a physics course. It might be nice to learn a new math concept, but this is not a math course. Thus, I would not have taught you about the dot product unless there was some physics behind it.

To learn the physics behind the dot product, you need to recall the concept of **work** from your first-year physics course. Do you remember how we define work mathematically? Try to see if this doesn't jog your memory:

$$W = F_{\parallel} \cdot x \tag{1.7}$$

In this equation, "W" represents work , "x" stands for the displacement over which the force was applied, and "$F_{\parallel}$" is used to indicate the component of the force vector that is parallel to the direction of motion.

To remember why Equation (1.7) uses only that portion of the applied force that is parallel to the motion, consider Figure 1.7.

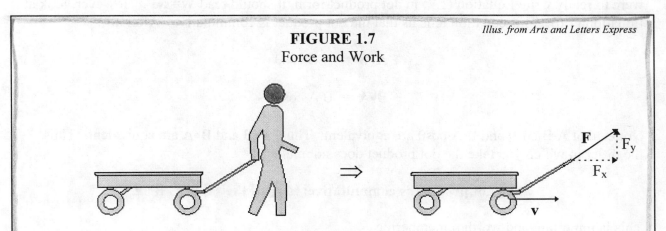

FIGURE 1.7
Force and Work

Illus. from Arts and Letters Express

In the left side of this figure, a boy is pulling a wagon. If we remove the picture of the boy (right side of the figure) and just look at the vectors involved, we see several things. First, the wagon travels in a straight, horizontal line, as indicated by the horizontal velocity vector (**v**). The force that the boy is applying (**F**) goes in the same direction as the wagon's handle. As a result, his pulling force is not parallel with the motion. Since the force is a two-dimensional vector, we can split it into vertical (F_y) and horizontal (F_x) components. The horizontal component is parallel to the motion and, as you can see, is the only portion of the force that contributes to the motion. In contrast, there is no motion in the perpendicular direction. In other words, the wagon is not moving upwards. In the end, the perpendicular portion of the force fights gravity. Since it is not strong enough to overcome gravity, the wagon does not move up. Remember, when a force is applied but there is no motion, there is no work. Thus, the perpendicular component of the boy's pulling force is wasted. It causes no motion, and therefore it accomplishes no work. That's why only the portion of the force parallel to the motion is considered when calculating the work done by that force.

So, when you are faced with a situation in which you must calculate the work done by a force which takes place over a certain displacement, you can use Equation (1.7). Wait a minute, however. Equation (1.7) tells you to take the magnitude of one vector (the displacement vector, **x**), and multiply it by the magnitude of the component of another vector (the force vector, **F**) which is parallel to the first vector. What does that sound like? It sounds like the *dot product*! Thus, we can re-write the definition of work in dot product notation:

$$W = \mathbf{F} \bullet \mathbf{x} \qquad (1.8)$$

Now remember, work is a scalar. It doesn't tell us anything about direction. That makes sense, since the result of the dot product is a scalar.

If you have been paying close attention, there may be something puzzling you at this point. In the dot product, we take the magnitude of the first vector, and multiply it by the magnitude of the component of the second vector which is parallel to the first vector. Thus, if I were to really write Equation (1.7) in dot product form, it should read W=x•F. However, look at Equation (1.6). This equation tells us that the dot product is commutative. After all,

$$\mathbf{A \bullet B} = A \cdot B \cdot \cos\theta$$

$$\mathbf{B \bullet A} = B \cdot A \cdot \cos\theta$$

Notice that $A \cdot B \cdot \cos\theta$ and $B \cdot A \cdot \cos\theta$ are equivalent. Thus, **A•B** and **B•A** are equivalent. Thus, the order in which you take the dot product does not matter.

The dot product is commutative: A•B is the same as B•A

This is important and worth remembering.

Now that you know the physical significance of the dot product, solve the following "on your own" problems.

ON YOUR OWN

1.11 A particle undergoes a displacement **x** = (1.5 m)·**i** - (2.3 m)·**j** while being acted upon by a constant force **F** = (5.6 N)·**i** - (3.4 N)·**j**. What is the work done?

1.12 A person applies a force of 16.6 Newtons to an object as the object travels 9.2 meters. If the work done was 14.5 J, what was the angle between the force vector and the displacement vector?

The Cross Product

The dot product of two vectors produces a scalar. It only makes sense that if there is a way to multiply two vectors to produce a scalar, there must be a way to multiply two vectors to produce a vector. Indeed, there is. We call it the **cross product**. In the cross product, we are still multiplying the magnitude of one vector with the magnitude of another vector. In this case, however, we are multiplying the magnitude of the first vector with the component of the second vector which is *perpendicular* to the first vector. In addition to using a different component of the second vector, the cross product also produces a *vector, not a scalar*. Thus, the cross product has both magnitude and direction. Let's deal with the magnitude first.

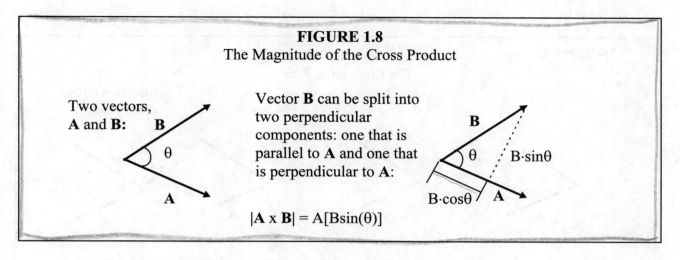

FIGURE 1.8
The Magnitude of the Cross Product

Two vectors, **A** and **B**:

Vector **B** can be split into two perpendicular components: one that is parallel to **A** and one that is perpendicular to **A**:

$|A \times B| = A[Bsin(\theta)]$

Once again, we have our old friends vector **A** and vector **B**. They can be drawn tail-to-tail, and the resulting angle between them is called θ. If we split vector **B** into two components: one parallel to **A** and one perpendicular to **A**, we find that the perpendicular component is B·sinθ. Thus, since the cross product involves multiplying the magnitude of the first vector and the magnitude of the component of the second vector which is perpendicular to the first, the magnitude of the cross product is:

$$|A \times B| = A \cdot B \cdot sin\theta \qquad (1.9)$$

The vertical lines enclosing **A** x **B** simply mean "magnitude." Thus, "|**A** x **B**|" means "the magnitude of the vector **A** x **B**."

So that's how we get the magnitude of the cross product. The cross product produces a vector, however, so there is also direction to consider. How do we come up with the direction of the cross product? We use something called the **right hand rule**.

Right hand rule - To determine the direction of the cross product **A** x **B**, take your right hand and point your fingers in the direction of **A**. Then, curl your fingers towards **B**, along the arc of the angle between the vectors. Your thumb will then point in the direction of the cross product

The right hand rule is illustrated in Figure 1.9.

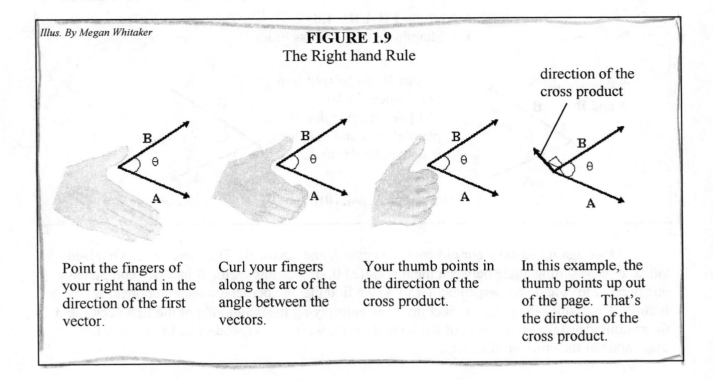

FIGURE 1.9
The Right hand Rule

Illus. By Megan Whitaker

direction of the
cross product

Point the fingers of
your right hand in the
direction of the first
vector.

Curl your fingers
along the arc of the
angle between the
vectors.

Your thumb points in
the direction of the
cross product.

In this example, the
thumb points up out
of the page. That's
the direction of the
cross product.

When determining the direction of the cross product, then, you take your right hand and point your fingers in the direction of the first vector. Then, you curl your fingers towards the second vector, along the arc of the angle between them. Your thumb will then point in the direction of the cross product. Think about what this means for a moment.

The direction of the cross product of two vectors will <u>always</u> be perpendicular to *both* vectors.

The right hand rule has another implication. Look at Figure 1.9 and use the right hand rule to determine the direction of **B** x **A**. Remember, you point the fingers on your right hand in the direction of the *first vector* (**B**), and you then curl towards the *second vector* (**A**). Where does your thumb point? It points down towards the paper. That's the *opposite direction* as that shown in the figure. Thus, unlike the dot production, the cross product is *not commutative*.

The cross product is not commutative: A x B = -(B x A)

This is important to remember.

Okay, there is one more thing you need to learn about the cross product. You need to know how to calculate the cross product using unit vector notation. However, before you can do that, you need to see how we define unit vectors in three-dimensional space.

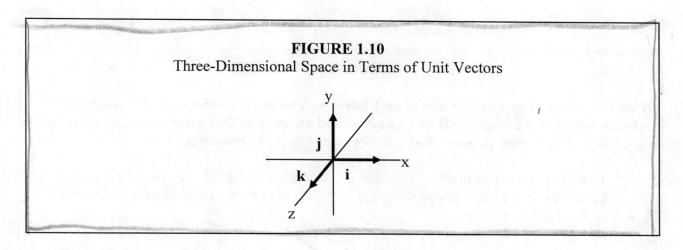

FIGURE 1.10
Three-Dimensional Space in Terms of Unit Vectors

When we add another dimension (the z-axis), we can represent that in unit vector notation with just another unit vector. Notice that **i** is still the unit vector in the horizontal direction and **j** is still the unit vector in the vertical direction. To represent three-dimensional space, then, we simply add a third unit vector, **k**, which points out of the plane of the paper, towards you. If we multiply by -1, the unit vector **-k** points behind the paper.

Now that you know how three-dimensional space is represented in vector notation, you can learn how we compute the cross product. First, let's start with the simple case of two-dimensional vectors.

For two-dimensional vectors in the i/j plane: $\mathbf{A} \times \mathbf{B} = (A_x \cdot B_y - A_y \cdot B_x) \cdot \mathbf{k}$ (1.10)

Notice the restriction placed on this equation. To use this equation, you must be taking the cross product of two-dimensional vectors which exist only in the plane defined by the horizontal (**i**) and vertical (**j**) axes. Thus, this is a pretty restrictive equation. However, most of the physics problems that you do will involve such vectors, so it is probably what you will use most often for calculating cross products.

For completeness sake, I will give you the total equation for calculating the cross product between any three-dimensional vectors:

$$\mathbf{A} \times \mathbf{B} = (A_y \cdot B_z - A_z \cdot B_y) \cdot \mathbf{i} + (A_z \cdot B_x - A_x \cdot B_z) \cdot \mathbf{j} + (A_x \cdot B_y - A_y \cdot B_x) \cdot \mathbf{k}$$ (1.11)

Notice that Equation (1.11) reduces to Equation (1.10) for two-dimensional vectors in the **i/j** plane. After all, the z-component of such a two-dimensional vector is zero. Thus, the term $(A_y \cdot B_z - A_z \cdot B_y) \cdot \mathbf{i}$ is zero, as is the term $(A_z \cdot B_x - A_x \cdot B_z) \cdot \mathbf{j}$. As a result, the only term in the equation that is non-zero is $(A_x \cdot B_y - A_y \cdot B_x) \cdot \mathbf{k}$, and that gives us Equation (1.10).

I know that this is a lot to throw at you, but hopefully the following example problems will clear up any confusion that may still be in your mind.

EXAMPLE 1.10

A velocity vector has a magnitude of 56.1 m/sec and an angle of 45.0 degrees. Another velocity vector has a magnitude of 12.2 m/sec and an angle of 290.1 degrees. Calculate the magnitude of the cross product and give the vector in unit vector notation.

Calculating the magnitude of the cross product is not bad at all. We just use Equation (1.9). To do that, however, we need the angle between the vectors. To determine that we will have to draw the two vectors:

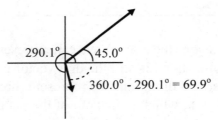

If the angle of the second vector as defined from the positive x-axis is 290.1, then the angle from the positive x-axis *down* to the vector must be $69.9°$, because the total angle must be $360.0°$. Well, the angle from the positive x-axis *up* to the first vector is $45.0°$. The angle between the two vectors, then, must be $69.9° + 45.0° = 114.9°$. Now we can use Equation (1.9):

$$|\mathbf{A} \times \mathbf{B}| = A \cdot B \cdot \sin\theta = (56.1 \text{ m/sec}) \cdot (12.2 \text{ m/sec}) \cdot \sin(114.9°) = 621 \text{ m}^2/\text{sec}^2$$

The magnitude of the cross product, then, is <u>621 m²/sec²</u>.

What about the direction? For that, we use the right hand rule. We point the fingers of our right hand in the direction of the first vector, then we curl along the arc of the $114.9°$ angle in between the vectors. When we do that, our thumb points down into the page. Thus, the vector is in the negative **k** direction. That tells us what we need to know for unit vector notation. After all, we know the vector's magnitude ($621 \text{ m}^2/\text{sec}^2$), and we know that it is pointed in the negative **k** direction. Thus, the vector is <u>-(621 m²/sec²)·**k**</u>.

Given the following vectors, calculate A x B and determine the angle between the vectors:

$$\mathbf{A} = 3.4 \cdot \mathbf{i} + 4.5 \cdot \mathbf{j}$$
$$\mathbf{B} = 2.4 \cdot \mathbf{i} + 1.1 \cdot \mathbf{j}$$

Notice that these two vectors are two-dimensional and have only **i** and **j** unit vectors. Thus, they are in the **i**/**j** plane, and we can use the simpler version of the cross product equation, Equation (1.10):

$$\mathbf{A} \times \mathbf{B} = (A_x \cdot B_y - A_y \cdot B_x) \cdot \mathbf{k}$$

$$\mathbf{A} \times \mathbf{B} = [3.4 \cdot 1.1 - 4.5 \cdot (2.4)] \cdot \mathbf{k} = \underline{-7.1 \cdot \mathbf{k}}$$

That's the cross product. Based solely on the unit vector notation, you know that it is pointing behind the plane of the paper. What about the angle? Well, we now know the magnitude of the vector (if the vector is composed solely of 7.1 times $\mathbf{k}$, then the magnitude is 7.1, because $\mathbf{k}$ has a magnitude of 1), so we can use Equation (1.9):

$$|\mathbf{A} \times \mathbf{B}| = A \cdot B \cdot \sin\theta$$

Remember, "$|\mathbf{A} \times \mathbf{B}|$" means "magnitude of $\mathbf{A} \times \mathbf{B}$," so that's 7.1. We don't have the magnitudes of $\mathbf{A}$ and $\mathbf{B}$, but we can use their components to calculate them:

$$A = \sqrt{3.4^2 + 4.5^2} = 5.6$$
$$B = \sqrt{(2.4)^2 + 1.1^2} = 2.6$$

Now we can use Equation (1.9):

$$|\mathbf{A} \times \mathbf{B}| = A \cdot B \cdot \sin\theta$$

$$7.1 = (5.6) \cdot (2.6) \cdot \sin\theta$$

$$\theta = \sin^{-1}\left(\frac{7.1}{(5.6) \cdot (2.6)}\right) = \underline{29°}$$

Given the following vectors, calculate the cross product and the angle between them:

$$A = -1.4 \cdot \mathbf{i} + 4.2 \cdot \mathbf{j} - 5.6 \cdot \mathbf{k}$$
$$B = 2.4 \cdot \mathbf{i} - 1.1 \cdot \mathbf{j} + 3.2 \cdot \mathbf{k}$$

This is essentially the same as the problem above. However, these are three-dimensional vectors, so we have to use the larger formula, Equation (1.11):

$$\mathbf{A} \times \mathbf{B} = (A_y \cdot B_z - A_z \cdot B_y) \cdot \mathbf{i} + (A_z \cdot B_x - A_x \cdot B_z) \cdot \mathbf{j} + (A_x \cdot B_y - A_y \cdot B_x) \cdot \mathbf{k}$$

$$\mathbf{A} \times \mathbf{B} = (4.2 \cdot 3.2 - [-5.6] \cdot [-1.1]) \cdot \mathbf{i} + (-5.6 \cdot 2.4 - [-1.4] \cdot 3.2) \cdot \mathbf{j} + ([-1.4] \cdot [-1.1] - 4.2 \cdot 2.4) \cdot \mathbf{k}$$

$$\mathbf{A} \times \mathbf{B} = \underline{7.2 \cdot \mathbf{i} - 8.9 \cdot \mathbf{j} - 8.6 \cdot \mathbf{k}}$$

Just as we did before, we can calculate the magnitudes of the two vectors and then determine the angle between them using Equation (1.9). The only difference now is that the magnitude of the cross product is not as easy to determine. We must calculate it like we calculate the magnitudes of all vectors:

$$A = \sqrt{(-1.4)^2 + 4.2^2 + (-5.6)^2} = 7.1$$
$$B = \sqrt{2.4^2 + 1.1^2 + 3.2^2} = 4.1$$

$$|A \times B| = \sqrt{7.2^2 + (-8.9)^2 + (-8.6)^2} = 14$$

Now that we have all of the magnitudes involved, we can use Equation (1.9):

$$|A \times B| = A \cdot B \cdot \sin\theta$$

$$14 = (7.1) \cdot (4.1) \cdot \sin\theta$$

$$\theta = \sin^{-1}\left(\frac{14}{(7.1) \cdot (4.1)}\right) = \underline{29^\circ}$$

ON YOUR OWN

1.13 Vector **A** is defined as 3.2 feet at 45.1°, and vector **B** is defined as 1.1 feet at 70.1°. What is the cross product? Give your answer in unit vector notation.

1.14 Given the following vectors, calculate the cross product and the angle between them:

$$A = -7.1 \cdot i + 4.2 \cdot j$$
$$B = 3.4 \cdot i - 4.1 \cdot j$$

The Physical Significance of the Cross Product

As was the case with the dot product, there is physical significance to the cross product. We will apply the cross product in at least three different areas of physics, but for right now, I will concentrate on only one: the concept of **torque**. As you learned in your first-year physics course, when we apply a force some distance away from an axis of rotation, the result is a torque, which can cause rotational motion. In your first-year physics course, you learned the equation used to calculate torque.

$$\tau = F_\perp \cdot r \tag{1.12}$$

Where "τ" represents torque, "r" represents the magnitude of the vector drawn from the axis of rotation to the point at which the force is applied, and "$F_\perp$" represents the component of the force which is perpendicular to that vector. Figure 1.11 illustrates the concept of torque.

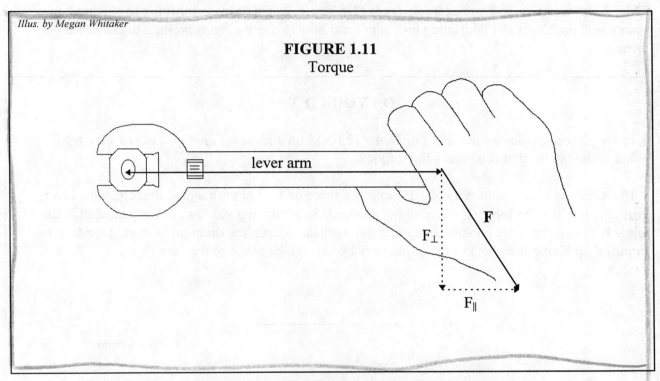

Illus. by Megan Whitaker

FIGURE 1.11
Torque

Now remember what torque is. It is the counterpart of force when one is considering *rotational motion*. Remember, force causes acceleration in a straight line. Torque causes rotational acceleration. In the figure, the wrench is going to turn the screw. To do that, it will have to give the screw rotational acceleration so that it starts to turn in a circle. Torque is the impetus which will cause that rotational acceleration.

Notice from the figure that only a portion of the force used can generate torque. Any component of the force that is parallel to the vector defined from the axis of rotation to the point at which the force is applied (the **lever arm**) is lost. Thus, the magnitude of the torque is given by the magnitude of the lever arm times the component of the force which is perpendicular to the lever arm.

Well, since the cross product takes the magnitude of a vector and multiplies it by the magnitude of a second vector's component which is perpendicular to the first vector, torque can be calculated using the cross product.

$$\tau = r \times F$$ (1.13)

There are two things to note about this equation. First, torque is a vector. Remember, the cross product results in a vector. That's why the "τ" is bold. Second, remember that the cross product is NOT commutative. Thus, the order of the vectors *is* important, so one must take the vector of the lever arm (**r**) and cross it with the vector representing the force (**F**), *in that order*.

Since you already know how to do cross products, calculating the torque is pretty easy. Thus, I will not give you any examples of it. However, you should perform the following "on your own" problems to make sure you understand how to use the cross product to calculate torque.

ON YOUR OWN

1.15 A person applies a force $\mathbf{F} = (15\ \text{N}){\cdot}\mathbf{i} + (23\ \text{N}){\cdot}\mathbf{j}$ on a lever arm $\mathbf{r} = (1.2\ \text{m}){\cdot}\mathbf{i} + (1.1\ \text{m}){\cdot}\mathbf{j}$. What is the vector that represents the torque?

1.16 A man is trying to turn a bolt. He exerts a force of 15.2 N with a pipe that creates a lever arm which is 0.36 m long. If the plumber succeeds in producing 4.9 N·m of torque, what is the angle between the force he is exerting and the wrench? Given the diagram below, is the torque pointing up above the plane of the paper or back behind the plane of the paper?

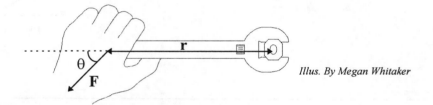

Illus. By Megan Whitaker

Summing Up

This module contained some concepts which were review for you and others which were new. That will be the case with most of the modules in this course. In each module, I will review some of the highlights of your first-year physics course and then go deeper into each subject. In addition, completely new concepts will be brought in from time to time. Thus, if there is something that really baffles you in this course, you should review your first-year course to see if it is explained there.

ANSWERS TO THE ON YOUR OWN PROBLEMS

1.1 To solve this problem, we simply have to convert miles to centimeters and hours to seconds. It doesn't matter that they are both a part of our original unit. As long as we use the factor-label method, everything will work out:

$$\frac{65 \text{ miles}}{1 \text{ hour}} \times \frac{1609 \text{ m}}{1 \text{ mile}} \times \frac{1 \text{cm}}{0.01 \text{m}} \times \frac{1 \text{ hour}}{3600 \text{ s}} = 2900 \ \frac{\text{cm}}{\text{s}}$$

Notice that I converted from miles to meters and then meters to centimeters. I had to do that, since I was not given a direct relationship between miles and centimeters. Sixty-five miles per hour is the same as 2900 cm/s.

1.2 We can't use the conversion of 3 feet in 1 yard right away, because we want to convert from square feet into square yards. Thus, we need a relationship between those quantities. We can get such a relationship by squaring both sides of the relationship that we do have:

$$3 \text{ ft} = 1 \text{ yd}$$

$$9 \text{ ft}^2 = 1 \text{ yd}^2$$

Now we can do the conversion:

$$\frac{1600 \text{ ft}^2}{1} \times \frac{1 \text{ yd}^2}{9 \text{ ft}^2} = 180 \text{ yd}^2$$

The house has an area of 180 square yards. If your answer was 177.8, go back and review significant figures from your first-year course.

1.3 To convert from Joules ($\frac{\text{kg} \cdot \text{m}^2}{\text{sec}^2}$) to ergs ($\frac{\text{g} \cdot \text{cm}^2}{\text{sec}^2}$), I need to convert kg into g and m^2 into cm^2. That's not bad. We know that 1 kg = 1,000 g. We also know:

$$1 \text{ cm} = 0.01 \text{ m}$$

To get the relationship between cm^2 and m^2, we just square both sides:

$$1 \text{ cm}^2 = 0.0001 \text{ m}^2$$

This leads us to:

$$\frac{151 \text{ kg} \cdot \text{m}^2}{1 \text{ sec}^2} \times \frac{1,000 \text{ g}}{1 \text{ kg}} \times \frac{1 \text{ cm}^2}{0.0001 \text{ m}^2} = 1.51 \times 10^9 \ \frac{\text{g} \cdot \text{cm}^2}{\text{sec}^2}$$

1.4 In this problem, we are given the x- and y-components of a vector and are asked to calculate its magnitude and direction. Getting the magnitude is not too bad:

$$\text{Magnitude} = \sqrt{V_x^{\,2} + V_y^{\,2}} = \sqrt{(23\,\frac{m}{sec})^2 + (11\,\frac{m}{sec})^2} = 25\,\frac{m}{sec}$$

To get the angle, we start with this equation:

$$\theta = \tan^{-1}\left(\frac{V_y}{V_x}\right) = \tan^{-1}\left(\frac{11\frac{m}{sec}}{23\frac{m}{sec}}\right) = 26^\circ$$

We aren't necessarily finished yet, however. We have to determine which region of the Cartesian coordinate system that the vector is in. Since both its components are positive, this tells us that the vector is to the right and above the origin, which means that the vector is in region I. According to our rules, we don't need to do anything to the result of the equation when the vector is in region I, so 26° is the proper angle. Thus, <u>the vector has magnitude of 25 m/sec and direction of 26°</u>.

1.5 In this problem, we are asked to add two-dimensional vectors together. Before we do this mathematically, let's do it graphically:

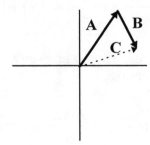

As we learned before, the dotted arrow (vector **C**) gives us the sum.

The first step in adding vectors mathematically is to break both vectors down into their components:

$$A_x = (3.1\,\frac{m}{sec}) \cdot \cos(60.0^\circ) = 1.6\,\frac{m}{sec}$$

$$A_y = (3.1\,\frac{m}{sec}) \cdot \sin(60.0^\circ) = 2.7\,\frac{m}{sec}$$

$$B_x = (1.4 \; \frac{m}{sec}) \cdot \cos(290.0°) = 0.48 \; \frac{m}{sec}$$

$$B_y = (1.4 \; \frac{m}{sec}) \cdot \sin(290.0°) = -1.3 \; \frac{m}{sec}$$

Now that we have the individual components, we can add them together.

$$C_x = A_x + B_x = 1.6 \; \frac{m}{sec} + 0.48 \; \frac{m}{sec} = 2.1 \; \frac{m}{sec}$$

$$C_y = A_y + B_y = 2.7 \; \frac{m}{sec} + -1.3 \; \frac{m}{sec} = 1.4 \; \frac{m}{sec}$$

Now that we have the components to our answer, we can get the magnitude and direction of the sum.

$$\text{Magnitude} = \sqrt{C_x^2 + C_y^2} = \sqrt{(2.1 \; \frac{m}{sec})^2 + (1.4 \; \frac{m}{sec})^2} = 2.5 \; \frac{m}{sec}$$

$$\theta = \tan^{-1}\left(\frac{C_y}{C_x}\right) = \tan^{-1}\left(\frac{1.4 \; \frac{\cancel{m}}{\cancel{sec}}}{2.1 \; \frac{\cancel{m}}{\cancel{sec}}}\right) = 34°$$

Since the x- and y-components are both positive, the vector is in the first region of the Cartesian coordinate plane. This is consistent with the graphical answer we drew to begin with, and it means that we do not need to do anything to the result the equation. Thus, the sum of vectors **A** and **B** has a magnitude of 2.5 m/sec at a direction of 34°.

1.6 To draw the vector, we simply need to realize that the number multiplying **i** is the x-component and the number multiplying **j** is the y-component.

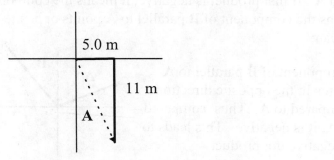

To get the magnitude and direction, we just use the formulas in Figure 1.2.

$$A = \sqrt{A_x^2 + A_y^2} = \sqrt{(5.0\,\text{m})^2 + (-11\,\text{m})^2} = 12\ \text{m}$$

$$\theta = \tan^{-1}\left(\frac{-11\ \text{m}}{5.0\ \text{m}}\right) = -66°$$

Now remember, the angle may not be defined correctly at this point. Based on the components, we see that this vector is in region IV of the Cartesian coordinate plane. Thus, we must add 360.0° to it. Thus, the answer is <u>12 m at a direction of 294°</u>.

1.7 To add vectors, we add the x-components and y-components. In unit vector notation, the formula is given by Equation (1.2):

$$\mathbf{A} + \mathbf{B} = (A_x + B_x)\mathbf{i} + (A_y + B_y)\mathbf{j} = (5\ \text{m} + {-11}\ \text{m})\mathbf{i} + (-11\ \text{m} + 22\text{m})\mathbf{j} = \underline{(-6\ \text{m})\mathbf{i} + (11\ \text{m})\mathbf{j}}$$

The difference is given by Equation (1.3):

$$\mathbf{A} - \mathbf{B} = (A_x - B_x)\mathbf{i} + (A_y - B_y)\mathbf{j} = (5\ \text{m} - {-11}\text{m})\mathbf{i} + (-11\ \text{m} - 22\ \text{m})\mathbf{j} = \underline{(16\ \text{m})\mathbf{i} - (33\ \text{m})\mathbf{j}}$$

1.8 In unit vector notation, scalar multiplication is given by Equation (1.2):

$$k\mathbf{A} = (kA_x)\mathbf{i} + (kA_y)\mathbf{j}$$

$$6\mathbf{C} = (6\text{x}2.0\ \text{m/sec})\mathbf{i} + (6\text{x}3.0\ \text{m/sec})\mathbf{j} = \underline{(12\ \text{m/sec})\mathbf{i} + (18\ \text{m/sec})\mathbf{j}}$$

1.9 Using Equation (1.5):

$$\mathbf{A} \bullet \mathbf{B} = A_x \cdot B_x + A_y \cdot B_y$$

$$\mathbf{A} \bullet \mathbf{B} = (-2.3\ \text{m}) \cdot (1.2\ \text{m}) + (-1.2\ \text{m}) \cdot (4.3\ \text{m}) = -8.0\ \text{m}^2$$

The dot product, then, equals <u>-8.0 m²</u>. What does the minus sign mean? Well, remember, the dot product is the product of the magnitude of **A** and the magnitude of the component of **B** parallel to **A**. If that product is negative, it means the component of **B** parallel to **A** is negative. That means the component of **B** parallel to **A** points opposite of **A**. Draw the two vectors to see what I mean:

Component of **B** parallel to **A** points in the opposite direction compared to **A**. Thus, compared to **A**, it is negative. This leads to a negative dot product.

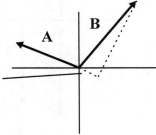

1.10 This problem requires you to understand that the dot product **A**•**B** is the magnitude of **A** times the magnitude of the component of **B** which lies parallel to **A**. You are given those two things, so you can compute the dot product:

$$\textbf{A} \bullet \textbf{B} = (\text{magnitude of } \textbf{A}) \cdot (\text{magnitude of the component of } \textbf{B} \text{ parallel to } \textbf{A})$$

$$\textbf{A} \bullet \textbf{B} = (15.1 \text{ m}) \cdot (1.2 \text{ m}) = 18 \text{ m}^2$$

Now that we have the dot product, we can solve Equation (1.6) for the magnitude of **B**.

$$\textbf{A} \bullet \textbf{B} = A \cdot B \cdot \cos\theta$$

$$18 \text{ m}^2 = (15.1 \text{ m}) \cdot B \cdot \cos(61.0°)$$

$$B = \frac{18 \text{ m}^2}{(15.1 \text{ m}) \cdot \cos(61.0°)} = \underline{2.5 \text{ m}}$$

1.11 This is a straightforward application of Equation (1.8):

$$W = \textbf{F} \bullet \textbf{x} = (5.6 \text{ N}) \cdot (1.5 \text{ m}) + (3.4 \text{ N}) \cdot (2.3 \text{ m}) = 16.2 \text{ N} \cdot \text{m} = \underline{16.2 \text{ J}}$$

Remember from your first-year course that a N·m is the standard unit for energy or work, and that unit is called the **Joule** in honor of James Prescott Joule.

1.12 Remember, work is the dot product of **F** and **x**. Thus,

$$W = F \cdot x \cdot \cos\theta$$

In this problem, we have all of the variables except θ, so we can solve for it:

$$W = F \cdot x \cdot \cos\theta$$

$$14.5 \text{ J} = (16.6 \text{ N}) \cdot (9.2 \text{ m}) \cdot \cos\theta$$

$$\theta = \cos^{-1}\left(\frac{14.5 \text{ N} \cdot \text{m}}{(16.6 \text{ N}) \cdot (9.2 \text{ m})}\right) = \underline{85°}$$

Notice that in the last line, I replaced the unit Joule with its definition, N·m, to show that the units cancel out. Remember, when dealing with a trigonometric function, the argument should have no units. Thus, any units in the problem need to fully cancel, as they do above.

1.13   To calculate the magnitude of the cross product, we just use Equation (1.9). To do that, however, we need the angle between the vectors:

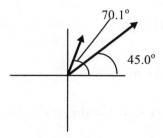

This angle is easy, it's just $70.1° - 45.0° = 25.1°$. Now we can use Equation (1.9):

$$|\mathbf{A} \times \mathbf{B}| = A \cdot B \cdot \sin\theta = (3.2 \text{ feet}) \cdot (1.1 \text{ feet}) \cdot \sin(25.1°) = 1.5 \text{ feet}^2$$

To determine direction, we use the right hand rule. We point the fingers of our right hand in the direction of the first vector, then we curl along the arc of the $25.1°$ angle in between the vectors. When we do that, our thumb points up out of the page. Thus, the vector is in the positive $\mathbf{k}$ direction. That tells us what we need to know for unit vector notation. Thus, the vector is $\underline{(1.5 \text{ feet}^2) \cdot \mathbf{k}}$.

1.14   Notice that the vectors are two-dimensional and have only $\mathbf{i}$ and $\mathbf{j}$ unit vectors. Thus, we can use the simpler version of the cross product formula, Equation (1.10):

$$\mathbf{A} \times \mathbf{B} = (A_x \cdot B_y - A_y \cdot B_x) \cdot \mathbf{k}$$

$$\mathbf{A} \times \mathbf{B} = [(-7.1) \cdot (-4.1) - 4.2 \cdot 3.4] \cdot \mathbf{k} = \underline{15 \cdot \mathbf{k}}$$

That's the cross product. What about the angle? Well, we just need the magnitudes of all three vectors and Equation (1.9). The magnitude of the cross product is easy; it's just 15. What about $\mathbf{A}$ and $\mathbf{B}$?

$$A = \sqrt{(-7.1)^2 + (4.2)^2} = 8.2$$
$$B = \sqrt{(3.4)^2 + (-4.1)^2} = 5.3$$

Now we can use Equation (1.9):

$$|\mathbf{A} \times \mathbf{B}| = A \cdot B \cdot \sin\theta$$

$$15 = (8.2) \cdot (5.3) \cdot \sin\theta$$

$$\theta = \sin^{-1}\left(\frac{15}{(8.2) \cdot (5.3)}\right) = \underline{2.0 \times 10^{1 \; \circ}}$$

Notice that I had to put the answer in scientific notation. The rules indicate that I must have 2 significant figures. The number 20 has only 1 significant figure. Thus, I had to make that zero significant by putting the whole number in scientific notation.

1.15 This is an easy one. We are given the vectors for **r** and **F**, so we can just use Equation (1.13). Since these are two-dimensional vectors in the **i/j** plane, we can use the simplified cross product formula, Equation (1.10).

$$\boldsymbol{\tau} = \mathbf{r} \times \mathbf{F} = (r_x \cdot F_y - r_y \cdot F_x) \cdot \mathbf{k} = [(1.2 \text{ m}) \cdot (23 \text{ N}) - (1.1 \text{ m}) \cdot (15 \text{ N})] \cdot \mathbf{k} = \underline{(11 \text{ N} \cdot \text{m}) \cdot \mathbf{k}}$$

1.16 In this problem, we are dealing only with magnitudes. Since we want to figure out the angle between the vectors, we are going to use Equation (1.9):

$$|\mathbf{A} \times \mathbf{B}| = A \cdot B \cdot \sin\theta$$

$$4.9 \text{ N} \cdot \text{m} = (0.36 \text{ m}) \cdot (15.2 \text{ N}) \cdot \sin\theta$$

$$\theta = \sin^{-1}\left(\frac{4.9 \text{ N} \cdot \text{m}}{(0.36 \text{ m}) \cdot (15.2 \text{ N})}\right) = \underline{64^\circ}$$

To determine the direction, we use the right hand rule. Point the fingers of your right hand from the nut to the hand. That is along the lever arm. Now, curl your fingers towards the force, along the arc of the angle between the lever arm and the force. Your thumb should be pointed up away from the paper. Thus, the torque points above the plane of the paper.

REVIEW QUESTIONS FOR MODULE #1

1. What is the conversion relationship between m^2 and km^2?

2. Two vectors are written below. Draw them on a Cartesian coordinate plane so that they each start at the origin.

    A: 55 miles/hour at 45 degrees   **B**: 20 miles/hour at 210 degrees

3. A position vector, **P**, is given as 36 miles at 15 degrees. What are the magnitude and angle of -2·**P**?

4. In which region of the Cartesian coordinate system do you find the vector
A = 1.2·**i** - 3.4·**j**?

5. You are given the vector **S** = -3.4·**i** - 4.5·**j** and must determine the angle at which it is pointing. You use the fact that $\tan\theta = S_y/S_x$ to get the angle. However, what do you have to do to the result of that equation in order to report the angle so that it is defined properly?

6. The dot product **A**•**B** is equal to 34.2 m^2. What is the value of **B**•**A**?

7. Fill in the blank:

The dot product takes the magnitude of one vector and multiplies it by the magnitude of the second vector's component which is ___Parallel___ to the first vector.

8. Suppose a person applies a force to an object, but the object travels in a direction that is perpendicular to the force. How much work is being done?

9. The cross product **A** x **B** is equal to (45 m^2/sec^2)·**k**. What is the cross product **B** x **A**?

10. Given the diagram below, determine the direction of the vector **A** x **B**. Is the vector going back behind the plane of the paper or coming out above the plane of the paper?

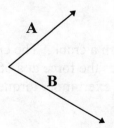

PRACTICE PROBLEMS FOR MODULE #1

1. Convert an acceleration of 845 feet/hour^2 into meters/sec^2. (1 m = 3.281 feet)

2. A Newton is a $\dfrac{kg \cdot m}{sec^2}$. Convert 15.1 Newtons into $\dfrac{g \cdot cm}{minute^2}$.

3 The velocity vector of an object is **v** = (13 m/sec)·**i** - (11 m/sec)·**j**. What are the magnitude and direction of the velocity vector?

4. Vector **A** has a magnitude of 2.2 m/sec at an angle of 35.0 degrees, and vector **B** has a magnitude of 3.4 m/sec at an angle of 120.0 degrees. Graphically add these two vectors together, and then compute the magnitude and direction.

5. Given the following vectors:

A = (1.5 miles)·**i** + (7.1 miles)·**j**
B = (1.8 miles)·**i** - (2.2 miles)·**j**

What is **A** + **B**? What is **A** - **B**? Give your answers in unit vector notation.

6. Given the following vector:

C = (12.0 m)·**i** + (13.0 m)·**j**

What is -5·**C** in unit vector notation?

7. An object undergoes a displacement **x** = (-5.2 m)·**i** + (1.1 m)·**j** while being acted upon by a constant force **F** = (1.5 N)·**i** - (4.3 N)·**j**. What is the work done?

8. A person applies a force of 18 Newtons to an object as the object travels 3.4 meters. The angle between the force and the displacement is 35.1 degrees. How much work was done?

9. A construction worker is using a crowbar to pry a rock out of the ground. He applies a force **F** = (-55 N)·**i** - (34 N)·**j** + (43 N)·**k** at a lever arm **r** = (0.23 m)·**i** + (0.25 m)·**j** + (0.22 m)·**k**. What is the vector that represents the torque?

10. A person applies a force in order to turn a crank. The crank is 0.50 meters long, and he applies a force of 15 Newtons. If he applies the force at a 65 degree angle relative to the crank, what is the torque? How could the person exert more torque without increasing the force or changing the lever arm?

Module #2: Kinematics

Introduction

Motion is a fundamental part of Creation. It is everywhere around you. Birds fly; insects buzz around in the air or crawl on the ground; dogs chase each other; and your eyes move while you read. Indeed, you can see motion all around you. There is also an enormous amount of motion that you *cannot* see. For example, the molecules which make up the air around you are speeding around the room, colliding into one another and also into you. In fact, the speed at which they move and the violence with which they collide with your body determines whether you feel hot, warm, cool, or cold. Even the molecules which make up the ink and paper of this book are vibrating back and forth at a dizzying rate.

Kinematics is the study of motion. It does not try to explain *how* the motion was started or why it is continuing. It simply tries to describe the motion in detail.

Kinematics – A study of an object's motion which determines its displacement, velocity, and acceleration

You should be familiar with the terms **displacement, velocity,** and **acceleration** from your first-year physics course. In this course, we want to delve deeper into these concepts so that you have a detailed view of kinematics.

Position Versus Time Graphs

In your first-year physics course, you should have learned that the velocity of an object can be calculated by determining the slope of a position versus time graph, such as the one pictured below.

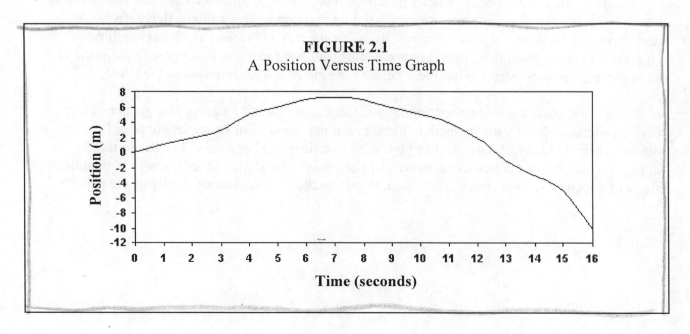

FIGURE 2.1
A Position Versus Time Graph

Remember that velocity is the rate at which position changes with respect to time. Mathematically, it can be represented as:

$$\mathbf{v} = \frac{\Delta \mathbf{x}}{\Delta t} \qquad (2.1)$$

where "$\Delta \mathbf{x}$" is the change in the position and "Δt" is the change in time. Look at the graph in Figure 2.1. What does Equation (2.1) represent on this graph? It represents the *slope* of the graph. Thus, if we have a graph of position versus time, we can calculate the velocity by determining the slope of the graph. This is an important point.

The velocity of an object can be determined by the slope of its position versus time curve.

Now remember, to calculate velocity, we choose a time interval (Δt) and determine the change in position during that time interval. Since the velocity may, indeed, change over this time interval, we refer to the results of Equation (2.1) as the **average velocity**. In other words, the results of Equation (2.1) give us the velocity of the object, averaged over the time interval chosen.

If we want to know the velocity of an object at a specific instant in time, we need to determine the **instantaneous velocity** of the object. We really cannot do that with Equation (2.1) unless a specific situation exists, which I will explain in a moment. We can *approximate* the instantaneous velocity with Equation (2.1), as long as we choose a short time interval. The shorter the time interval (the smaller the Δt), the less the velocity can change over the time interval, so the closer we are to measuring the object's instantaneous velocity. However, unless the time interval is infinitely short, we cannot truly determine the object's instantaneous velocity.

How can instantaneous velocity be determined? Well, if you take calculus, you will learn how to measure the slope of a curve at any point on that curve. It is called a **derivative**. The derivative of a position versus time curve gives you the instantaneous velocity at any time. However, I cannot assume that you know calculus, so I want to show you a graphical means of determining the slope of a displacement versus time curve at a given point on the curve.

As you should have learned from mathematics, the slope of a curve at a given point is defined as the slope of a line tangent to the curve at that point. For example, suppose I wanted to determine the velocity of the object in Figure 2.1 at a time of 11 seconds. I could do that by drawing a line that is tangent to the curve at 11 seconds. The slope of that line would then be the slope of the curve *at that point*. That, then, would be the instantaneous velocity of the object.

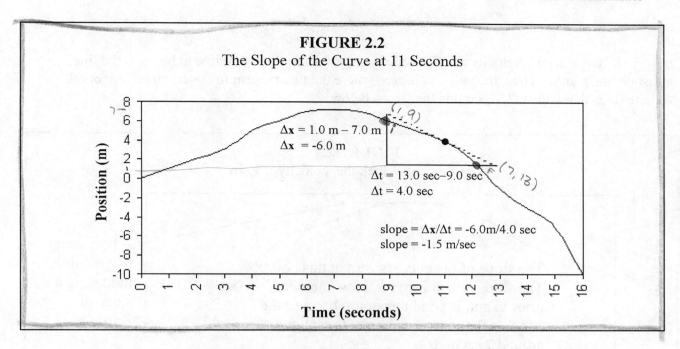

FIGURE 2.2
The Slope of the Curve at 11 Seconds

The instantaneous velocity of the object at 11 seconds, then, is -1.5 m/sec. Remember what the negative means. We are dealing with motion in one dimension here, so positive and negative signs tell us direction. If we define motion to the right as the positive direction, then this velocity tells us that at 11 seconds, the object is traveling to the *left* with a speed of 1.5 m/sec. This technique, then, allows us to determine the instantaneous velocity of the object at any point in time, as long as we have the position versus time curve.

A little while ago, I told you that we cannot really use Equation (2.1) to determine instantaneous velocity unless a certain condition exists. What condition is that? Well, look at the curve from 0 seconds to 3 seconds. Notice that the curve in that region of the graph is really a straight line. What do we know about straight lines? The slope of a straight line is always constant. Thus, the slope of the curve is the same from 0 seconds all the way to 3 seconds. This means that between zero and 3 seconds, the velocity is constant. Thus, it does not change during that time interval. As a result, *during that time interval*, the average velocity is also the instantaneous velocity. This is another important point.

When the position versus time curve is a straight line, the velocity is constant and thus there is no difference between instantaneous and average velocity.

There is one point on the graph that is of particular interest. We know that the object must have been moving in one direction, and then it must have turned around and started moving the other direction. We know this because the slope of the curve from 0 to just under 7 seconds is clearly positive, and therefore the velocity is positive. If motion to the right is defined as positive, this means that the object was moving to the right. From just over 7 seconds to 16 seconds, the slope of the curve is negative. That means the velocity is negative, and therefore the object was moving to the left during that time frame. When did it stop and turn around? It stopped and turned around where the velocity was zero.

Where was the velocity zero? Well, in order for the slope of a line to be zero, the line must be horizontal. Thus, the velocity is zero where the line tangent to the curve is horizontal. Where does that happen?   Examine the figure below.

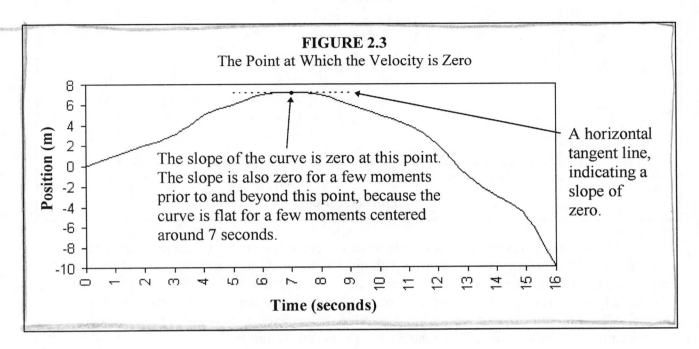

FIGURE 2.3
The Point at Which the Velocity is Zero

The slope of the curve is zero at this point. The slope is also zero for a few moments prior to and beyond this point, because the curve is flat for a few moments centered around 7 seconds.

A horizontal tangent line, indicating a slope of zero.

This is the last important thing you need to remember about these graphs.

The velocity is zero when the line tangent to the position versus time curve is horizontal.

Why did I go through this displacement versus time curve so carefully? Well, one reason was to give you some experience trying to determine the instantaneous velocity by looking at the slope of the line tangent to the curve. The other reason is that if you keep in mind the three boldfaced statements you have read, you can actually do an incredible thing with the displacement versus time curve. To see what I mean, study the following example.

EXAMPLE 2.1

Given the position versus time curve in the figure above, sketch a curve that estimates how the velocity varies with time.

Although the task given in the problem sounds incredibly difficult, it really is not at all. Think about it. We know that the slope of the displacement versus time curve is the velocity. Thus, if we calculate the slope at a few points, we can graph the velocity versus time. The real issue, however, is to determine *where* to calculate the slope. Well, any point on the graph in which the velocity is zero is easy to spot. Thus, that should be one point at which we calculate the slope. Also, any region over which the curve looks linear would be another easy region in which to determine the slope. Then, if we do one or two more points in between, we will be all set. We know, for example, that the slope of the curve is zero for a few moments centered around 7 seconds. That's a point we can graph. We also determined that at 11 seconds, the slope was -1.5 m/sec. That's another point we can graph. Here are some other points and regions:

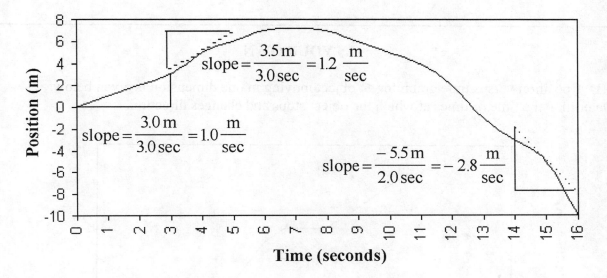

Between zero and 3 seconds, the curve is a straight line, so the velocity is 1.0 m/sec during that entire time. The velocity then increases (the curve gets steeper). At 4 seconds, it is 1.2 m/sec. It then slows down (the curve gets less steep) until the velocity reaches zero around 7 seconds. The curve then has a negative slope, indicating that the velocity becomes negative. At 11 seconds, we already measured the velocity to be -1.5 m/sec. The curve gets even more sharply negative after 11 seconds, indicating that the velocity gets more negative. At 15 seconds, it is -2.8 m/sec and gets even more negative after that. Putting in the points we measured and following the trends we just discussed, we get this graph:

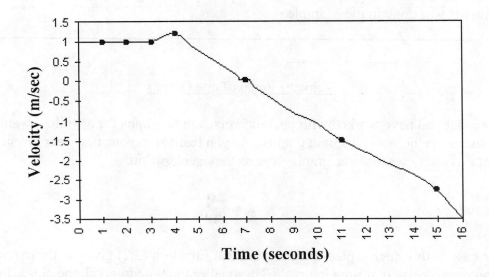

Now please understand two things about this example. First, the graph we just drew is an estimate. It would require a lot more points to be exact. Also, the curves that I am going to ask you to analyze in this way will be much simpler. See what I mean by trying the "on your own" problems which follow.

ON YOUR OWN

2.1 A position versus time graph for an object moving in one dimension is given below. Determine the time or times at which the object stops and changes direction.

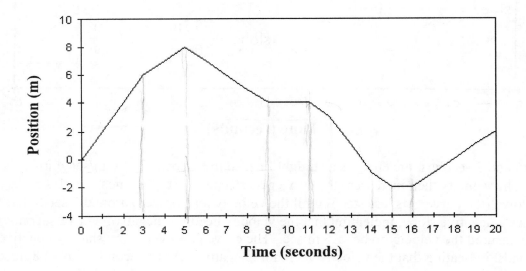

2.2 Sketch the velocity versus time graph for the object whose position versus time graph appears above. Note that the graph is composed entirely of straight lines. That makes the task easier than what was done in the example.

Velocity Versus Time Graphs

Now that you have worked with position versus time graphs for a while, I want to switch gears and discuss velocity versus time graphs. As you learned in your first-year physics course, the slope of a velocity versus time graph gives us the **acceleration**.

$$\mathbf{a} = \frac{\Delta \mathbf{v}}{\Delta t}$$

(2.2)

As was the case with velocity, please understand that Equation (2.2) gives us the *average* acceleration over a particular time interval. The smaller the time interval, the closer Equation (2.2) approximates the instantaneous acceleration at a time within that time interval. To get the true instantaneous acceleration at a given time, however, we would have to calculate the slope of a line tangent to the velocity versus time curve at that point. If you know calculus, you can do this by taking the derivative of the curve. If you do not know calculus, you can manually draw a line tangent to the curve and then calculate the slope of that line.

All of the skills that you just learned about analyzing a position versus time curve can be applied to a velocity versus time curve as well. Of course, the slope does not give you the velocity anymore. Instead, it gives you the acceleration. Thus, you could analyze the slope of a velocity versus time curve at several points and sketch the resulting acceleration versus time curve. You will be given an "on your own" problem to make sure that you can do this.

In this section, I want to concentrate on one very interesting aspect of a velocity versus time curve:

The area under an object's velocity versus time curve is the total displacement that object experiences during its motion.

You were probably told this fact in your first-year course, and it may have even been used to derive the motion equations we will revisit in the next section of this course. However, you probably do not have any direct experience working with this fact. I want to give you that experience now.

Before we jump into an example, however, I want to make a brief point. The mathematical discipline of calculus allows us to calculate the area under a curve rather easily. It is called taking the **definite integral** of the curve. Once again, I cannot assume that you know calculus, so I will show you a graphical way to calculate the area under a curve. This method has its limitations, but it is better than nothing.

Notice that in the last two sections, I have discussed three things (velocity, acceleration, and total displacement) that are best determined using calculus. The velocity of an object is the slope of its position versus time curve, and the acceleration of an object is the slope of its velocity versus time curve. These can best be calculated using the calculus technique called the "derivative." Thus, we can say that velocity is the derivative of displacement versus time, while acceleration is the derivative of velocity versus time. Also, we can say that displacement is the definite integral of velocity versus time. This gives you an idea of how intimately linked calculus is with physics. Once you have a firm grasp on calculus, you might consider taking a calculus-based physics course to really appreciate the link between the two.

This, however, is not a calculus-based physics course, so I now want to show you how to calculate the area under a curve without using a definite integral. As I said before, this method has its limitations, but it is better than nothing.

EXAMPLE 2.2

The behavior of an object's one-dimensional velocity with respect to time is given below. What is the total displacement of the object over the entire time represented by the graph?

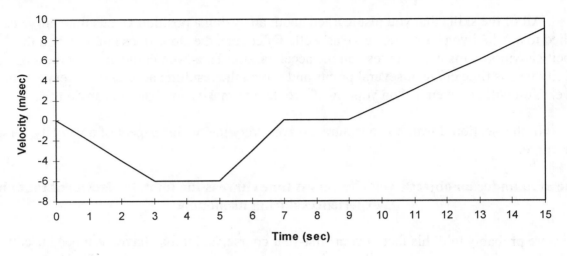

To determine the displacement, we must figure out the area under the curve. How do we do that? Well, first you need to know what "area under the curve" means. It means the area encompassed by the curve and the x-axis. Thus, if we redraw the graph, we can shade the area under the curve:

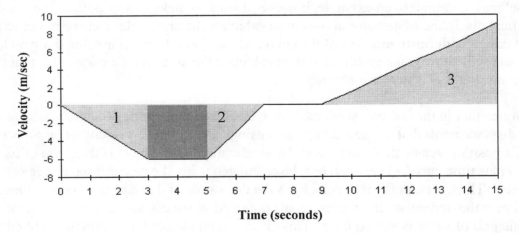

How do we determine the area here? Well, notice that I have shaded the area into four regions. Because the graph is composed of straight lines, the light gray areas (1, 2, and 3) are triangles, and the dark gray area is a rectangle. We know formulas to calculate the areas of these shapes. Thus, we can determine the area under the curve by adding the areas of the triangles (light gray regions) and the area of the rectangle (dark gray region).

How do we calculate the area of the triangles? Well, we know that the area of a triangle is given by:

$$\text{Area of a triangle } = \frac{1}{2} \cdot (\text{base}) \cdot (\text{height})$$

Let's look triangle #1.

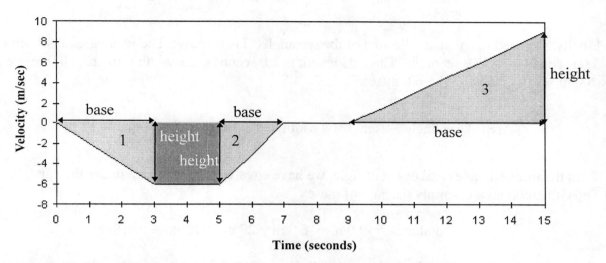

What is its height? The height of a triangle is defined as the length of a line drawn from the apex to the base so that it is perpendicular to the base. If you look at time = 3.0 seconds, you will see that there is a line which extends from the tip of the triangle to the x-axis. What is the length of the line? Read the graph. The line starts at y = 0.0 and travels to the tip of the triangle at -6.0 m/sec. Thus, the height is -6.0 m/sec. Don't let it bother you that the length of the line is negative. Remember, we are dealing with vector quantities here and, in one dimension, the sign represents direction.

What is the base? That's the length of the bottom line. The triangle starts at t = 0.0 seconds and ends at t = 3.0 seconds. Thus, the base is 3.0 seconds. Now we can calculate the area:

$$\text{Area of triangle \#1} = \frac{1}{2} \cdot (3.0 \text{ sec}) \cdot (-6.0 \frac{m}{sec}) = -9.0 \text{ m}$$

Notice two things about this number. First, the units work out so that the answer has the units of meters. That makes sense, since the area is suppose to tell us the displacement, which has units of length. Second, notice that the answer is negative. Even though you might think it odd that an area has a negative value, remember that signs tell us directions. Thus, this tells us that the object's displacement from t = 0.0 seconds to t= 3.0 seconds is in the negative direction.

Okay, triangle #2 starts at t = 5.0 seconds and continues through t = 7.0 seconds. This means its base is 2.0 seconds. Its height is -6.0 m/sec, because the apex is at -6.0 m/sec, and the line perpendicular to the base stops at 0.0 m/sec.

$$\text{Area of triangle \#2} = \frac{1}{2} \cdot (2.0 \text{ sec}) \cdot (-6.0 \frac{m}{sec}) = -6.0 \text{ m}$$

The last triangle starts at t = 9.0 seconds and runs to t=15.0 seconds. That's a base of 6.0 seconds. The apex is at 9.0 m/sec, so the height is 9.0 m/sec.

$$\text{Area of triangle \#3} = \frac{1}{2} \cdot (6.0 \text{ sec}) \cdot (9.0 \frac{m}{sec}) = 27 \text{ m}$$

Finally, we need to calculate the area of the rectangle. That's easy. The rectangle runs from t = 3.0 seconds to t = 5.0 seconds. Thus, its length is 2.0 seconds. Its width runs from 0.0 m/sec to -6.0 m/sec, so the width is -6.0 m/sec.

$$\text{Area of rectangle} = (\text{length}) \cdot (\text{width}) = (2.0 \text{ sec}) \cdot (-6.0 \frac{m}{sec}) = -12 \text{ m}$$

With the three triangles and one rectangle, we have covered all of the area under the curve. Thus, the total area is simply the sum of these:

$$\text{Total area} = -9.0 \text{ m} + -6.0 \text{ m} + 27 \text{ m} + -12 \text{ m} = 0 \text{ m}$$

The area under the curve, which also is the *displacement* of the object, is 0 m. What does this mean? Well, it means that the object ended up right where it started. Why? Look at the velocity. It started out negative, stayed negative for a while, eventually became zero, and then became positive. Thus, the object started moving in the negative direction, then slowed down to a stop, and then started moving in the positive direction. In the end, the object moved in the negative direction as far as it did in the positive direction. As a result, the overall displacement was zero.

Now that you have seen me work a problem like this, work one on your own so that you are certain you understand the process.

ON YOUR OWN

2.3 An object traveling in one dimension has the velocity versus time graph given below. What is the total displacement of the object?

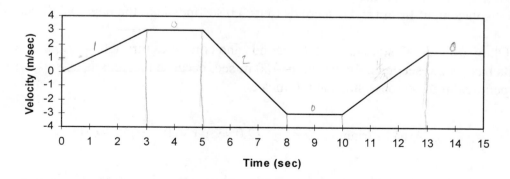

2.4 Sketch the acceleration versus time graph for this object.

The Major One-Dimensional Motion Equations

Now that you know how to fully analyze graphs related to motion in one dimension, it is time to revisit the major one-dimensional kinematic equations you learned in your first-year course. We have already discussed two of them, Equations (2.1) and (2.2). However, there are three more with which you need to work:

$$v = v_o + at \tag{2.3}$$

$$v^2 = v_o^2 + 2ax \tag{2.4}$$

$$x = v_o t + \frac{1}{2}at^2 \tag{2.5}$$

These equations contain the major kinematic variables - the velocity (v), the initial velocity (v_o), the acceleration (a), the displacement (x), and the time (t). You use one or more of Equations (2.1) - (2.5) depending on the information given in a problem. Remember, *these equations work only under conditions of <u>constant</u> acceleration*. If the acceleration varies, these equations cannot be used. To help "clear the cobwebs out of your mind," I want to work through two example problems, each of which should be review for you.

EXAMPLE 2.3

An object travels in one dimension with a constant acceleration of 0.56 m/sec² to the west. If it starts with an initial velocity of 3.2 m/sec east and travels for 15.0 seconds, what is its displacement?

In this problem, we are given the initial velocity (3.2 m/sec east), the acceleration (0.56 m/sec² west), and the time (15.0 sec). We are asked to calculate the displacement (x). From Equations (2.1) - (2.5), the only one which relates all of these quantities is Equation (2.5). Thus, that's the equation we will use. Now remember, we must be *very careful to consider direction* in this situation. Notice that the initial velocity is directed to the east but the acceleration is directed to the west. What does that mean? It means that acceleration *opposes* the initial velocity. Thus, the object is initially slowing down.

Mathematically, we take these directions into account with positive and negative signs. First, we define our directions. I will define motion to the west as negative and motion to the east as positive. The definition could be reversed. As long as we *stick to the definition*, which way is positive and which way is negative is irrelevant. Taking this definition into account, we can plug into the equation:

$$x = v_o t + \frac{1}{2}at^2$$

$$\mathbf{x} \;=\; (3.2\,\tfrac{m}{\text{sec}})\cdot(15.0\,\text{sec}) \;+\; \frac{1}{2}\cdot(-0.56\,\tfrac{m}{\text{sec}^2})\cdot(15.0\,\text{sec})^2 \;=\; -15\;m$$

The displacement, then, is <u>-15 m</u>, which means 15 meters to the west. The object, therefore, actually started out moving east, but it ended up west of its initial position. This means that the object started out traveling east (the initial velocity was positive). However, since acceleration opposed velocity, the object started slowing down. Since the objected ended up west of its initial position, we know that the object eventually slowed to a halt and then started traveling west. At that point, the acceleration and velocity were pointed in the same direction, so the object began speeding up. That continued, and by the end of the 15.0 seconds, the object was 15 meters west of its initial position.

What was the velocity of the object at the end of the 15.0 seconds?

At this point, either Equation (2.3) or Equation (2.4) would work, since we have all of the variables in each equation except for the final velocity (**v**). Equation (2.3) is much easier to handle, so I will use it:

$$\mathbf{v} = \mathbf{v}_o + \mathbf{at}$$

$$\mathbf{v} = 3.2\,\frac{m}{\text{sec}} + (-0.56\,\frac{m}{\text{sec}^2})\cdot(15.0\,\text{sec}) = -5.2\,\frac{m}{\text{sec}}$$

The final velocity, then, is <u>5.2 m/sec to the west</u>. We knew that it had to be pointed to the west, since the displacement told us that in the end, it was moving west. The negative sign on the velocity simply confirms this fact.

Okay, now that you are starting to remember how these equations are used, I want to remind you about **free fall**. As you should have learned in your first-year course, objects near the surface of the earth experience the same acceleration due to gravity. Whether the object weighs an ounce or a million pounds, the acceleration it experiences due to gravity does not change. In the absence of **air resistance**, then, all objects fall with exactly the same acceleration. This is called "free fall." Of course, air resistance reduces the acceleration due to gravity. A feather falls much more slowly than a rock not because of gravity but because of air resistance. A feather experiences the same acceleration due to gravity as does the rock. However, since air resistance affects the feather more strongly than the rock, the feather falls more slowly than the rock.

As you should recall from your first-year course, the acceleration due to gravity is 9.81 m/sec^2 downwards in metric units and 32.2 ft/sec^2 downwards in English units. You will be required to know those values from memory. Since the acceleration due to gravity is constant while an object is near the surface of the earth, free fall is a real-world example of motion under constant acceleration, and it is an excellent situation in which to use Equations (2.1) - (2.5).

EXAMPLE 2.4

A person stands on a bridge that is 25.0 meters above a river. He throws a ball straight up in the air with an initial velocity of 10.0 m/sec. Ignoring air resistance, what will the velocity of the ball be when it strikes the water below?

When doing these kinds of problems, you must be keenly aware of direction and use the proper signs. In this problem, you are given the initial velocity and the distance. You also know the acceleration. Because the object is in free fall, its acceleration is the acceleration due to gravity. The problem wants us to calculate the final velocity, so Equation (2.4) is the equation to use.

If you don't take direction into account properly, you will not get the right answer. Thus, we first must *define* direction. I will call motion upwards positive and motion downwards negative. Thus, the initial velocity is 10.0 m/sec, because the ball is being thrown upwards. The acceleration is -9.81 m/sec^2, because gravity accelerates objects downward. What is the displacement? The river is 25.0 m *below* the point at which the ball was thrown. Thus, the displacement is -25.0 meters. Now that we have all of the proper signs, we can plug the numbers into the equation.

$$v^2 = v_o{}^2 + 2ax$$

$$v^2 = (10.0 \frac{m}{sec})^2 + 2 \cdot (-9.81 \frac{m}{sec^2}) \cdot (-25.0 \, m)$$

$$v^2 = 1.00 \times 10^2 \frac{m^2}{sec^2} + 491 \frac{m^2}{sec^2}$$

$$v^2 = 591 \frac{m^2}{sec^2}$$

$$v = \pm 24.3 \frac{m}{sec}$$

Notice two things about the solution. First, I had to report 100 as 1.00×10^2 because I needed three significant figures. The number 100 has only one significant figure, so I had to use scientific notation to write the answer to the proper number of significant figures. Also, notice that the velocity has a ± in it. Remember, when you take a square root (the final step of the solution), you do not know whether the answer is positive or negative, because both signs work. However, we can reason out which is right. The ball is moving downwards when it hits the water. Since upwards is the positive direction, we know that the ball's velocity must therefore be negative. Thus, the answer is -24.3 m/sec, or 24.3 m/sec downwards.

What is the maximum height (relative to the river) that the ball reaches in its path?

As you learned in your first-year course, the velocity of the ball will be zero when it reaches its maximum height. Thus, we know that the final velocity at that point is zero. We also know the initial velocity and the acceleration, so Equation (2.4) is the equation to use again. Keeping the direction definitions the same:

$$v^2 = v_o{}^2 + 2ax$$

$$(0)^2 = (10.0 \ \frac{m}{sec})^2 + 2 \cdot (-9.81 \frac{m}{sec^2}) \cdot (x)$$

$$x = \frac{-1.00 \times 10^2 \ \frac{m^2}{sec^2}}{(2) \cdot (-9.81 \ \frac{m}{sec^2})} = 5.10 \ m$$

Notice that the displacement is positive. That makes sense. The highest point will be above the point from which it was thrown. However, this is *not* the answer. The question asks what is the height *relative to the river*. Remember, displacement gives the position *relative to the initial starting point*, which is 25.0 m above the river. Thus, the highest point relative to the river is 5.10 m + 25.0 m = 30.1 m. Notice here that because I am adding, I do not count significant figures. Instead, I go by precision. Since both numbers go out to the tenths place, the answer goes out to the tenths place.

How long does the ball stay in the air before hitting the river?

You could use two equations to solve for this. We know the final velocity when it strikes the river (-24 m/sec), we know the acceleration (-9.81 m/sec^2), we know the initial velocity (10.0 m/sec), and we know the displacement (-25.0 m). Thus, *either* Equation (2.3) or (2.5) will work. Equation (2.3) does not involve solving a quadratic equation, however, so I will use it. Once again, remember that the signs must be right!

$$\mathbf{v} = \mathbf{v}_o + \mathbf{at}$$

$$-24 \ \frac{m}{sec} = 10.0 \ \frac{m}{sec} + (-9.81 \frac{m}{sec^2}) \cdot t$$

$$t = \frac{-24 \ \frac{m}{sec} - 10.0 \ \frac{m}{sec}}{-9.81 \frac{m}{sec^2}} = \frac{(-34 \ \frac{m}{sec})}{-9.81 \frac{m}{sec^2}} = 3.5 \ sec$$

When students are first faced with problems like the first one in the example box, they typically think about splitting the problem up into sections. They first determine the velocity that the ball has as it falls past the point from which it was thrown (which is easy - equal and opposite of its initial velocity) and then start another problem with the ball falling down from that point with that initial velocity. Similarly, most students take the last problem in the example box and split it up into two parts. They calculate the time it takes for the ball to travel up and then back down to the point from which it was thrown, and then they calculate the time it takes the ball to fall the rest of the way. Finally, they then add the two times. Although you certainly *can* solve problems like that, there is no reason to. It is more work and you have more chances of messing up. You can solve virtually all one-dimensional motion problems by just using one equation once, as long as you define your directions properly and stick to those definitions. Perform the following experiment to give you more practice with defining directions.

EXPERIMENT 2.1
Measuring Your Vertical Pitching Speed

Supplies:

- A ball that is easy to throw but not too light (Use a baseball or golf ball or something that is heavy enough so that air resistance is not a factor.)
- A tape measure or meter stick
- A stopwatch
- Someone to help you

Introduction - In order to test the speed at which a baseball pitcher throws, baseball teams usually employ radar guns, which use the Doppler effect to determine the speed of the ball. However, you can get a pretty good estimate of the speed at which you throw by simply using the kinematics equations in a situation which involves *mostly* one-dimensional motion.

Procedure:

1. Find an area outdoors where you can throw the ball around but not risk breaking things. The area should be level within a circle of at least 1.5 meters from where you are standing.
2. Stand the way that you normally would stand when you throw a ball, and hold your arm straight up as high as it will go.
3. Have your helper measure the distance from the center of your palm to the ground. Record that distance.
4. Hold the ball in one hand and the stopwatch in the other. Do not adjust your stance.
5. Now throw the ball *straight up* in the air, extending your arm fully in the release. When the ball leaves your hand, start the stopwatch. When it hits the ground, stop the stopwatch. In order for this experiment to work, the ball must land pretty near where you are standing, telling you that it traveled mostly in one dimension (straight up and straight back down). Ideally, you should have to jump out of the way to avoid being hit. However, as long as the

ball lands within 1.5 meters of where you are standing, the motion is *mostly* one-dimensional, and the error associated with the slight motion in the other dimension is not large. If the ball landed within 1.5 meters of where you are standing, record the time. If not, ignore the time.

6. Repeat step #5 until you have 10 times recorded. Thus, you have 10 trials in which you have measured the time it takes for the ball to travel up and then back down to the ground.

7. Average your 10 times to get the average time it took the ball to travel. The process of averaging, as you should already know, compensates for random experimental errors such as not starting the stopwatch at precisely the time the ball leaves your hands or not stopping the stopwatch at precisely the time that the ball hits the ground.

8. Now you have all of the information you need in order to calculate the initial velocity, which is the velocity at which you can throw a ball straight up in the air. The displacement is the distance measured from the center of the palm to the ground. Remember, however, that the sign is important. Define upwards motion as positive. With that definition, the displacement is negative. In addition, you know the acceleration: -9.81 m/sec^2 or -32.2 ft/sec^2, depending on the units with which you want to work. Finally, you know the time (the average of your 10 trials). If you put those numbers into Equation (2.5), you have everything except the initial velocity, so you can solve for it.

9. So that the number has some meaning for you, convert it to miles per hour. You can use the fact that 1 m = 0.000621 miles and 1 hour = 3600 seconds. Your answer will probably be somewhere between 15 and 70 miles per hour. When I did this experiment, my throwing speed was 28 miles per hour.

Now please understand that there are errors associated with this experiment. Most people can throw faster horizontally than vertically, because the mechanics are easier and the whole body can aid in the throw. Also, the fact that the motion is not perfectly one-dimensional adds error as well. Air resistance also plays a very small role. Overall, however, this experiment gives you a basic idea of how fast a ball is moving when you throw it.

Now remember, one-dimensional motion concepts like this should be review for you. However, you should be so comfortable with them from your first-year course and this quick refresher that you can now easily do problems which would have been considered incredibly tough when you took physics before. Make sure that this is the case by solving the "on your own" problems which follow.

ON YOUR OWN

2.5 A baseball player throws a ball into the air with an initial velocity of 22.0 m/sec upwards. It travels up and then right back down, hitting the ground 4.58 seconds later.

a. From what height was the ball thrown?
b. How long did it take the ball to reach its maximum height?
c. What was the ball's acceleration at its maximum height?

2.6 An object is given an initial shove which provides it with an unknown initial velocity. Its acceleration is measured to be a constant 1.5 m/sec². At a time of 3.0 seconds after the shove, its velocity is measured to be -12.0 m/sec. How fast will it be traveling at a time of 5.0 seconds after the shove?

Air Resistance and Terminal Velocity

During the entire discussion of free fall, you were told to ignore air resistance. In many cases, that introduces only a small error in the calculation, since air resistance is negligible in many situations. However, air resistance *can* be a factor, especially when an object is large, has a small mass, or is traveling very quickly. Why does it become important in these cases? Well, consider this equation for the force due to air resistance:

$$F_{drag} = \frac{1}{2}C\rho Av^2 \tag{2.6}$$

In this equation, "F_{drag}" is the force due to air resistance (air resistance is often called "drag"), "C" is a dimensionless constant related to the shape of the object, "ρ" is the density of the air, "A" is the area of the largest cross section of the object which is perpendicular to the path of travel, and "v" is the speed of the object.

Now before I go into the details of this equation, I want you to look at it conceptually. Ignoring "C," what does the equation tell us about the air resistance an object experiences? First, it depends on the density of the air. The more dense the air, the more air resistance there is. This should make sense. After all, if there are a *lot* of molecules in the air through which you are traveling, there will be a lot of resistance. The fewer molecules, the lower the resistance.

Now do you see why airplanes like to fly at high altitudes? The higher the altitude, the less dense the air. Thus, the higher a plane flies, the less air resistance it experiences. This means that the higher a plane flies, the less fuel it consumes, because the less it has to fight air resistance. Now, of course, it takes extra fuel to climb to a high altitude, since while the airplane climbs, it is working against gravity. As a result, the trip has to be long enough to be worth getting to a higher altitude. Nevertheless, in general, airplanes like to fly as high as is realistic to reduce the density of the air through which they are traveling so as to reduce drag.

The force of air resistance also depends on the size of the object. The larger the cross section that is perpendicular to the direction of travel, the more the air resistance. This should also make sense. If an object travels through the air, the part of the object that must "shove" air out of the way is the part that will cause the drag. Thus, the cross section of the object which is perpendicular to its velocity vector will be the one that affects drag. The larger the cross section, the more air that must be "shoved" out of the way so as to allow the object to move. Thus, the more air resistance it will experience. You can see the effect that the cross section of an object has on air resistance by performing this simple experiment.

EXPERIMENT 2.2
The Effect of Cross Section on Air Resistance

Supplies

- Two round balloons (They need to both be the same size before they are inflated.)
- A stepladder or other platform on which to stand

Introduction - The force of air resistance depends on the cross-sectional area of an object. This experiment demonstrates that effect.

Procedure:

1. Take one balloon and inflate it mostly full. Tie it off so that it stays inflated.
2. Take the second balloon and inflate it only slightly. Make sure you have inflated it enough so that it has the proper shape, but it should be no more than half the size of the other balloon.
3. Climb up on the ladder with the two balloons. **BE CAREFUL!!!**
4. Hold one balloon in each hand at the same height, and drop them at the same time.
5. Note which one hits the ground first.
6. Repeat the experiment once or twice to make sure your results make sense.

What happened in the experiment? The small balloon should have hit the ground noticeably sooner than the large balloon. Why? They were roughly the same shape, so the "C" for each object was the same. They were traveling through the same air, so " ρ "was the same for each balloon. Their initial velocities were the same so, at least initially, "v" was the same in both cases. However, the cross section perpendicular to the motion (A) for each balloon was different. The "A" for the large balloon was significantly larger than the "A" for the small balloon. As a result, the large balloon experienced more drag and was thus slower at reaching the ground.

Finally, the force of air resistance also depends on the speed of the object as it travels. In fact, it depends on the speed of the object more than it depends on the other factors. The force of air resistance increases as the *square* of the speed. Thus, if the object moves three times as fast, it experiences *nine times* the air resistance! Supersonic jets such as the Concorde airplane fly at very high altitudes - much higher than that of slower jets. The main reason for this is that the effect of velocity on air resistance is so high that a supersonic jet must do anything it can to counteract air resistance. About the only thing it can do is climb to very high altitudes where the density of air is as low as possible. In general, then, the faster a jet travels, the higher it travels so as to try and counteract the strong effect that its speed has on the air resistance.

Okay, now that you have learned the basic factors which affect air resistance, I want to apply Equation (2.6) to the concept of **terminal velocity**. Since air resistance depends on speed, the faster an object travels, the larger the air resistance. Well, consider what this means for an object which is falling. As it falls, its velocity increases. This means the air resistance increases.

What does that do to the acceleration of the object? It *decreases* the acceleration. Thus, the farther an object falls, the *less* it accelerates, because air resistance increases with increasing speed. At some point, the object will be traveling so fast that the air resistance becomes strong enough to *completely counteract the force of gravity*. At that point, the object will still fall because it has velocity in the downward direction. However, since there is no more acceleration, the velocity will not change. No matter how far the object falls after that point, its speed will not increase. That speed is called the object's "terminal velocity."

Since we have an equation for air resistance, and since you already know a lot of physics from your first-year course, we can actually develop an equation for the terminal velocity of any object. How do we do that? Well, let's first think about the forces acting on an object that is falling. Gravity is pulling down on the object with a force that is equal to the mass times the acceleration of gravity (you should know that $F_{gravity} = mg$ from your first-year physics course). The only other force acting on the object is air resistance. This force opposes the force due to gravity. Thus, the *total* force acting on the object is simply:

$$F_{total} = F_{gravity} - F_{air\ resistance}$$

Using the fact that $F_{gravity} = mg$ and Equation (2.6), we get.

$$F_{total} = mg - \frac{1}{2}C\rho Av^2$$

Now remember, Newton's Second Law says that the *total* force on any object is equal to the mass of the object times its acceleration.

$$ma = mg - \frac{1}{2}C\rho Av^2$$

Dividing through by the mass of the object, we get:

$$a = g - \frac{1}{2}\frac{C\rho Av^2}{m}$$

When will an object reach terminal velocity? That happens when the acceleration is zero. Thus, terminal velocity is defined as the velocity at which $a = 0$.

$$0 = g - \frac{1}{2}\frac{C\rho Av_{terminal}^2}{m}$$

Now we can simply solve for $v_{terminal}$.

$$v_{terminal} = \sqrt{\frac{2mg}{C\rho A}} \tag{2.7}$$

Notice, then, that if you know the mass, cross-sectional area, and "C" for any object, you can calculate its terminal velocity. Mass and cross-sectional area are rather easy to determine, but what is "C?" As I noted before, "C" is a quantity which depends on the shape. For a perfect sphere, C = 0.50. The more irregular the shape, the larger the value for "C." Some very irregularly-shaped objects have a "C" as high as 2.

EXAMPLE 2.5

The International Tennis Federation regulates the size, shape and mass of tennis balls so that their air resistance is standard from tennis match to tennis match. A regulation tennis ball must be spherical (C = 0.50), have a diameter within 5% of 6.67 cm, and have a mass within 3% of 56.69 grams. Given the fact that the density of air at 1.00 atm is 1290 g/m^3, what is the terminal velocity of a tennis ball?

This is a simple application of Equation (2.7). First, however, we need to determine the area of the cross section of the tennis ball. The largest cross section of a sphere is given by πr^2. If the diameter is 6.67 cm, the radius is 3.34 cm, which is 0.0334 m. Thus, the area is:

$$\text{Area} = \pi r^2 = (3.1415) \cdot (0.0334 \text{ m})^2 = 0.00350 \text{ m}^2$$

Now we can plug the numbers into the equation:

$$v_{terminal} = \sqrt{\frac{2mg}{C\rho A}}$$

$$v_{terminal} = \sqrt{\frac{2 \cdot (56.69 \text{ g}) \cdot (9.81 \frac{m}{sec^2})}{(0.50) \cdot (1290 \frac{g}{m^3}) \cdot (0.00350 \text{ m}^2)}} = \sqrt{490 \frac{m^2}{sec^2}} = \underline{22 \frac{m}{sec}}$$

If a tennis ball is dropped from a very large height, then, the maximum velocity it can ever reach is 22 m/sec downwards.

Before I leave this section, I want to make two quick points about Equation (2.7). First of all, this equation is only valid for objects that are either large or moving at reasonably high speeds. This equation applies to most objects in free fall, since free fall produces large speeds. For small objects traveling slowly, a completely different equation applies, which I do not want to discuss. Equation (2.7) is, by far, the most widely-applicable equation for objects and situations with which we are familiar. I just want to make it clear that it is not applicable in *all* situations. Second, this equation actually applies to object moving through *any* fluid (as far as physicists are concerned, air is a fluid). Thus, if you substitute the density of water for the density of air in Equation (2.7), you will end up calculating the terminal velocity of the object as it falls in a deep pool of water.

ON YOUR OWN

2.7 A 0.22-caliber rifle (a standard rifle used for target practice and to hunt small animals) fires a bullet whose diameter is 0.22 inches and whose mass is 38.0 grams. Given that the density of air is 1290 g/m^3 and C = 0.50, what is the terminal velocity of a bullet shot from a 0.22-caliber rifle?

Kinematics in Two Dimensions

Now that you are thoroughly refreshed on kinematics in one dimension, it is time to review and go deeper into the concepts of kinematics in two dimensions. Remember, so far we have dealt with motion in a straight line. The direction of motion is simply given by positive or negative signs. Motion in two dimensions is more difficult to analyze, since motion can occur both left or right and, at the same time, up or down. Consider, for example, the motion of a football being kicked by a football player.

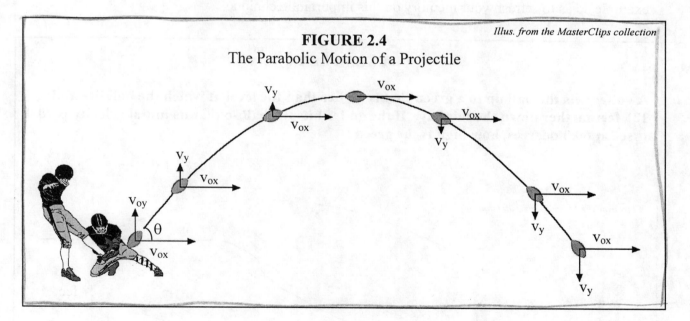

Illus. from the MasterClips collection

FIGURE 2.4
The Parabolic Motion of a Projectile

In this situation, the ball is given a kick by the football player. This gives the ball an initial velocity ($\mathbf{v}_o$), which can be specified by an initial speed (v_o) and an angle relative to the horizontal (θ). Thus, the initial velocity has a component which is horizontal to the ground (v_{ox}), which makes the ball travel to your right as you look at the figure. It also has a component which is perpendicular to the ground (v_{oy}), making the ball travel up in the air initially.

As you learned in your first-year course, the path traveled by the ball will be in the shape of a parabola. Why? Well, once the ball has left the kicker's foot, the only force acting on the ball is gravity. However, gravity works only to pull the ball *downwards*. As shown in the figure, then, gravity will start decreasing the upwards component of the velocity until that component of the velocity reaches zero. At that point, the ball reaches the maximum height in its trajectory. After that, since gravity is still accelerating the ball downwards, the ball will start to fall, its downward velocity increasing until it reaches the ground (or some other obstacle).

Ignoring air resistance, there is NO force acting on the ball in the horizontal direction. Thus, the horizontal component of the initial velocity stays constant throughout the entire trajectory. As a result, the ball travels horizontally in a very steady fashion. The superposition of its vertical motion with its horizontal motion results in the shape of a parabola, as shown in the figure.

Notice the reasoning that I am using here. I discussed the vertical motion of the projectile without referring to its horizontal motion at all. In the same way, I discussed its horizontal motion without discussing its vertical motion. That's because *we analyze two-dimensional motion by breaking it down into two one-dimensional situations*. That's how you were taught to analyze these things in your first-year course. If you need to solve a two-dimensional motion problem, simply break it down into two one-dimensional motion problems. Study the following example so as to refresh your memory on this important technique.

EXAMPLE 2.6

A golfer hits the ball up to a green that is higher than the level at which the ball lies and 121 feet farther down the fairway. If the golfer hits the ball so that its initial velocity is 70.0 ft/sec at 60.0 degrees, how high is the green?

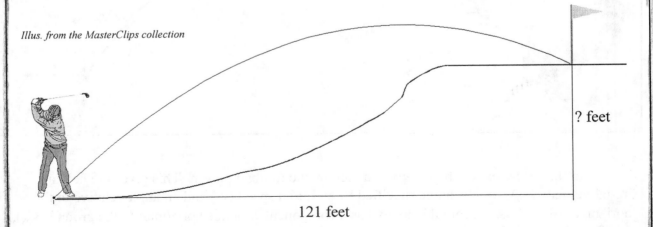

Illus. from the MasterClips collection

? feet

121 feet

This is definitely a two-dimensional problem. The ball travels both horizontally and vertically to the green. Thus, we split it into two one-dimensional problems. Now, we want to learn something about the vertical dimension (we want to know how *high* the hill is). In these problems, we typically learn something from one dimension and then use that knowledge to learn something about the other dimension. In this case, then, we will start with the horizontal dimension. We can probably learn something from that dimension to apply to the vertical dimension.

What do we know about the horizontal dimension? Well, we know that the acceleration in that dimension is zero. There are no forces working on the ball in the horizontal dimension once it leaves the golf club. Thus, the acceleration in that dimension is zero. We also know the initial velocity in the horizontal dimension: the horizontal component of the velocity vector.

$$v_{ox} = v_o \cdot \cos\theta$$

$$v_{ox} = (70.0 \; \frac{ft}{sec}) \cdot \cos(60.0) = 35.0 \; \frac{ft}{sec}$$

Finally, we know that the distance the ball travels in the horizontal dimension is 121 feet. What can we learn from this information? We can learn the *time* it takes for the ball to travel.

$$\mathbf{x} = \mathbf{v_o}t + \frac{1}{2}\mathbf{a}t^2$$

$$121 \; ft = (35.0 \; \frac{ft}{sec}) \cdot t + \frac{1}{2} \cdot (0) \cdot t^2$$

$$t = \frac{121 \; ft}{35.0 \; \frac{ft}{sec}} = 3.46 \; sec$$

Okay, we know that the ball was in the air for 3.46 seconds. Now we can look at the vertical dimension and see *how high* the ball is at 3.46 seconds. That will tell us the height of the green. First, however, we need to know the initial velocity in the vertical dimension.

$$v_{oy} = v_o \cdot \sin\theta$$

$$v_{oy} = (70.0 \; \frac{ft}{sec}) \cdot \sin(60.0) = 60.6 \; \frac{ft}{sec}$$

We also need to know the acceleration in the vertical dimension. Unlike the horizontal dimension, there is a force acting on the golf ball in the vertical dimension. It is *gravity*. Gravity is constantly pulling the ball towards the ground. Thus, the acceleration is -32.2 ft/sec². The acceleration is negative because the ball is being pulled downwards, and since I made the initial velocity positive, that tells you that the upwards direction is positive. I could have made the initial velocity negative. Had I done that, the acceleration would be positive.

So, we know the initial velocity, acceleration, and time. From that, we can determine how far the ball traveled in the y-dimension.

$$\mathbf{x} \;=\; \mathbf{v}_o \mathbf{t} \;+\; \frac{1}{2}\mathbf{a}\mathbf{t}^2$$

$$\mathbf{x} = (60.6\;\frac{\text{ft}}{\text{sec}})\cdot(3.46\;\text{sec}) + \frac{1}{2}\cdot(-32.2\;\frac{\text{ft}}{\text{sec}^2})\cdot(3.46\;\text{sec})^2 = 17\;\text{ft}$$

The green, then, is <u>17 ft</u> above the ball.

Hopefully, that example helped you remember how to analyze two-dimensional problems. Now I want to go through a more difficult two-dimensional problem to give you an idea of what I expect from you in this course. Before I do that, however, I want to remind you of an equation that has limited usefulness but is nevertheless convenient: the **range equation** for a projectile.

$$R = \frac{(v_o{}^2)\cdot \sin(2\theta)}{g} \tag{2.8}$$

In this equation, "R" is the horizontal distance over which the projectile travels, "v_o" is the initial speed of the projectile, "θ" is the launch angle, and "g" is the acceleration due to gravity. Now remember

Equation (2.8) only works when the projectile lands at the same height as that from which it was launched

This equation, then, was not applicable to the example given above, since the ball landed higher than the spot from which it was launched. Nevertheless, it is useful in some instances, and it is an equation you should know.

EXAMPLE 2.7

A field-goal kicker is trying to kick a long field goal. He aims his kick so that the ball will leave at an angle of 25.0° relative to the ground. In order for the field goal to be good, it must pass *over* the crossbar, which is 2.44 m high. Thus, we will say that when it reaches the goal post, the ball must be at least 2.45 m off of the ground.   If the goal post is 60.0 yards (54.8 m) away, what minimum initial speed must he supply to the ball?

   This is a tougher question than you ever saw in your first-year course. Nevertheless, we attack all of these problems the same way. We split them up into two one-dimensional problems. We usually start with the dimension in which we are not interested, as useful information can be found there. Thus, we will start with the horizontal dimension. We need to use the velocity in the horizontal dimension, but we don't know the magnitude of the initial velocity. Thus, we will have to keep that as a variable.

$$v_{ox} = v_o \cdot \cos\theta = v_o \cdot \cos(25.0) = 0.906 \cdot v_o$$

We know the distance at which the ball must be 2.45 m high (it must be at that height after it has traveled 54.8 m in the horizontal dimension). Thus, we could try to find the time it takes for the ball to get to that point.

$$\mathbf{x} = \mathbf{v}_o t + \frac{1}{2}\mathbf{at}^2$$

$$54.8 \text{ m} = (0.906 \cdot v_o) \cdot t + \frac{1}{2} \cdot (0) \cdot t^2$$

You might think that we are stuck now, since there are two unknowns. However, remember that there are more equations to be found in the other dimension! Thus, let's go ahead and solve for the time in terms of v_o. Perhaps we can use that in the vertical dimension.

$$t = \frac{54.8 \text{ m}}{0.906 \cdot v_o} = \frac{60.5 \text{ m}}{v_o}$$

Now let's go to the vertical dimension. We know that at the time noted above, the height *must* be 2.45 m. Once again, we do not know v, so we cannot completely calculate the initial vertical velocity. However, we can develop an equation for it:

$$v_{oy} = v_o \cdot \sin\theta = v_o \cdot \sin(25.0) = 0.423 \cdot v_o$$

Now let's see what we can do with this information.

$$\mathbf{x} = \mathbf{v}_o t + \frac{1}{2}\mathbf{at}^2$$

$$2.45 \text{ m} = (0.423 \cdot v_o) \cdot \frac{60.5 \text{ m}}{v_o} + \frac{1}{2} \cdot (-9.81 \frac{m}{\sec^2}) \cdot (\frac{60.5 \text{ m}}{v_o})^2$$

$$2.45 \text{ m} = 25.6 \text{ m} + \frac{-1.80 \times 10^4}{v_o^2} \frac{m^3}{\sec^2}$$

$$\frac{1.80 \times 10^4}{v_o{}^2} \frac{m^3}{sec^2} = 25.6 \; m - 2.45 \; m$$

$$\frac{1.80 \times 10^4}{v_o{}^2} \frac{m^3}{sec^2} = 23.2 \; m$$

$$v_o{}^2 = \frac{1.80 \times 10^4 \; \dfrac{m^3}{sec^2}}{23.2 \; \cancel{m}} = 776 \; \frac{m^2}{sec^2}$$

$$v_o = \pm 27.9 \; \frac{m}{sec}$$

When you take a square root, you always have a +/- sign to deal with. However, we know that speed is always positive so the initial speed that he must give the ball is 27.9 m/sec.

Now what made that problem difficult? It was just another two-dimensional motion problem. However, it was clearly more difficult than the previous one. The reason it was more difficult is that you could not get a *number* for the time. Instead, you had to leave it as an expression in terms of the initial speed. This always bothers students. Somehow, students are more comfortable working with numbers rather than expressions. Nevertheless, sometimes you have to use expressions rather than numbers. Let's try one more so that you are comfortable with this kind of problem.

EXAMPLE 2.8

A ship is firing its guns (v_o = 750.0 ft/sec) at another ship which has run out of ammunition. To avoid the guns, the other ship is trying to hide. It gets behind an island that has a large mountain (2000.0 feet high) on it. That way, the mountain is between the two ships. The ship that is firing is 2600.0 feet from the tip of the mountain. How far from the tip of the mountain must the hiding ship stray before the firing ship can hit it? The firing ship can fire its guns at any angle.

Illus. by Megan Whitaker

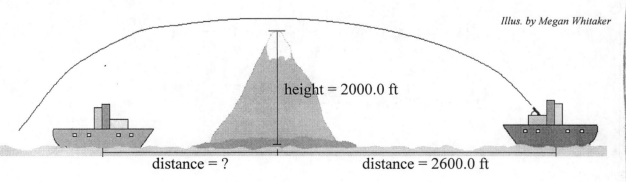

height = 2000.0 ft

distance = ?   distance = 2600.0 ft

If you think about it, the mountain puts constraints on the range of angles that the firing ship can use. After all, if the angle is too shallow or too steep, the projectiles will hit the mountain and be stopped. Thus, we know that the projectiles must be at least 2000.0 feet high when they are 2600.0 feet from the ship, or they will never get over the mountain. That's the constraint. Well, at what time will the projectiles be at 2600.0 feet away from where they were launched? We can look in the horizontal dimension to find out. Of course, we do not know θ, so the initial velocity in the horizontal dimension must be left in terms of theta:

$$v_{ox} = v_o \cdot \cos\theta = (750.0 \frac{ft}{sec}) \cdot \cos\theta$$

Now we can determine the time:

$$2600.0 \text{ ft} = (750.0 \frac{ft}{sec}) \cdot \cos\theta \cdot t + \frac{1}{2} \cdot (0) \cdot t^2$$

$$t = \frac{3.467 \text{ sec}}{\cos\theta}$$

At that time, the projectiles *must* be at least 2000.0 ft high. Thus, we can take that time and put it into the equation for the vertical dimension. Once again, we do not know θ, so the initial velocity in the vertical dimension is left in terms of θ:

$$v_{oy} = v_o \cdot \sin\theta = (750.0 \frac{ft}{sec}) \cdot \sin\theta$$

Now we can plug the information into the equation:

$$x = v_o t + \frac{1}{2} at^2$$

$$2000.0 \text{ ft} = (750.0 \frac{ft}{sec}) \cdot \sin\theta \cdot (\frac{3.467 \text{ sec}}{\cos\theta}) + \frac{1}{2} \cdot (-32.2 \frac{ft}{sec^2}) \cdot (\frac{3.467 \text{ sec}}{\cos\theta})^2$$

$$2000.0 \text{ ft} = (2.600 \times 10^3 \text{ ft}) \cdot (\frac{\sin\theta}{\cos\theta}) - (194 \text{ ft}) \cdot (\frac{1}{\cos^2\theta})$$

? Shouldn't this be squared?

This looks like a *bad* equation, but to solve it, all we have to do is remember three trigonometric identities. The first two are easy. You know that sine over cosine is tangent. You also know that $\frac{1}{\cos\theta}$ is secθ.

$$2000.0 \text{ ft} = (2.600 \times 10^3 \text{ ft}) \cdot \tan\theta - (194 \text{ ft}) \cdot (\sec^2\theta)$$

?

The next trigonometric identity is kind of obscure.

$$\sec^2 \theta = 1 + \tan^2 \theta$$

Plugging that into the equation gives us:

$$2000.0 \text{ ft} = (2.600 \times 10^3 \text{ ft}) \cdot \tan\theta - (194 \text{ ft}) \cdot (1 + \tan^2\theta)$$

$$(194 \text{ ft}) \cdot \tan^2 \theta - (2.600 \times 10^3 \text{ ft}) \cdot \tan\theta + \underline{2194 \text{ ft}} = 0$$

Shouldn't this be 2000?

What is this? This is a quadratic equation with $\tan\theta$ as the variable. Thus, we can use the quadratic formula to solve for $\tan\theta$:

$$\tan\theta = \frac{2.600 \times 10^3 \text{ ft} \pm \sqrt{(2.600 \times 10^3 \text{ ft})^2 - 4 \cdot (194 \text{ ft}) \cdot (2194 \text{ ft})}}{2 \cdot (194 \text{ ft})} = \frac{2.600 \times 10^3 \text{ ft} \pm 2249 \text{ ft}}{388 \text{ ft}}$$

This gives us two possible answers. First,

$$\tan\theta = \frac{351}{388} \qquad \tan\theta = \frac{4849}{388}$$

or

$$\theta = 42.1° \qquad \theta = 85.4°$$

What does this mean? Well, if you think about it, there is a minimum angle and a maximum angle at which the gun must aim to get the projectile over the mountain:

Illus. by Megan Whitaker

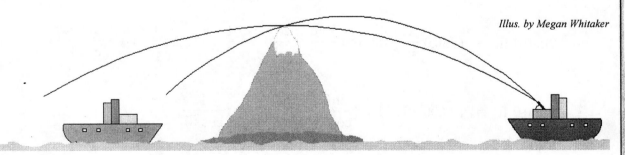

Our results tell us that the minimum angle is 42.1 degrees and the maximum angle is 85.5 degrees. Now, we have done *a lot* of work but have still not answered the question. How far must the hiding boat be from the tip of the mountain before the firing boat can hit it? Well, if you think about it, the maximum angle will result in the projectile falling closest to the tip of the mountain (see the figure above). Thus, we just need to calculate how far that projectile travels in the horizontal dimension. That's easy, given the range equation. This is a situation in which the range equation is applicable, so we might as well use it.

$$R = \frac{(v_o{}^2) \cdot \sin(2\theta)}{g} = \frac{(750.0 \, \frac{ft}{sec})^2 \cdot \sin(2 \cdot 85.4)}{32.2 \, \frac{ft}{sec^2}} = \frac{(562500 \, \frac{ft^2}{sec^2}) \cdot (0.160)}{32.2 \, \frac{ft}{sec^2}} = 2.80 \times 10^3 \, ft$$

Of course, that's *still not quite the answer*. The question asked how far the hiding boat must be from the tip of the mountain in order for the other boat's projectiles to hit it. Well, the mountain is 2,600.0 ft from the firing ship, and the projectile travels a total of 2,800 ft. Thus, it will land 200 ft from the tip of the mountain. Thus, if the hiding ship is 2.0x10² feet from the tip of the mountain, the other ship will be able to hit it. If it can stay closer to the mountain than that, the other ship will never be able to hit it.

That was a hard problem, wasn't it? What made it hard? Two things made it hard. The first was that, once again, you could not work with numbers. You had to leave θ in as a variable. The other thing that made it hard was the fact that you had to recall trigonometric identities. This actually brings up an important point. Precalculus is a prerequisite for this course. Thus, you have to *remember* what you learned in that course so that you can use it in this one. Therefore, I will hold you responsible for remembering trigonometric identities. I will say this, however.

You will never have to remember a trigonometric identity that I did not cover within the module.

Thus, any identities you need to know will be used or listed in the module. If they are not there, you need not remember them. I might *give* them to you on a test, but you will not need to memorize them unless I specifically used them in the module you are studying. For the test in this module, then, you must know the three trigonometric identities I just used to solve the example. If there are any others that you need to use on the test, *they* will be provided.

ON YOUR OWN

2.8 A person is shooting cannonballs at a castle. The cannon is 150.0 meters from the castle wall, and the wall is 45.0 m high. It can shoot its projectiles with a speed of 65.0 m/sec, and it is currently aimed at an angle of 25.0 degrees. Will the projectiles pass over the wall? If not, how high will they be when they hit the wall?

2.9 For the situation above, what range of firing angles must be used in order to get the projectiles over the wall?

2.10 Any projectile following a parabolic path will pass thorough every height (except for its maximum height) twice. Develop an equation that gives the *time in between* the first time it reaches any height, h, and the second time it reaches the same height. The equation should be given in terms of h, the initial speed (v_o), the launch angle (θ), and gravitation acceleration (g).

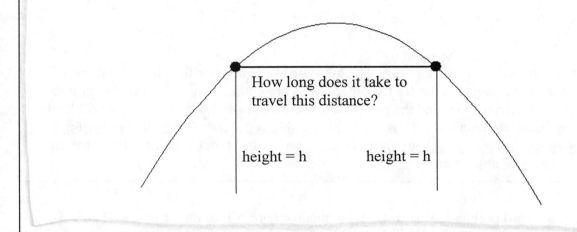

How long does it take to travel this distance?

height = h   height = h

ANSWERS TO THE ON YOUR OWN PROBLEMS

2.1 The object stops when the slope of the curve is zero. That happens in three places:

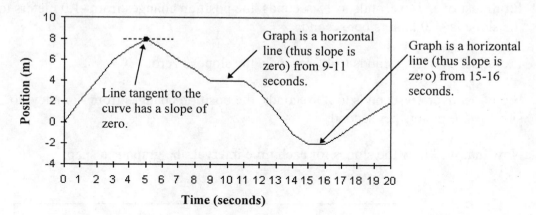

Although the velocity is zero in three regions of the graph, the question asked at what times did the object stop *and change direction*. That happens at 5 seconds, because the slope goes from positive before 5 seconds to negative after 5 seconds. However, between 9 and 11 seconds, the velocity is zero, but the slope before 9 seconds is negative as is the slope after 11 seconds. Thus, the object did not change directions. Finally, from 15-16 seconds, the velocity is zero and the slope changes from negative prior to 15 seconds to positive after 16 seconds. In the end, then, the object stopped and changed directions twice: once at 5 seconds and once from 15 to 16 seconds.

2.2 To sketch the velocity versus time curve, we must calculate slopes at different points. This is reasonably easy to do, however, since the curve is made of straight lines. Thus, we just section off the straight lines and calculate the slope of each line.

From 0 - 3 seconds, the curve is a straight line. Over 3.0 seconds, the position goes from 0.0 m to 6.0 meters. Thus, the velocity is 2.0 meters per second.

From just over 3 seconds to 5 seconds, we have another straight line. During those 2.0 seconds, the displacement goes from 6.0 meters to 8.0 meters, so the slope is 1.0 meters per second.

At 5 seconds, the slope is zero.

From just over 5 seconds to 9 seconds, we have another straight line. During that time, the position changes from 8.0 m to 4.0 meters. Thus, the slope is -1.0 meters per second.

From just over 9 seconds to 11 seconds, the slope is zero.

From just over 11 seconds to 12 seconds, the position changes from 4.0 meters to 3.0 meters, so the slope is -1.0 meters per second.

From just over 12 seconds to 14 seconds, the position changes from 3.0 meters to -1.0 meters, so the slope is -2.0 meters per second.

From just over 14 seconds to 15 seconds, the position changes from -1.0 meters to -2.0 meters, so the slope is -1.0 meters per second.

From just over 15 seconds to 16 seconds, the slope is zero.

From just over 16 seconds to 20 seconds, the position changes from -2 meters to 2 meters, so the slope is 1.0 meters per second.

Now that we know the slopes for each time interval, the graph is a snap!

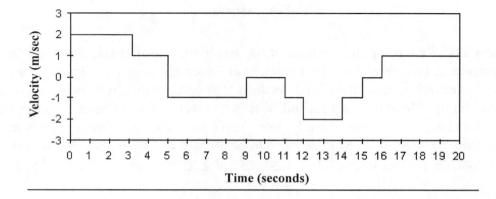

Please note that the stair-step shape of the graph is due to the fact that the position versus time curve is made up of straight lines with no smooth transitions. Thus, the slope stays constant for a given time interval and then changes instantaneously to a new constant value. If the displacement versus time graph were smooth, this graph would look more smooth as well. These are the kinds of graphs you will be required to make.

2.3 To determine the area under the curve, we must split the graph into regions for which we can calculate the area:

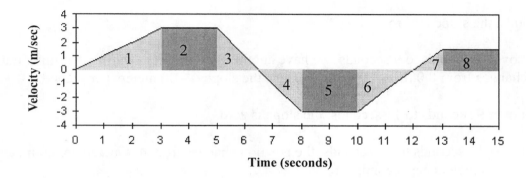

In this graph, then, we have 5 triangles (areas 1, 3, 4, 6, and 7) and 3 rectangles (areas 2, 5, and 8). That's a lot of areas to figure, but it's not really difficult:

$$\text{Area of region \#1 (a triangle)} = \frac{1}{2} \cdot (3.0 \text{ sec}) \cdot (3.0 \frac{m}{sec}) = 4.5 \text{ m}$$

$$\text{Area of region \#2 (a rectangle)} = (2.0 \text{ sec}) \cdot (3.0 \frac{m}{sec}) = 6.0 \text{ m}$$

$$\text{Area of region \#3 (a triangle)} = \frac{1}{2} \cdot (1.5 \text{ sec}) \cdot (3.0 \frac{m}{sec}) = 2.3 \text{ m}$$

$$\text{Area of region \#4 (a triangle)} = \frac{1}{2} \cdot (1.5 \text{ sec}) \cdot (-3.0 \frac{m}{sec}) = -2.3 \text{ m}$$

$$\text{Area of region \#5 (a rectangle)} = (2.0 \text{ sec}) \cdot (-3.0 \frac{m}{sec}) = -6.0 \text{ m}$$

$$\text{Area of region \#6 (a triangle)} = \frac{1}{2} \cdot (2.0 \text{ sec}) \cdot (-3.0 \frac{m}{sec}) = -3.0 \text{ m}$$

$$\text{Area of region \#7 (a triangle)} = \frac{1}{2} \cdot (1.0 \text{ sec}) \cdot (1.5 \frac{m}{sec}) = 0.75 \text{ m}$$

$$\text{Area of region \#8 (a rectangle)} = (2.0 \text{ sec}) \cdot (1.5 \frac{m}{sec}) = 3.0 \text{ m}$$

The total displacement, then, is simply the sum of the areas:

Total displacement = 4.5 m + 6.0 m + 2.3 m + -2.3 m + -6.0 m + -3.0 m + 0.75 m + 3.0 m = <u>5.3 m</u>

2.4 This problem is not too bad because the graph is made up of straight lines.

From t = 0.0 sec to t = 3.0 sec, the slope is $\dfrac{3 \frac{m}{sec}}{3.0 \text{ sec}} = 1.0 \frac{m}{sec^2}$.

From t = 3.0 sec to t = 5.0 sec, the slope is $0 \frac{m}{sec^2}$.

From t = 5.0 sec to t = 8.0 sec, the slope is $\dfrac{-6.0\,\frac{m}{sec}}{3.0\ sec} = -2.0\,\dfrac{m}{sec^2}$.

From t = 8.0 sec to t = 10.0 sec, the slope is $0\,\dfrac{m}{sec^2}$.

From t = 10.0 sec to t = 13.0 sec, the slope is $\dfrac{4.5\,\frac{m}{sec}}{3.0\ sec} = 1.5\,\dfrac{m}{sec^2}$.

From t = 13.0 sec to t = 15.0 sec, the slope is $0\,\dfrac{m}{sec^2}$.

Thus, the graph is:

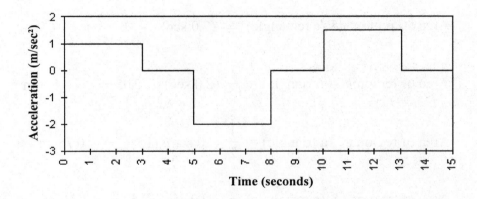

2.5 In this problem, we should define upward motion as positive and downward motion as negative. If that's the case, the initial velocity is 22.0 m/sec, the acceleration is -9.81 m/sec^2, and the time is 4.58 seconds.

a. In this part, we need to calculate the height. That's displacement. The only equation which relates displacement to the quantities we have is Equation (2.5).

$$x \;=\; (22.0\tfrac{m}{sec})\cdot(4.58\,sec) + \tfrac{1}{2}\cdot(-9.81\tfrac{m}{sec^2})\cdot(4.58\,sec)^2 = 101\,m - 103\ m = -2\,m$$

I can have only one significant figure in the end because the final thing I do is subtract the two numbers. Since they both go out to the ones place, the answer can go only to the ones place. Notice that the displacement is negative. What does that mean? That means the ground is 2 meters *down* from the initial starting place. Thus, the initial height of the ball is 2 meters above the ground.

b. At its maximum height, the velocity of the ball is zero. We know its initial velocity, and we want the time, so the easiest equation to use is Equation (2.3):

$$v = v_o + at$$

$$0 \; \frac{m}{sec} = 22.0 \; \frac{m}{sec} + (-9.81 \; \frac{m}{sec^2}) \cdot t$$

$$t = \frac{-22.0 \; \frac{m}{sec}}{-9.81 \; \frac{m}{sec^2}} = \underline{2.24 \; sec}$$

Notice that I do not worry about the significant figures associated with the final velocity. That's because the final velocity is *exactly* 0 m/sec, because it is stopped. Thus, the number has infinite precision (0.00000000000000000....).

c. This question was designed to make you remember something VERY important. When an object's velocity is zero, its acceleration need not be zero. When the ball reaches its maximum height, its velocity is zero. However, the acceleration is a constant $\underline{-9.81 \; m/sec^2}$. Think about it. If the ball were to have zero acceleration when it had zero velocity, it would *never move again*. Thus, it would reach the top of its trajectory and just float there!

2.6 In this question, you have to get used to thinking through the problem and redefining things that you can redefine. We have no idea what the initial velocity is. However, we don't need to know. We know its acceleration (1.5 m/sec^2). We also know that at t=3.0 seconds, the velocity is -12.0 m/sec. This tells us the object is slowing down because the acceleration opposes the velocity. We need to know the velocity at 5.0 seconds. Think about it. Let's just redefine the term "initial." We know that at t=3.0 seconds, it is traveling at -12.0 m/sec. Let's just assume the problems *starts* there. Thus, the *initial velocity* (assuming that t = 3.0 seconds is when the situation begins) is -12.0 m/sec. We need to know the velocity at 5.0 seconds. That's 2.0 seconds after the time that we know the velocity. Thus, in the situation we are defining, the time is 2.0 seconds. Now the solution is simple:

$$v = v_o + at$$

$$v = -12.0 \; \frac{m}{sec} + (1.5 \; \frac{m}{sec^2}) \cdot (2.0 \; sec) = \underline{-9.0 \; \frac{m}{sec}}$$

Now, of course, the way we redefined things would not have worked had we wanted to know something about the situation *prior to* t = 3.0 seconds. However, we did not need to know anything about that time frame, so our redefinition worked fine.

2.7 A bullet is cylindrical. However, it travels so that circular part of the cylinder is perpendicular to the direction of motion. Thus, the area of the cylinder's circle (πr^2) is the cross sectional area we need to calculate. However, we need the unit to be m^2, so we must convert 0.11 inches (half the diameter) to m. That works out to 0.0028 m.

$$\text{Area} = \pi r^2 = (3.1415)\cdot(0.0028 \text{ m})^2 = 2.5\times10^{-5}\text{ m}^2$$

Now we can plug the numbers into the equation:

$$v_{terminal} = \sqrt{\frac{2mg}{C\rho A}}$$

$$v_{terminal} = \sqrt{\frac{2\cdot(38.0\text{g})\cdot(9.81\frac{m}{\sec^2})}{(0.50)\cdot(1290\frac{g}{m^3})\cdot(2.5\times10^{-5}\text{ m}^2)}} = \sqrt{46,000\frac{m^2}{\sec^2}} = \underline{210\frac{m}{\sec}}$$

Thus, if a 0.22-caliber rifle were shot directly into the air, it would fall back down to the earth with a maximum speed of 210 m/sec.

2.8 To get over the wall, the projectile must be at a height of 45.0 m once it travels 150.0 m from the cannon. Thus, we need to determine the height of the projectile when it is that far from the cannon. To do that, we start in the horizontal dimension to get the time.

$$v_{ox} = v_o \cdot \cos\theta$$

$$v_{ox} = (65.0\frac{m}{\sec})\cdot\cos(25.0) = 58.9\frac{m}{\sec}$$

$$\mathbf{x} = \mathbf{v}_o t + \frac{1}{2}\mathbf{a}t^2$$

$$150.0 \text{ m} = (58.9\frac{m}{\sec})\cdot t + \frac{1}{2}\cdot(0)\cdot t^2$$

$$t = \frac{150.0\;\cancel{m}}{58.9\frac{\cancel{m}}{\sec}} = 2.55 \text{ sec}$$

Okay, we know that the projectile will encounter the wall after traveling for 2.55 seconds. At what height will it be then?

$$v_{oy} = v_o \cdot \sin\theta$$

$$v_{oy} = (65.0 \,\frac{m}{sec}) \cdot \sin(25.0) = 27.5 \,\frac{m}{sec}$$

$$x = v_o t + \frac{1}{2}at^2$$

$$x = (27.5\,\frac{m}{sec}) \cdot (2.55 \,\text{sec}) + \frac{1}{2} \cdot (-9.81\,\frac{m}{sec^2}) \cdot (2.55\,\text{sec})^2 = 38.2 \text{ m}$$

This is not higher than the wall. Thus, <u>the projectile will not get over the wall; it will hit the wall at a height of 38.2 m.</u>

2.9 This is similar to the last example. We know that the height must be 45.0 m when the projectile is 150.0 m from the cannon. We do not know θ, so we must leave v_{ox} and v_{oy} in terms of θ.

$$v_{ox} = v_o \cdot \cos\theta = (65.0\,\frac{m}{sec}) \cdot \cos\theta$$

Now we can determine the time:

$$150.0 \text{ m} = (65.0\,\frac{m}{sec}) \cdot \cos\theta \cdot t + \frac{1}{2} \cdot (0) \cdot t^2$$

$$t = \frac{2.31 \text{ sec}}{\cos\theta}$$

At that time, the projectile *must* be at least 45.0 m high. Thus, we can take that time and put it into the equation for the vertical dimension.

$$v_{oy} = v_o \cdot \sin\theta = (65.0\,\frac{m}{sec}) \cdot \sin\theta$$

Now we can plug the information into the equation:

$$x = v_o t + \frac{1}{2}at^2$$

$$45.0 \text{ m} = (65.0 \frac{\text{m}}{\cancel{\text{sec}}}) \cdot \sin\theta \cdot (\frac{2.31 \cancel{\text{sec}}}{\cos\theta}) + \frac{1}{2} \cdot (-9.81 \frac{\text{m}}{\text{sec}^2}) \cdot (\frac{2.31 \cancel{\text{sec}}}{\cos\theta})^2$$

$$45.0 \text{ m} = (1.50 \times 10^2 \text{ m}) \cdot (\frac{\sin\theta}{\cos\theta}) - (26.2 \text{ m}) \cdot (\frac{1}{\cos^2\theta})$$

Now we can use the three identities:

$$45.0 \text{ m} = (1.50 \times 10^2 \text{ m}) \cdot \tan\theta - (26.2 \text{ m}) \cdot (1 + \tan^2\theta)$$

$$(26.2 \text{ m}) \cdot \tan^2\theta - (1.50 \times 10^2 \text{ m}) \cdot \tan\theta + 71.2 \text{ m} = 0$$

Now we can use the quadratic formula to solve for $\tan\theta$:

$$\tan\theta = \frac{1.50 \times 10^2 \text{ m} \pm \sqrt{(1.50 \times 10^2 \text{ m})^2 - 4 \cdot (26.2 \text{ m}) \cdot (71.2 \text{ m})}}{2 \cdot (26.2 \text{ m})} = \frac{1.50 \times 10^2 \cancel{\text{m}} \pm 123 \cancel{\text{m}}}{52.4 \cancel{\text{m}}}$$

This gives us two possible answers.

$$\tan\theta = \frac{27}{52.4} \qquad\qquad \tan\theta = \frac{273}{52.4}$$

or

$$\theta = 27° \qquad\qquad\qquad \theta = 79.1°$$

Thus, the cannon can be aimed <u>between 27° and 79.1°</u> to get the projectiles over the wall.

2.10 This is actually not a tough problem if you are comfortable with using variables instead of numbers. In fact, you need do nothing with the horizontal dimension. In the vertical dimension, the initial velocity is $v_o \cdot \sin\theta$, the height is h, and the acceleration is -g (gravity pulls down). Thus, the time can be solved for as follows:

$$\mathbf{x} = \mathbf{v}_o t + \frac{1}{2}\mathbf{a}t^2$$

$$h = v_o \cdot \sin\theta \cdot t - \frac{1}{2} \cdot g \cdot t^2$$

$$\left(\frac{1}{2} \cdot g\right) \cdot t^2 - (v_o \cdot \sin\theta) \cdot t + h = 0$$

This is a quadratic equation in t. Thus, we can solve for t using the quadratic formula.

$$t = \frac{v_o \cdot \sin\theta \pm \sqrt{(v_o \cdot \sin\theta)^2 - 4 \cdot \left(\frac{1}{2} \cdot g\right) \cdot h}}{2 \cdot \left(\frac{1}{2} \cdot g\right)} = \frac{v_o \cdot \sin\theta \pm \sqrt{(v_o \cdot \sin\theta)^2 - 2gh}}{g}$$

What does this mean? It means that there are two times at which the projectile passes through a height of h. The first time (the smallest) is

$$t = \frac{v_o \cdot \sin\theta - \sqrt{(v_o \cdot \sin\theta)^2 - 2gh}}{g}$$

The second time (the largest) is

$$t = \frac{v_o \cdot \sin\theta + \sqrt{(v_o \cdot \sin\theta)^2 - 2gh}}{g}$$

What do we want to calculate? We want to calculate the *difference* in those two times. After all, the time between these two heights is simply the second time minus the first time:

$$\text{time difference} = \frac{v_o \cdot \sin\theta + \sqrt{(v_o \cdot \sin\theta)^2 - 2gh}}{g} - \frac{v_o \cdot \sin\theta - \sqrt{(v_o \cdot \sin\theta)^2 - 2gh}}{g}$$

$$\text{time difference} = \underline{\frac{2\sqrt{(v_o \cdot \sin\theta)^2 - 2gh}}{g}}$$

The underlined formula uses only v_o, θ, g, and h, so it is the equation we wanted.

REVIEW QUESTIONS FOR MODULE #2

1. At a certain time, an object's velocity vector is given by the following arrow:

One second later, the velocity vector is given by this arrow:

Draw the vector which represents the object's average acceleration during that one second.

2. A student observes several instances of motion with constant acceleration and then makes the following statement:

"If the acceleration of an object is constant, it must travel in a straight line."

Is the statement true? Why or why not?

3. Under what specific condition of acceleration will instantaneous velocity and average velocity be the same at all times?

4. One student throws a ball up into the air and determines the time it takes for the ball to hit the ground. A second student, at the same instant, drops a ball and times how long it takes for his ball to hit the ground. Compare the times measured by the two students. Compare the acceleration of the two balls.

5. A ball is dropped off of a building. At the same instant a second, identical ball is thrown off of a building with an initial velocity in the downwards direction. Which ball will experience more air resistance in the few moments right after the experiment begins? Which ball has the highest terminal velocity?

6. Consider an object moving at constant speed. Can you conclude that the acceleration of the object is zero? Why or why not?

7. Consider a projectile launched at an angle of 45 degrees relative to the ground. Describe the relative directions of the acceleration vector and velocity vector in both the horizontal and vertical dimensions over the entire path of the projectile, assuming that it eventually lands on the ground again.

8. A projectile is launched from level ground with a velocity whose magnitude is v and whose direction is θ. What are the magnitude and direction of the velocity when the projectile reaches the ground again, providing that it hits at the same height as the height from which it was launched?

9. Which of the following would follow a parabolic trajectory:

a. A baseball thrown horizontally from the roof of a building
b. An airplane flying from one city to another
c. A rocket leaving the launch pad, firing its engines
d. A rocket after the engines have burned out but still under the influence of earth's gravity

10. A student throws a ball horizontally at 30.0 m/sec. A second student drops a ball from exactly the same height at the same instant. Compare the time at which the balls hit the ground.

PRACTICE PROBLEMS FOR MODULE #2

1. An object travels in one dimension with the following position versus time graph.

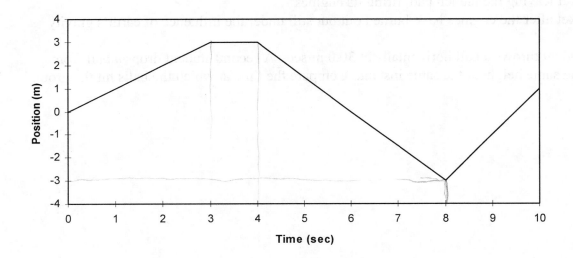

   a. Over what time interval is the object moving with the greatest speed?
   b. At what times is the object stopped?
   c. At what times does the object change directions?
   d. Sketch the velocity versus time graph for the same time interval.

2. An object travels in one dimension according to the following graph:

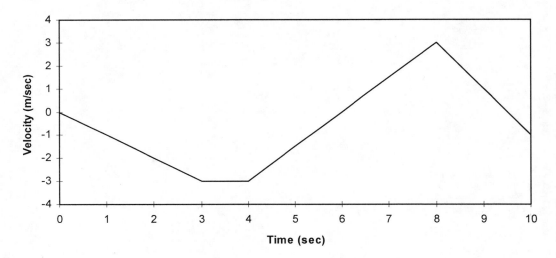

   a. During which time intervals is the object speeding up?
   b. At what times is the object at rest?
   c. Sketch the acceleration versus time graph.

3. A rock is dropped off of a cliff. It takes 1.5 seconds for it to fall half the distance to the ground. What is the total time it will take to fall from the top of the cliff to the ground? Ignore air resistance.

4. Starting from rest, an object travels with an acceleration of 2.0 m/sec^2 for 25 seconds and, at the end of that time period, it begins traveling with an acceleration of -2.0 m/sec^2 for another 25 seconds.

a. What is the final velocity?
b. What is the maximum speed attained during the trip?
c. What is the total displacement over the entire trip?

5. Two bikers start at the same point and travel in opposite directions at constant speed. The speed of the first biker is twice that of the second biker. At the end of 30.0 minutes, they are 9401 meters apart from one another. What is the speed of each biker?

6. A boy stands on a ladder and throws a ball straight up into the air with an initial velocity of 5.0 ft/sec. If the boy releases the ball 15 feet above the ground and it falls straight back down, how fast will it be going when it impacts the ground? Ignore air resistance.

7. A gun has a maximum range of 500.0 meters on level ground. If the gun is fired at an angle of 30.0 degrees relative to the ground, what is its range?

8. A cannon shoots a projectile horizontally off the edge of a cliff. It is aiming at a ship that sits on the ocean, 500.0 meters below and 2500.0 meters west of the cliff. At what speed must the projectile be fired in order to hit the ship?

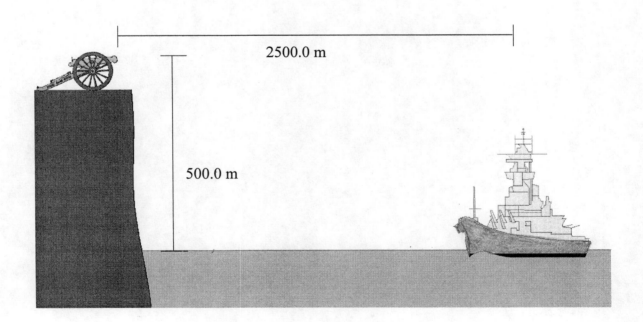

2500.0 m

500.0 m

9. Suppose in problem number 8 that the cannon can only shoot its projectiles with one speed: 300.0 m/sec. At what angle must the cannon aim to hit the ship?

10. A football player just scored a touchdown and wants to throw the ball to a fan that's wearing his jersey. The fan is 300.0 ft (horizontally) from the player, but he is also up in the stands, which are 50.0 ft above the point where the football player will release the ball. If the football player aims the ball at 30.0° relative to the horizontal, at what speed will he have to release the ball so that the ball hits his fan?

Module #3: Newton's Laws of Motion

Introduction

Although kinematics allows us to analyze motion in a very detailed way, it does not tell us *why* this motion occurs. It simply allows us to study the motion. The study of *why* motion occurs is called **dynamics**, and it begins with a discussion of the scientific laws formulated by Sir Isaac Newton.

Sir Isaac Newton, as you learned in your first-year physics course, was a brilliant man. He was also a dedicated (although unorthodox) Christian. He studied the Bible just as fervently as he studied science, and he studied science just as reverently as he studied the Bible. To him, science and Scripture were related. He believed that studying science was a means of understanding God. Of course, he understood that the Bible was a more direct way of understanding God, and he spent a great deal of time studying it. However, he also believed that he was able to learn about God by studying His creation.

As a result of studying God's creation, Newton published a monumental work entitled *The Mathematical Principles of Natural Philosophy*. Later on, it became known simply as *The Principia*. Most historians consider the publication of this work in the year 1687 as the beginning of the scientific discipline we call physics. In *The Principia*, Newton discussed his views on dynamics. He laid out three basic laws of motion and discussed the consequences of those laws. These laws contradicted long-held beliefs in the scientific community, but Newton used rigorous experiments to provide evidence for his laws.

The remainder of *The Principia* is divided into three books in which Newton applied his laws of motion to several situations. In the first book, he concentrated on how his laws of motion affected the motion of bodies in different situations. The second book covered the motion of bodies in fluids. That book also explored the behavior of the fluids themselves. Finally, the third book dealt with the motion of the planets, moons, and comets in the solar system. In that book, he developed his universal law of gravitation, which we will study in the next module.

The genius of Newton is best demonstrated by the fact that his laws still form the basis of most of the physics that we study today. Certainly there is more to modern physics than Newton's laws. For example, the foundation of modern physics is a theoretical framework known as quantum mechanics, which we will discuss in the final few modules of this course. Quantum mechanics has been successful in describing most of the features of the atomic and subatomic world, which are situations in which Newton's Laws do not work. However, when you move out of the atomic and subatomic worlds and observe the macroscopic world, you find out that the laws of quantum mechanics actually become Newton's Laws.

In the end, then, most physicists think of Newton's Laws as a special case of quantum mechanics. When dealing with the world that we can see and touch, the laws of quantum mechanics are the same as Newton's Laws. When we deal with the atomic and subatomic world, however, quantum mechanics and Newton's Laws differ somewhat, and the experimental evidence indicates that quantum mechanics is correct. Thus, quantum mechanics gives rise to Newton's Laws when applied to the macroscopic world.

Newton's Three Laws of Motion

In your first-year physics course, you learned about Newton's three laws of motion. I want to list them again in order to review.

Newton's First Law (The Law of Inertia) - An object in motion (or at rest) will tend to stay in motion (or at rest) until it is acted upon by an outside force.

Newton's Second Law - When an object is acted on by one or more outside forces, the sum of those forces is equal to the mass of the object times the resulting acceleration.

Newton's Third Law - For every action, there is an equal and opposite reaction.

The first of these laws, also called the **Law of Inertia**, was probably considered the most controversial statement in *The Principia*. It squarely contradicted the teachings of Aristotle, a Greek philosopher who lived from 384 to 322 BC. Aristotle was revered by scientists throughout the ages, and he said that the "natural state" of an object is at rest. Thus, an object would "like" to be at rest, and a force has to act on an object to keep it from being at rest. Newton's First Law says that there is no "natural state" for an object. Instead, objects simply move (or don't move) until acted on by an outside force. Thus, if an object is moving, it will continue to move *forever* unless a force acts to stop it. Even though this law was controversial, rigorous experiments demonstrated that it was true.

The Second Law is the one that physics students use most often. It gives rise to the famous equation

$$\mathbf{F} = \mathbf{m} \cdot \mathbf{a} \qquad (3.1)$$

which gives rise to many other equations in physics. Now remember from your first-year course that "**F**" in this formula is the *vector sum of all forces acting on the object*. Thus, if three forces act on an object, those forces must be added, and the *sum* is equal to the mass times the acceleration.

The Third Law tells us that if there is a force being exerted on an object, there is an equal force being exerted in the opposite direction. If object #1 exerts a force on object #2, then object #2 exerts an equal but opposite force on object #1. For example, consider the earth and the moon. The moon stays in orbit around the earth because the earth exerts a gravitational force on the moon. However, the moon *also* exerts an equal force on the earth. Thus, the earth's gravity pulls the moon towards the earth, but the moon's gravity also pulls the earth towards the moon.

These two gravitational forces are equal in magnitude, but opposite in direction. As a result, the earth and moon are called an **action/reaction pair**.

Most of what has been covered in this section should be review. Now I want to take each of these laws and discuss them in more depth than what was done in your first-year course.

Inertial Reference Frames and Inertial Mass

There are two aspects of Newton's First Law which I want to discuss in this module. They both lead to definitions. Before I tell you the definitions, however, I need to remind you about something from your first-year course. Remember that velocity is *relative*. It must be defined relative to something else. Suppose, for example, that two spaceships are flying in space and are approaching one another such that they get 10000 meters closer to one another every second. You could analyze their motion in several different ways. You could say that the first ship is approaching the second ship with a velocity of 10000 meters per second and that the second ship is standing still in space. You could also say that the second ship is approaching the first ship with a velocity of -10000 meters and the first ship is standing still in space. You could also say that both ships are moving, one with a velocity of 5000 meters per second and the other with a velocity of -5000 meters per second.

Which analysis would be correct? Physics says that there is *no way to tell*. Velocity is relative. One ship may be moving and the other stationary, or both ships may be moving at virtually any speed. The only thing you know is that the difference between their velocities is 10000 meters per second, because you know that they are approaching one another at that speed.

Now you might say that all you have to do is look for the nearest planet. Then you could use that as a reference to see which ship is moving and which ship isn't. However, that doesn't solve the problem. *That planet* might be moving, too. Thus, you are now just defining motion *relative to the planet*. In the end, there is no absolute way to tell what is moving and what is not. You can only determine velocity by defining it relative to something.

When we choose a reference, we are really choosing a **reference frame**. For example, if we define the motion of the space ships based on the nearest planet, then we are defining the motion of the spaceships relative to all things that are moving with the planet. We would say, therefore, that the motion of the space ships is being defined in the reference frame of the planet. If a ship does not move relative to the planet, its velocity is zero in the planet's reference frame. If it is traveling with a speed of 3500 m/sec at a heading of 23.0 degrees relative to the planet, then its velocity in the planet's reference frame is 3500 m/sec at 23.0 degrees. In another reference frame, however, its velocity is probably completely different, depending on the definition of that reference frame.

Now this might seem odd to you because we are so used to dealing with a predetermined reference frame. We are sitting on the surface of the earth. To us, it looks like the surface of the earth is not moving. Thus, we define that as our reference frame. As a result, it seems to us that we can tell whether something is moving or whether it is not. After all, if you walk across the street, you "know" that you are moving, right? WRONG! You only know that *relative to the surface of the earth* you are moving. Suppose someone was looking at you through a telescope from the surface of the moon. From that standpoint, the earth's surface is *not* stationary. It is moving because the earth rotates on its axis and because the moon orbits the earth. Thus, in the reference frame of the moon, the earth's surface is moving.

Have you heard the term **geosynchronous orbit**? A satellite is in geosynchronous orbit if it never moves relative to some fixed point on the earth. If you want a satellite to always be above the same point on the earth, you put it in geosynchronous orbit. If you were to look at a satellite in geosynchronous orbit, you would say that the satellite isn't moving. However, relative to the sun, the other planets, the moon, and any non-geosynchronous satellites, that satellite is moving like crazy. Thus, in the reference frame of the earth's surface, the satellite is stationary. In the sun's reference frame, however, it is moving. Velocity, then, depends on how you define your *reference frame*.

Now you are ready for the definition:

Inertial Reference Frame - A frame of reference in which an object that is subject to no force travels at constant velocity

What does this definition mean? It means that an **inertial reference frame** is any reference frame in which Newton's First Law of motion is true.

That last statement probably surprised you. Isn't Newton's First Law *always* true? Well, that's actually hard to say. It depends on how you define things. Consider, for example, a man driving a car. He has just picked up a beautiful birthday cake for his daughter's birthday, and it is sitting on the seat next to him. On his way home, he turns a corner too quickly, and the cake moves across the seat, falling onto the floor. The cake, of course, is ruined as a result. Now think about what the man saw. He saw the cake *at rest* next to him. Then, without anything pushing or pulling on the cake, the cake suddenly moved, eventually falling on the floor. To *the man driving the car*, Newton's First Law of motion did not seem to be true. The cake was at rest and then suddenly started moving of its own accord.

Why did Newton's First Law of motion seem to be false in this situation? It's because *the car was not an inertial reference frame*. When the car began to turn the corner, it *accelerated*. Even if it continued to move at the same speed, it still accelerated, because it changed direction. You learned in your first-year course that when an object moves in a circle, it experiences a **centripetal force**, which causes a **centripetal acceleration**. That centripetal acceleration causes the object to move in a circle. Thus, as the car turned the curve, it experienced centripetal acceleration.

Now, before I tell you why this means the car is not an inertial reference frame, consider what a person standing on the street watching this situation would see. Assume that the car is transparent so that the observer can see everything going on in the car. At first, the observer would see the car and the cake both traveling with the same velocity. Then suddenly, the observer would see the car begin to turn, which would tell him that the car is experiencing acceleration. However, he would see the cake continue to move in the direction in which it was originally moving. It would slow down (because of friction between it and the seat), but it would not turn with the car. Instead, it would continue in the direction it was originally moving. Since the car turned and the cake did not, the cake moved relative to the car, causing it to fall on the floor.

To the observer, Newton's First Law was true. The car and cake were traveling at the same speed. Then, the car experienced a force (the friction between the turned tires and the road) which caused it to accelerate (change direction). This is completely consistent with Newton's First Law. The cake, on the other hand, did not experience that force. As a result, it continued to move the way it was heading. That's also completely consistent with Newton's First Law. For the observer, then, Newton's First Law worked, because *he* was in an inertial reference frame.

What about the driver? He turned with the car. Well, the observer would probably realize that the friction between the driver and the seat was greater than that between the cake and the seat. In addition, if the driver was wearing a seat belt, that would hold him to the car. Also, the driver's grip on the wheel would hold him to the car as well. As a result, the *car* would exert the force necessary to turn the driver with the car. Once again, that's all consistent with Newton's First Law. The driver changed his velocity because the car exerted a centripetal force on him.

Have you heard of the term **centrifugal force**? In your first-year course, you should have learned that there is no such thing. It is a mythical force. Now you know why people who do not know physics very well think that such a force exists. Centrifugal force is a force people made up to explain actions of objects in non-inertial reference frames. In the reference frame of the car, the cake moved. To a person who does not know about inertial reference frames, it would therefore follow that a force must have acted on the cake. That force is called the centrifugal force. However, such reasoning is faulty. No force acted on the cake. Since the car was not an inertial reference frame, it does not follow that a force acted on the cake to make it move. Centrifugal force, then, is a term developed to try to explain the motion of objects in certain non-inertial reference frames.

All right, then. Not all reference frames are inertial, so not all reference frames follow Newton's First Law. Well, what reference frames *are* inertial? Actually, there are probably not very many truly inertial reference frames. You see, in order for a reference frame to be inertial, it must not be acted on by any outside forces. Thus, it cannot experience any acceleration. As a result, even the earth is not an inertial reference frame. It is being acted on by many gravitational forces, the largest of which is the gravitational force between it and the sun. As a result, it experiences centripetal acceleration towards the sun and thus is not an inertial reference frame. In addition, the earth revolves on its axis. Thus, every *point* on the surface of the earth is spinning around the axis of the earth, so each point experiences centripetal acceleration in the direction of the center of the earth.

However, compared to the accelerations with which you and I are accustomed to working, the centripetal accelerations mentioned above are negligible. Thus, even though it is not true, we can *treat* the earth as an inertial reference frame for most situations in which we find ourselves.

We will treat the earth as an inertial reference frame because it is close to one. It is not a true inertial reference frame, however. Any reference frame moving with a constant velocity with respect to the earth, then, will also be considered an inertial reference frame.

Newton was able to discover his laws because the earth is close to an inertial reference frame. Thus, for all practical purposes, Newton's First Law works on the earth.

So in the example of the man driving the car with a cake on the seat, the observer was, for all practical purposes, in an inertial reference frame. He was standing on the side of the road. Thus, relative to the surface of the earth (which we consider to be an inertial reference frame), he was moving with a constant velocity (zero). As a result, Newton's First Law applied in his reference frame, and he could properly understand what happened to the cake. The reference frame of the car, however, was *not* an inertial reference frame, because it was accelerating relative to the surface of the earth. Thus, Newton's First Law does not apply in that reference frame. As a result, the driver might believe that a force moved the cake. However, he would be wrong, because the car is not an inertial reference frame.

Notice the third sentence in boldface type. If a reference frame moves with constant velocity relative to an inertial reference frame, then *it* is an inertial reference frame as well. Think about it. The car is not an inertial reference frame because it is accelerating. Thus, if a reference frame travels with constant velocity relative to an inertial reference frame, it is also an inertial reference frame, since it is not accelerating. Another way to think about an inertial reference frame is that an inertial reference frame is one which does not accelerate.

The first and second laws of motion lead us to the other definition, that of **inertial mass**.

<u>Inertial mass</u> - A measure of an object's resistance to a change in its state of motion

What does this definition mean? It means that when you try to change an object's velocity (either get it moving from rest or change its speed and/or direction while it is moving), it will resist that change. The amount by which it resists depends on its inertial mass. In fact, that's really what the second law says. Equation (3.1) says that the force required to accelerate (change the velocity of) an object depends on the mass. If one object has twice the mass of a second object, the second object will require only one-half of the force to change its velocity to the same degree.

Now wait a moment, you might be thinking. Isn't mass a measure of the amount of *matter* in an object? Yes, it certainly is. However, that concept of mass is often referred to as **gravitational mass**, because the more matter an object contains, the more gravitational force it experiences when exposed to another object. Inertial mass, however, is a wholly different concept. It is a measure of how much an object resists changes in its velocity. What is the relationship between these two masses? They are numerically equal. If an object has a gravitational mass of 10.0 grams, it will have an inertial mass of 10.0 grams.

Why bother to make the distinction, then? It is a rather interesting phenomenon. Think about it. Inertial mass *resists* changes in motion. However, gravitational mass *encourages* changes in motion. After all, the larger the gravitational mass of an object, the larger the gravitational force it experiences when exposed to another massive object. The larger the force, the more the change in velocity. These two different concepts of mass, then, actually lead to two different behaviors when it comes to different situations. Einstein used the fact that gravitational mass and inertial mass are numerically equal as a major point in developing his theory of general relativity, which we will discuss near the end of this course.

ON YOUR OWN

3.1 If an object is at rest in an inertial reference frame, can we conclude that no forces are acting on it?

3.2 Two observers move with constant velocity relative to one another. Are they both in inertial reference frames?

Newton's Second Law: A Few Reminders

In the next section of the course, I want to dive into some detailed applications of Newton's Second Law. Before I can do that, however, I need to remind you of a few things from your first-year physics course. Please understand that this is review, so I will be going through it quickly. If you are confused about the things I present in this section, please review your first-year physics course.

The first thing you need to remember is that weight and mass are two different things. There are two ways of looking at mass, and we discussed them above. Weight, however, is entirely different. Weight is a measure of the force with which gravity pulls on an object. Using Equation (3.1) and the fact that the acceleration due to gravity is constant near a planet's surface, we can say

$$\text{Weight} = m \cdot g \qquad (3.2)$$

where "g" is the acceleration due to gravity for that planet. For the earth, g is 9.81 m/sec^2 or 32.2 ft/sec^2. Of course, since the value for "g" varies from planet to planet, the weight of an object varies from planet to planet. The mass, however, does not.

Weight is an important concept because it figures into most physics problems in one way or another. If an object is hanging from a rope, for example, the weight of the object is a force which pulls the object down. The rope, then, has to exert an equal but opposite force to keep the object from falling to the ground. Even if the object is sitting on the ground, weight plays a role, because the weight of an object affects the **normal force** that the ground exerts on the object. Remember, when an object sits on a surface, the surface exerts a force, pushing against the object's weight. That force is called the "normal force," because it is exerted perpendicular (or normal) to the surface.

Why is the normal force important? It is important because it affects the **friction** an object experiences. When an object sits on a surface, it experiences friction according to the equation:

$$F_{friction} = \mu \cdot F_n \qquad (3.3)$$

The "μ" is called the **coefficient of friction**, and it comes in two forms. There is a **coefficient of static friction** (μ_s) which governs the frictional force which is applicable when the object is at rest, and a **coefficient of kinetic friction** (μ_k) which is applicable when the object is moving. For reasons discussed in your first-year course, the coefficient of kinetic friction for a surface is smaller than the coefficient of static friction for that same surface. Also, note that there are no vectors in Equation (3.3). It is a scalar equation. However, force is a vector. Thus, you have to "reason out" the direction of the frictional force. That's not too hard, however, since friction always opposes motion.

Now that you have been reminded about weight and friction, you can be reminded about **equilibrium**. An object is in **translational equilibrium** when the sum of the forces acting on the object is zero. Under those conditions, the object has no acceleration. It might be at rest, or it might be moving at a constant velocity. Either situation is considered a state of translational equilibrium. An object is in **static equilibrium** if it is at rest.

There is just one more thing to cover before I jump into some detailed problems related to Newton's Second Law. Remember that when dealing with situations in two dimensions, we split things up into the vertical and horizontal dimensions. However, as mentioned in Module #1, those aren't the only dimensions in which a two-dimensional problem can be analyzed. We can analyze a two dimensional problem with *any two perpendicular dimensions*. In some cases, it makes more sense to use dimensions other than the horizontal and vertical dimensions. For example, examine Figure 3.1.

FIGURE 3.1
An Object on an Incline

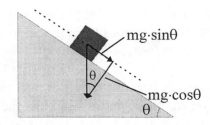

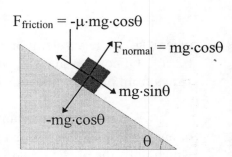

The object is subject to two forces: gravity pulling straight down and friction, which opposes the motion.

We can take the gravitational force and split it into two components: one parallel to and one perpendicular to the surface of the incline.

Now all of the forces are either parallel to or perpendicular to the surface of the incline. This makes analysis *much* easier!

Notice the situation in the figure. There are two forces at play: gravity and friction. Friction always directly opposes the motion. Thus, it is pointed up along the incline, since the object wants to slide down along the incline. Gravity always pulls objects straight down with a force of m·g. The directions of these two forces present a problem, because they are not parallel or perpendicular to one another. Thus, the analysis will be tough. We can fix that, however, by splitting up the gravitational force into two perpendicular components: one parallel to and one perpendicular to the surface of the incline. Following the geometry of the situation, we can find that the component parallel to the surface is mg·sinθ, and the component perpendicular to the surface is mg·cosθ.

Now look what we have on the right-hand side of the figure. There are two forces parallel to the surface of the incline: mg·sinθ and friction. These forces oppose one another. There are also two forces perpendicular to the incline. The component mg·cosθ pushes down on the surface of the incline. In response, the incline pushes back with an equal and opposite force, which we call the normal force. Thus, the normal force is mg·cosθ. This is a good thing to know because, once we know the normal force, we know the frictional force, according to Equation (3.3). Thus, the frictional force is -μmg·cosθ. This analysis, then, gives us a way of examining all of the forces at play so that they all fall in either one dimension or another. That's how we will do problems which involve inclines.

Before I leave this section, I want to go through a couple of basic problems for you. These are the kinds of problems you covered in your first-year physics course, but I want to go through them so that you remember the basics.

EXAMPLE 3.1

A 900.0 g picture is hung according to the diagram shown below. Calculate the tension in each of the three strings.

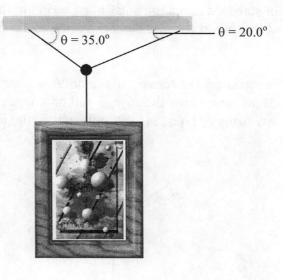

To do this problem, we first have to realize that the picture is hanging still. Thus, its acceleration is zero. Next, we have to look at the forces in the problem. First, we look at the forces acting on the picture. There are only two. Gravity is pulling the picture straight down. It has a strength equal to the weight of the picture, which is mg. The string is exerting **tension**, pulling the picture up. Thus, the forces look like this:

Since the picture is not moving, we know it is not accelerating. This means that the sum of the forces on the picture is zero. However, we need to sum up the forces as *vectors*. They are each in the same dimension (the vertical dimension), so we use signs to indicate direction. I will define down as negative, so the force due to the weight is -mg. This means that the sum of the forces, which equals zero is:

$$T_1 - mg = 0$$

We know m and we know g, so we can calculate T_1.

$$T_1 = m \cdot g = (0.9000 \text{ kg}) \cdot \left(9.81 \frac{m}{sec^2}\right) = 8.83 \text{ N}$$

Remember, to stay in standard units, the mass must be in kg, the length in meters, and the time in seconds. Thus, I had to convert the mass to kg in order to get the standard unit for force, the Newton.

Okay, we already know the tension in the bottom string. What about the other two strings? Well, let's think about how the strings pull on one another. The bottom string pulls down on the other two strings. They, in turn, pull against the bottom string. Thus, the situation looks like this:

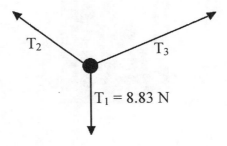

Since the place where the strings connect is not moving, we know that its acceleration is zero and thus the sum of these forces is zero. Since the two top strings do not point straight up and down, however, we need to look individually at the horizontal and vertical dimensions.

Looking in the horizontal dimension, we see that there is no horizontal component to T_1. However, both T_2 and T_3 have horizontal components. Thus, I can sum up their components and set them equal to zero, since the acceleration is zero in the horizontal dimension. Remember, I have to define direction, so I will say that a force pulling to the right is positive, while a force pulling to the left is negative. Thus, the sum of the forces in the horizontal dimension is:

$$T_3 \cdot \cos(20.0) - T_2 \cdot \cos(35.0) = 0$$

This is an equation with two unknowns. That's okay, however. Let's solve for one in terms of the other, and then we can look in the vertical dimension to see if there's something else we can learn.

$$T_3 \cdot \cos(20.0) = T_2 \cdot \cos(35.0)$$

$$T_3 = \frac{T_2 \cdot \cos(35.0)}{\cos(20.0)} = 0.872 \cdot T_2$$

That's the best we can do. Now let's go to the vertical dimension. That should give us more information. In that dimension, the point connecting the strings is not moving. Thus, acceleration is zero. That means the sum of the forces is zero. T_1 is pulling straight down (the negative direction), while the vertical components of T_2 and T_3 are pulling straight up.

$$T_3 \cdot \sin(20.0) + T_2 \cdot \sin(35.0) - 8.83\,N = 0$$

Now let's take the equation we have for T_3 from the horizontal dimension and stick it into this equation. That will result in only one variable for which to solve.

$$0.872 \cdot T_2 \cdot \sin(20.0) + T_2 \cdot \sin(35.0) - 8.83\,N = 0$$

$$0.298 \cdot T_2 + 0.574 \cdot T_2 = 8.83\ N$$

$$T_2 = 10.1\ N$$

Now that we have T_2, we can determine T_3:

$$T_3 = 0.872 \cdot T_2 = 0.872 \cdot (10.1\ N) = 8.81\ N$$

The tensions on the strings, then, are 8.83 N, 10.1 N, and 8.81 N.

Notice the basic reasoning used here. We summed up the forces on an object and set that sum equal to the mass times the acceleration. In this case, the mass times the acceleration was zero, because the object was at rest. However, that does not have to be the case. The object may be accelerating. That doesn't change the analysis, however. We still sum up the forces and set them equal to the mass times the acceleration. Notice also that we actually dealt with two objects. First, we dealt with the picture. That had only two forces acting on it, however, and the equation allowed us to calculate the tension in only one string. To determine the tension in the other strings, we had to concentrate on another object. The second object we concentrated on was the point that joined the three strings.

This is a very typical situation in physics. When you have more than one object in a situation, *you often deal with the objects separately*. You sum up the forces on one of the objects, and you set that sum equal to the mass of that object times its acceleration. Then, you sum up the forces on the other object and set that sum equal to the mass of that object times its acceleration. I want to make sure you understand this by doing one more example. Once again, this should be review.

EXAMPLE 3.2

Atwood's machine is a common mechanism in physics. It consists of two unequal masses joined together by a string. The string is hung vertically over a light pulley, and the motion of the system can then be analyzed. Determine the acceleration of the masses in Atwood's machine in terms of each mass and the acceleration due to gravity.

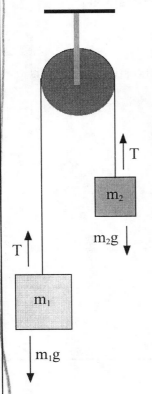

You know what will happen in a situation like this. The heavier mass will begin to accelerate downward while the lighter mass will accelerate upwards. However, we need to know more than that. We need to know the acceleration. In order to analyze this situation, you need to realize two things. First, since the masses are connected by one string, the tension is the same throughout the string. Thus, the string pulls on m_1 with the same force as that with which it pulls on m_2. Second, since the string stays tight and does not "bunch up," the masses must be moving with the same acceleration. Thus, the acceleration of each mass is equal in magnitude.

Given those facts, how can we analyze this situation? Well, we look at *each mass separately* and sum up the forces, setting the sum equal to the mass times the acceleration. Look, for example, at the first mass. There are two forces acting on it. Gravity pulls it down (the negative direction) with a strength of m_1g, and the tension on the string pulls it up. Thus, we can sum up the forces as:

$$T - m_1g = m_1a$$

What are the unknowns in the equation? Remember, we want to determine the acceleration in terms of the masses and the acceleration due to gravity. Thus, we can treat m_1, m_2, and g as givens. That means there are two unknowns, T and a. However, if we solve for T in terms of a, we might then learn something else by looking at the other mass.

$$T = m_1a + m_1g$$

Now let's look at the other mass. Once again, there are two forces acting on it. Gravity pulls it down with a strength of m_2g, while the tension in the string pulls it up. Pulleys, however, present a problem. They *change the direction*. Think about it. Mass 1 is moving downward. When that happens, mass 2 moves upward. As a result, *downward motion for mass 1 is upward motion for mass 2.* In terms of mass 2, then, upward motion must be defined as *negative* and downward motion must be defined as *positive*.

You need to be sure you understand this point. We defined negative motion when we dealt with mass 1. We said that negative motion for mass 1 is downward motion. However, when mass 1 moves in the negative direction, mass 2 moves *upwards*. Thus, for mass 2, *upwards motion is negative*. This is very important. When I define the sign for direction, it must be consistent. The pulley makes negative motion for mass 1 upward motion for mass 2. Thus, for mass 1, downward motion is negative. That means for mass 2, upward motion is negative.

$$m_2g - T = m_2a$$

Now, we can substitute the equation we derived for T into this equation, which will reduce this equation to one unknown:

$$m_2g - (m_1a + m_1g) = m_2a$$

$$m_2g - m_1a - m_1g = m_2a$$

$$a = \left(\frac{m_2 - m_1}{m_1 + m_2}\right) \cdot g$$

Notice how this equation works out to give you the direction of the acceleration. If m_2 is larger than m_1, then the acceleration is positive. According to our definition of direction, positive motion is upward motion for mass 1 and downward motion for mass 2. Thus, the equation tells us that if m_2 is larger than m_1, mass 1 rises while mass 2 falls. That is, of course, what one expects. If, on the other hand, m_1 is larger than m_2, the acceleration is negative. That means mass 1 will fall and mass 2 will rise, as you would expect. That's why it is important to understand how to do sign definitions with pulleys. Since pulleys reverse the direction of motion from one side to the other, you have to be careful in determining the signs associated with the forces at play.

To give you a little practical experience with Atwood's Machine, perform the following Experiment.

EXPERIMENT 3.1
Building and Using Atwood's Machine

Supplies:

- Two Ziplock® bags (The smaller the bag, the better)
- A string that is about 1.5 meters in length
- Sand (Kitty litter, dirt, or small gravel will work as well.)
- A mass scale (It can be one of the scales used to measure food, which cost about $6 at any grocery store. It should be marked off in grams, and it should have a range of no more than 500 grams.)
- A pulley (You can get these at any hardware store. They are plastic and are typically called "clothesline" pulleys. Get one that is at least 2.5 inches in diameter.)
- A stopwatch
- Meter stick or other metric ruler
- A high place to which you can attach the pulley (I used the shower curtain rod in my shower.)

Introduction - Atwood's machine can be used for many different applications. It is sometimes used to measure the acceleration due to gravity. We will use it to get an idea of the friction associated with the pulley.

Procedure:

1. Place one of the bags on the scale and fill it with sand until it has a mass of 50 grams. Remember, the scale can be read to one decimal place more than what it is marked off. Thus, your reading should really be 5.0×10^1 grams.
2. Take that bag off and put the other bag on the scale. Fill it with sand until it has a mass of 6.0×10^1 grams.
3. Zip both bags sealed.
4. Tie one bag to one end of the string. Probably the easiest way to do this is to punch a hole through the bag near the top and then thread the string through the hole.
5. Tie the pulley to a rod or other structure that is at least 1.5 meters above the ground. I used the curtain rod in my shower.
6. Thread the string through the pulley, and then attach the other bag to the free end of the string.
7. You now have a working version of Atwood's machine. The bags of sand are the masses, and when you release them, the lighter mass will rise and the heavier mass will fall.
8. Now we want to measure the acceleration of your Atwood's machine. To do this, hold the stopwatch in one hand and the lighter bag in the other.
9. Pull the lighter bag down so that the heavier bag is all the way at the top, touching the pulley.

10. Release the bag and, at the same time, start the stopwatch. Stop the stopwatch when the lighter mass reaches the pulley.

11. While the system is in this configuration, measure the length of the string from the pulley to the heavier bag. This is the distance that the lighter mass traveled from the time you released it to the time that it touched the pulley.

12. Repeat steps 8-10 nine more times. If one or two of the times are significantly (30% or so) different than the others, discard that trial and try again.

13. Average your 10 time measurements to get one average time.

14. You now have the distance that your masses traveled and the time it took them to travel that distance. Using Equation (2.5), you can calculate the acceleration of the masses. Remember, the initial velocity is zero.

15. The acceleration you calculated in #14 is the experimental acceleration. Now, use the equation we just derived for the acceleration of Atwood's machine (Example 3.2) to calculate the *theoretical* acceleration of your Atwood's machine.

16. Compare the two accelerations. The experimental number should be *lower* than the theoretical number. Why? Because of three things that were ignored in the example. First, friction was ignored. Second, it actually takes energy to turn the pulley. You will learn more about that later. Also, the mass of the string was ignored. After all, it has to accelerate as well. All of these effects will slow down the system, reducing the acceleration.

17. Take the experimental acceleration and divide it by the theoretical acceleration. This gives you an idea of how much friction plays a role in the machine. For example, my experimental acceleration was 82% of the theoretical value. That tells me that the factors I ignored in the calculation reduced the acceleration by roughly 18%.

18. So that you can take a shower again, remove the Atwood's machine from the shower, and clean everything up as well.

ON YOUR OWN

3.3 In Figure 3.1, I split up the force due to gravity in terms of components that were parallel to and perpendicular to the surface of the incline. In the middle of the figure, I show that the angle opposite of the parallel component is the angle of the incline, θ. Use geometry to prove this fact.

3.4 In the following situation, $m_1 = 40.0$ kg and $m_2 = 20.0$ kg. Neglecting friction, the mass of the string, and the mass of the pulley, what is the acceleration?

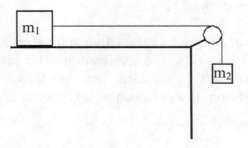

3.5 Now take the friction between m_1 and the table into account in Problem 3.4. If the coefficient of sliding friction is 0.25, what is the acceleration?

Newton's Second Law: Some Detailed Applications

Now that you have reminded yourself about the applications associated with Newton's Second Law, it is time to discuss such applications in detail. Let's start out with an analysis of a non-inertial reference frame. Let's suppose that, for some insane reason, you decided you wanted to weigh yourself in an elevator. Thus, you take your bathroom scale into the elevator, set it on the floor, and jump on the scale. The elevator is still and, in a moment, the scale reads that you weigh 122 pounds.

Now let's suppose that someone calls the elevator from a floor high above the floor you are on. Thus, the elevator begins to move upwards. If you watched the scale while the elevator began to move upward, you would see your weight as read by the scale *increase*. Then, as the elevator reached a constant velocity on the ride upward, the scale would go back to reading 122 pounds. Then, as the elevator began to slow down, you would see your weight as read by the scale *decrease*. When the elevator stopped, your weight would go back to 122 pounds.

Why does your weight fluctuate like that? During parts of the trip in the elevator, you are not in an inertial reference frame. Why? Because during parts of the trip, the elevator was *accelerating*. Since you were not in an inertial reference frame, your weight appeared to fluctuate. To understand why your weight appeared to fluctuate, you must analyze the situation from an inertial reference frame. Then, you can reason out what happened physically. What would be a proper reference frame from which to analyze the situation? If an observer stood outside of the elevator and observed the motion, that observer would be in an inertial reference frame, because he or she would be at rest relative to the earth. Thus, let's analyze the situation from *that* perspective.

EXAMPLE 3.3

A man weighs himself on an elevator while the elevator is at rest. The weight is 122 pounds. Then, the elevator begins to move upward with an acceleration of 8.00 ft/sec². What weight does the scale read then?

Notice that now we are analyzing things relative to the inertial reference frame of the earth. Inside the elevator, there is no observed acceleration. The man and the bathroom scale are at rest relative to the elevator. Relative to the earth, however, they are accelerating at 8.00 ft/sec². If we view the situation from this perspective, it is easy to understand it.

Illus. by Megan Whitaker

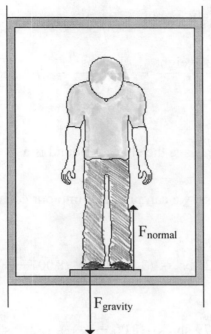

As shown above, from the perspective of someone standing on the floor of the building, there are two forces working on the man: the force of gravity and the normal force that the scale exerts on him. The normal force is what the scale actually reads. Using the standard definition that the upward direction is positive, these forces add to equal the mass of the man times his acceleration:

$$F_{normal} - F_{gravity} = ma$$

The gravitational force is, of course, the man's weight.

$$F_{normal} - 122\ lbs = ma$$

When the elevator is at rest, or when it is moving at a constant velocity, the acceleration is zero.

$$F_{normal} - 122\ lbs = 0$$

$$F_{normal} = 122\ lbs$$

Since the scale reads the normal force, the scale reads the man's weight (122 lbs) when the elevator is at rest or moving with a constant velocity.

What happens when the elevator accelerates, however? Well, when that happens, the sum of the forces is no longer zero, because acceleration is no longer zero. Thus, we will need to solve the equation again, but this time with a nonzero acceleration. Before we can solve the equation, however, we need to know the man's mass. Remember, weight = mg. Since we know the man's weight, we can calculate his mass:

$$weight = mg$$

$$m = \frac{weight}{g} = \frac{122\,lbs}{32.2\,\frac{ft}{sec^2}} = 3.79\ slugs$$

Remember, the English unit for mass is the slug. A pound is a $\frac{slug \cdot ft}{sec^2}$, so the units work.

Now that we have the mass, we can plug that into our equation along with the acceleration:

$$F_{normal} - 122\ lbs = (3.79\ slugs) \cdot (8.00\,\frac{ft}{sec^2})$$

$$F_{normal} = (3.79\ slugs) \cdot (8.00\,\frac{ft}{sec^2}) + 122\ lbs = \underline{152\ lbs}$$

As the elevator accelerates upward, then, the scale reads a weight *larger* than the man's true weight. When the elevator slows down, the acceleration becomes negative. If you plug a negative acceleration into the problem, you will find that the scale reads a weight *smaller* than the man's true weight.

We can see, then, that while the man is in a non-inertial reference frame (while the elevator is accelerating), the scale does not read the proper weight. If the elevator is accelerating upwards, the weight is larger than the man's true weight. If the elevator is accelerating downwards (either by slowing its upward velocity or by moving downwards), the scale reads a weight lower than the true weight.

What would happen if the elevator cable were cut, and the elevator began to free fall? Well, at that point, the man's acceleration would be -g. If you put that into the equation we developed above, you would see that the scale would read zero. Thus, in that situation, the man would appear to be weightless. This is, in fact, the way we *simulate* weightlessness here on earth. If we put an experiment in a container that falls freely, the experiment can be considered to occur in weightless conditions, because in that reference frame, the experiment has no weight. The National Aeronautics and Space Administration (NASA), for example, has a 430 feet deep shaft called the "drop tower" which is used to simulate weightlessness.

In fact, there is a common misconception that there is no gravity in space. That's because we see pictures of astronauts floating around while in spaceships. They are *not* floating around because there is no gravity in space. If there were no gravity in space, the planets would not orbit the sun nor would the moons orbit the planets! The reason you see astronauts float in spaceships is that those spaceships are in orbit, and while in orbit, the spaceship is accelerating downwards!

Suppose, for example, you could climb a ladder that was 300 miles tall. That is a height at which the space shuttle orbits the earth. If the space shuttle flew by and you looked in the window, you would see all of the people inside floating around weightless. However, you would *not* be weightless. In fact, you would weigh 85% of your weight on the earth's surface. If you jumped off the ladder, you would fall to your death, because gravity would pull you back to the earth.

Why would the people in the space shuttle be weightless while you were not? Remember, for an object to move in a circle, it must experience centripetal acceleration directed towards the center of the circle. Thus, an orbiting spaceship experiences gravitational acceleration. As a result, those inside the spaceship seem weightless, just as a person in a freely-falling elevator seems weightless. In fact, in the making of the movie *Apollo 13*, the scenes in which the astronauts are shown floating in the spaceship were actually shot in an airplane that was in free fall! Of course, the plane would pull out of free fall before it was too late, so that the actors could get ready for the next segment of filming!

Now let's look at two more applications of Newton's Second Law. This next one looks deceptively simple.

EXAMPLE 3.4

Two blocks (m_1 = 40.0 kg, m_2 = 25.0 kg) are touching one another and sitting on the floor (μ_s = 0.450, μ_k = 0.250). A person pushes the blocks with a force of 200.0 Newtons. What is the acceleration of the system? What force pushes on the 25.0 kg mass?

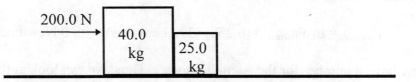

The 40.0 kg object is the one that actually experiences the force of the person pushing. What are all of the forces acting on it? Well, gravity pulls the object downwards, and the floor exerts a normal force up on the block. As a result of the contact between the block and the floor, there is also a friction force which opposes the motion. In addition, the 200.0 N force acts on the block. There is, however, one more force. Do you know what it is? The 40.0 kg block pushes against the 25.0 kg block, right? What does Newton's third law say *must* happen in response? The 25.0 block must push against the 40.0 kg block with an equal and opposite force. We will call this force "P," because it results from the fact that the blocks push against each other. This force is often referred to as a **contact force**. Thus, the forces working on this object are shown below:

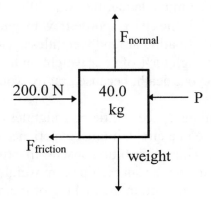

That's a lot of forces. We are interested in the horizontal direction, because that's where all of the action takes place. However, we do need to look at the vertical dimension. After all, friction is involved. To determine the force due to friction, we must determine the normal force. Therefore, let's start in the vertical dimension. There is no acceleration in the vertical dimension. Thus, the sum of the forces is zero. As a result:

$$F_{normal} - weight = 0$$

$$F_{normal} = weight = (40.0 \text{ kg}) \cdot (9.81 \frac{m}{sec^2}) = 392 \text{ Newtons}$$

Now that we know the normal force, we can calculate the frictional force with Equation (3.3). Since the system is moving, we will use μ_k:

$$F_{friction} = \mu_k \cdot F_{normal} = (0.250) \cdot (392 \text{ Newtons}) = 98.0 \text{ Newtons}$$

We now have a number for the frictional force. Thus, we can look at the horizontal dimension. Using the convention that motion to the right is positive, we get the following equation from Newton's Second Law:

$$200.0 \text{ N} - F_{friction} - P = m \cdot a$$

$$200.0 \text{ N} - 98.0 \text{ N} - P = (40.0 \text{ kg}) \cdot a$$

There are two unknowns in this equation, so we cannot solve it completely. However, if we get one of the unknowns in terms of the other, then perhaps looking at the other mass will allow us to finish the problem.

$$200.0 \text{ N} - 98.0 \text{ N} - P = (40.0 \text{ kg}) \cdot a$$

$$P = 102.0 \text{ N} - (40.0 \text{ kg}) \cdot a$$

Now let's look at the other mass. The 25.0 kg mass is also affected by gravity, the normal force, and friction. In addition, it is being pushed with a force of "P" by the 40.0 kg block. Remember, this "P" is equal in magnitude to the "P" we just solved for, because of Newton's Third Law. It is simply pointed in the opposite direction:

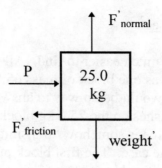

Notice that there is a prime in the notations for the normal force, frictional force, and weight. This just emphasizes that the values for these forces are *different* than the values for the normal, frictional, and weight forces acting on the first mass. The contact force is the same, however, so there is no prime on P. Once again, to get a number for the frictional force, I must first look at the vertical dimension:

$$F'_{normal} - weight' = 0$$

$$F'_{normal} = weight' = (25.0 \text{ kg}) \cdot (9.81 \, \frac{m}{sec^2}) = 245 \text{ Newtons}$$

Now we can calculate the frictional force:

$$F'_{friction} = \mu_k \cdot F'_{normal} = (0.250) \cdot (245 \text{ Newtons}) = 61.3 \text{ Newtons}$$

Next, we sum up the forces in the horizontal dimension and set them equal to mass times acceleration:

$$P - F'_{friction} = m \cdot a$$

$$P - 61.3 \text{ N} = (25.0 \text{ kg}) \cdot a$$

Since the "P" in this equation is the same as the "P" we had when we analyzed the previous mass, I can use the expression I determined for P in terms of a:

$$102.0 \text{ N} - (40.0 \text{ kg}) \cdot a - 61.3 \text{ N} = (25.0 \text{ kg}) \cdot a$$

$$(65.0 \text{ kg}) \cdot a = 40.7 \text{ N}$$

$$a = \frac{40.7 \text{ N}}{65.0 \text{ kg}} = 0.626 \frac{\text{m}}{\text{sec}^2}$$

The acceleration, then, is <u>0.626 m/sec^2</u>.

    The acceleration is actually much easier to find. All you have to do is add the masses together and treat the entire system as one block of mass 65.0 kg. Thus, there is only one equation to solve. However, there would be no way to answer the second part of the question. The second part asks what force pushes on the 25.0 kg block. Many students would say a force of 200.0 N, because the 200.0 N force is somehow "transmitted" through the first block and to the second. However, that is not the case. The first block pushes on the second block with a contact force. We have an equation for that contact force, so we can use it:

$$P = 102.0 \text{ N} - (40.0 \text{ kg}) \cdot a = 102.0 \text{ N} - (40.0 \text{ kg}) \cdot (0.626 \frac{\text{m}}{\text{sec}^2}) = 77.0 \text{ N}$$

The force pushing on the second block, then, is nowhere near 200.0 N. It is <u>77.0 N</u>.

    Notice that the method I used in this problem was the same as that which I employed when analyzing Atwood's Machine in the previous section. I looked at the masses individually, treating them each as an individual problem. Whenever you see a situation in which two objects are used, this is almost certainly the method you have to employ. Let me go through one more example so that you see exactly what I mean.

EXAMPLE 3.5

    A block (m = 50.0 kg) is being pulled up an incline (θ = 30.0°) with a 75.0 kg block that is hung on a pulley and attached to the 50.0 kg block via a string. If the coefficient of kinetic friction between the block and the incline is 0.310, what is the acceleration of the system and the tension in the string?

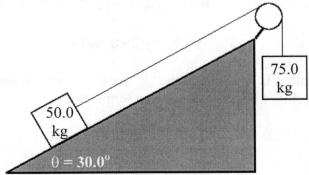

As with most problems like this, we start by looking at the blocks individually and summing up the forces on each of them. Starting with the 50.0 kg block, there are several forces acting on it. First, gravity is pulling straight down with a strength of mg. However, since this block is on an incline, we split that into two components. The component parallel to the incline is mg·sinθ, and the component perpendicular is mg·cosθ, as shown in the previous section. In addition, the incline exerts a normal force on the block. That normal force is, by definition, perpendicular to the incline. Also, friction exerts a force against the motion (thus parallel to the incline). Finally, the string exerts a tension pulling the block up the incline (and parallel to it).

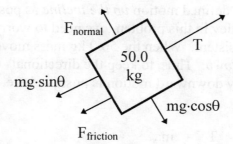

In the vertical dimension, there is no acceleration. Thus, the sum of the forces equals zero.

$$F_{normal} - mg \cdot \cos\theta = 0$$

$$F_{normal} - (50.0 \text{ kg}) \cdot (9.81 \, \frac{m}{sec^2}) \cdot \cos(30.0) = 0$$

$$F_{normal} = 425 \text{ N}$$

With this information, then, we can calculate $F_{friction}$:

$$F_{friction} = \mu F_{normal} = (0.310) \cdot (425 \text{ N}) = 132 \text{ N}$$

Now we can sum up the forces parallel to the incline and set them equal to the mass times the acceleration. Let's use the convention that motion up the incline is positive.

$$T - mg \cdot \sin\theta - F_{friction} = ma$$

$$T - (50.0 \text{ kg}) \cdot (9.81 \, \frac{m}{sec^2}) \cdot \sin(30.0) - 132 \text{ N} = (50.0 \text{ kg}) \cdot a$$

There are two unknowns here, so let's solve for T in terms of a.

$$T = (50.0 \text{ kg}) \cdot a + (50.0 \text{ kg}) \cdot (9.81 \, \frac{m}{sec^2}) \cdot \sin(30.0) + 132 \text{ N}$$

$$T = (50.0 \text{ kg}) \cdot a + 377 \text{ N}$$

Now we can look at the other block. It is *much* easier to analyze. In that block, there are only two forces. The string's tension pulls up on the block, and gravity pulls down. Thus, we can sum these two forces up and set them equal to the mass times the acceleration. Now remember, the tension here *must* be the same as the tension in the string that is attached to the other block, because it is all the same string. Also, these blocks move together, so the acceleration is the same for each block as well. There is just one more thing to think about. We already defined motion *up the incline* as positive motion. Since we are using a pulley in this problem, we need to worry about making that definition consistent. When the 50.0 kg mass moves up the incline, *this mass will move down*. Thus, to keep the directional definition consistent, we must say downward motion is positive here.

$$mg \ - \ T \ = \ ma$$

$$(75.0 \text{ kg}) \cdot (\ 9.81 \ \frac{m}{\sec^2}) - T = (75.0 \text{ kg}) \cdot a$$

Since the T in this equation is the same as the T in the previous equation, let's plug the expression for T that we got above into this equation.

$$(75.0 \text{ kg}) \cdot (\ 9.81 \ \frac{m}{\sec^2}) - [(50.0 \text{ kg}) \cdot a + 377 \text{ N}] = (75.0 \text{ kg}) \cdot a$$

$$359 \text{ N} = (125.0 \text{ kg}) \cdot a$$

$$\underline{a = 2.87 \frac{m}{\sec^2}}$$

With the acceleration, we can now use our expression for T to calculate the tension:

$$T = (50.0 \text{ kg}) \cdot a + 377 \text{ N} = (50.0 \text{ kg}) \cdot (2.87 \ \frac{m}{\sec^2}) + 377 \text{ N} = 521 \text{ N}$$

The string, then, is stretched with a <u>tension of 521 N</u>.

Now I want you to perform an experiment that is set up much like "on your own" Problem 3.4. Unlike that problem, however, we are not going to ignore friction. Instead, we are going to use this experiment as a means of *measuring* the coefficient of kinetic friction between a board and an object.

EXPERIMENT 3.2
Measuring the Coefficient of Kinetic Friction

Supplies:

- A Ziplock® bag
- A block of wood or some other object with a flat surface (I used a small cardboard box with some sand inside.)
- A board that is as wide as the block and about 1.5 meters long
- A string that is as long as the board.
- Sand (Kitty litter, dirt, or small gravel will work as well.)
- A mass scale
- A pulley
- Hammer and nails
- A stopwatch
- Meter stick or other metric ruler
- A table or desk. (The closer the height is to 1.5 meters, the better.)

Introduction - In your first-year course, you should have learned how to measure the coefficient of static friction between a board and a block by tilting the block. That, however, measures only the coefficient of static friction. This method, by contrast, will measure the coefficient of kinetic friction. You will do this using a setup that looks like the drawing for "on your own" problem 3.4.

Procedure:

1. Take the board and attach the pulley to the board with nails. This can be the tricky part. You want the pulley to be at the right height. Make sure that the top of the pulley is not higher than the top of the block as it rests on the board.
2. You will need to attach the string to the block of wood. If the block has no place to attach the string, drive a nail into it so that you can attach the string to the nail. Place the nail so that the string will stretch *in a straight line which is parallel to the board* from the block to the pulley. This will ensure that the string exerts a force on the block which is parallel to the board.
3. Measure the mass of the block.
4. As you did in the previous experiment, fill a Ziplock® bag with sand. You want the mass of the bag and sand to be about equal to the mass of the block.

5. Seal the bag and punch a hole through it near the top so that you can thread the string through it.
6. Attach the string to the block, place it over the pulley, and attach the other end of the string to the bag.
7. Now you have a system that looks much like the drawing for "on your own" problem 3.4.
8. Lay the board/pulley system on the desk so that the bag hangs over the edge of the table and the pulley turns freely.
9. Pull the block back along the board so that the bag is lifted to where it is just touching the pulley.
10. Release the block. If the block slides across the board, your setup is working. If not, the friction between the board and the block is too large, and you need to add more mass to the bag.
11. Once the system allows the block to slide across the board when it is released, you are ready to begin the experiment. Repeat steps (9) - (10) ten times, each time using the stopwatch to measure the time from when you released the block to when the bag touches the ground. Average those 10 results so that you have a good idea of the time that it took for the bag to fall.
12. Pull the bag up so that it is just touching the pulley as you did each time in step (9).
13. Measure the distance between the bottom of the bag and the floor. That is the distance over which the bag dropped.
14. Now you can calculate the coefficient of sliding friction between the board and the block. First, use the time and distance you measured in Equation (2.5) to determine the acceleration of the system.
15. Next, analyze the two masses in the system independently. If you are unsure how to do this, review the solution to "on your own" problem 3.5. The best way to begin the analysis is with the bag. There are only two forces on the bag: gravity and tension. Since you have measured the acceleration, you can get a value for the tension in the string.
16. Now look at the block. There are two forces acting horizontally on the block: the tension on the string (you determined its value in the previous step) and friction. Once again, since you know the acceleration, you can determine the size of the frictional force.
17. Since the frictional force is just the coefficient of sliding friction times the normal force, and since the normal force is just the mass of the block times g, you can now solve for the coefficient of sliding friction. The number should be less than one. Mine was 0.58.
18. You can try this with different boards. The smoother the board, the lower your coefficient should be.
19. Clean everything up.

ON YOUR OWN

3.6 In the drawing to the right, the block on the incline has a mass of 150.0 kg, and the block hanging from the pulley has a mass of 100.0 kg. Neglecting friction, what value of θ will allow the 150.0 kg mass to move up the incline at a constant velocity?

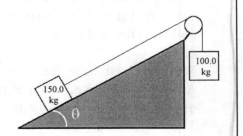

3.7 Referring to the setup in problem 3.6, assume that the coefficient of static friction is 0.300 and the coefficient of kinetic friction is 0.200. Set up an equation that tells you for what value of theta the masses will just start moving. The equation should have θ as its only variable. Do not solve the equation.

3.8 Consider the situation depicted in the drawing to the right. If the coefficient of kinetic friction is 0.250 and the system is moving, what is the acceleration of the system and the tension in each string?

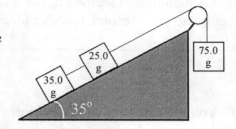

3.9 Three masses are pushed along a floor that has a coefficient of kinetic friction equal to 0.35. The force used to push the masses is 375.0 Newtons.

a. What is the acceleration of the system?
b. List the values of all forces which act on the 15.0 kg block.

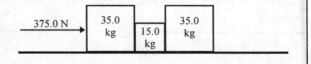

A Few Words About Newton's Third Law

Although I have already explained Newton's Third Law, I want to spend just a moment discussing a consequence of this very important law. You have already used Newton's Third Law in the previous two sections of the course. You use it, for example, to calculate the value of the frictional force. When an object rests on a surface, it exerts a force on that surface. If the surface is horizontal, the force the object exerts on the surface is equal to its weight. In response, the surface exerts a normal force, which is equal in size but opposite in direction. That, of course, is the equal and opposite force demanded by Newton's Third Law.

You also used Newton's Third Law when analyzing systems in which blocks touch each other and are pushed across a surface together. In "on your own" problem 3.9, for example, the 15.0 kg mass moves because the 35.0 kg block to the left exerts a force on it. In turn, however, the 15.0 kg mass exerts an equal but opposite force on the 35.0 kg mass. This force slows down the 35.0 kg mass so that it does not accelerate as quickly as it could were it not in contact with the 15.0 kg mass.

In your first-year physics course, you also dealt with Newton's Third Law quite a bit. Remember, for example, that the moon stays in orbit around the earth because the earth exerts a gravitational force on the moon. In turn, the moon exerts an equal but opposite gravitational force on the earth, and one of the consequences of that force is the tides that we see in the ocean.

Notice what's going on here, then. *Every time* a force is exerted, *an equal and opposite force* is exerted. This tells us something very important:

There is no such thing as a single, isolated force. ALL forces come in pairs, which are called action/reaction pairs.

This statement might seem odd, but it is nevertheless true. It is impossible to exert a force without *causing* a second, reactive force. That's a consequence of Newton's Third Law.

ON YOUR OWN

3.10 You are caught in a sudden storm with high winds and rain. You take shelter from the wind and rain under a tree and notice that the wind is so strong that the tree is actually bending. Thus, the wind is exerting a strong force on the tree, and you see the evidence of that force because the tree bends. What is the equal and opposite force as demanded by Newton's Third Law? What is the evidence you find for the force?

ANSWERS TO THE ON YOUR OWN PROBLEMS

3.1 <u>No, we cannot</u>. If it is at rest (or moving with a constant velocity), we can conclude that the *sum of the forces* acting on the object is zero. It is entirely possible that two or more forces are acting on the object. They simply cancel each other out.

3.2 <u>Not necessarily</u>. If they move with constant velocity *relative to each other*, that means either they have no acceleration (and thus are in inertial reference frames) or have *the same acceleration*. Two cars each accelerating at 3.5 m/sec^2 in the same direction will move at constant velocity with respect to each other. However, they are not inertial reference frames.

3.3 Let's start by drawing a horizontal line where the gravitational vector and the incline meet. When we do that, we can use the geometric law that says when two parallel lines are cut by a transversal, corresponding angles are congruent.

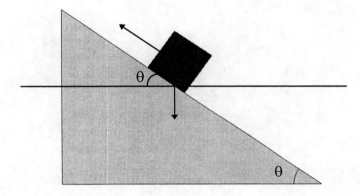

Geometry also tells us that vertical angles are congruent. Thus:

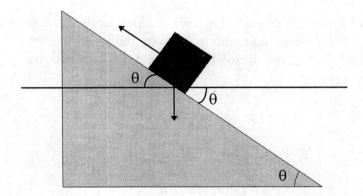

Since the gravitational vector forms a right angle with the horizontal, we can say that the angle next to the theta we just drew is 90-θ.

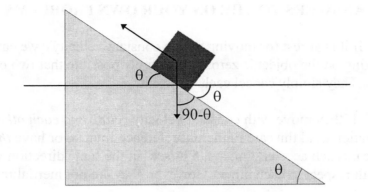

When we split the gravitational force vector into components parallel to and perpendicular to the incline, a right triangle is formed. Since the internal angles of a triangle must add to 180, that means the remaining angle must be θ.

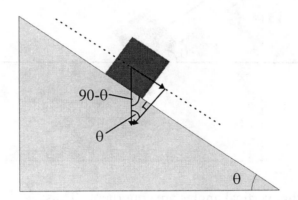

3.4   In all problems like this, we treat the masses independently. The second mass is the easiest to analyze first. It has two forces acting on it. Gravity pulls it down, and the tension in the string pulls it up. Using the normal definition of down being negative motion :

$$T - m_2 \cdot g = m_2 \cdot a$$

$$T = m_2 \cdot a + m_2 \cdot g$$

$$T = (20.0 \text{ kg}) \cdot (a) + 196 \text{ N}$$

With that equation for T, we can move to the first mass to calculate the acceleration. Since friction is not being considered, the only horizontal force acting on the mass is tension. There are vertical forces acting on the mass, but we need not consider them since we are ignoring friction. Now, we *must* worry about the signs used. We defined negative motion as m_2

moving down. When m_2 moves downward, however, m_1 moves to the right. Thus, the motion of m_1 to the right is negative. This means:

$$- T = m_1 \cdot a$$

We can plug the equation we had previously for T into this equation and solve for a:

$$(-20.0 \text{ kg}) \cdot a - 196 \text{ N} = (40.0 \text{ kg}) \, a$$

$$a = \frac{-196 \text{ N}}{60.0 \text{ kg}} = -3.27 \, \frac{\text{m}}{\text{sec}^2}$$

Notice that the acceleration is negative, which means that m_1 is moving to the right. There is a simpler way to do this problem and get this answer. However, you need to know how to do problems this way, because the simple method will only work in very simple cases. For example, you cannot use the simple method to do the next problem. That's why I do not teach it.

3.5 Now we have to take friction into account. However, friction affects only m_1. As a result, our analysis of m_2 stays the same. Thus, from m_2 we get the same equation:

$$T = (20.0 \text{ kg}) \cdot (a) + 196 \text{ N}$$

When we look at m_1, however, things change. Remember, friction depends on the normal force, which is a vertical force. Thus, we have to consider vertical forces now. In the vertical dimension, gravity pulls the mass down and the normal force pushes it back up. Since there is no motion in that dimension, we know that the sum of these forces is zero.

$$F_{normal} - m_1 \cdot g = 0$$

$$F_{normal} = m_1 \cdot g = 392 \text{ N}$$

Now we can use that to calculate the frictional force:

$$F_{friction} = \mu \cdot F_{normal} = (0.25) \cdot (392 \text{ N}) = 98 \text{ N}$$

Now we can sum up the forces in the horizontal dimension. Remember, however, that in analyzing m_2, we already defined the motion. When m_2 moves downward the motion is negative. Thus, when m_1 moves to the right, motion is negative. This means:

$$F_{friction} - T = m_1 \cdot a$$

$$98 \text{ N} - T = (40.0 \text{ kg}) \cdot a$$

Now we can plug in the equation we got for T from m_2 and solve for a:

$$98 \text{ N} - (20.0 \text{ kg}) \cdot a - 196 \text{ N} = (40.0 \text{ kg}) \cdot a$$

$$a = \frac{98 \text{ N} - 196 \text{ N}}{60.0 \text{ kg}} = -1.6 \, \frac{m}{\sec^2}$$

Once again, the negative simply means that m_1 is moving to the right and m_2 is moving downwards.

3.6 In this situation, we must once again analyze the masses individually. Let's start with the 100.0 kg mass. There are two forces, tension and gravity. If the system moves at *constant velocity*, that means *acceleration is zero*. Thus, the sum of the forces is zero. Let's say that motion of the 100.0 kg mass downwards is negative. That means:

$$T - (100.0 \text{ kg}) \cdot g = 0$$

$$T = (100.0 \text{ kg}) \cdot g = 981 \text{ N}$$

Instead of getting an equation for T this time, we actually got a number. That should make the next step even easier!

Now we look at the other block. This block has two forces working on it in the dimension parallel to the incline. The tension of the string is pulling it up the incline, and the component of the gravitation force that is parallel to the incline is pushing it down the incline. There are forces in the dimension vertical to the incline but, since we are ignoring friction, we can ignore them.

Since motion of the 100.0 kg mass downwards is negative motion, that means motion up the incline is negative. This means that the sum of the forces (which equals zero) is:

$$(150.0 \text{ kg}) \cdot g \cdot \sin\theta - T = 0$$

We know what T is, so we can plug that number in and solve for theta:

$$(150.0 \text{ kg}) \cdot (9.81 \frac{\text{m}}{\text{sec}^2}) \cdot \sin\theta - 981 \text{ N} = 0$$

$$\theta = \sin^{-1}\left(\frac{981 \text{ N}}{(150.0 \text{ kg}) \cdot (9.81 \frac{\text{m}}{\text{sec}^2})} \right) = 41.8°$$

If the angle of the incline is <u>41.8 degrees</u>, the masses will move at a constant velocity.

3.7 In this situation, the only difference is that there is a frictional force. In order to get the system moving, the force exerted on the 150.0 kg mass by the string must overcome both the gravitational force that pulls the 150.0 kg mass down the incline and the static friction. In order to overcome the static friction, the sum of the forces must be just barely greater than zero. Thus, we will set the sum of the forces equal to zero as a lower limit.

Since friction affects *only* the block on the incline, our analysis of the 100.0 kg block in problem 3.6 does not change. Thus, we know that T = 981 N. Now let's look at the 150.0 kg block.

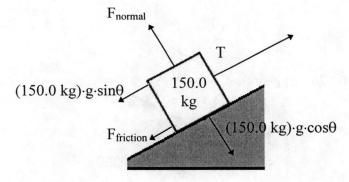

In the dimension perpendicular to the incline, there is no motion. Thus:

$$F_{normal} - (150.0 \text{ kg}) \cdot g \cdot \cos\theta = 0$$

$$F_{normal} = (150.0 \text{ kg}) \cdot g \cdot \cos\theta$$

Now we can determine the frictional force. Remember, we are trying to determine what is required to get the system moving. Thus, we use the coefficient of static friction:

$$F_{friction} = \mu \cdot F_{normal} = (0.300) \cdot (150.0 \text{ kg}) \cdot g \cdot \cos\theta = (441 \text{ N}) \cdot \cos\theta$$

With an equation for the frictional force and a value for T, we can now sum up the forces in the dimension parallel to the incline. Remember, motion to the right is negative because we defined motion of the 100.0 kg block downwards as negative.

$$(150.0 \text{ kg}) \cdot g \cdot \sin\theta + (441 \text{ N}) \cdot \cos\theta - 981 \text{ N} = 0$$

$$\underline{(1.47 \times 10^3 \text{ N}) \cdot \sin\theta + (441 \text{ N}) \cdot \cos\theta = 981 \text{ N}}$$

This is as far as I wanted you to go. It is an equation that tells you for what value of theta the static friction is overcome. Now you see why I did not want you to solve the equation!

3.8 Let's analyze the easiest mass first: the 75.0 g mass. There are only two forces acting on it, and they sum to give the mass times the acceleration. Note that mass is not in the standard units, so we must convert to kg. If downward motion is negative:

$$T_1 - (0.0750 \text{ kg}) \cdot g = (0.075 \text{ kg}) \cdot a$$

$$T_1 = (0.0750 \text{ kg}) \cdot a + 0.736 \text{ N}$$

This gives us an equation for the tension in the *first* string. However, there are two strings, so that complicates matters. Now let's look at the 25.0 g mass:

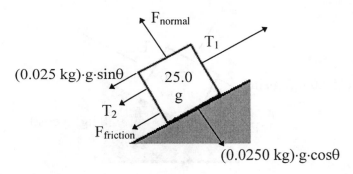

The tension in the second string, the component of the gravitational force parallel to the incline, and friction all pull downward on the mass. Only the tension of the first string pulls upward on the mass. Since we are dealing with friction, we have to determine the normal force. That's easy, however. The sum of the forces perpendicular to the incline tells us that $F_{normal} = (0.0250 \text{ kg}) \cdot g \cdot \cos\theta$. Since we know g and θ we can evaluate this. The normal force is 0.201 N. This means the kinetic frictional force is 0.0503 N.

Now we can sum up the forces parallel to the incline that work on this block:

$$T_2 + F_{friction} + (0.0250 \text{ kg}) \cdot g \cdot \sin\theta - T_1 = (0.0250 \text{ kg}) \cdot a$$

Plugging in what we know ($F_{friction}$, g, θ, and the equation for T_1):

$$T_2 + 0.0503 \text{ N} + 0.141 \text{ N} - (0.0750 \text{ kg}) \cdot a - 0.736 \text{ N} = (0.0250 \text{ kg}) \cdot a$$

We can't solve this equation because it has two unknowns. However, we can solve for T_2 in terms of a and hope that the last mass gives us what we need.

$$T_2 = 0.545 \text{ N} + (0.100 \text{ kg}) \cdot a$$

The last mass is a bit easier. It has T_2 pulling it up the incline, and friction plus the gravitational force component parallel to the incline pulling it down. Since we are dealing with friction, we must also use the dimension perpendicular to the incline to determine the normal force.

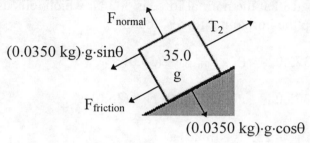

The vertical dimension tells us that $F_{normal} = (0.0350 \text{ kg}) \cdot g \cdot \cos\theta$. This tells us that the frictional force is 0.0703 N. Summing up the forces parallel to the incline gives us:

$$(0.0350 \text{ kg}) \cdot g \cdot \sin\theta + F_{friction} - T_2 = (0.0350 \text{ kg}) \cdot a$$

Now we can plug in what we know and solve for a:

$$0.197 \text{ N} + 0.0703 \text{ N} - 0.545 \text{ N} - (0.100 \text{ kg}) \cdot a = (0.0350 \text{ kg}) \cdot a$$

$$a = \frac{-0.278 \text{ N}}{0.135 \text{ kg}} = -2.06 \ \frac{\text{m}}{\text{sec}^2}$$

This allows us to calculate both T_2 and T_1:

$$T_1 = (0.0750 \text{ kg}) \cdot a + 0.736 \text{ N} = \underline{0.582 \text{ N}}$$

$$T_2 = 0.545 \text{ N} + (0.100 \text{ kg}) \cdot a = \underline{0.339 \text{ N}}$$

3.9 You could get the acceleration of the system by just adding up the masses and treating the three as one large mass. However, to answer the second part of the question, you have to do a full analysis. Thus, you might as well do it right away. The first block has the 75.0 N force pushing to the right, which I will define as the positive direction. It pushes against the second block, which in turn pushes back to the left. I will call that force P_1. Finally, friction pushes to the left. Since we are dealing with friction, we have to determine the normal force.

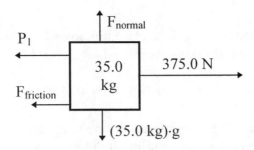

The vertical dimension tells us that the normal force is 343 N, which tells us the frictional force is 1.20×10^2 N. Summing up the horizontal forces, then:

$$375.0 \text{ N} - P_1 - F_{friction} = (35.0) \cdot a$$

$$375.0 \text{ N} - P_1 - 1.20 \times 10^2 \text{ N} = (35.0) \cdot a$$

$$P_1 = 255 \text{ N} - (35.0) \cdot a$$

Now we can move on to the next mass:

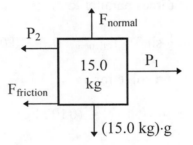

In this mass, the force with which the first mass pushes is pointed to the right. However, this mass pushes against the third mass, and in turn that third mass pushes back with an equal but opposite force, which I will call P_2. The vertical dimension tells us that the normal force is 147 N, which means the frictional force is 51.5 N.

$$P_1 - F_{friction} - P_2 = (15.0) \cdot a$$

$$255 \text{ N} - (35.0) \cdot a - 51.5 \text{ N} - P_2 = (15.0) \cdot a$$

$$P_2 = 203 \text{ N} - (50.0) \cdot a$$

Finally, we reach the last block:

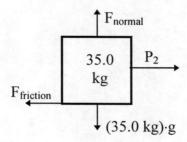

The vertical dimension tells us that the normal force is 343 N, which tells us the frictional force is 1.20×10^2 N. Summing up the horizontal forces, then:

$$P_2 - F_{friction} = (35.0 \text{ kg}) \cdot a$$

$$203 \text{ N} - (50.0) \cdot a - 1.20 \times 10^2 \text{ N} = (35.0 \text{ kg}) \cdot a$$

$$a = \frac{83 \text{ N}}{85.0 \text{ kg}} = \underline{0.98 \ \frac{m}{sec^2}}$$

b. Now that we know a, we can figure out P_1 and P_2, which will tell us all of the forces acting on the 15.0 kg block.

$$P_1 = 255 \text{ N} - (35.0) \cdot a = 221 \text{ N}$$

$$P_2 = 203 \text{ N} - (50.0) \cdot a = 154 \text{ N}$$

The forces acting on the 15.0 kg block are:

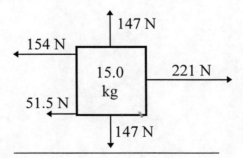

3.10 <u>The tree exerts a force on the wind. The evidence for that force is the fact that you do not feel the wind nearly as strongly as you stand behind the tree.</u>

REVIEW QUESTIONS FOR MODULE #3

Questions 1-3 refer to the following situation:

You are inside a large room, and there is a ball hanging on a string that is attached to the ceiling. The ball hangs straight down. As you watch, the ball seems to swing to the right of its own accord. Slowly, the ball begins to drift back to the point from which it started, and it once again hangs straight down from the ceiling. Throughout this entire time, there was no wind or other motion in the room.

1. While the ball is moving, are you in an inertial reference frame? Why or why not?

2. What was the net direction of the sum of forces acting on the room while the ball was swinging to the right?

3. When the ball once again hung straight down from the ceiling, were you in an inertial reference frame?

4. Suppose you are in a car with a ball that hangs from a string attached to the ceiling. As you move with constant speed, the ball hangs straight down. Suppose you were to follow a curve in the road, never altering your speed. Which way would the ball swing?

5. Consider Atwood's machine. Suppose the string and pulley were weightless and there was no friction. If the masses on the machine move with constant velocity, how does the mass of the second compare to the first?

6. Suppose you were sitting on a car seat that could read the force with which your back pushed against the seat. When the car is at rest, the car seat reads 20 pounds, indicating that you are leaning back in the seat. Assume that you do not adjust the way you are sitting.

a. As the car started to accelerate, would the reading go up or down?
b. When the car reaches a constant speed, what will the chair read?
c. As the car slowed to a halt, would the chair read higher or lower than 20 pounds?

Questions 7-9 refer to the following situation:

Two people, one of mass 75 kg and the other of mass 150 kg are skating. There is essentially no friction. They stand at rest, and then the 75 kg skater puts her hands on the other skater and pushes.

7. Both skaters will begin to move. Why?

8. What direction will the 150 kg skater move in, compared to the 75 kg skater?

9. Compare the acceleration of the 150 kg skater to that of the 75 kg skater.

10. A football kicker kicks a ball in the air. Identify the action/reaction forces when the ball is kicked. Once in the air, identify the action/reaction forces, if there are any. Ignore air resistance, air pressure, and wind.

PRACTICE PROBLEMS FOR MODULE #3

1. Find the tensions in each string if the ball in the figure has a mass of 100.0 kg.

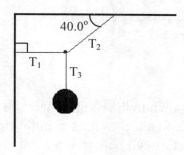

2. Consider the variation on Atwood's machine shown to the right. If $m_1 = 50.0$ kg, $m_2 = 30.0$ kg, and $m_3 = 30.0$ kg, calculate the acceleration of the system and determine the tension in each string.

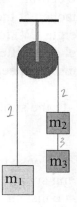

3. Consider the same Atwood's machine shown to the right. If someone were to grasp m_1 and pull down, what force would be required to keep m_1 moving downwards at a constant speed?

4. Consider the following drawing:

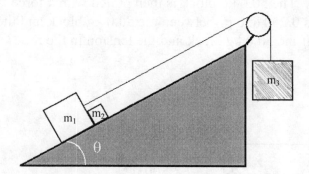

If $m_1 = 50.0$ kg, $m_2 = 15.0$ kg, and $\theta = 35.0°$ what must m_3 be to make m_1 and m_2 accelerate up the incline at 1.00 m/sec²? Assume that the pulley and string have no mass and experience no friction. However, take the friction between the blocks and the incline into account, assuming $\mu_k = 0.200$.

5. For the situation in the problem above, draw and label all of the forces that work on m_1. Include the magnitudes of the forces in your drawing.

6. A bosun's chair (developed for use on ships) consists of a chair attached to a rope that is slung over a pulley. As illustrated on the right, the person sitting on the chair then pulls down on the rope, and the chair lifts up. Suppose the chair and the person have a mass of 125 kg. What force must the person pull down with in order to lift the chair at a constant speed?

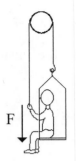

7. A block-and-tackle system is set up as shown to the right. There are three separate ropes. The first is the one which attaches the top pulley to the ceiling. The second is the one that goes through both pulleys and is attached at the bottom of the upper pulley. The last one attaches the weight (W) to the lower pulley. When you pull down on the rope, the weight is lifted up. Calculate the force needed to lift the weight at a constant speed. Leave your answer in terms of W.

8. In the situation shown to the right, what is T_1 in terms of W?

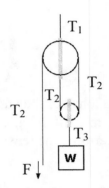

9. Suppose the W in the block-and-tackle system shown was a bosun's chair, with the F being supplied by the occupant of the chair. What force would be required to lift the chair at a constant speed?

10. In the drawing below, a 10.0 kg block is attached to the wall by a rope and then placed on top of a 50.0 kg block. The 50.0 kg block is then pulled with a force of 300.0 N. If μ_k between the two blocks is 0.250 and μ_k between the 50.0 kg block and the floor is 0.350, what is the acceleration of the 50.0 kg block and the tension in the rope?

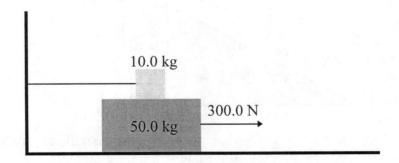

Module #4: Energy and Momentum

Introduction

Newton's laws provided an incredible boost to the science of physics, and using those laws as a framework, scientists began to learn many details regarding motion. In about 100 years, scientists decided that they had to incorporate another concept into the science of physics: the concept of **energy**. Of course, you covered many energy concepts in your first-year course, so in this course, I want to apply those concepts to many different situations, including the collision of two objects. When we analyze collisions, we will also have to use the concept of **momentum**, which you also learned about in your first-year course.

Review of Energy Concepts and Equations

Before I start applying energy concepts to different situations, I want to quickly review what you should have learned in your first-year course. First, the definition of energy is:

Energy - The ability to do work

The definition of work is best given by an equation, which was introduced in Module #1:

$$W = \mathbf{F} \bullet \mathbf{x} \qquad\qquad (1.8)$$

Remember, the dot product between two vectors is the product of the magnitude of each vector and the cosine of the angle between them. Thus:

$$W = F \cdot x \cdot \cos\theta \qquad\qquad (4.1)$$

There are two basic forms of energy: **potential energy** and **kinetic energy**:

Potential Energy (PE) - Energy that is stored, ready to do work

Kinetic Energy (KE) - Energy in motion

A rock sitting at the top of a hill, for example, has potential energy. It is not in motion, but if it were to roll down the hill, it would start moving faster and faster, thus gaining kinetic energy. Where does the kinetic energy come from? Well, as the ball rolls down the hill, its potential energy is converted into kinetic energy.

The **Law of Energy Conservation**, which is also called the **First Law of Thermodynamics**, says that the *total* energy (TE) of any object stays the same. In mathematical terms:

$$TE = \text{constant} \qquad\qquad (4.2)$$

This tells us that if you add up *all* of the energy of an object (its KE, its PE, and any work done on or by the object), the sum will always remain the same.

Of course, to track the total energy of an object, we need to know how to calculate potential energy, kinetic energy, and work. Well, Equation (1.8) tells you how to calculate work, and there are also equations that we can use to calculate kinetic and potential energy. Kinetic energy is the easier of the two. Since kinetic energy is energy in motion, the amount of kinetic energy an object has depends on mass and speed:

$$KE = \frac{1}{2} \cdot m \cdot v^2 \tag{4.3}$$

Notice that the "v" is not in boldface type, so it refers to speed, not velocity.

What about potential energy? Well, there are also equations for potential energy, but the equation depends on the situation. For example, suppose you have a rock sitting at the top of a hill. The potential energy that the rock has is based on the force due to gravity. Near the surface of the earth, it can be calculated with the formula:

$$PE = m \cdot g \cdot h \tag{4.4}$$

Where "g" is the acceleration due to gravity and "h" is the height of the rock relative to some other surface. Consider, for example, a ball that is sitting at the top of a staircase. The ball has potential energy relative to the first step, and that could be calculated using Equation (4.4), as long as the value for "h" is the height of the ball relative to that first step. However, the ball has potential energy relative to *every other step* on the staircase as well. Thus, the value for potential energy in Equation (4.4) depends on the surface relative to which height is measured.

Equation (4.4), however, is only one possible equation for potential energy. It is applicable only for objects that sit at a height relative to another surface, and it is only applicable near the surface of the earth (or some other planet, assuming you use the appropriate value for "g"). There are, however, other ways in which an object can have potential energy. For example, a charged particle can be placed in an electric field. In that situation, the charged particle has potential energy related to the electromagnetic force. That potential energy can be calculated via the following equation:

$$PE = q \cdot V \tag{4.5}$$

Where "q" is the charge (include the sign of the charge: positive or negative) and "V" is the **electrical potential**:

$$V = \frac{k \cdot Q}{r} \tag{4.6}$$

In this equation, "k" is the Coulomb constant ($8.99 \times 10^9 \ \frac{N \cdot m^2}{C^2}$), "Q" is the charge of the particle which is making the electrical field (once again, include the sign), and "r" is the distance from the particle of charge "Q."

Okay, I've just thrown a lot of equations at you, so I want you to think about all of this for a moment. This should really be review for you, and that's why I went through it quickly. Nevertheless, you need to remember these concepts and be comfortable working with them. To get you thinking about these concepts again, I want you to perform an experiment that utilizes Equation (4.4).

EXPERIMENT 4.1
Ping Pong Pendulums

Supplies:

- Two ping pong balls
- Thread
- Scissors
- Cellophane tape
- Double-stick cellophane tape
- Ruler
- Pencil
- Sheet of lined paper (If you don't have lined paper, you can make the lines yourself.)
- Two nails (Small finishing nails are ideal.)
- Hammer
- A board that is at least a few inches wide and a few inches long. It must be thick enough to hammer the nails into the edge of the board.

Introduction - Colliding pendulums provide an excellent opportunity to study the energy concepts you learned in your first-year physics course.

Procedure:

1. Take the board and hammer the nails into one end of the board so that they are roughly centered and about 4 cm away from each other. The board should look like the following sketch if viewed from above:

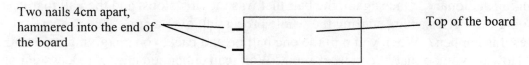

Two nails 4cm apart, hammered into the end of the board

Top of the board

2. Cut two lengths of thread approximately 25 cm long. Use the regular (not the double-stick) cellophane tape to attach one end of each thread to each of the ping pong balls. Now you have two ping pong balls, each of which hangs from a thread.

3. Place the board on a desk or some other surface with a solid wall beneath it. For example, I used the top of a filing cabinet. You are going to hang the ping pong balls from the nails, but there must be a surface behind those ping pong balls to which you can tape the paper.

4. Tie the free end of each thread to each of the nails in the board. You now have two ping pong balls hanging from threads which are attached to the nails in the board. Adjust the board so that the nails hang far enough over the edge so that the balls are very close to but not touching the surface behind them.

5. The ping pong balls should be just barely touching each other. Adjust them so that they are at the same height. The best way to adjust them is to take the ball that is hanging lower and start to wrap its thread around the nail from which it hangs. That will raise the ball up until it is even with the other ball.

6. Now you are going to tape the lined paper to the surface which is behind the ping pong balls. If your paper does not have lines, make lines which are 1.0 cm apart. The paper should be taped so that the lines run horizontally, level with the floor, and one of the lines should run through the center of the two ping pong balls. Your setup should look something like this:

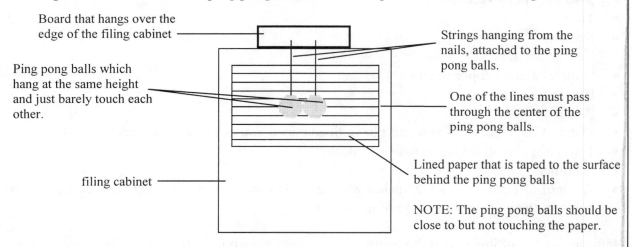

Board that hangs over the edge of the filing cabinet

Ping pong balls which hang at the same height and just barely touch each other.

filing cabinet

Strings hanging from the nails, attached to the ping pong balls.

One of the lines must pass through the center of the ping pong balls.

Lined paper that is taped to the surface behind the ping pong balls

NOTE: The ping pong balls should be close to but not touching the paper.

7. If you have paper with lines, measure the distance between the lines.

8. Now you are ready to begin the experiment. Pull one ball up and to the side so that the string stays taut. In essence, you want to turn this ball into a pendulum. Release the ball and let it swing.

9. Note what happens. When the swinging ball hits the ball that is still hanging straight down, the swinging ball stops and the ball that was just hanging there begins to swing upwards. It eventually reaches a maximum height and falls back down, hitting the other ball which is now hanging stationary. Once again, the ball that was moving stops, and the ball that was just hanging there rises again, starting the whole process all over again.

10. Why does this happen? When you pull the one ball up and back, you are giving it potential energy. How do you do that? You *work* on it. Work can either add energy to a system or take energy away, depending on the nature of the work. In this case, your work (lifting the ball) adds potential energy to the system. When you release the ball, that potential energy is

converted into kinetic energy, and the ball begins to move. When it collides with the hanging ball, almost all of its energy is transferred to the other ball via the collision. Thus, the ball that was originally moving stops, because it has no more energy. However, the ball that was hanging now moves, because it has all sorts of kinetic energy. The ball then rises until all of that kinetic energy is converted into potential energy. Once that happens, the ball stops rising and starts falling, converting its potential energy back into kinetic energy.

11. Okay, now it is time to get a bit more detailed. Stop the balls so that they both hang down again, and note the line that runs through the center of the balls. We will call that line the "zero line," because it represents the lowest position the balls can reach. Thus, it corresponds to a height of zero.

12. Now, lift one ball up and back again so that the string stays taut. Lift it high enough so that the center of the ball is even with the line which is 5 lines above the zero line. This corresponds to a height of 5 times the distance between the lines. If the distance between the lines is 0.85 cm, for example, this corresponds to a height of 4.25 cm.

13. Release the ball, and use the lines to read the maximum height that the other ball reaches after the collision. If the situation were ideal, this height would be identical to the first one. However, it will not work out that way. The height reached by the second ball will be lower than the height at which the first ball was released.

14. Now think about the energetics of this situation. Why doesn't the second ball reach the height from which the first ball was released? Well, in addition to the potential and kinetic energy considerations I have discussed so far, there is one more consideration: the work done by friction. As the balls move and collide, friction (mostly air resistance) works against the motion. This removes energy from the system. You can actually use your data to determine how much work friction performed.

15. The mass of an official ping pong ball is 2.2 grams. Use Equation (4.4) to calculate the potential energy of the first ball before it was released. Remember, mass must be in kg, and height must be in meters (standard units) for the units to work out. If the lines on the paper were 0.85 cm, apart, for example, the PE of the first ball would be 9.2×10^{-4} J.

16. Use the maximum height of the second ball to calculate the maximum potential energy of the second ball. Ideally, this should be the same as the potential energy of the first ball. After all, as the first ball fell, it converted all of its potential energy into kinetic energy. When it hit the second ball, the second ball received that kinetic energy and then began to rise, converting the kinetic energy back into potential energy. If that were the end of the story, then, the maximum potential energy of the second ball would be the same as that of the first. However, it will be lower, because friction worked on the balls, removing energy from the system.

17. Calculate how much energy friction removed from the system by taking the difference between the two potential energies. That number is the work done by friction.

18. Now I want you to modify your experiment a bit. Cover the two balls with double-stick tape so that when they collide, they will stick to one another.

19. Repeat the experiment. Notice that in this situation, the two balls stick together and rise to about half of the height that the second ball rose to in the first part of the experiment. Why? Well, when the balls stick together, the object rising has twice as much mass. Thus, by Equation (4.4), it needs to reach only half of the height to have the same potential energy.

20. Clean everything up.

I hope this experiment helped to remind you about the energy concepts you learned in your first-year physics course. Remember, in the absence of an outside force, the kinetic energy plus the potential energy of a system must stay constant. However, if an outside force is working on the system, that work can either add energy or take energy away from the system. This is often referred to as the **work-energy theorem**.

Work-energy Theorem - The work done on an object is equal to the change in its kinetic energy

If the work done is positive, it adds kinetic energy to the object, increasing its speed. If the work done is negative, it lowers the kinetic energy of the object, decreasing its speed.

In the experiment, friction removed energy from the balls by working on them as they fell and as they collided. In this case, then, the work done was negative. Since work and energy have the same units, any work done either directly adds to or subtracts from the kinetic energy of the system. Perform the following "on your own" problems to make sure you remember these energy concepts.

ON YOUR OWN

4.1 Consider a block that is sitting at the top of a hill (height = 1.5 m). It starts from rest and slides to the bottom. Ignoring friction, what will its speed be at the bottom of the hill? Note: you do not need the mass of the block to answer this question!

4.2 Now let's consider friction in the problem above. Suppose the mass of the block is 150.0 grams. In addition, suppose its speed at the bottom of the hill is 4.0 m/sec. How much work did friction do as the block slid down the hill?

4.3 A charged particle (Q = 4.5 C) is fixed so that it cannot move. Another charged particle (q = -1.5 C, m = 15.0 g) is placed 3.5 m from the fixed particle. It is held there for a moment and then released. How quickly will the charged particle be traveling when it is 1.0 m from the fixed particle?

More Applications of Energy Concepts

Now that you are up to speed on the energy concepts you learned in your first-year physics course, it is time to work on more applications. Let's start by dealing with friction in more detail. Remember, friction does work which slows down the motion of an object. Thus, the work that it performs is negative. According to the work-energy theorem, then, it reduces the kinetic energy of the object. I want to illustrate this with an example problem.

EXAMPLE 4.1

A mass slides down an incline that has an angle of 30.0 degrees relative to the horizontal. The height of the incline is 1.00 m, and the mass is initially at rest. The coefficient of kinetic friction between the mass and the incline is 0.450. How fast will the mass be moving when it reaches the bottom of the incline?

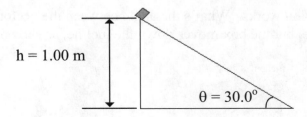

$h = 1.00$ m

$\theta = 30.0°$

If the mass starts at rest, its only energy is potential energy, and we can use Equation (4.4) to develop an expression for it:

$$PE = m \cdot g \cdot h = (m) \cdot (9.81\, \frac{m}{sec^2}) \cdot (1.00\ m) = 9.81 \cdot m\ J$$

We do not know "m," so we will just have to leave it in the expression, hoping it will eventually cancel out. As the box slides down the ramp, this potential energy is converted to kinetic energy. Once it reaches the bottom of the ramp, all of the potential energy has been converted to kinetic energy. Thus, *without friction*, the kinetic energy of the box at the bottom of the ramp would be 9.81·m J. However, friction does come into play, so we must take it into account.

How do we take friction into account? Well, if we can calculate the work done by friction, we can simply add that to the kinetic energy, and the result will be the kinetic energy that the box has after taking friction into account. How can we calculate the work done by friction? Well, we can calculate the frictional force and then use Equation (1.8). The frictional force is easy. We did that a lot in the previous module:

$$F_{friction} = \mu \cdot F_{normal} = \mu \cdot m \cdot g \cdot \cos\theta = (0.450) \cdot (m) \cdot (9.81\, \frac{m}{sec^2}) \cdot \cos(30.0) = 3.82 \cdot m\ N$$

Now that we have the frictional force, we can calculate the work by multiplying the force by the distance and then multiplying that by the cosine of the angle between the vectors. What is the distance? Well, friction works over the entire length of the ramp. Thus, we need to learn the distance that the box travels along the ramp. That distance is the hypotenuse of the triangle formed by the incline. If the height is 1.00 m and the angle is 30.0 degrees, the length of the hypotenuse can be calculated using the definition of sine:

$$\sin\theta = \frac{opposite}{hypotenuse}$$

$$\sin(30.0) = \frac{1.00 \text{ m}}{\text{hypotenuse}}$$

$$\text{hypotenuse} = \frac{1.00 \text{ m}}{\sin(30.0)} = 2.00 \text{ m}$$

That's the distance over which friction works. What's the angle between the vectors? The frictional force points up the incline, but the box moves down the incline, as shown below:

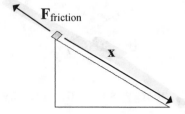

Thus, the angle between them is 180.0 degrees.

$$W = F \cdot x \cdot \cos\theta = (3.82 \cdot m \text{ N}) \cdot (2.00 \text{ m}) \cdot \cos(180.0) = -7.64 \cdot m \text{ J}$$

The work is negative because it is fighting the motion and thus subtracting from the kinetic energy. Now, we can use the work-energy theorem to take friction into account. Without friction, the energy of the mass at the bottom of the ramp would be $9.81 \cdot m$ J. The work done by friction takes away $7.64 \cdot m$ J of that energy, so the final kinetic energy is $2.17 \cdot m$ J (Don't worry that you do not have a number for the kinetic energy - an expression is just as good!). Now we can use the kinetic energy and Equation (4.3) to determine the speed:

$$KE = \frac{1}{2} \cdot m \cdot v^2$$

$$2.17 \cdot \cancel{m} \text{ J} = \frac{1}{2} \cdot (\cancel{m}) \cdot v^2$$

$$v = \sqrt{2 \cdot (2.17 \text{ J})} = \underline{2.08 \frac{m}{sec}}$$

Notice that "m" finally did cancel out. You *must* get comfortable leaving variables in your equations as you solve problems. Students always hate to do this, but sometimes, you simply must! Now please realize that we could have solved this problem using Newton's Laws. We could have summed up the gravitational force parallel to the incline and the frictional force, and from that, we could have calculated the acceleration. Then, using the motion equations, we could have determined the resulting speed. However, using energy concepts involved a *lot less work!*

Now let's look at a problem that would be very difficult to solve using just Newton's Laws. This problem involves electrical attraction, so we will use Equations (4.5) and (4.6) when calculating potential energy.

EXAMPLE 4.2

In the Bohr model of a hydrogen atom, an electron (m = 9.11x10^{-31} kg, q$_e$ = -1.60x10^{-19} C) orbits a proton (m = 1.67x10^{-27} kg, q$_p$ = 1.60x10^{-19} C) in a circular orbit whose radius is 5.29x10^{-11} m. However, if the electron is supplied with the proper amount of energy, it can jump to an orbit whose radius is 2.12x10^{-10} m. If the kinetic energy of the electron is given by the equation $KE = \dfrac{k \cdot q_p \cdot (-q_e)}{2 \cdot r}$**, how much energy must the electron be given to make the jump?**

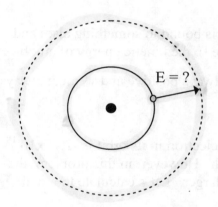

We will discuss the Bohr model of the atom in much more detail later on in the course. For right now, however, it gives us an excellent opportunity to apply energy concepts to a real situation. In this problem, we have an electron orbiting a proton in a circle. We know the radius of the circle, and we are given an equation to calculate the kinetic energy of the electron as it orbits. Thus, we have all that we need in order to calculate the total energy of the electron as it orbits:

$$TE = KE + PE$$

To calculate the KE of the situation, we simply use the formula that was given:

$$KE = \frac{k \cdot q_p \cdot (-q_e)}{2 \cdot r}$$

$$KE = \frac{(8.99x10^9 \; \frac{N \cdot m^2}{C^2}) \cdot (1.60x10^{-19} \; C) \cdot (1.60x10^{-19} \; C)}{2 \cdot (5.29x10^{-11} \; m)} = 2.18x10^{-18} \; J$$

The potential energy is given by Equation (4.5).

$$PE = q_e \cdot V$$

When we substitute Equation (4.6) into Equation (4.5), we get:

$$PE = q_e \cdot \frac{k \cdot q_p}{r} = (-1.60 \times 10^{-19} \ \cancel{C}) \cdot \frac{(8.99 \times 10^9 \ \frac{N \cdot m^2}{\cancel{C^2}}) \cdot (1.60 \times 10^{-19} \ \cancel{C})}{5.29 \times 10^{-11} \ \cancel{m}} = -4.35 \times 10^{-18} \ J$$

Does it bother you that potential energy is negative? It should not. As discussed in your first-year course, potential energy can be positive or negative, based on how it is defined. In fact, even *total* energy can be negative. It is in this case:

$$TE = PE + KE = -4.35 \times 10^{-18} \ J + 2.18 \times 10^{-18} \ J = -2.17 \times 10^{-18} \ J$$

What does it mean when an object has a total energy that is negative? In physics, it means that the object is *bound* by another object. In other words, the object cannot move freely. It is held to some other object. In fact, that's the situation with an electron in an atom. An electron in an atom is bound to that atom and cannot leave it unless given enough energy to make its total energy greater than zero.

Although total energy can be negative (when an object is bound to something else) and potential energy can be negative (depending on how it is defined), the kinetic energy of an object is always positive. After all, $KE = \frac{1}{2} \cdot m \cdot v^2$. Since mass is always positive and v^2 must always be positive, KE must be positive as well.

Okay, then. We now know that the total energy of the electron in its orbit is -2.17×10^{-18} J. What does that mean? Well, by itself it doesn't tell us much. However, in this problem, the electron is supposed to jump to another orbit, whose radius is larger. Let's calculate the total energy of the electron in that orbit:

$$KE = \frac{k \cdot q_p \cdot (-q_e)}{2 \cdot r}$$

$$KE = \frac{(8.99 \times 10^9 \ \frac{N \cdot m^2}{\cancel{C^2}}) \cdot (1.60 \times 10^{-19} \ \cancel{C}) \cdot (1.60 \times 10^{-19} \ \cancel{C})}{2 \cdot (2.12 \times 10^{-10} \ \cancel{m})} = 5.43 \times 10^{-19} \ J$$

$$PE = q_e \cdot \frac{k \cdot q_p}{\cdot r} = (-1.60 \times 10^{-19} \ \cancel{C}) \cdot \frac{(8.99 \times 10^9 \ \frac{N \cdot m^2}{\cancel{C^2}}) \cdot (1.60 \times 10^{-19} \ \cancel{C})}{2.12 \times 10^{-10} \ \cancel{m}} = -1.09 \times 10^{-18} \ J$$

$$TE = KE + PE = 5.43 \times 10^{-19} \ J + -1.09 \times 10^{-18} \ J = -5.5 \times 10^{-19} \ J$$

Now let's not get so lost in the mathematics that we forget what we are doing here! We now know that when the electron is in its original orbit, it has a total energy of -2.17×10^{-18} J. When it jumps to the orbit that is farther from the proton, it has an energy of -5.5×10^{-19} J. Now think about it. The number 5.5×10^{-19} is *smaller* than 2.17×10^{-18}. Thus, the number -5.5×10^{-19} is *bigger* (less negative) than -2.17×10^{-18}. In order for the electron to make the jump, then, the electron must *gain energy*. How much energy? Well,

$$\Delta E = E_{final} - E_{initial} = -5.5 \times 10^{-19} \text{ J} - (-2.17 \times 10^{-18} \text{ J}) = 1.62 \times 10^{-18} \text{ J}$$

Thus, in order for the electron to jump from the first orbit to the second orbit, it must absorb 1.62×10^{-18} J of energy.

So far, we have analyzed situations which involve potential energy associated with gravity near the surface of the earth [Equation (4.4)] and electrical potential energy [Equation (4.5)]. Before I end this section, I want to discuss one other way in which potential energy forms. Look at the situation depicted in Figure 4.1.

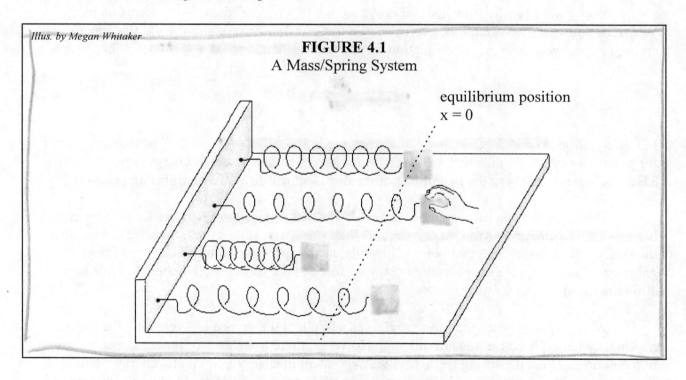

Illus. by Megan Whitaker

FIGURE 4.1
A Mass/Spring System

equilibrium position
x = 0

In your first-year physics course, you should have analyzed this system in terms of **simple harmonic motion**. The spring has a certain equilibrium length. When the mass is attached to the spring, and the spring is at its equilibrium position, the mass is at a position of $\mathbf{x} = 0$. At that position, the spring exerts no force on the mass. However, if a person were to pull (or push) the mass away from $\mathbf{x} = 0$, the spring would exert a **restoring force**, designed to pull the mass back to the equilibrium position. For a spring that has not been stretched too far, the restoring force is given by **Hooke's law**:

Hooke's Law $$\mathbf{F}_{spring} = -k \cdot \mathbf{x}$$ (4.7)

In this equation, the displacement "$\mathbf{x}$" is calculated relative to the equilibrium position of the mass, and "k" is called the **spring constant**. The spring constant describes the strength of the spring. The larger the spring constant, the harder it is to stretch or compress the spring.

Notice that in Equation (4.7), the force is *opposite* the displacement (that's the purpose of the negative sign). Thus, if you pull the mass to the right of $\mathbf{x} = 0$, the spring pulls back with a force directed to the left. As a result, when the mass is released, it starts accelerating towards the equilibrium position. When it reaches $\mathbf{x} = 0$, however, the spring no longer exerts a force on the mass, but the mass still is moving. Thus, it overshoots $\mathbf{x} = 0$, compressing the spring. As a result, the spring starts exerting a force opposite the compression, and that slows the mass down until it stops. At that point, however, the spring is pushing with a lot of force, so the mass starts accelerating in the other direction. In the absence of friction, this would happen over and over again, and the resulting motion is called simple harmonic motion.

Now I want you to think about this system not in terms of force, but in terms of energy. When the spring is stretched, it begins to exert a force. Since force can do work, that means the spring has *potential energy*. The equation for the **potential energy of a spring** is rather simple:

$$U_{spring} = \frac{1}{2} \cdot k \cdot x^2$$ (4.8)

In this equation, "k" and "x" are defined as they are in Hooke's Law, and "U" is another symbol for potential energy. Notice that x is not a vector here, because potential energy is not a vector. Thus, "x" refers simply to the magnitude of the displacement from the equilibrium position.

Think about what this equation means. When $x = 0$, $U_{spring} = 0$. That means the spring has no potential energy when it is at its equilibrium position. This makes complete sense, since the spring exerts no force at that point. However, as the spring is stretched or compressed, it gains potential energy. That potential energy is stored in the spring until the mass is released, allowing the spring to do work.

What happens when the mass is released? Well, at the instant it is released, the mass has no kinetic energy, because it is not moving. However, there is all sorts of potential energy stored in the spring. Thus, the spring begins converting potential energy into kinetic energy. This gets the mass moving. As the mass moves, more potential energy is converted to kinetic energy, and the mass begins to move faster. However, when it reaches $x = 0$, there is no more potential energy in the spring. However, there is a lot of kinetic energy in the mass. Thus, the mass begins to compress the spring. This, however, reduces the speed of the mass, decreasing its kinetic energy. Of course, the potential energy of the spring increases as a result. Thus, when the mass eventually stops, the spring will have a lot of potential energy stored up. That potential energy will start being converted to kinetic energy, and the mass will start sliding the other way.

Now really, all of that should be review for you from your first-year physics course. Let's now think of this situation in a little more detail.

EXAMPLE 4.3

In the mass/spring system illustrated in Figure 4.1, assume that the block has a mass of 50.0 grams, the spring constant is 1.50 Newtons/meter, the block is pulled back 15.0 cm, and the mass of the spring can be ignored.

a. If we ignore friction, what is the maximum speed of the mass and where will it occur?
b. Now take friction into account. If the coefficient of kinetic friction is 0.100, what will the maximum speed of the block be?

To solve part (a), we just need to think about the energy. When the block is pulled back 15.0 cm from the equilibrium position, the spring stores up a certain amount of potential energy:

$$U_{spring} = \frac{1}{2} \cdot k \cdot x^2$$

$$U_{spring} = \frac{1}{2} \cdot (1.50 \frac{N}{m}) \cdot (0.150 \, m)^2 = 0.0169 \, N \cdot m = 0.0169 \, J$$

The units work out here because a Newton ($\frac{kg \cdot m}{sec^2}$) times a meter (m) is a Joule ($\frac{kg \cdot m^2}{sec^2}$).

While pulled back, the block has no kinetic energy, because it is at rest. Thus, the total energy is also 0.0169 J. When will the speed be greatest? It will be greatest when all of the potential energy is converted to kinetic energy. Thus, when potential energy is zero, the kinetic energy will be 0.0169, and we can solve for the speed:

$$KE = \frac{1}{2} \cdot m \cdot v^2$$

$$0.0169 \, J = \frac{1}{2} \cdot (0.0500 \, kg) \cdot v^2$$

$$v = \sqrt{\frac{2 \cdot (0.0169 \, J)}{0.0500 \, kg}} = 0.822 \, \frac{m}{sec}$$

Where will this happen? Well, potential energy is zero at $x = 0$, so it will happen at the equilibrium position.

Now let's take friction into account. Since we have the mass and the coefficient of kinetic friction, we can calculate the frictional force.

$$F_f = \mu_k \cdot F_n = (0.100) \cdot (0.0500 \text{ kg}) \cdot (9.81 \text{ m/sec}^2) = 0.0491 \text{ N}$$

What does friction do? It works against the motion. How much work does it do? Well, the block travels a distance of 15.0 cm to get back to the equilibrium position. That displacement is 180 degrees to the direction of the frictional force (the frictional force opposes the motion), so calculating the work done is easy:

$$W = F \cdot x \cdot \cos\theta = (0.0491 \text{ N}) \cdot (0.150 \text{ m}) \cdot \cos(180) = -0.00737 \text{ J}$$

The work is negative, of course, because it removes energy from the system. Thus, once friction is taken into account, the kinetic energy of the mass at the equilibrium position will be 0.0169 J minus 0.00737 J, or 0.0095 J. Thus, the speed of the mass after friction is taken into account is:

$$KE = \frac{1}{2} \cdot m \cdot v^2$$

$$0.0095 \text{ J} = \frac{1}{2} \cdot (0.0500 \text{ kg}) \cdot v^2$$

$$v = \sqrt{\frac{2 \cdot (0.0095 \text{ J})}{0.0500 \text{ kg}}} = 0.62 \frac{\text{m}}{\text{sec}}$$

Try analyzing situations like this by solving the following "on your own" problems.

ON YOUR OWN

4.4 A block slides down a ramp (h=1.00 m, $\theta = 45.0°$). It then slides across a level floor (length = 0.200 m) and up another ramp (h = 0.250 m, $\theta = 30.0°$) to another flat surface. If the coefficient of kinetic friction between all of the surfaces and the block is 0.150, what will the speed of the block be when it reaches the top of the second ramp?

4.5 In the mass/spring system given in Example 4.3 (part b), what is the total distance that the block will travel before coming to rest?

4.6 An Atwood's machine (see Example 3.2) contains a 40.0 kg mass and a 20.0 kg mass. Neglecting friction, the mass of the string, and the mass of the pulley, what is the speed of the masses once they have each traveled 0.500 m?

<u>Power</u>

There is one more energy concept that I must address before I move on to collisions, and that is **power**. As you learned in your first-year physics course, power is the rate of energy transfer. Since energy is transferred via work, we can give the following formula for power:

$$P = \frac{W}{t}$$

(4.9)

In this equation, "P" represents power, "W" is work and "t" is time. Thus, the standard unit for power is the unit J/sec, which is also called a **Watt**.

Now, according to Equation (4.1), $W = F \cdot x \cdot \cos\theta$. If force and displacement are parallel ($\theta = 180°$), then Equation (4.1) becomes $W = F \cdot x$. If we substitute that into Equation (4.9), we get:

$$P = F \cdot v$$

(4.10)

This equation is relatively useful for calculating the power required in certain situations. However, be sure you understand its limits. Equation (4.10) is only applicable when force and displacement are parallel. Also, it is only applicable when velocity is constant. If velocity changes, or if the force and displacement are not parallel, then you must use Equation (4.9). The following example shows you how this works.

Illus. from the MasterClips collection

EXAMPLE 4.4

You are designing an elevator that has a mass of 1200.0 kg and must be capable of lifting at least 1000.0 kg of load. You estimate that an average frictional force of 5000.0 N fights its motion. What average power must the elevator motor provide in order to be able to accelerate the elevator and its full load at 2.00 m/sec² upwards? Assume that the motor must accelerate the elevator until it reaches its "cruising speed" of 3.50 m/sec. Once it reaches that speed, how much power will the motor need to supply to keep the elevator moving upwards?

You have to be very careful in doing a problem like this, because you are given a speed and some forces, and your first inclination might be to use Equation (4.10). However, the first part of the problem discusses the situation when the elevator is *accelerating*. Thus, velocity is not constant, and as a result, we must use Equation (4.9). Our first task, then, is to determine the work that the motor must do. To determine that, we need to know the force exerted by the motor.

As you see in the drawing above, the force exerted by the motor (F_{motor}) is working against three other forces. The weight of the elevator (F_{weight}) pulls down; the weight of the load that is being carried also pulls down (F_{load}); and the force of friction ($F_{friction}$) fights the motion, so it pulls down as well. To get the force required for acceleration, we sum up all of the forces and set them equal to mass times acceleration. We will call upward motion positive, leading to this equation:

$$F_{motor} - F_{weight} - F_{load} - F_{friction} = m \cdot a$$

What is the mass in the equation? Well, both the elevator and the load are being accelerated, so the mass is the sum of the two (2200.0 kg). Now let's plug in all of the numbers we know:

$$F_{motor} - (1200.0 \text{ kg}) \cdot (9.81 \, \frac{m}{sec^2}) - (1000.0 \text{ kg}) \cdot (9.81 \, \frac{m}{sec^2}) - 5000.0 \text{ N} = (2200.0 \text{ kg}) \cdot (2.00 \, \frac{m}{sec^2})$$

$$F_{motor} = 3.10 \times 10^4 \text{ N}$$

Now, what is the distance? Well, for that, we need to remember our one-dimensional motion equations, because we know the acceleration, and we know the final cruising speed. Thus:

$$v^2 = v_o^2 + 2 \cdot a \cdot x$$

$$(3.50 \, \frac{m}{sec})^2 = 0 + 2 \cdot (2.00 \, \frac{m}{sec^2}) \cdot x$$

$$x = 3.06 \text{ m}$$

We can now calculate work.

$$W = F \cdot x \cdot \cos\theta$$

$$W = (3.10 \times 10^4 \text{ N}) \cdot (3.06 \text{ m}) \cdot \cos(0) = 9.49 \times 10^4 \text{ J}$$

That's work, but what about time? Well, we can determine time from our one-dimensional motion equations:

$$v = v_o + a \cdot t$$

$$3.50 \, \frac{m}{sec} = 0 + (2.00 \, \frac{m}{sec^2}) \cdot t$$

$$t = 1.75 \text{ sec}$$

Now we can finally calculate the power:

$$P = \frac{W}{t} = \frac{9.49 \times 10^4 \text{ J}}{1.75 \text{ sec}} = \underline{5.42 \times 10^4 \text{ Watts}}$$

That only answers the first part of the question! However, the second part is really easy. To keep the elevator going at a constant velocity, the sum of the forces is zero. Thus,

$$F_{motor} - F_{weight} - F_{load} - F_{friction} = 0$$

$$F_{motor} = 2.66 \times 10^4 \text{ N}$$

Also, since the velocity is constant and the force and displacement are parallel, we can use Equation (4.10).

$$P = F \cdot v = (2.66 \times 10^4 \text{ N}) \cdot (3.50 \frac{m}{sec}) = \underline{9.31 \times 10^4 \text{ Watts}}$$

Notice that the power delivered once the elevator stops accelerating is *greater* than the power delivered while it is accelerating. That might seem strange to you, since the force required is lower once the elevator is no longer accelerating. However, remember that power is work divided by time. As the elevator accelerates, the motor applies a constant force, but the faster the elevator moves, the longer the distance traveled (and hence the greater the work) each second. Thus, the power consumption *increases* with increasing speed. So the power given in the first part of the problem is the *average* power. More power is used at the end of the acceleration period than is used at the beginning of the acceleration period. Once the speed is constant, the work per unit time is constant, so the power is constant as well.

ON YOUR OWN

4.7 A worker pushes a 150.0 kg crate horizontally along the floor at a constant rate of 1.55 m/sec. If the coefficient of kinetic friction between the crate and the floor is 0.251, what is the worker's power output?

Momentum and Impulse

In your first year physics course, you learned about linear momentum, which is a measure of the impetus behind translational motion. The definition of momentum is given by the equation

$$\mathbf{p} = m \cdot \mathbf{v} \tag{4.11}$$

Since momentum is given by mass times velocity, it has the standard unit of $\frac{kg \cdot m}{sec}$. Remember also that momentum is a vector, so it contains directional information.

When you learned about momentum in your first-year course, you learned that in an isolated system (one with no forces working on it), momentum is always conserved. Reasonably enough, this concept is called the **conservation of linear momentum.** You probably used that concept to analyze collisions between objects. You calculated the total momentum of the objects prior to the collision, and then you determined what had to happen in order to make sure that the total momentum after the collision was the same.

At the same time, you should have learned about **impulse.** If an external force works on an object in motion, the momentum will change because of the work done by the force. The impulse delivered by a force can be calculated as follows:

$$J = F \cdot \Delta t \qquad (4.12)$$

where "**J**" is impulse, **F** is the average force exerted on the object, and Δt is the time interval over which the force acts. When an object is subjected to an impulse, its momentum will change accordingly:

$$J = \Delta p \qquad (4.13)$$

Note that because force and momentum are vector quantities, impulse is a vector quantity as well.

In the remainder of this module, I want to take the concepts of energy that you just learned and join them with the concepts of momentum and impulse that you learned in your previous course. The results are a very powerful analysis of many situations which occur in Creation. I want to illustrate this with an experiment.

EXPERIMENT 4.2
Conservation of Momentum and Energy

Supplies:

- A ping pong ball
- A golf ball
- A hard floor

Introduction - Bouncing balls provide an excellent chance to use energy and momentum concepts together.

Procedure:

1. Hold a ping pong ball about chest high and release it, allowing it to bounce on the floor. Note approximately how high it bounces off of the floor. You don't have to measure the

height. Just approximate how high it bounced relative to the height from which it was released.

2. Repeat step (1) with the golf ball.
3. Now place the ping pong ball on top of the golf ball, holding them both together in one hand.
4. Release the balls so that they fall together, with the ping pong ball on top of the golf ball. It might take a few tries to get it just right, but you want the golf ball to hit the floor, bounce back up, and immediately collide with the ping pong ball. That way, the ping pong ball hits the golf ball and bounces straight up in response. If you don't drop the balls correctly, the ping pong ball will bounce away at an angle. Continue to try dropping the balls until the ping pong ball bounces straight up after hitting the gold ball.
5. Note the height that the ping pong ball reaches when dropped in this way. Compare it to the height that the ping pong ball bounced in step (1).

How can we explain the results of the experiment? The first two steps are easy. When a ball is held at a height, it has potential energy. As it drops, the potential energy changes to kinetic energy, and the ball speeds up, gaining momentum. When the ball hits the floor, the floor exerts a force on the ball over a small time interval. This generates an impulse, changing the momentum of the ball, and the ball starts moving in the opposite direction. As the ball starts moving up, its kinetic energy begins to be converted to potential energy. When all kinetic energy is converted to potential energy, the ball reaches is maximum height.

In steps (1) and (2), you noticed that the ball did not bounce as high as the height from which it was dropped. Why? Think about it. The impulse changes the momentum, but there are limits to the amount that the momentum can change. The collision with the floor cannot result in *more* energy than what was in the system before the collision. Thus, the impulse can change the direction of the velocity (thus changing the momentum), but it cannot supply a larger *magnitude* for the velocity, because that would result in the object having more kinetic energy. Since all of the energy is kinetic during the collision, this would increase the total energy of the system to something more than what existed in the system prior to the collision. In fact, as I am sure you already knew, friction from the collision *lowers* the total energy of the system. Thus, the ball rebounds from the floor with a lower speed than that with which it hit the floor. As a result, after the rebound, the ball cannot even reach the height from which it was dropped.

What happened in step (4), however? In that step, the ping pong ball bounced *much* higher than the height from which it was dropped. In fact, if you do the drop properly, it can bounce almost *nine times higher* than the height from which it was dropped. How do we explain that? The explanation is a bit detailed, but it is very worthwhile, so I want to go through it.

First, let's assume that the collision with the floor is elastic. In an **elastic collision**, no energy is lost to friction or any other outside force. Had the collisions in steps (1) and (2) in the experiment been elastic, the balls would have bounced back to the same height as that from which they were released. That did not happen, but we will assume it did in order to make our analysis easier. In step (4) of the experiment, the golf ball hits the floor first. It then bounces back, hitting the ping pong ball. Let's examine *that* collision (the one between the golf ball as it travels upward and the ping pong ball as it travels downward), and let's assume that *that collision* is elastic as well. This is actually not a bad assumption, as the friction involved in this collision is pretty minor.

No impulse is being generated in this collision, so the conservation of momentum holds here. Let's call the mass of the ping pong ball "m_p" and the mass of the golf ball "m_g." Furthermore, let's call the initial and final velocity of the ping pong ball $\mathbf{v}_{pi}$ and $\mathbf{v}_{pf}$, and let's call the initial and final velocity of the golf ball $\mathbf{v}_{gi}$ and $\mathbf{v}_{gf}$. The conservation of momentum tells us that the sum of the momenta after the collision must be the same as the sum prior to the collision:

$$m_p \cdot \mathbf{v}_{pi} + m_g \cdot \mathbf{v}_{gi} = m_p \cdot \mathbf{v}_{pf} + m_g \cdot \mathbf{v}_{gf} \tag{4.14}$$

That gives us one relationship between the velocities. However, assuming that we can measure the initial velocities and the masses, we are still left with two final velocities. Two unknowns require two equations. Do we have another equation?

Of course we have another equation, or I would not have started this discussion! The other equation comes from the assumption that the collision is elastic. If that is the case, then the total energy prior to and after the collision is the same. Since all of the energy is kinetic just prior to and just after the collision, we can say that the kinetic energy before and after the collision remains the same. That tells us:

$$\tfrac{1}{2} m_p \cdot v_{pi}{}^2 + \tfrac{1}{2} m_g \cdot v_{gi}{}^2 = \tfrac{1}{2} m_p \cdot v_{pf}{}^2 + \tfrac{1}{2} m_g \cdot v_{gf}{}^2 \tag{4.15}$$

This gives us a second relationship with which we can work.

Now we have to do some algebra. Let's get rid of the ½ in Equation (4.15), because it appears in every term. Then, let's group the ping pong ball terms together on one side of the equation and the golf ball terms on the other side:

$$m_p \cdot (v_{pi}{}^2 - v_{pf}{}^2) = m_g \cdot (v_{gf}{}^2 - v_{gi}{}^2) \tag{4.16}$$

That's just a restatement of Equation (4.15) after a little algebra. Now look at what we have. On each side of the equation, we have the difference of two squares. In algebra, you learned that the difference of two squares can be factored. Let's do that here:

$$m_p \cdot (v_{pi} - v_{pf}) \cdot (v_{pi} + v_{pf}) = m_g \cdot (v_{gf} - v_{gi}) \cdot (v_{gf} + v_{gi}) \tag{4.16}$$

Once again, this is still just a restatement of Equation (4.15). How in the world did I decide that I should do that? Well, remember that we are working with two equations here, and that the first equation, Equation (4.14), does not contain any squares. Now I have the second equation, Equation (4.15), written with no squares as well. That has to be a good thing.

Now let's rearrange Equation (4.14) so that it looks more like Equation (4.16). We can do that by once again grouping the ping pong ball terms on one side and the golf ball terms on the other:

$$m_p \cdot (v_{pi} - v_{pf}) = m_g \cdot (v_{gf} - v_{gi}) \qquad (4.17)$$

Notice what this says. It says that $m_p \cdot (v_{pi} - v_{pf})$ is the *same as* $m_g \cdot (v_{gf} - v_{gi})$. Notice that in Equation (4.16), we have $m_p \cdot (v_{pi} - v_{pf})$ on the left of the equal sign and $m_g \cdot (v_{gf} - v_{gi})$ on the right. However, according to Equation (4.17), they are the same. Thus, they cancel:

$$\cancel{m_p \cdot (v_{pi} - v_{pf})} \cdot (v_{pi} + v_{pf}) = \cancel{m_g \cdot (v_{gf} - v_{gi})} \cdot (v_{gf} + v_{gi}) \qquad (4.18)$$

$$(v_{pi} + v_{pf}) = (v_{gf} + v_{gi}) \qquad (4.19)$$

Now let's rearrange this equation, grouping the initial velocities and the final velocities.

$$(v_{pi} - v_{gi}) = -(v_{pf} - v_{gf}) \qquad (4.19)$$

Now before you understand what the equation means, remember the assumption used to generate the equation. This equation is valid *only* for elastic collisions. What does it say? It says that *for elastic collisions*, the *relative velocity* (we get relative velocity by subtracting velocities) prior to the collision must be equal in magnitude and opposite in direction as compared to the *relative velocity* after the collision.

Before I tell you how this explains the experiment, I want to make sure the mathematics did not cover up the physics of the situation. The physics of the situation was simple: momentum and energy both had to be conserved. That led us to two equations - the conservation of momentum equation [Equation (4.14)] and the conservation of energy equation [Equation (4.15)]. The rest was just mathematics. In solving problems, you will become *very* familiar with starting with those two equations and solving them simultaneously to get two unknowns. The mathematics will be a bit more straightforward when you do this to solve problems, as will be illustrated in the example below.

Now, how does this explain step (4) in the experiment? Well, think about the situation just prior to the collision. The golf ball had bounced off of the floor. Even though that collision wasn't elastic, let's assume that it was almost elastic. Thus, the golf ball lost just a bit of energy in the rebound. The ping pong ball was still falling down, but it had converted *most* of its potential energy into kinetic energy. Because the golf ball and ping pong ball fell from essentially the same height, and since the golf ball's collision with the floor was almost elastic, the golf ball and ping pong ball had essentially equal and opposite velocities. Let's say that the golf ball had a velocity of v, and the ping pong ball a velocity of -v. Thus, the relative velocity $(v_{pi} - v_{gi})$ is equal to -2v.

Equation (4.19), then, says that the relative velocity after the collision must be +2v. Well, think about the golf ball. It is moving upward with a speed of approximately v. The ping pong ball is very light compared to the golf ball, so when the golf ball hits the ping pong ball, the golf ball continues moving upward. The collision slowed it down some, but since the ping pong ball was very light, the golf ball lost only a small amount of energy to the ping pong ball. Thus, it continued to move upward at a speed that is slightly lower than, but still pretty much equal to v. Well, if the relative velocity ($\mathbf{v}_{pf}$ - $\mathbf{v}_{gf}$) must be equal to +2v, the velocity of the ping pong ball must have been 3v. Thus, the ping pong ball rebounds with a velocity of about 3v, which is three times larger than the velocity it would have had if it had bounced elastically off the ground.

What does that tell you about the kinetic energy of the ping pong ball? Well, kinetic energy is $\frac{1}{2} \cdot m \cdot v^2$. Thus, if the velocity is three times higher than what it would have had if it just bounced off of the floor, the energy it had was *nine (3^2) times* higher. With nine times the energy, it can reach a height (determined by PE = $m \cdot g \cdot h$) nine times higher than had it bounced off of the floor. That's why the ping pong ball bounced so high when it bounced off of the golf ball. Now please understand that this explanation is a direct result of the constraints of momentum conservation with the constraints of energy conservation. Together, they produce Equation (4.19), which leads us to the explanation. I want to do a problem using these principles now so that you can see how you use them in other situations.

EXAMPLE 4.5

Two billiard balls of equal mass are heading directly towards each other and collide head on in an elastic collision. The first one is traveling at a speed of 9.00 m/sec and the other at 11.00 m/sec. Ignoring friction, what are the velocities of each ball after the collision?

In this problem, momentum is conserved (no external forces are providing an impulse). Thus, the total momentum before the collision must equal the total momentum after:

$$m_1 \cdot \mathbf{v}_{1i} + m_2 \cdot \mathbf{v}_{2i} = m_1 \cdot \mathbf{v}_{1f} + m_2 \cdot \mathbf{v}_{2f}$$

$$\mathbf{v}_{1i} + \mathbf{v}_{2i} = \mathbf{v}_{1f} + \mathbf{v}_{2f}$$

Notice that since the masses are equal, they all cancel out of the equation. The collision is elastic. That means energy is conserved as well.

$$\frac{1}{2} \cdot m_1 \cdot v_{1i}^2 + \frac{1}{2} \cdot m_2 \cdot v_{2i}^2 = \frac{1}{2} \cdot m_1 \cdot v_{1f}^2 + \frac{1}{2} \cdot m_2 \cdot v_{2f}^2$$

$$v_{1i}^2 + v_{2i}^2 = v_{1f}^2 + v_{2f}^2$$

Once again, the masses (and the ½'s) cancel because they are equal in every term. This gives us two equations - the first comes from momentum conservation, and the second comes from energy conservation. We know the initial velocities, but the final velocities are unknown. That's okay, however, since we have two equations. If we have two equations, we can solve for two unknowns. Let's use the first equation to get $\mathbf{v}_{1f}$ in terms of $\mathbf{v}_{2f}$.

$$v_{1i} + v_{2i} = v_{1f} + v_{2f}$$

$$9.00 \frac{m}{sec} + -11.00 \frac{m}{sec} = v_{1f} + v_{2f}$$

$$v_{1f} = -v_{2f} - 2.00 \frac{m}{sec}$$

Now let's take that equation and stick it into the energy conservation equation:

$$v_{1i}^2 + v_{2i}^2 = v_{1f}^2 + v_{2f}^2$$

$$\left(9.00 \frac{m}{sec}\right)^2 + \left(-11.00 \frac{m}{sec}\right)^2 = \left(-v_{2f} - 2.00 \frac{m}{sec}\right)^2 + v_{2f}^2$$

$$202.0 \frac{m^2}{sec^2} = v_{2f}^2 + 4.00 \frac{m}{sec} \cdot v_{2f} + 4.00 \frac{m^2}{sec^2} + v_{2f}^2$$

$$2 \cdot v_{2f}^2 + 4.00 \frac{m}{sec} \cdot v_{2f} - 198.0 \frac{m^2}{sec^2} = 0$$

We can now use the quadratic equation to solve for v_{2f}.

$$v_{2f} = \frac{-b \pm \sqrt{b^2 - 4ac}}{2 \cdot a} = \frac{-4.00 \frac{m}{sec} \pm \sqrt{\left(4.00 \frac{m}{sec}\right)^2 - 4 \cdot (2) \cdot (-198.0 \frac{m^2}{sec^2})}}{2 \cdot (2)} = \frac{-4.00 \frac{m}{sec} \pm 40.0 \frac{m}{sec}}{4}$$

As always, the quadratic equation gives us two possible solutions for v_{2f}: -11.0 m/sec and 9.00 m/sec. Since -11.0 m/sec is the original velocity, the velocity *after* the collision must be the other choice, 9.00 m/sec. To get v_{1f}, we can just use the equation we derived from momentum conversion:

$$v_{1f} = -v_{2f} - 2.00 \frac{m}{sec} = -9.00 \frac{m}{sec} - 2.00 \frac{m}{sec} = -11.00 \frac{m}{sec}$$

Notice, then, that the two balls simply "exchanged" velocities. The first ball was moving with a velocity of 9.00 m/sec and, after the collision, moves with a velocity of -11.00 m/sec. The second ball started out with a velocity of -11.0 m/sec, and after the collision, it moves with a velocity of 9.0 m/sec.

Before I leave this section, I want to discuss two other kinds of collisions: **inelastic collisions** and **perfectly inelastic collisions**. In an inelastic collision, momentum is conserved but energy is not conserved. This usually means that some energy was dissipated by friction. In reality, the vast majority of collisions are inelastic. However, when the amount of energy dissipated by friction is very small compared to the total energy of the system, an inelastic collision can be assumed to be elastic. A perfectly inelastic collision is a collision in which momentum is conserved and the two colliding partners stick together. As a result, they move together at the same speed. In your first-year course, you probably worked problems with both of those types of collisions. You might not have *known* that they had names, but those kinds of collisions are typical for first-year students to analyze.

ON YOUR OWN

4.8 In my research as a nuclear chemist, I studied neutrons which had been emitted from a nuclear reaction. I detected these neutrons with a liquid that was rich in hydrogen atoms. When the neutrons collided elastically with the hydrogen atoms, energy would be transferred from the neutron to the hydrogen atom. The atom would then release that energy in the form of light, which could be detected. If the hydrogen atom was initially at rest and the neutron was moving, what fraction of the neutron's energy would be transferred to the hydrogen atom in a head-on collision? Assume that the masses are equal. This is not quite true, but it is close. The neutron is actually 0.12% heavier than the hydrogen atom.

4.9 Two objects ($m_1 = 5.00$ kg, $m_2 = 9.00$ kg) are moving in one dimension. The lighter one is traveling with a velocity of 4.50 m/sec, and the heavier one with a velocity of -1.40 m/sec. After they collide, the lighter mass moves with a velocity of -2.50 m/sec, while the heavier mass moves in the positive direction at an unknown speed. What type of collision (elastic, inelastic, or perfectly inelastic) is this?

Collisions in Two Dimensions

So far, we have concentrated on collisions that occur in one dimension. In other words, the collision partners are moving along a straight line, and after they collide, they continue to move along that line. However, most collisions occur in at least two dimensions. On a pool table, for example, the billiard balls rarely hit each other head on and stay in one dimension. Instead, they usually hit each other in a glancing collision that sends the balls traveling off at different angles. It is important that you be able to analyze those kinds of collisions as well. Luckily, if you understand collisions in one dimension, collisions in two dimensions are really the same. They just require more work, because like two-dimensional motion, we can analyze two-dimensional collisions by splitting them into two, one-dimensional problems. In *each dimension*, momentum must be conserved. Thus, we can do two one-dimensional momentum conservation problems. Study the following example so that you understand what I mean.

EXAMPLE 4.6

Two cars (m₁ = 2407 kg, m₂ = 3316 kg) approach
an intersection. The lighter car is moving with a
velocity of 25.7 m/sec north, and the heavier car is
moving with a velocity of 21.2 m/sec east. Neither
driver is paying attention, so they collide. The
collision is perfectly inelastic. What is the velocity
of the two cars as they move together after the
collision?

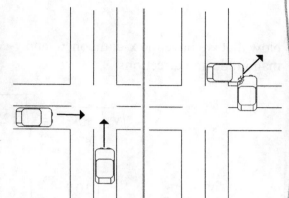

Notice that this is a two-dimensional
problem. Thus, we must split it up into two one-
dimensional problems. Let's first look at the east/west dimension, which we will call the x-
dimension. In the x- dimension, the total momentum must be conserved. Thus, we have:

$$m_1 \cdot v_{1i} \cdot \cos\theta_1 + m_2 \cdot v_{2i} \cos\theta_2 = (m_1 + m_2) \cdot v_x$$

Notice what I did. I multiplied the velocity of the cars by the cosine of theta to get their x-
components. Also, notice that since the cars are moving together after the collision, they make
up just one object, whose mass is the sum of the cars' masses. Since this is just the x-dimension,
we get only the x-component of the cars' final velocity. Filling in what we know and defining
the angle counterclockwise from the east:

$$(2407 \text{ kg}) \cdot (25.7 \frac{m}{sec}) \cdot \cos(90.0) + (3316 \text{ kg}) \cdot (21.2 \frac{m}{sec}) \cdot \cos(0.00) = (2407 \text{ kg} + 3316 \text{ kg}) \cdot v_x$$

$$v_x = \frac{(3316 \text{ kg}) \cdot (21.2 \frac{m}{sec}) \cdot}{(5723 \text{ kg})} = 12.3 \frac{m}{sec}$$

Now let's do the same thing in the y-dimension:

$$m_1 \cdot v_{1i} \cdot \sin\theta_1 + m_2 \cdot v_{2i} \cdot \sin\theta_2 = (m_1 + m_2) \cdot v_y$$

$$(2407 \text{ kg}) \cdot (25.7 \frac{m}{sec}) \cdot \sin(90.0) + (3316 \text{ kg}) \cdot (21.2 \frac{m}{sec}) \cdot \sin(0.00) = (2407 \text{ kg} + 3316 \text{ kg}) \cdot v_y$$

$$v_y = \frac{(2407 \text{ kg}) \cdot (25.7 \frac{m}{sec})}{5723 \text{ kg}} = 10.8 \frac{m}{sec}$$

Now that we have the x-component and y-component of the final velocity, we can get the magnitude and direction:

$$v = \sqrt{v_x^2 + v_y^2} = \sqrt{\left(12.3 \frac{m}{sec}\right)^2 + \left(10.8 \frac{m}{sec}\right)^2} = 16.4 \frac{m}{sec}$$

$$\theta = \tan^{-1}\left(\frac{10.8 \frac{m}{sec}}{12.3 \frac{m}{sec}}\right) = 41.3°$$

The two-car system, then, travels with a velocity of 16.4 m/sec at 41.3°.

Two-dimensional collisions, then, are really no more difficult to analyze than are one-dimensional collisions. All you have to do is look at each dimension individually, and in the end, you simply have two one-dimensional collisions to analyze. I want to do one more example, which will demonstrate an important fact.

EXAMPLE 4.7

Two billiard balls of equal mass hit each other in a glancing (not head-on) collision. One ball is at rest, and the other ball is moving at 5.00 m/sec. After the collision, the ball that was initially moving has a velocity of 2.89 m/sec at 54.7°. What is the velocity of the ball that was initially at rest?

Before Collision   After Collision

To solve this kind of problem, we split it up into two, one-dimensional problems. It turns out that the y-dimension is a bit easier in this case, since initially, there is no momentum in the y-dimension. Thus, we will start there:

$$m_1 \cdot v_{1i} \cdot \sin\theta_{1i} + m_2 \cdot v_{2i} \cdot \sin\theta_{2i} = m_1 \cdot v_{1f} \cdot \sin\theta_{1f} + m_2 \cdot v_{2f} \cdot \sin\theta_{2f}$$

Since the masses are equal, they cancel. That leaves:

$$v_{1i} \cdot \sin\theta_{1i} + v_{2i} \cdot \sin\theta_{2i} = v_{1f} \cdot \sin\theta_{1f} + v_{2f} \cdot \sin\theta_{2f}$$

Filling in what we know (always defining angle counterclockwise from the +x axis):

$$(5.00 \, \frac{m}{sec}) \cdot \sin(0.00) + (0) \cdot \sin\theta_{2i} = (2.89 \, \frac{m}{sec}) \cdot \sin(54.7) + v_{2f} \cdot \sin\theta_{2f}$$

$$v_{2f} = \frac{-2.36 \, \dfrac{m}{sec}}{\sin\theta_{2f}}$$

That gives us two unknowns, but that's okay, because we have another dimension to investigate. Recognizing that the masses will cancel in the x-dimension as well, we get:

$$v_{1i} \cdot \cos\theta_{1i} + v_{2i} \cdot \cos\theta_{2i} = v_{1f} \cdot \cos\theta_{1f} + v_{2f} \cdot \cos\theta_{2f}$$

$$(5.00 \, \frac{m}{sec}) \cdot \cos(0.00) + (0) \cdot \cos\theta_{2i} = (2.89 \, \frac{m}{sec}) \cdot \cos(54.7) + v_{2f} \cdot \cos\theta_{2f}$$

$$3.33 \, \frac{m}{sec} = v_{2f} \cdot \cos\theta_{2f}$$

Let's take the equation we got for v_{2f} from the y-dimension and stick it into this equation:

$$3.33 \, \frac{m}{sec} = \frac{-2.36 \, \dfrac{m}{sec}}{\sin\theta_{2f}} \cdot \cos\theta_{2f}$$

$$\frac{3.33 \, \dfrac{m}{sec}}{-2.36 \, \dfrac{m}{sec}} = \frac{1}{\tan\theta_{2f}}$$

$$\tan\theta_{2f} = \frac{-2.36 \, \dfrac{m}{sec}}{3.33 \, \dfrac{m}{sec}}$$

$$\theta_{2f} = -35.3°$$

Notice that I had to recognize that $\cos\theta/\sin\theta$ is the same as $1/\tan\theta$ to solve this. That is an identity ($\tan\theta = \sin\theta/\cos\theta$) you will have to know. You already should have it ingrained in your head from trigonometry. Now based on the way the *drawing* is made, that is θ_{2f}. However, the angle is not really defined properly. To give the properly-defined angle, you must add 360.0° to it (it is in quadrant IV), so the properly-defined angle is 324.7°.

Now we can use the relationship between v_{2f} and $\sin\theta_{2f}$ to get the speed:

$$v_{2f} = \frac{-2.36\,\dfrac{m}{sec}}{\sin\theta_{2f}} = \frac{-2.36\,\dfrac{m}{sec}}{\sin(324.7)} = 4.08\,\frac{m}{sec}$$

The velocity of the other ball, then, is <u>4.08 m/sec at 324.7°</u>.

Okay, then, that is another example of how to analyze two-dimensional collisions. However, this example tells you something else as well. It is a specific example of an important principle in collision physics. Let's calculate the energy of the system *before* the collision:

$$TE = PE + KE = 0 + \tfrac{1}{2}\cdot m \cdot v^2 = \tfrac{1}{2}\cdot m \cdot (25.0\ m^2/sec^2)$$

We don't know the mass of the billiard balls, but we can just leave it in terms of "m." What is the energy *after* the collision? At that point, there are two balls moving and still no potential energy. Thus:

$$TE = PE + KE = 0 + \tfrac{1}{2}\cdot m \cdot v_{1f}^2 + \tfrac{1}{2}\cdot m \cdot v_{2f}^2 = \tfrac{1}{2}\cdot m \cdot (8.35\ m^2/sec^2) + \tfrac{1}{2}\cdot m \cdot (16.6\ m^2/sec^2)$$

$$TE = \tfrac{1}{2}\cdot m \cdot (25.0\ m^2/sec^2)$$

What does that tell you? It tells you that *this collision is elastic*. I did not tell you that to begin with, because you did not need that fact to solve the problem. Nevertheless, the calculations show that the collision is elastic.

What's the big deal? Look at the two angles. Use their values to calculate the *angle between the velocities of the two balls*. The relative angle between the velocities of the two balls is 54.7° + 35.3° = 90.0°. This is no accident. When two objects of equal mass collide elastically in a glancing collision and one mass is initially at rest, the relative angle between the objects after the collision will always be 90.0°. This is an insanely useful bit of information, so I want you to know it by heart.

When two equal masses have a glancing, elastic collision and one of them is initially at rest, they will move away at a right angle relative to each other.

Please commit that little fact to memory, because you will need to use it on the practice problems and the test.

ON YOUR OWN

4.10 Two balls of equal mass collide with one another in a glancing, elastic collision. One ball is at rest, and the other moves with a velocity of 3.5 m/sec towards the ball at rest. If the ball that was initially moving travels at an angle of 40.0 degrees relative to its initial velocity, what is its speed?

ANSWERS TO THE ON YOUR OWN PROBLEMS

4.1 When sitting on top of the hill, the block has only potential energy. Thus, its total energy is:

$$TE \ = \ PE \ + \ KE \ = \ m \cdot g \cdot h + 0 = m \cdot (9.81 \ \frac{m}{sec}) \cdot (1.5 \ m)$$

We can't get a number for TE, but that's okay, because we can just continue on and hope that we can either solve for mass or that it will cancel out. At the bottom of the hill, the total energy will be all kinetic:

$$TE \ = \ PE \ + \ KE \ = \ 0 + \frac{1}{2} \cdot m \cdot v^2$$

We don't know either m or v, so that's the best we can do. Now, energy conservation says that (ignoring outside forces like friction which work on the system) the total energy must stay the same. Thus:

$$m \cdot (9.81 \ \frac{m}{sec}) \cdot (1.5 \ m) = \frac{1}{2} \cdot m \cdot v^2$$

Now we see that mass cancels, leaving only v as the unknown:

$$\cancel{m} \cdot (9.81 \frac{m}{sec}) \cdot (1.5 \ m) = \frac{1}{2} \cdot \cancel{m} \cdot v^2$$

$$v = \sqrt{2 \cdot (9.81 \ \frac{m}{sec}) \cdot (1.5 \ m)} = \underline{5.4 \ \frac{m}{sec}}$$

4.2 Had friction done no work in the problem above, the block would have a speed of 5.4 m/sec. Friction, however, worked against motion, lowering the kinetic energy. How much energy does it have at the end?

$$TE \ = \ PE \ + \ KE \ = \ 0 + \frac{1}{2} \cdot m \cdot v^2 = \frac{1}{2} \cdot (0.1500 \ kg) \cdot (4.0 \ \frac{m}{sec})^2 = 1.2 \ J$$

Notice that I had to convert from grams to kg to keep things in the standard units. That tells us how much energy the block had at the end. How much energy did it have at the beginning?

$$TE \ = \ PE \ + \ KE \ = \ m \cdot g \cdot h + 0 = (0.1500 \ kg) \cdot (9.8 \ \frac{m}{sec}) \cdot (1.5 \ m) = 2.2 \ J$$

Why was there more energy at the beginning than at the end? Friction *worked* on the block, removing kinetic energy. Thus, the difference between the energy before and after (2.2 J - 1.2 J) represents the work done by friction. Thus, friction did 1.0 J of work.

4.3 What is the total energy before the charged particle is released?

$$TE = PE + KE = q \cdot V + 0$$

Once we plug in the equation for electrical potential (V), we get:

$$TE = \frac{k \cdot q \cdot Q}{r}$$

We know the value for k ($8.99 \times 10^9 \ \frac{N \cdot m^2}{C^2}$), and we are given the charges of both particles (q and Q) as well as the distance between them (r).

$$TE = \frac{(8.99 \times 10^9 \ \frac{N \cdot m^2}{C^2}) \cdot (-1.5 \ C) \cdot (4.5 \ C)}{3.5 \ m} = -1.7 \times 10^{10} \ J$$

Before I go on, note something that you should have learned in your first-year physics course. The total energy associated with gravity typically is on the order of a few Joules for macroscopic objects. On the other hand, the potential energy associated with electricity is *much* greater. That's because the electrical force is *significantly* stronger than the gravitational force. Also, note that total energy is negative. Remember, that should not bother you. Only *kinetic* energy must be positive.

When the moving particle is 1.0 m from the charged particle, it will have *both* kinetic and potential energy:

$$TE = PE + KE = q \cdot V + \frac{1}{2} \cdot m \cdot v^2 = \frac{(8.99 \times 10^9 \ \frac{N \cdot m^2}{C^2}) \cdot (-1.5 \ C) \cdot (4.5 \ C)}{1.0 \ m} + \frac{1}{2} \cdot (0.015 \, kg) \cdot v^2$$

Energy conservation tells us that the total energy must stay -1.7×10^{10} J. Thus:

$$\frac{(8.99 \times 10^9 \ \frac{N \cdot m^2}{C^2}) \cdot (-1.5 \ C) \cdot (4.5 \ C)}{1.0 \ m} + \frac{1}{2} \cdot (0.015 \, kg) \cdot v^2 = -1.7 \times 10^{10} \ J$$

$$v = \sqrt{\frac{2 \cdot [(-1.7 \times 10^{10} \ J) + (6.0 \times 10^{10} \ J)]}{0.015 \ kg}} = \underline{2.4 \times 10^6 \ \frac{m}{sec}}$$

4.4 Let's draw what's happening here:

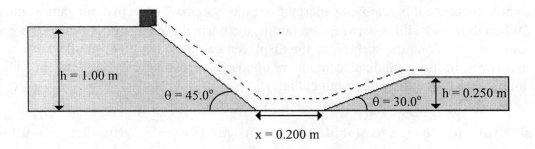

At first, the block has only potential energy. Thus, the total energy is:

$$TE = KE + PE = 0 + m \cdot g \cdot h = (m) \cdot (9.81 \frac{m}{sec^2}) \cdot (1.00\,m) = 9.81 \cdot m\ J$$

Notice that we have to leave "m" in as a variable. Hopefully, it will cancel out later. If there were no friction, then the block would have 9.81·m J at the end of the journey. However, there is friction. Thus, we must calculate the work that friction does and remove that energy from the total energy of the object. This is where we have to be a bit careful. On the inclines, the normal force is *not* m·g. It is m·g·cosθ, because only a portion of the weight is perpendicular to the surface. Thus, the frictional force on the first ramp is:

$$f = \mu_k \cdot F_n = (0.150) \cdot m \cdot g \cdot cos\theta = (0.150) \cdot (m) \cdot (9.81 \frac{m}{sec^2}) \cdot cos(45.0) = 1.04 \cdot m\ N$$

Okay, that's the frictional force while the block is on the first incline. To get the work done by friction, we multiply the force by the distance and by the cosine of the angle between force and displacement. What is that angle? Well, the frictional force works *along* the surface of the incline. We can calculate the distance down the incline using trigonometry:

$$sin\theta = \frac{opposite}{hypotenuse}$$

$$sin(45.0) = \frac{1.00\ m}{length\ of\ incline}$$

$$length\ of\ incline = 1.41\ m$$

Of course, the block slides *down* the incline, so that's the direction of the displacement. The frictional force works *up* the incline, so the angle between force and displacement is 180.0°. The work done by friction while sliding down the first ramp, then, is:

$$W_{f\_ramp1} = (1.04 \cdot m \text{ N}) \cdot (1.41 \text{ m}) \cdot \cos(180.0) = -1.47 \text{ J}$$

Work is negative because it is *removing* energy from the system. That's just one part of the trip, however. When the block slides between the ramps, the normal force is m·g, because the surface is flat. Friction works along the surface, so the displacement is the length of the flat surface, 0.200 m. However, friction and displacement are opposed, so the angle is 180.0° again. Thus, the work done by friction during that segment is:

$$W_{f\_flat} = f \cdot x \cdot \cos(180.0) = \mu_k \cdot m \cdot g \cdot x \cdot \cos(180.0) = -(0.150) \cdot (m) \cdot (9.81 \frac{m}{sec^2}) \cdot (0.200 \text{ m}) = -0.294 \cdot m \text{ J}$$

There is still one more segment. As the block slides up the next ramp, friction works on it again, but the normal force is less now that it is once again on the ramp. To get the work, we will need to know the displacement again, which is 180.0° relative to friction:

$$\sin\theta = \frac{\text{opposite}}{\text{hypotenuse}}$$

$$\sin(30.0) = \frac{0.250 \text{ m}}{\text{length of incline}}$$

$$\text{length of incline} = 0.500 \text{ m}$$

We can now calculate the work done by friction in the last segment:

$$f = \mu_k \cdot F_n = (0.150) \cdot m \cdot g \cdot \cos\theta = (0.150) \cdot (m) \cdot (9.81 \frac{m}{sec^2}) \cdot \cos(30.0) = 1.27 \cdot m \text{ N}$$

$$W_{f\_ramp2} = (1.27 \cdot m \text{ N}) \cdot (0.500 \text{ m}) \cdot \cos(180.0) = -0.635 \cdot m \text{ J}$$

The *total* work done by friction is just the sum of the work done in each segment, or -2.40·m J. This adds to the original energy, to give us the total energy after the block reaches the final flat surface:

$$TE_{after} = 9.81 \cdot m \text{ J} - 2.40 \cdot m \text{ J} = 7.41 \text{ J}$$

The block has potential energy (it is higher than the floor) and kinetic energy. Thus:

$$TE = PE + KE = m \cdot g \cdot h + \frac{1}{2} \cdot m \cdot v^2$$

$$7.41 \cdot \cancel{m} \text{ J} = (\cancel{m}) \cdot (9.81 \frac{m}{\sec^2}) \cdot (0.250 \text{ m}) + \frac{1}{2} \cdot (\cancel{m}) \cdot v^2$$

$$v = 3.15 \underline{\frac{m}{\sec}}$$

So the mass did, eventually cancel. As I have said before, you must get used to using variables and expressions just as easily as you use numbers. That's an integral part of mastering physics (and chemistry as well)!

4.5 The spring constant and initial displacement of the block gives us the potential energy with which the system begins. There is no initial kinetic energy, as the block is being held.

$$\text{TE} = \text{KE} + \text{PE} = 0 + \frac{1}{2} \cdot k \cdot x^2 = \frac{1}{2} \cdot (1.50 \frac{N}{m}) \cdot (0.150 \text{ m})^2 = 0.0169 \text{ J}$$

The work due to friction is easy to calculate, because the block is on a flat surface:

$$W_f = f \cdot x \cdot \cos(180.0) = \mu_k \cdot m \cdot g \cdot x \cdot \cos(180.0) = -(0.100) \cdot (0.0500 \text{ kg}) \cdot (9.81 \frac{m}{\sec^2}) \cdot x = -(0.0491 \frac{kg \cdot m}{\sec^2}) \cdot x$$

We can calculate x by realizing that when the total energy plus the work done by friction is zero, the system will stop moving:

$$0.0169 \text{ J} - (0.0491 \frac{kg \cdot m}{\sec^2}) \cdot x = 0$$

$$x = \underline{0.344 \text{ m}}$$

4.6 In Atwood's machine, the heavier block travels down, and the lighter block travels up. Thus, the lighter block gains potential energy, but since it is accelerating, it gains kinetic energy as well. The heavier block loses potential energy and gains kinetic energy. To determine how all of this "pans out," we first need to define potential energy *relative* to something. Remember, potential energy has to be defined relative to a point, so let's choose the most convenient point. We know that, in the end, the heavy block will move at least 0.500 m down, since we are asked to calculate speed at that point. Thus, let's make that the definition of zero potential energy. If anything is 0.500 m lower than the point the blocks started, we will call that zero potential energy.

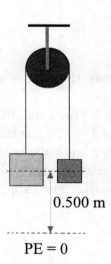

Okay, then, what is the total energy before the masses are released? There is no kinetic energy, but both masses have potential energy:

$$TE = PE + KE = m_1 \cdot g \cdot h_1 + m_2 \cdot g \cdot h_2$$

$$TE = (20.0\,\text{kg}) \cdot (9.81\frac{m}{sec^2}) \cdot (0.500\,m) + (40.0\,\text{kg}) \cdot (9.81\frac{m}{sec^2}) \cdot (0.500\,m) = 294\ J$$

After the masses have traveled 0.500 m, both will have kinetic energy, but the heavy one (m_2) will be at the point we have defined as zero potential energy, so it will have *no* potential energy. The lighter mass (m_1), however, will now be 1.000 m *above* the zero potential energy point, so it will definitely have potential energy.

$$TE = PE + KE = m_1 \cdot g \cdot h_1 + \frac{1}{2} \cdot m_1 \cdot v_1^2 + \frac{1}{2} \cdot m_2 \cdot v_2^2$$

$$294\ J = (20.0\ \text{kg}) \cdot (9.81\frac{m}{sec^2}) \cdot (1.000\ m) + \frac{1}{2} \cdot (20.0\ \text{kg}) \cdot v_1^2 + \frac{1}{2} \cdot (40.0\ \text{kg}) \cdot v_2^2$$

$$98\ J = \frac{1}{2} \cdot (20.0\ \text{kg}) \cdot v_1^2 + \frac{1}{2} \cdot (40.0\ \text{kg}) \cdot v_2^2$$

You might think that we are stuck here because we have one equation and two unknowns. However, remember that these masses start at rest, and, since they are attached by a string that doesn't "bunch up," they accelerate at the same rate. Thus, they will always have the same speed since they start off with the same velocity and experience acceleration of the same magnitude. Thus,

$$98\ J = \frac{1}{2} \cdot (20.0\ \text{kg}) \cdot v^2 + \frac{1}{2} \cdot (40.0\ \text{kg}) \cdot v^2$$

$$v = 1.8\ \frac{m}{sec}$$

Note that you could have used Newton's laws to solve this, as discussed in the previous module.

4.7 Force and displacement are parallel, and velocity is constant. Thus, we can use Equation (4.10). To use that equation, we need to know the force that is doing the work and the velocity. We know the velocity. What about the force? To be moving the crate at a constant velocity, Newton's Second Law says that the sum of the forces on the crate must be zero. Thus, the worker must supply just enough force to counteract friction.

$$f = \mu_k \cdot F_n = (0.251) \cdot m \cdot g = (0.251) \cdot (150.0\ \text{kg}) \cdot (9.81\ \frac{m}{sec^2}) = 369\ N$$

Now we can use Equation (4.10).

$$P = F \cdot v = (369 \text{ N}) \cdot (1.55 \, \frac{m}{sec}) = \underline{572 \text{ Watts}}$$

The units work out here because a N·m is a Joule, thus, the units multiply to give J/s, which is a Watt.

4.8 Since the collision is elastic, energy is conserved. The only initial energy is the kinetic energy of the neutron. Since the masses are equal, I will refer to them both as "m." Thus:

$$\tfrac{1}{2} \, m \cdot v_n^2 = \tfrac{1}{2} m \cdot v_{Hf}^2 + \tfrac{1}{2} m \cdot v_{nf}^2$$

$$v_{ni}^2 = v_{Hf}^2 + v_{nf}^2$$

This seems strange, since we have 3 unknowns here. However, it will work out if we just continue to plug through the math. Let's go to momentum conservation:

$$m \cdot v_{ni} = m \cdot v_{Hf} + m \cdot v_{nf}$$

$$v_{ni} = v_{Hf} + v_{nf}$$

Putting v_{nf} in terms of v_{ni} and v_{Hf}:

$$v_{nf} = v_{ni} - v_{Hf}$$

Putting that in the energy equation:

$$v_n^2 = v_{Hf}^2 + (v_{ni} - v_{Hf})^2$$

$$v_{ni}^2 = v_{Hf}^2 + v_{Hf}^2 - 2 \, v_{Hf} \cdot v_{ni} + v_{ni}^2$$

Does that help at all? Actually, it does. After all, we need to know what fraction of the neutron's energy is transferred to the hydrogen atom. Thus, let's take the equation above and solve for v_{Hf}^2:

$$2 \cdot v_{Hf}^2 - 2 \, v_{Hf} \cdot v_{ni} = 0$$

$$2 \cdot v_{Hf}(v_{Hf} - v_{ni}) = 0$$

Well, for this equation to be true, v_{Hf} must be either 0 or v_{ni}. Remember, an equation with a square will always give you two answers. You should be able to eliminate one of them. In this case, we will eliminate $v_{Hf} = 0$, since that was the initial condition. Thus, $v_{Hf} = v_{ni}$.

What does this tell us? Well, from momentum conservation, we got that:

$$v_{nf} = v_{ni} - v_{Hf}$$

Since $v_{Hf} = v_{ni}$, that means the final neutron velocity (v_{nf}) is zero. Thus, the elastic, head-on collision caused *all* of the neutron's energy to be transferred to the hydrogen atom. As a result, the neutron is at rest, and when the hydrogen releases its energy, all of the neutron's kinetic energy is released in the energy of light emitted by the hydrogen atom. Now it turns out that head-on collisions are rare in this situation. Most collisions are glancing, and that reduces the amount of energy transferred to the hydrogen atom. In the next section of this module, you will learn how to deal with those kinds of collisions.

4.9 We do not know what kind of collision this is, so we only have momentum conservation. That is enough in this situation, however.

$$m_1 \cdot v_{1i} + m_2 \cdot v_{2i} = m_1 \cdot v_{1f} + m_2 \cdot v_{2f}$$

$$(5.00 \text{ kg}) \cdot (4.50 \frac{m}{sec}) + (9.00 \text{ kg}) \cdot (-1.40 \frac{m}{sec}) = (5.00 \text{ kg}) \cdot (-2.50 \frac{m}{sec}) + (9.00 \text{ kg}) \cdot (v_{2f})$$

$$v_{2f} = 2.49 \frac{m}{sec}$$

That does not answer the question, however. We need to determine the type of collision. It is not perfectly inelastic, because the two masses move at different velocities. However, is it elastic or inelastic? For that, we have to look at the energy before and after the collision:

$$TE_i = PE_i + KE_i = 0 + \frac{1}{2} \cdot m_1 \cdot v_{1i}^2 + \frac{1}{2} \cdot m_2 \cdot v_{2i}^2$$

$$TE_i = \frac{1}{2} \cdot (5.00 \text{ kg}) \cdot (4.50 \frac{m}{sec})^2 + \frac{1}{2} \cdot (9.00 \text{ kg}) \cdot (1.40 \frac{m}{sec})^2 = 59.4 \text{ J}$$

$$TE_f = PE_f + KE_f = 0 + \frac{1}{2} \cdot m_1 \cdot v_{1f}^2 + \frac{1}{2} \cdot m_2 \cdot v_{2f}^2$$

$$TE_f = \frac{1}{2} \cdot (5.00 \text{ kg}) \cdot (2.50 \frac{m}{sec})^2 + \frac{1}{2} \cdot (9.00 \text{ kg}) \cdot (2.49 \frac{m}{sec})^2 = 43.5 \text{ J}$$

Energy was lost. Thus, this is an inelastic collision.

4.10 Since the two balls have equal mass, and since the collision is elastic, we know that in a glancing collision, their relative angles will be 90.0°. Thus, if the first ball has a velocity angle of 40.0°, the other ball angles off at 50.0° below the line defined by the collision:

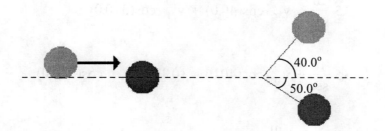

To do the vector math, however, we need to DEFINE the angles properly. The first angle, 40.0° is defined properly already. However the angle we deduced is not 50.0°. It is 310.0°. That's what we need to use in the vector equations.

Now let's conserve momentum in each dimension. Let's start with the y-dimension:

$$m_1 \cdot v_{1i} \cdot \sin\theta_{1i} + m_2 \cdot v_{2i} \cdot \sin\theta_{2i} = m_1 \cdot v_{1f} \cdot \sin\theta_{1f} + m_2 \cdot v_{2if} \cdot \sin\theta_{2f}$$

Since the masses are equal, they cancel. That leaves:

$$v_{1i} \cdot \sin\theta_{1i} + v_{2i} \cdot \sin\theta_{2i} = v_{1f} \cdot \sin\theta_{1f} + v_{2f} \cdot \sin\theta_{2f}$$

Filling in what we know:

$$(3.5 \frac{m}{sec}) \cdot \sin(0.00) + (0) \cdot \sin\theta_{2i} = (v_{1f}) \cdot \sin(40.0) + v_{2f} \cdot \sin(310.0)$$

$$v_{2f} = 0.839 \cdot v_{1f}$$

That gives us two unknowns, but that's okay, because we have another dimension to investigate. Recognizing that the masses will cancel in the x-dimension as well, we get:

$$v_{1i} \cdot \cos\theta_{1i} + v_{2i} \cdot \cos\theta_{2i} = v_{1f} \cdot \cos\theta_{1f} + v_{2f} \cdot \cos\theta_{2f}$$

$$(3.5 \frac{m}{sec}) \cdot \cos(0.00) + (0) \cdot \cos\theta_{2i} = v_{1f} \cdot \cos(40.0) + v_{2f} \cdot \cos(310.0)$$

$$3.5 \frac{m}{sec} = v_{1f} \cdot \cos(40.0) + v_{2f} \cdot \cos(310.0)$$

Taking the equation from the y-dimension and sticking it into this equation:

$$3.5 \frac{m}{sec} = v_{1f} \cdot \cos(40.0) + v_{2f} \cdot \cos(310.0)$$

$$3.5 \frac{m}{sec} = v_{1f} \cdot \cos(40.0) + (0.839 \cdot v_{1f}) \cdot \cos(310.0)$$

$$v_{1f} = 2.7 \frac{m}{sec}$$

That's actually all the problem asked for. You could go back to the equation developed in the y-dimension and find out that $v_{2f} = 2.25$ m/sec. One way you could see whether or not the answers are correct is to confirm that energy is conserved. Indeed, since the square of the initial speed is equal to the sum of the squares of the final speeds, and since the masses are equal, energy is conserved.

REVIEW QUESTIONS FOR MODULE #4

1. As you learned in your first-year course, in order for an object to move in a circle, it must experience a centripetal force which is directed towards the center of the circle. If an object moves in a circle of radius 1.0 m with a constant speed of 2.0 m/sec, how much work is done by the centripetal force in one trip around the circle?

2. A ball hits a wall and bounces straight back along the same path. What is the impulse delivered to the ball by the wall in terms of the ball's mass (m) and the ball's speed (v)?

3. Two objects collide with one another and move away from each other. There are no net forces acting on the objects. Could the collision be elastic? Could it be inelastic? Could it be perfectly inelastic?

4. Consider the situation described in question #3. Suppose the total kinetic energy of the objects after the collision is lower than it was before the collision. What kind of collision was it? Was momentum conserved?

5. Is energy ever conserved in a perfectly inelastic collision? If so, under what conditions?

6. Is momentum ever conserved in a perfectly inelastic collision? If so, under what conditions?

7. A student sees a laboratory notebook in which the following notation is made:

"Total Energy is -2.3 Joules."

The student says that this must be wrong, since energy cannot be negative. Why is the student wrong?

8. In this module, we used the equation PE = m·g·h quite often. When is that equation valid?

9. Two machines do *exactly* the same amount of work, but the second requires twice as much power. Assuming both machines are equally efficient, what can you say about the time it takes for each machine to get the job done?

(There is one more review question on the next page.)

10. Consider the desktop toy made by suspending four balls of equal mass. When ball 1 is pulled to the right and released, it falls, striking the other balls. In response, ball 4 will begin moving at the same speed as that which ball 1 had the instant  before the collision. This, of course, is because of momentum conservation. If balls 1 and 2 are both lifted and released together, they will hit balls 3 and 4, and *both* ball 3 and ball 4 will begin moving, each with the same speeds that balls 1 and 2 had the instant before the collision. Once again, momentum is conserved.   However, momentum *could* be conserved if ball 4 began moving at twice the speed of balls 1 and 2 and all of the other balls remained motionless. That never happens, however. Why not?

PRACTICE PROBLEMS FOR MODULE #4

1. A person skis down a hill that is covered with snow. Assume that there is no friction on the snow. If the hill is 150 meters high, how fast will the skier be moving at the bottom of the hill? Ignore air resistance and any initial shove that the skier uses to get started.

2. For the skier in problem #1, assume that when he reaches the bottom of the hill, the snow is sparse, and as a result, the coefficient of kinetic friction is 0.550. Assume that the ground at the bottom of the hill is flat. How far will the skier (m= 75 kg) travel before stopping ?

3. A student drops a rock off the edge of a cliff. When the rock is halfway down the cliff, what is its speed in terms of its speed right before it hits bottom?

4. A box sits on top of a ramp with a height of 1.00 m and an angle of 45.0 degrees. The μ_k is 0.150. When it reaches the bottom of the hill, it slides on a frictionless surface and goes around a loop (also frictionless) that is 0.300 m high at its tallest point. What is the speed of the box at the top of the loop?

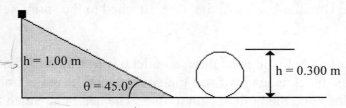

5. A toy is moving across a surface which is not frictionless. Its motor supplies the force that it needs to overcome friction. The velocity of the car is given by the graph shown on the right.

a. Is the motor exerting more force at t = 8.0 seconds or at t = 5.0 seconds?

b. Is the motor exerting more power at t = 2.0 seconds or t = 9.0 seconds?

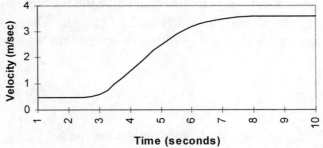

6. An object with a charge of 1.50 milliCoulombs is pushed towards a stationary charge of 2.50 milliCoulombs. The charged object was initially very far away from the stationary object and ends up only 0.500 meters away from it. If this process took 10.0 minutes, what is the average power used?

7. A ball of mass 5.0 kg is kicked with a 55 N force. If the ball begins traveling at 3.5 m/sec as a result, how long did the force act on the ball?

8. A mass (10.0 kg) is attached to a spring (k = 15.1 N/m) which is attached to a wall. While it is sitting at its equilibrium position, another mass (15.0 kg) is set on the floor, touching the first mass. The mass attached to the spring is so smooth that there is virtually no friction between it and the floor. The 15.0 kg mass, however, is rough, and the coefficient of kinetic friction between it and the floor is 0.250. The mass attached to the spring is pushed 50.0 cm towards the wall and then released so that it collides elastically with the other mass.

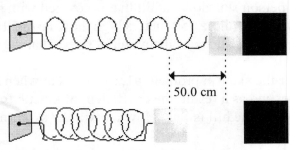

50.0 cm

a. How far will the 15.0 kg mass travel before it stops?

b. How far back will the mass attached to the spring rebound?

9. In a ballistic pendulum, a bullet of mass m is fired at a block of mass M suspended by a string. The block is made of soft material so that the bullet imbeds itself into the block. As a result, the block and the bullet begin to rise. The height at which the block rises (h) is then measured. This is a means by which the speed of the bullet can be measured.

a. What is the speed of the bullet in terms of m, M, and h?

b. A student suggests that you solve the problem by first calculating the potential energy gained by the block and the bullet as (M + m)·g·h. Then, you can say that this energy must have all been from the kinetic energy of the bullet, so that leads to the equation:

$$(M + m) \cdot g \cdot h = \frac{1}{2} \cdot m \cdot v^2$$

Then, you can simply solve this equation for v to get the speed of the bullet. Why is the student wrong?

10. Two balls of equal mass collide elastically. Ball 1 is initially at rest, and ball 2 moves with an unknown velocity. After they collide, the ball initially at rest moves with a velocity of 2.00 m/sec at an angle of 45.0 degrees relative to the initial velocity of the ball that was moving. What was the initial velocity of ball 2?

Module #5: Rotational Motion

Introduction

So far, we have discussed bodies in **translational motion**, which is motion from one point to another point in space. In your first-year physics course, you probably concentrated on that type of motion as well. However, there is another type of motion that we encounter every day. Consider a wheel on a car. The wheel rotates around a fixed point (the car's axle). That kind of motion is, not surprisingly, called **rotational motion**, and that's where I want to start in this module. Now please remember that these two types of motion are not necessarily isolated. They can, indeed, interact. For example, consider once again the wheel on a car. The wheel rotates, so it is involved in rotational motion. However, because of friction between the wheel and the road, the car (and the wheel along with it) moves from one point to another. Thus, the wheel engages in *both* translational motion *and* rotational motion.

The Center of Mass

Before I discuss rotational motion, I need to tell you a few things about the **center of mass** (sometimes called the "center of gravity"). The center of mass is an important concept when dealing with objects or systems of objects. You can think of it as the "average position" of the mass. Consider, for example, a system composed of two particles. If the particles are of equal mass, the "average position" of the mass will be directly in between the two. After all, there is just as much mass on one side of the point as there is on the other. Thus, that point represents the "average position" of the mass in the system. However, if one particle has twice the mass of the other, the center of mass will be weighted towards the more massive particle, because the extra mass skews the average.

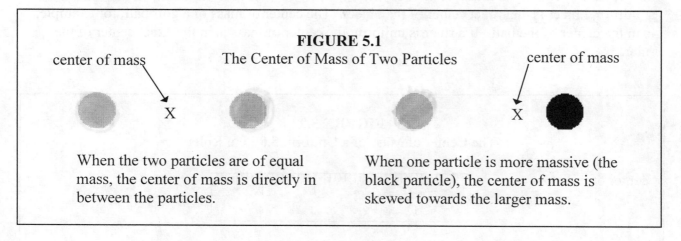

FIGURE 5.1
The Center of Mass of Two Particles

center of mass

center of mass

X

X

When the two particles are of equal mass, the center of mass is directly in between the particles.

When one particle is more massive (the black particle), the center of mass is skewed towards the larger mass.

If you are dealing with a system of many particles instead of just two, you can calculate the system's center of mass with the following formula:

Center of mass

$$\mathbf{x}_{cm} = \frac{m_1 \cdot \mathbf{x}_1 + m_2 \cdot \mathbf{x}_2 + m_3 \cdot \mathbf{x}_3 \dots m_n \cdot \mathbf{x}_n}{m_1 + m_2 + m_3 \dots m_n} \qquad (5.1)$$

In this equation, "$\mathbf{x}_{cm}$" is the position of the center of mass, and "n" is the number of particles in the system. The term "m_1" represents the mass of the first particle; "m_2" represents the mass of the second particle; and so on; "$\mathbf{x}_1$" is the position of the first particle; "$\mathbf{x}_2$" is the position of the second particle; etc. To calculate the center of mass in a system of particles, then, you just multiply the position of each particle by its mass, sum up the products, and then divide by the total mass of the system. That will give you the position of the system's center of mass.

Although so far I have just talked about the center of mass in terms of a system of particles, every object that takes up space has a center of mass as well. It is much harder to calculate the center of mass of a single object, but it can be done. For example, consider a regulation golf ball. You could imagine that the golf ball is really just a composite of thousands of tiny "golf ball particles." If you measured the position of each particle and its mass and then used Equation (5.1), you would find that the center of mass of the golf ball is in the very center of the ball. In fact, when you take calculus, you will find that the **integral** is a calculus concept which does just that. It allows you to calculate the center of mass of the golf ball by hypothetically splitting it up into infinitesimally small sections and then multiplying the mass of each section times its position. When you then divide by the total mass, you get the center of mass of the object.

Since this is not a calculus class, we will not use integrals to calculate the center of mass of a single object. Instead, we will keep things relatively "simple." When dealing with individual objects in this class, we will always assume that the object is uniform throughout. What good does that do? It makes finding the center of mass a snap. Just as the center of mass of a system of two equal masses is directly in the center of the two masses, the center of mass of a uniform object is the direct center of the object. The center of mass of a golf ball, for example, is in the center of the ball. If a ruler is uniform, the center of mass is in the exact center of the ruler.

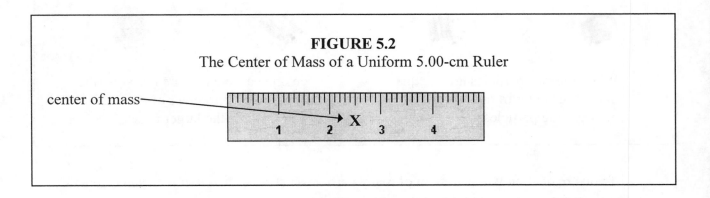

FIGURE 5.2
The Center of Mass of a Uniform 5.00-cm Ruler

center of mass

Before I go any further, I want to make sure that you understand *how* to determine the center of mass. Thus, I want to go through a couple of example problems.

EXAMPLE 5.1

Consider a system of three particles as illustrated in the diagram to the right. The gray particles are three times as massive as the white particle, and they are each located 50.0 cm from the white particle. What is the center of mass of this system?

To determine the center of mass, we must first define a coordinate system. We could do that any number of ways, but I will consider the white particle to be the origin of the coordinate system. Now this is clearly a two-dimensional problem, so we need to calculate an x-coordinate and a y-coordinate for the center of mass. How will we do that? We will do it like we do *any* two-dimensional problem: we will split it up into two one-dimensional problems! Let's start with the x-dimension. In the x-dimension, the white mass has a position of x = 0. In addition, the gray mass directly above the white mass also has a position of x = 0. The other gray mass has a position of x = 50.0 cm, because it is 50.0 cm to the right of the origin. Equation (5.1), then, becomes:

$$x_{cm} = \frac{m_1 \cdot x_1 + m_2 \cdot x_2 + m_3 \cdot x_3 \dots m_n \cdot x_n}{m_1 + m_2 + m_3 \dots m_n}$$

$$x_{cm} = \frac{m \cdot 0 + 3m \cdot 0 + 3m \cdot (50.0 \text{ cm})}{m + 3m + 3m} = \frac{\cancel{m} \cdot (1.50 \times 10^2 \text{ cm})}{7 \cdot \cancel{m}} = 21.4 \text{ cm}$$

That's the x-coordinate of the center of mass. To get the y-coordinate, we do the same in the y-dimension. The y-coordinate of both the white mass and the gray mass to its right are both 0. The y-coordinate of the gray mass directly above the white mass is y = 50.0 cm.

$$y_{cm} = \frac{m_1 \cdot y_1 + m_2 \cdot y_2 + m_3 \cdot y_3 \dots m_n \cdot y_n}{m_1 + m_2 + m_3 \dots m_n}$$

$$y_{cm} = \frac{m \cdot 0 + 3m \cdot 0 + 3m \cdot (50.0 \text{ cm})}{m + 3m + 3m} = \frac{\cancel{m} \cdot (1.50 \times 10^2 \text{ cm})}{7 \cdot \cancel{m}} = 21.4 \text{ cm}$$

That's the y-coordinate of the center of mass. Thus, <u>the center of mass is 21.4 cm to the right and 21.4 cm above the white mass</u>.

A system of three uniform rods is shown to the right. The top rod is twice as massive as the rod on the left, and the rod on the right is three times as massive as the rod on the left. If the top rod has a length of "L," and the side rods have lengths of "K," what is the center of mass of the system?

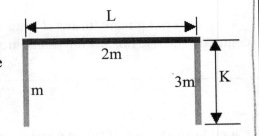

You might think that this problem requires calculus to solve, because each of the rods has a center of mass that must be determined. However, they are uniform rods. Thus, the center of mass of each rod is at the exact center of the rod. Thus, if we look at just the center of mass of each rod, this is the situation:

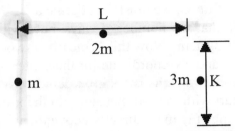

Looking at this picture, then, we really just have a system of three particles. If we define the origin as the upper, left-hand corner of the assembly, the mass labeled "2m" is at $x = \frac{1}{2} \cdot L$, $y = 0$. The mass labeled "m" is at $x = 0$, $y = -\frac{1}{2} \cdot K$, and the mass labeled "3m" is at $x = L$, $y = -\frac{1}{2} \cdot K$. Now we can use Equation (5.1):

$$x_{cm} = \frac{m_1 \cdot x_1 + m_2 \cdot x_2 + m_3 \cdot x_3 \dots m_n \cdot x_n}{m_1 + m_2 + m_3 \dots m_n}$$

$$x_{cm} = \frac{(2m) \cdot (\frac{1}{2} \cdot L) + m \cdot 0 + 3m \cdot (L)}{m + 3m + 2m} = \frac{m \cdot (4 \cdot L)}{6 \cdot m} = \frac{2}{3} \cdot L$$

$$y_{cm} = \frac{m_1 \cdot y_1 + m_2 \cdot y_2 + m_3 \cdot y_3 \dots m_n \cdot y_n}{m_1 + m_2 + m_3 \dots m_n}$$

$$y_{cm} = \frac{(2m) \cdot 0 + m \cdot (-\frac{1}{2} \cdot K) + 3m \cdot (-\frac{1}{2} \cdot K)}{m + 3m + 2m} = \frac{m \cdot (-2 \cdot K)}{6 \cdot m} = -\frac{1}{3} \cdot K$$

The center of mass, then, is 2/3·L to the right of the upper, left-hand corner, and 1/3·K below the upper, left-hand corner. If you think about it, that makes perfect sense. Since the bar to the right is heavier than the bar to the left, the center of mass is weighted to the right (2/3·L is to the right of halfway in between the bars). Since the upper bar is heavier than the other two bars, the center of mass is weighted up (-1/3·K is only one-third of the way down the bars).

Now that you know how to calculate the center of mass, you might wonder why in the world you would want to do such a thing. The answer is simple:

An extended body or a system of individual particles will behave as though all of the mass is concentrated at the center of mass.

That might be a bit hard to believe, so I want you to do the following experiment.

Photos by Kathleen J. Wile

EXPERIMENT 5.1
The Center of Mass

NOTE: I learned this experiment from Brian Clay - preacher, actor, consultant, and all-around great guy.

Supplies:

- A teaspoon (Not a measuring teaspoon - a normal teaspoon you use at the table)
- A fork roughly as long as the spoon (The fork will probably be a bit longer, but that's okay.)
- Wooden matches
- A glass

Introduction - This experiment demonstrates that a system behaves as if all of its mass is concentrated at its center of mass.

Procedure:

1. Set the glass on the top of a table.
2. Interlock the spoon in the tines of the fork. The middle tines should touch the back of the spoon, while the outer tines should touch the front of the spoon. In the end, the spoon and fork should form a "V," as shown in the picture to the right.

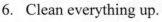

3. Take a match and stick one end (not the end you strike - the other end) between the tines of the fork under the spoon so that the entire "V" assembly balances on the match.
4. Now balance the entire assembly on the edge of the glass by placing the match on the lip of the glass, as shown in the picture to the right.
5. You might think that the match has something to do with the balance of the assembly on the glass. It does not. The match serves only to provide a surface for the assembly to hang on the glass. To demonstrate this, light a match and use it to light the head of the match that the assembly sits on. The match will burn until it reaches the edge of the glass, and then it will go out. Carefully use the match you have in your hand to break off the burnt part of the match. The assembly will still stay balanced on the glass.
6. Clean everything up.

Why did the fork/spoon assembly balance on the glass even when the match was burnt from one end? It's because the center of mass of the assembly is sitting on the edge of the glass. Think about the spoon. The majority of the spoon's mass is in the ladle. Thus, the center of mass is on the handle but near the ladle of the spoon. For the fork, the center of mass is near the tines as well, because the mass of the fork is concentrated on the part of the fork that forms the tines. Since the handles both bend in towards the glass, the center of mass of the entire assembly ends up being located in the same plane as the edge of the glass. Well, since extended objects behave as if their mass was concentrated at the center of mass, the fork/spoon assembly behaved as if its mass was concentrated on the edge of the glass. Thus, it balanced. That's why the center of mass is so important in physics. An object that is difficult to analyze can simply be replaced by a point that contains all of the object's mass. That point is the center of mass.

ON YOUR OWN

5.1 A man (m = 85.0 kg) stands in the center of a uniform raft (m = 150.0 kg), 2.50 meters from one edge. The raft is 15.0 meters long and 4.00 meters wide.

a. What is the center of mass of this system?
b. The raft is floating motionless in the water. If the man walks to the other side of the raft so that he is now 2.50 m from the other edge of the raft, how far will the raft move in response?

5.2 A shoulder-fired rocket launcher fires a projectile (from ground level) with an initial speed of 125 m/sec at an angle of 30.0° relative to the horizontal. The projectile then explodes into ten pieces. Where will the center of mass of those ten pieces be when they hit the ground?

Torque and Static Rotational Equilibrium

As mentioned in Module #1, whereas force causes translational acceleration, **torque** causes rotational acceleration (usually called **angular acceleration**). Thus, if an object is at rest and you want it to move from one point to another, you must apply a force to get it moving. If that same object is at rest and you want to get it rotating, you must apply a torque to make it start rotating. In the same way, if an object is in translational motion and you want to stop it, you must apply force that opposes the motion. If the object is rotating and you want to stop it, you must apply a torque that opposes the rotation. Torque was defined in Module #1:

$$\tau = r \times F \tag{1.13}$$

Using the definition of the magnitude of the cross product, we can say:

$$\tau = r \cdot F \cdot \sin\theta \tag{5.2}$$

where "τ" is the magnitude of the torque, "r" is the distance between the force and the axis around which the object rotates (called the "lever arm"), and "θ" is the angle between **r** and **F**.

In Module #3, we dealt with Newton's Laws. In that module, we analyzed situations in which a object was in **static translational equilibrium**. In other words, the object was not moving. To analyze the situation, we said that in order for the object to be not moving, the sum of the forces on the object had to be zero. Well, if an object is not rotating, it is in **static rotational equilibrium**, and thus the sum of the torques must equal zero. In your first-year physics course, you probably did some problems with see-saws, summing up the torques and making sure that the sum equaled zero. That allowed the see-saw to be in static rotational equilibrium. I want you to review those kinds of problems by performing the following experiment.

EXPERIMENT 5.2
Static Rotational Equilibrium

Supplies:

- A wooden pencil
- A wooden ruler
- At least 5 U.S. quarters, preferably more

Introduction - This experiment allows you to use what you learned in the previous section as well as what you learned about static rotational equilibrium in your first-year physics course.

Procedure:

1. Set the pencil on the table.
2. Balance the ruler on the pencil so that neither end of the ruler hits the table. If your ruler is uniform, it will balance when the halfway mark of the ruler is sitting on the middle of the pencil, because that is the center of mass of the ruler. If it is not the center of the ruler, note where it is.
3. Now you are going to weigh your ruler. How are you going to do that without a scale? Put a quarter on the end of the ruler so that one end of the quarter touches the zero mark on the ruler. Read the mark that corresponds to the center of the quarter. If you are using an English ruler, for example, the center of the quarter will be at the ½-inch mark.
4. Now find the point at which the ruler balances again. You will discover that it is not the halfway mark of the ruler. Instead, a shorter portion of the ruler will be on the same side of the pencil as is the quarter.
5. Read the ruler to find the distance from the center of the quarter to the point at which the ruler is balancing on the pencil.
6. Read the ruler to find the distance from the center of mass you determined in step (2) to the point at which the ruler balances.

7. Now think about the rotational motion aspect of this situation. When not balanced, the ruler rotates around the axis defined by the pencil. The rotation is short because it is interrupted by the table. Nevertheless, it *is* rotation. When the ruler balances, there is no rotation, so the sum of the torques is zero.

What is supplying the torques? The weight of the quarter supplies one torque. Let's say that rotation in that direction is

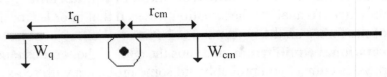

positive. The weight of the ruler (remember - it is concentrated at the center of mass) provides a torque in the opposite direction, which we will call negative. Thus, we have the following equation to represent the sum of the torques:

$$W_q \cdot r_q - W_{cm} \cdot r_{cm} = 0$$

In this equation, "W_q" is the weight of the quarter, "r_q" is the lever arm distance from the axis of rotation to the center (center of mass) of the quarter, "W_{cm}" is the weight of the ruler (concentrated at the center of mass), and "r_{cm}" is the lever arm distance from the ruler's center of mass to the axis of rotation.

8. The mass of a U.S. quarter is 5.75 grams. Now you can calculate "W_q." You measured "r_q" and "r_{cm}" in steps (5) and (6). Thus, the only thing you don't know in the equation above is the weight of the ruler. Thus, you can solve for it. This is actually a very accurate weight for the ruler, providing you did your calculations and measurement correctly.

9. Now that you know the weight of the ruler, I want you to set up another problem. Take the quarter off of the ruler and place the ruler so that the center of mass is even farther away from the pencil than it has been so far. Make sure that the change is significant (7-15 cm).

10. Use the equation in step (7) to calculate the weight of quarters that would be required to balance the ruler with this new setup, assuming that you put the quarters at the same place you had the one quarter before.

11. Divide the weight you calculated by the weight per quarter, and that will tell you the number of quarters you need to balance the ruler now. Most likely, the number will not be an integer.

12. Put the nearest whole number of quarters on the ruler in the same place you had the one quarter in the previous part of the experiment. In other words, if you calculated that you needed 3.2452 quarters to balance the ruler, put 3 quarters on the spot where you had just one before. Note that the ruler still tips to the side without any quarters.

13. Put one more quarter on the pile. Note that the ruler now tips to the side with the quarters. That's because with the addition of another quarter, the quarters are now supplying more torque than is the ruler.

14. You can continue to play with this. In my setup, my ruler had a weight of 0.205 N (a mass of 20.9 g). When I placed the pencil very near the end of the ruler, it could hold up a stack of 10 quarters.

15. Clean everything up.

When an object is not rotating, then, the sum of the torques on the object must equal zero. It turns out that we can combine this concept (static rotational equilibrium) with the concept of static translational equilibrium to be able to analyze some pretty complex situations, as shown in the following example:

EXAMPLE 5.2

One side of a uniform 50.0 kg rod (length = 1.00 m) is attached to a wall. The rod is also supported by a rope that is attached to the center of the rod and tied to the wall above the rod at a 40.0° angle. A 150.0 kg block hangs 20.0 cm from the free end of the rod. What is the tension in the rope?

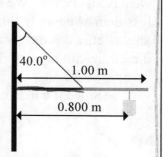

We could try to solve this problem using just the concept of static translational equilibrium. After all, the system is not moving. Thus, the sum of the forces must be zero. The first thing we should do is identify all of the forces. This might be tricky, as there is one force that you might not recognize:

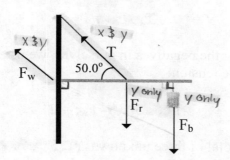

The tension in the rope (T) is an easy force to spot, as is the force from the weight of the block (F_b). However, the rod has mass as well. Thus, its weight will exert a force downward. Since any extended body behaves as if all of its mass was concentrated at the center of mass, the force due to the rod's weight (F_r) is located at the very center of the rod (since the rod is uniform). There is still one more force. After all, the rod is attached to the wall. Thus, the wall must be exerting a force on the rod (F_w). We do not know the direction of the force. I drew a vector for it, but that is just my guess as to the direction of the force. We will have to determine the direction when we solve the problem.

Okay, those are all of the forces. This is clearly a two-dimensional problem, so let's split it up into two, one-dimensional problems. Let's start with the y-dimension, defining upward motion as positive:

$$T_y + F_{wy} - F_r - F_b = \underline{0}$$

bcuz it is still

We know the mass of the rod and the block, so we can multiply by g and turn those into weights:

$$T_y + F_{wy} - 491 \text{ N} - 1470 \text{ N} = 0$$

natural force

Since the sum of angles in a triangle must be 180.0°, the angle that the rope makes relative to the rod is 50.0°. If we want to define that angle properly, it is 130.0°. However, we need to be careful here. In Newton's Laws problems, we typically define the directions ourselves. For example, in the equation above, we subtracted the weight of the rod and the weight of the block. Why? Because we know those forces are pointing down, and we defined down as negative. When we use angles that are properly defined, *those angles* keep track of direction for us. Thus, we have a choice. We can either use the reference angle of 50.0° (reference angles are always less than or equal to 90°) and *define the directions by putting in negative signs*, or we can use the angle defined properly and *never add any negative signs*. I personally like to reason the directions out myself. Thus, I will use the reference angle and put the negatives in myself.

Since the tension pulls upward, it is a positive force. That gives us:

bcuz we are in the y demension

$$T \cdot \sin(50.0) + F_{wy} - 491 \text{ N} - 1470 \text{ N} = 0$$

We are left with two unknowns. Let's go to the x-dimension and see what we can find out, defining motion to the right as positive:

negative becuz it is pointing to the left

$$-T_x - F_{wx} = 0$$

Once again, since we are putting the negatives in ourselves, we use the reference angle to calculate the x-component of the tension:

x demension

$$-T \cdot \cos(50.0) - F_{wx} = 0$$

This is a problem. We have a total of three unknowns (T, F_{wx}, F_{wy}). If we knew the angle of F_w, we could reduce that list to just two unknowns, but we don't. Thus, we are stuck with two equations and three unknowns.

This is where the concept of static rotational equilibrium comes into play. We also know that the rod is not rotating. Thus, the sum of the torques on the rod must be zero. So, we can just sum up the torques and set them equal to zero. However, to define a torque, we need to determine an axis about which this rod could potentially rotate. As I see it, there are two. If the rod were to come loose from the wall, it could rotate around its center, where the rope is attached. Alternatively, if the rope were to break, it could rotate around its end where it is attached to the wall. It turns out that *either* axis of rotation can be used to solve the problem. In fact, *any* axis of rotation could be used. However, if I choose the axis *carefully*, it will make the job *a lot* easier.

Remember how we define torque. We take the force, multiply by the distance to the axis of rotation (the lever arm), and then multiply by the sine of the angle. Well, if we choose the axis of rotation to be a point at which one of the unknown forces attaches, the torque generated by that force will be zero, because the distance between the force and the axis of rotation is zero. Thus, choosing the axis of rotation properly is a great way to get rid of unknown forces in the equation. Since the real mystery force here is F_w, let's choose the axis of rotation to be the point at which the rod attaches to the wall. That way, the torque generated by F_w is zero.

Okay, we have defined the axis of rotation. Now we have to define direction. Let's say that clockwise rotation is positive and counterclockwise rotation is negative. That means the block exerts a positive torque (it causes the rod to rotate clockwise about the end attached to the wall) as does the weight of the rod, and the rope exerts a negative torque (it causes the rod to rotate counterclockwise about the end attached to the wall). Thus:

r = distance of rotation

$$\underset{block}{F_b \cdot (r_b) \cdot \sin\theta_b} \overset{cw}{} + \underset{rod}{F_r \cdot (r_{cm}) \cdot \sin\theta_{cm}} \overset{cw}{} - \underset{rope}{T \cdot r_{rope} \cdot \sin\theta_{rope}} \overset{ccw}{} = 0$$

The distance from the axis of rotation to the block is 80.0 cm, so r_b is 0.800 m. The force exerted by the block is its weight, and the angle between the block and the rod is 90.0°. The force exerted by the rod is its weight, its distance is 50.0 cm (the center of the rod), and the angle is also 90.0°. We don't know the tension, but the distance is 50.0 cm (the rope is attached to the center of the rod), and the angle between the rope and the rod is 50.0°. Thus:

$$(1470\ N) \cdot (0.800\ m) \cdot \sin(90.0) + (491\ N) \cdot (0.500\ m) \cdot \sin(90.0) - T \cdot (0.500\ m) \cdot \sin(50.0) = 0$$

$$\underline{T = 3710\ N}$$

The application of static rotational equilibrium, then, allowed us to solve for the tension in the rope. That is, in fact, all that the problem wanted. Thus, had we started with static rotational equilibrium, we would already be done. For completeness sake, however, let's figure out F_w. Using the equation we got from the y-dimension:

$$T \cdot \sin(50.0) + F_{wy} - 491\ N - 1470\ N = 0$$

$$(3710\ N) \cdot \sin(50.0) + F_{wy} - 491\ N - 1470\ N = 0$$

$$F_{wy} = -881\ N$$

The negative means that this component is directed *opposite* of the way we defined it. We said it was pointing up, but since we got a negative answer, it must actually point down. Now let's move to the x-dimension:

$$-T \cdot \cos(50.0) - F_{wx} = 0$$

$$-(3710\ N) \cdot \cos(50.0) - F_{wx} = 0$$

$$F_{wx} = -2380\ N$$

The negative sign once again tells us that the wall force points *opposite* of what we thought. We thought it pointed left, but since we got a negative answer, it must point right. Thus, the arrow I originally drew was not correct. The force of the wall actually pulls slightly down and to the right. If you use the components to calculate the magnitude and direction of the force, you will find that the force is 2.54×10^3 N directed at an angle of 339.7°.

Make sure you can analyze situations like this by performing the following "on your own" problem.

ON YOUR OWN

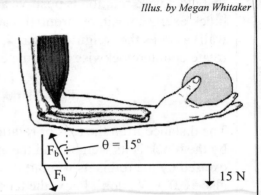

Illus. by Megan Whitaker

5.3 A man holds a 15.0-Newton ball in his hand (38.0 cm from the elbow) with his forearm flexed, as shown in the drawing below. The biceps, which flex the forearm, attach to the forearm roughly 3.50 cm from the elbow and pull at a 15.0° angle relative to the vertical. If the man wants to hold the ball stationary as shown, what force must the biceps exert (F_b)? What force must the arm bone (humerus) exert (F_h)?

A Few Terms in Rotational Motion

Now that you have been reminded that force causes translational acceleration and torque causes rotational acceleration, it should make sense to you that the concepts which apply to force in translational motion also apply to torque in rotational motion. In other words:

Torque is the rotational analogue of force.

For example, you know that Newton's Second Law of motion says that the sum of the forces on an object is equal to the mass of the object times its acceleration. Well, there is a "rotational motion version" of Newton's Second Law as well:

The sum of the *torques* on an object is equal to the *moment of inertia* of the object times the *angular acceleration* of the object.

To fully understand this statement, of course, you need to learn what **moment of inertia** and **angular acceleration** mean. I will explain those terms in a moment. I just want you to see the similarity of this statement and Newton's Second Law. This statement is essentially the same as Newton's Second Law, except that "force" has been replaced by "torque," "mass" has been replaced by "moment of inertia," and "acceleration" has been replaced by "angular acceleration." I will come back to this important point later.

First, I want to explain angular acceleration. In your first-year course, you probably learned about **angular velocity**. To remind you about that, you need to remember something about rotational motion.

FIGURE 5.3
Angular Velocity

Imagine a wheel that has a stripe along its radius. If the stripe starts out pointing directly up and the wheel beings to rotate, the position of the stripe will change:

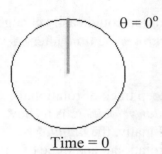
$\theta = 0°$

Time = 0

The stripe points straight up.

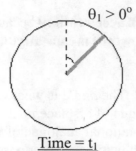
$\theta_1 > 0°$

Time = t_1

The stripe has moved so that it is at an angle relative to its original position.

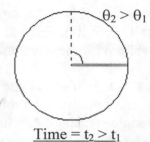
$\theta_2 > \theta_1$

Time = $t_2 > t_1$

The stripe has moved so that the angle relative to its original position is larger.

In rotational motion, you can keep track of how much an object has rotated by looking at how the *angle* has changed with respect to a specific point in time. In the figure above, the stripe starts out pointing straight up. However, as the wheel rotates, the stripe makes an angle with its original position. The more that the wheel rotates, the larger the angle becomes.

Thus, *angle* is a way to keep track of rotational motion. If an object rotates through an angle of $90.0°$ ($\frac{1}{2}\pi$ radians), you know that it has completed ¼ of a full rotation. An angular revolution of $180.0°$ (π radians) means half of a rotation, and if the wheel moves through an angle of $360.0°$ (2π radians), it makes one full revolution. Now compare that to translational motion. When an object moves from place to place, displacement is used to keep track of the object as it moves. Thus, in translational motion, we look at *displacement*. However, in rotational motion, we keep track of the object by looking at *angle*, not displacement.

What is angular velocity, then? Angular velocity (abbreviated with the lower case Greek letter omega, ω), is a measure of the rate at which the angle changes. Mathematically:

$$\omega = \frac{\Delta\theta}{\Delta t} \quad average \tag{5.3}$$

Remember, just as velocity can change over a given time frame, angular velocity can change as well. Thus, Equation (5.3) gives you the ***average* angular velocity** over the time interval. The smaller the time interval, the closer you come to measuring the ***instantaneous* angular velocity**.

All of that should be review for you. However, your first-year physics course probably did not discuss the concept of angular acceleration, so I will do that now. Angular acceleration (abbreviated with the lower case Greek letter alpha, α) is the change in angular velocity:

$$\alpha = \frac{\Delta\omega}{\Delta t} \quad average \tag{5.4}$$

Once again, this is the **average angular acceleration**, because acceleration could easily change over a given time interval. To get the **instantaneous angular acceleration**, the time interval would have to be infinitesimally small.

Do you see a pattern emerging? The *angle* is what we use to keep track of rotational motion. Thus, it is the rotational analogue of displacement. The *angular velocity* tells us how the angle is changing. Thus, it is the rotational analogue of velocity. Finally, the *angular acceleration* tells us how the angular velocity is changing, so it is the rotational analogue of acceleration. Since angle, angular velocity, and angular acceleration are simply the rotational "versions" of displacement, velocity, and acceleration, you might expect that there is a relationship between a translational quantity (like displacement) and its rotational analogue (like angle). Indeed, there is. These rotational analogues are all related to the corresponding translational quantity by the radius of the object that is rotating:

$$s = r \cdot \theta \tag{5.5}$$

$$v = r \cdot \omega \tag{5.6}$$

$$a = r \cdot \alpha \tag{5.7}$$

In these equations, "s" is the distance that a given point on the object moves as it is rotating. We use the symbol "s" rather than "x" because "x" is typically considered a linear distance. When an object is rotating, a point on that object will not travel a linear distance. Instead, it will follow an arc. The letter "s" is typically used as an abbreviation for **arc length**, which is the length of an arc swept out by an object moving in a circle. It is still a term that means "distance," but that distance is around an arc, not along a straight line.

Now that you have learned about angular acceleration, I want to explain moment of inertia. In Module #3, you learned about inertial mass. It was defined as a measure of an object's resistance to a change in its motion. In other words, the greater the mass, the harder it is to accelerate the object. Well, moment of inertia is a measure of an object's resistance to a change in its *rotational* motion:

Moment of inertia- A measure of an object's resistance to a change in its state of rotational
                    motion

Thus, the larger the moment of inertia, the harder it is to cause its rotation to change. Once again, then, we find that a physical quantity in rotational motion is an analogue of a physical quantity in translational motion. The *moment of inertia* is the rotational analogue of *mass*.

Now if you think about it, there are three factors which affect how difficult it is to change the rotation of an object. First, the mass plays a role. The more massive an object, the harder it will be to change the object's rotation. Second, the shape plays a role. Some shapes are just easier to rotate than others. Third, the *axis* about which the rotation occurs is also important.

When you take calculus, you will actually learn how you can use integration to determine the moment of inertia for any object. For right now, however, here is a figure that lists the moment of inertia (abbreviated as "I") for many common shapes. There is no need to memorize this figure. The information it contains will be provided on the test.

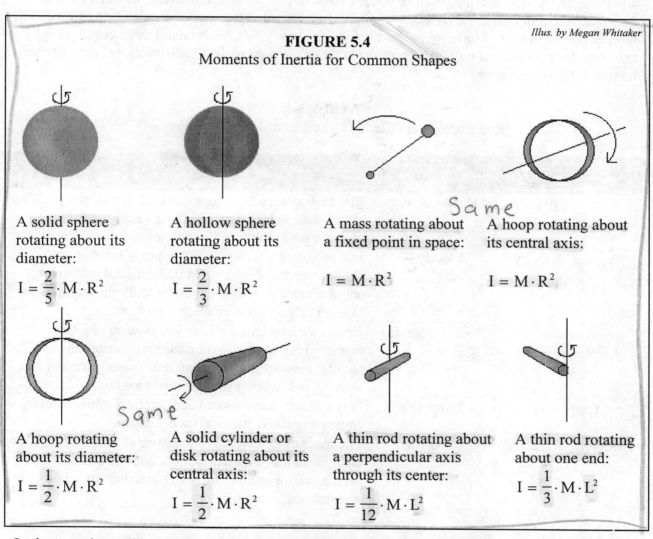

FIGURE 5.4
Moments of Inertia for Common Shapes

Illus. by Megan Whitaker

A solid sphere rotating about its diameter:
$$I = \frac{2}{5} \cdot M \cdot R^2$$

A hollow sphere rotating about its diameter:
$$I = \frac{2}{3} \cdot M \cdot R^2$$

A mass rotating about a fixed point in space:
$$I = M \cdot R^2$$

A hoop rotating about its central axis:
$$I = M \cdot R^2$$

A hoop rotating about its diameter:
$$I = \frac{1}{2} \cdot M \cdot R^2$$

A solid cylinder or disk rotating about its central axis:
$$I = \frac{1}{2} \cdot M \cdot R^2$$

A thin rod rotating about a perpendicular axis through its center:
$$I = \frac{1}{12} \cdot M \cdot L^2$$

A thin rod rotating about one end:
$$I = \frac{1}{3} \cdot M \cdot L^2$$

In the equations, "I" represents the moment of inertia; "M" represents the mass of the object; "R" is the radius; and "L" is the length.

Now don't get lost in all of the terminology and equations. Remember, the moment of inertia is simply a measure of how an object resists changes to its rotational motion. For example, suppose you had two spheres of equal mass and radius but one was solid while the other was hollow. If both were rotating about their diameters, and you tried to stop them from rotating, which would be harder to stop? Well, if you look at Figure 5.4, you will see that the moment of inertia of a solid sphere rotating about its diameter is $\frac{2}{5} \cdot M \cdot R^2$, while the moment of inertia of a hollow sphere rotating about its diameter is $\frac{2}{3} \cdot M \cdot R^2$. Since the mass and radius is the same for both spheres, the hollow sphere has the larger moment of inertia, since $\frac{2}{3}$ is greater than $\frac{2}{5}$. Thus, the hollow sphere would be harder to stop. That's what moment of inertia tells you.

We will use moment of inertia and angular acceleration in the analysis of physical situations in the next section. Before you move on to that section, however, you need to make sure that you understand the concepts of angle, angular velocity, angular acceleration, torque, and moment of inertia. As I have mentioned before, the best way to understand these concepts is by analogue to translational motion. Thus, the table below summarizes each rotational quantity and its translational analogue.

TABLE 5.1
Rotational Quantities and Their Translational Analogues

Rotational Quantity	Translational Analogue	Meaning
Angle (θ)	Displacement (x)	Just as displacement keeps track of an object's position in translational motion, the angle keeps track of the object's position in rotational motion.
Angular Velocity (ω)	Velocity (v)	Just as velocity tells you how quickly an object's displacement is changing in translational motion, angular velocity tells you how quickly the angle of an object is changing in rotational motion.
Angular Acceleration (α)	Acceleration (a)	Just as the acceleration tells you how an object's velocity is changing in translational motion, the angular acceleration tells you how quickly the angular velocity is changing in rotational motion.
Torque (τ)	Force (F)	Force causes translational acceleration, while torque causes angular (rotational) acceleration.
Moment of Inertia (I)	Mass (m)	The mass of an object is a measure of how it resists changes in translational motion, and the moment of inertia is a measure of how an object resists changes to its rotational motion.

ON YOUR OWN

5.4 A hoop is exposed to a torque so that it rotates around its central axis. The same hoop is then stopped and exposed to the same magnitude of torque, but the torque is oriented so that the hoop spins about its diameter. In which of the two situations will the angular acceleration be greater?

Rotational Dynamics

In the previous section, I already mentioned that Newton's Second Law also applies to rotational motion, as long as you replace the translational motion terms with their rotational analogues. As a result, in rotational motion, we say that the sum of the torques on an object is equal to the moment of inertia times the angular acceleration. In mathematical terms, we would say:

$$\tau_{net} = I \cdot \alpha \tag{5.8}$$

where "τ_{net}" is the sum of the torques, "I" is the moment of inertia, and "α" is the angular acceleration.

Equation (5.8) explains why the sum of the torques on an object must be zero if it is in static rotational equilibrium (not rotating). After all, if the sum of the torques were not zero, the object would be experiencing angular acceleration, which means it would be rotating. Of course, even if the sum of the torques is zero, the object *could still rotate*. After all, if the sum of the *forces* on an object is zero, the object is either not moving or moving with constant velocity (no acceleration). In the same way, if the sum of the *torques* on an object is zero, the object is either not rotating, or it is rotating with a constant angular velocity (no angular acceleration). If the latter is the case, we say that the object is in **dynamic rotational equilibrium** because it is rotating, but since there is no net torque on the object, its angular acceleration is zero.

How do we use Equation (5.8)? Not surprisingly, we use it a lot like we use Equation (3.1), which is its translational analogue. Study the following example to see what I mean.

EXAMPLE 5.3

A mass (m = 20.0 kg) hangs on a string that has been wrapped several times around a pulley (M = 500.0 g, r = 35.0 cm). At first, the pulley is held so that the system is not moving in any way. When the pulley is released, what is the angular acceleration of the pulley and the acceleration of the mass? Neglect friction and the mass of the string, and assume that the string never slips on the pulley.

If we were not dealing with the rotation of the pulley, this would be an easy problem. The only force acting on the block would be gravity, and the acceleration of the mass would be equal to g. However, since the pulley must rotate, its moment of inertia resists a change in its rotational motion. As a result, a tension develops on the string. This tension works against gravity. The resulting force diagram for the mass is shown on the right. This force diagram leads to the following equation:

$$T - m \cdot g = m \cdot a$$

Note that this equation tells you that I have defined upward motion as positive.

This gives us one equation, but there are two unknowns, because we do not know the value of T or a. Luckily, however, this is not the only equation. We have another body to consider - that of the pulley. The pulley is also exposed to a force, as shown in the diagram on the right. In this diagram, the string pulls down on the pulley at a distance away from its axis of rotation. Thus, the tension on the string provides a torque. Since the string pulls along a line tangent to the disk, and since the radius of any circle or disk is always perpendicular to any line drawn tangent to the circle or disk, the force that the tension exerts is perpendicular to the radius. As a result, the angle between **T** and **r** is 90.0 degrees, and Equation (5.2) becomes.

$$\tau = r \cdot F \cdot \sin\theta = (-T) \cdot r$$

bcuz it points down

where T is the tension of the string and r is the radius of the disk. Why do I have -T instead of T in this equation? Remember, up is positive. Thus, down is negative. That means the force that supplies the torque is -T, not T: We can take this equation and substitute it into Equation (5.8):

$$\tau_{net} = I \cdot \alpha$$

$$(-T) \cdot r = I \cdot \alpha$$

Since we know the shape, mass, and radius of the pulley, we can use Figure 5.4 to determine I. Thus, we really know I. We also know r. Thus, we have two unknowns in this equation - T and α. At this point, you might think we are stuck because we have two equations, but we have three unknowns (T, a, and α). However, you are forgetting that α is related to a via Equation (5.7):

$$a = r \cdot \alpha$$

Solving this equation for α gives us:

$$\alpha = \frac{a}{r}$$

Putting that into the Equation (5.8) gives us:

$$(-T) \cdot r = I \cdot \frac{a}{r}$$

Now we have two equations and two unknowns. Before we do the algebra, let's just remind ourselves of the two equations. The first comes from summing up the forces on the mass:

$$T - m \cdot g = m \cdot a$$

The second comes from summing up the torques on the pulley:

$$(-T) \cdot r = I \cdot \frac{a}{r}$$

We know m, g, and r, and we can determine I from Figure 5.4. Thus, the only unknowns are T and a. Let's solve for T in terms of a from the first equation:

$$T = m \cdot a + m \cdot g$$

Now let's put that into the second equation:

$$-(m \cdot a + m \cdot g) \cdot r = I \cdot \frac{a}{r}$$

$$-m \cdot a \cdot r - I \cdot \frac{a}{r} = m \cdot g \cdot r$$

$$m \cdot a \cdot r^2 + I \cdot a = -m \cdot g \cdot r^2$$

$$a = \frac{-m \cdot g \cdot r^2}{m \cdot r^2 + I}$$

Since the pulley is a disk rotating about its central axis, its moment of inertia (I), according to Figure 5.4 is given by:

$$I = \frac{1}{2} \cdot M \cdot R^2 = \frac{1}{2} \cdot (0.5000 \text{ kg}) \cdot (0.350 \text{ m})^2 = 0.0306 \text{ kg} \cdot \text{m}^2$$

Notice the unit on moment of inertia. Although the equation for moment of inertia changes, its standard unit is always $kg \cdot m^2$. Now that we have a number for I, we can calculate a:

$$a = \frac{-m \cdot g \cdot r^2}{m \cdot r^2 + I} = \frac{-(20.0 \text{ kg}) \cdot (9.81 \frac{m}{sec^2}) \cdot (0.350 \text{ m})^2}{(20.0 \text{ kg}) \cdot (0.350 \text{ m})^2 + 0.0306 \text{ kg} \cdot \text{m}^2} = -9.69 \frac{m}{sec^2}$$

Notice two things about the acceleration. First, it is negative. That makes sense, since I defined upward motion as positive. The mass obviously travels downwards, so the acceleration must be negative. Also, notice that it is just slightly smaller than g. This should make sense. After all, the motion of the pulley takes some energy away from the motion of the mass. Thus, the acceleration of the mass is slightly lower than it would be if the mass were to fall freely. The more massive the pulley and the larger the pulley's radius, the smaller the acceleration would be, because it would take more energy to get the pulley spinning.

What about the angular acceleration of the pulley? That's easy. The acceleration and angular acceleration are related by Equation (5.7):

$$a = r \cdot \alpha$$

$$\alpha = \frac{a}{r} = \frac{-9.69 \frac{m}{sec^2}}{0.350 \text{ m}} = -27.7 \frac{rad}{sec^2}$$

I will explain the unit in a moment. First, let's just review what we did. We used our knowledge of Newtons' Second Law and applied it both to translational motion (the motion of the mass) and rotational motion (the motion of the pulley) to give us a more accurate analysis of a system. The more accurate analysis tells us that the mass accelerates at -9.69 m/sec^2 and the pulley has an angular acceleration of -27.7 rad/sec^2.

Now what about that unit for angular acceleration? As you should recall from geometry, a "radian" is a measure of angle. An angle of $2 \cdot \pi$ radians, for example, is the same as 360.0°. An angle of π radians is 180.0°. When converting from translational motion into rotational motion, the radian unit must be inserted in place of "1" to preserve the integrity of the units. Thus, even though the math makes the units work out to 1/sec^2, the unit of radian is inserted in place of "1" in order to get rad/sec^2. In the same way, when converting from rotational motion into translational motion, the unit radian must be replaced with "1." For example, if you plugged numbers into Equation (5.7), you would get a unit of m·rad/sec^2 for acceleration. Instead, the unit radian is replaced by "1", to make m/sec^2.

Why do we have to do this? Well, geometry defines angle as the ratio of the arc length to the radius of a circle. Both of these quantities are measured in meters. Thus, when you divided arc length by radius, the units cancel and you are left with a number that has no units. This is called a **dimensionless quantity**. Physicists cannot stand to see a measurement without units, however. Thus, they insert "radian" where there is no unit. There is no problem with that if you deal purely with rotational motion. However, when you covert from rotational motion to translational motion (or vice versa), you run into a problem with the unit radian. Thus, you remove it when going from rotational motion to translational motion, and you add it when going from translational motion to rotational motion. You will get used to this as you do more problems.

Let's try one more problem to make sure you really understand this. We'll go back to an earlier system we analyzed (Atwood's machine), and see how much the analysis changes when considering the rotational motion of the pulley.

EXAMPLE 5.4

Let's consider Atwood's machine, but this time, we will include the rotation of the pulley. We ignored it the last time, but that's not really correct. Let's see how much the results change when we analyze the situation more correctly. The machine has two masses (m_1 and m_2). The pulley has mass M and radius r. What is the acceleration of the masses in terms of m_1, m_2, r, M, and g?

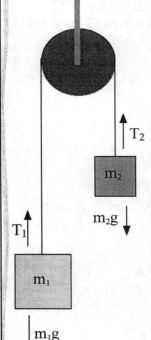

When we dealt with Atwood's machine in Module #3 (Example 3.2), we determined that the acceleration of the masses was:

$$a = \left(\frac{m_2 - m_1}{m_1 + m_2} \right) \cdot g$$

This, of course, is not quite right. How does the motion of the pulley affect Atwood's machine? Well, think about the torques on the pulley as shown on the right. There is one torque (T_1) trying to make the pulley rotate counterclockwise and another torque (T_2) trying to make the pulley rotate clockwise. They each act at the same distance (r) from the axis of rotation. If $T_1 = T_2$, the pulley would not rotate, because there would be two equal torques trying to get the pulley to rotate in opposite directions. Thus, the tension in the string on one side of the pulley (the side with the heavier mass) must be greater than the tension in the string on the other side of the pulley (the side with the lighter mass). *That's* where the motion of the pulley affects our analysis of Atwood's machine. When we did not consider the motion of the pulley, we just assumed that the tension along the string is constant. That's not true. The motion of the pulley makes the tension in the string different on one side than it is on the other. Thus, we really have three unknowns in our problem: T_1, T_2, and a. Let's reanalyze Atwood's machine taking this into account.

Looking at mass 1 and defining upward motion as positive (as we did in Module #3), we get:

Mass 1 $T_1 - m_1 \cdot g = m_1 \cdot a$

Looking at mass 2, we realize that *downward* motion of m_2 is the same as upward motion of m_1. Thus, downward motion of m_2 is positive:

Mass 2 $m_2 \cdot g - T_2 = m_2 \cdot a$

The last equation comes from looking at the pulley. T_1 and T_2 both exert torques on the pulley. T_1 is negative, but T_2 is positive because downward motion on that side of the pulley is positive. This should make sense, since the torques must have opposite signs because they cause the pulley to rotate in opposite directions. Since the tensions pull perpendicular to the radius, the torques are easy to calculate from Equation (5.2):

$$-r \cdot T_1 + r \cdot T_2 = I \cdot \alpha$$

Since α and acceleration are related through Equation (5.7), we can substitute for α:

$$-r \cdot T_1 + r \cdot T_2 = I \cdot \frac{a}{r}$$

We can calculate I by looking at Figure 5.4 again, so now we have three unknowns (T_1, T_2, and a) and three equations. That makes the math annoying, but not impossible! Let's use the equation from m_1 to solve for T_1 in terms of a:

$$T_1 = m_1 \cdot a + m_1 \cdot g$$

Now, let's use the equation from m_2 to get T_2 in terms of a:

$$T_2 = m_2 \cdot g - m_2 \cdot a$$

Finally, we can take these equations for T_1 and T_2 and plug them into the equation from the rotation of the pulley. That will then allow us to solve for a:

$$-r \cdot (m_1 \cdot a + m_1 \cdot g) + r \cdot (m_2 \cdot g - m_2 \cdot a) = I \cdot \frac{a}{r}$$

$$r^2 \cdot m_2 \cdot g - r^2 \cdot m_1 \cdot g = a \cdot (m_1 \cdot r^2 + m_2 \cdot r^2 + I)$$

$$a = \frac{r^2 \cdot m_2 - r^2 \cdot m_1}{m_1 \cdot r^2 + m_2 \cdot r^2 + I} \cdot g$$

We are actually almost done. We have the acceleration in terms of r, m_1, m_2, and g. We just need to replace I with something else. We can do that by looking at Figure 5.4 and realizing that the pulley is a disk rotating on its central axis. Thus, I $=\frac{1}{2}\cdot M \cdot r^2$.

$$a = \frac{r^2 \cdot m_2 - r^2 \cdot m_1}{m_1 \cdot r^2 + m_2 \cdot r^2 + I} \cdot g$$

$$a = \frac{\cancel{r}^2 \cdot m_2 - \cancel{r}^2 \cdot m_1}{m_1 \cdot \cancel{r}^2 + m_2 \cdot \cancel{r}^2 + \frac{1}{2}\cdot M \cdot \cancel{r}^2} \cdot g$$

$$a = \left(\frac{m_2 - m_1}{m_1 + m_2 + \frac{1}{2}\cdot M}\right)\cdot g$$

Now notice the difference between this equation and the one that we derived without considering the rotation of the pulley. The only difference is the $-\frac{1}{2}\cdot M$ term in the denominator of the fraction. What does this term do? Well, the more massive the pulley, the lower the acceleration. That should make sense. The more massive the pulley, the more it will resist the motion. Also, notice that if the pulley has no mass (M= 0), this equation turns into the original equation we derived. This should also make sense. If the mass of the pulley were zero (impossible, of course), then its moment of inertia ($\frac{1}{2}\cdot M \cdot r^2$) would be zero, and it would not resist change in its rotational state. Thus, it would not affect the acceleration of the masses.

Make sure you can analyze systems like this by solving the following "on your own" problems.

ON YOUR OWN

5.5 Consider the system shown on the right. You have analyzed it before, but you have ignored the mass of the pulley. Suppose m_1 = 20.0 kg, m_2 = 20.0 kg, and the pulley has a mass of 1.00 kg and a radius of 10.0 cm. Ignoring friction and the mass of the string, what are the acceleration of the system, the angular acceleration of the pulley, and the tensions in the string?

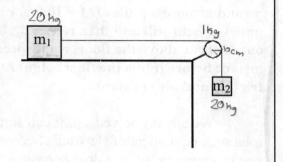

5.6 Two masses are hung from strings wound around a cylinder (mass = M, radius = R) which rotates without friction around its central axis. Develop an equation in terms of m_1, m_2, M, R, and g for the acceleration of the masses as they descend.

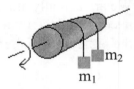

5.7. Given that m_1 = 1.00 kg, m_2 = 750.0 g, M = 450.0 g, and R = 15.0 cm, determine the angular acceleration of the cylinder.

Rotational Energy

In both Example 5.4 and "on your own" problem 5.5, when the rotation of the pulley is included in the analysis, the resulting acceleration is *lower* than the results of an analysis which does not consider the rotation of the pulley. Why? Well, it takes energy to rotate the pulley. How much energy? That's an easy question to answer. Remember, translational kinetic energy is given by $\frac{1}{2} \cdot m \cdot v^2$. Considering the analogues between translational and rotational motion, it should be easy to understand that the **rotational kinetic energy** of an object is given by:

$$KE_{rot} = \frac{1}{2} \cdot I \cdot \omega^2 \tag{5.9}$$

Notice that since the units on I are $kg \cdot m^2$ and the units of ω are rad/sec, the units resulting in this equation are $\dfrac{kg \cdot m^2 \cdot rad^2}{sec^2}$. However, we drop the radian unit (since it represents a dimensionless quantity), giving us $\dfrac{kg \cdot m^2}{sec^2}$, which is the same thing as a Joule. Thus, as you would expect, the unit for rotational kinetic energy is the Joule. Let's see how to take rotational energy into account when analyzing situations which involve rotational motion.

EXAMPLE 5.5

A mass (m = 150.0 g) is attached to a string which is wound around a pulley (M = 10.0 g, r = 11.0 cm). The pulley is held still and then released. If the mass started out 35.0 cm above the floor, what speed will it have the instant before it hits the floor? Ignore energy losses due to friction and air resistance.

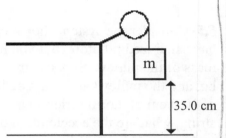

We already solved a problem similar to this using the rotational equivalent of Newton's Second Law. However, we can solve this problem using energy concepts, since it does not ask about acceleration. It asks only about speed. Think about the total energy of the system before it is released. The pulley is not moving, and neither is the mass. Thus, the only energy is the potential energy of the mass:

$$TE = m \cdot g \cdot h$$

Right before the mass hits the floor, there will be no potential energy, but there will be kinetic energy. The mass will be moving, so it has kinetic energy. However, the pulley will be rotating as well. Thus, *the pulley* will also have kinetic energy. Thus, the total energy will be:

$$TE = \frac{1}{2} \cdot m \cdot v^2 + \frac{1}{2} \cdot I \cdot \omega^2$$

Since there is no energy loss due to friction, the total energy must be the same at all times.

$$m \cdot g \cdot h = \frac{1}{2} \cdot m \cdot v^2 + \frac{1}{2} \cdot I \cdot \omega^2$$

Since the pulley is a disk, we know its moment of inertia is $\frac{1}{2} \cdot M \cdot r^2$. Also, Equation (5.6) gives us a relationship between ω and v. We can substitute these into the equation above to give us:

$$m \cdot g \cdot h = \frac{1}{2} \cdot m \cdot v^2 + \frac{1}{2} \cdot (\frac{1}{2} \cdot M \cdot r^2) \cdot (\frac{v}{r})^2$$

The only thing we don't know is v, so we can solve for it:

$$m \cdot g \cdot h = \frac{1}{2} \cdot m \cdot v^2 + \frac{1}{2} \cdot (\frac{1}{2} \cdot M \cdot \cancel{r^2}) \cdot (\frac{v}{\cancel{r}})^2$$

why only one?

$$v^2 \cdot (\frac{1}{2} \cdot m + \frac{1}{4} \cdot M) = m \cdot g \cdot h$$

$$v = \sqrt{\frac{m \cdot g \cdot h}{\frac{1}{2} \cdot m + \frac{1}{4} \cdot M}} = \sqrt{\frac{(0.1500\,\text{kg}) \cdot (9.81\,\frac{m}{\sec^2}) \cdot (0.350\,m)}{\frac{1}{2} \cdot (0.1500\,\text{kg}) + \frac{1}{4} \cdot (0.0100\,\text{kg})}} = 2.58\,\frac{m}{\sec^2}$$

Had we not considered the pulley, the speed would have been 2.62 m/sec². Notice that the radius of the pulley cancels out of the final equation. Thus, the radius of the pulley does not affect the speed of the system.

Now please understand that many of the motion problems you will analyze will involve *both* translational motion and rotational motion. If part or all of a system has translational motion, you must take it into account in the energy equations. If part or all of a system has rotational motion, you must also take that into account in the energy equations. A car, for example, has translational energy as it moves down the street, but its wheels have rotational energy. If you were to analyze the energy supplied by the engine, you would have to take into account the fact that some of the energy causes the rotational motion of the wheels and some of it causes the translational motion of the car.

Make sure you understand how to include rotational energy in the analysis of a system by solving the following "on your own" problems.

ON YOUR OWN

5.8 A sphere, a disk, and a hoop all sit at the top of a ramp, as shown to the right. Each of these objects have equal mass.

a. Which will make it to the bottom of the ramp first? Which will make it there last?

b. If the height of the ramp is 1.00 m, what will the speed of the hoop be as it reaches the bottom? Ignore any losses due to friction.

c. Even though you were told to ignore the losses due to friction in the problem above, if this is a rotational motion problem, we _must_ assume that there is friction. Why?

Angular Momentum

We have one more rotational analogue to discuss, and that is **angular momentum**. You probably learned something about angular momentum in your first-year course, but I want to delve a bit deeper into it. First of all, you need to know the formula for angular momentum:

$$\mathbf{L} = \mathbf{r} \times \mathbf{p} \tag{5.10}$$

In this equation, "**L**" is the angular momentum, "**r**" is the radius of the angular motion, and "**p**" is the translational momentum of a point on the edge of the object which is rotating. Notice that all of the quantities are vectors, because the cross product of two vectors gives us a vector whose direction is given by the right hand rule, as discussed in Module #1.

Now you might be a bit confused at this point if you remember what you learned in your first-year course, since this equation is probably a bit different than the one you learned before. However, I want to show you that the equation you learned before is simply a special case of this more general equation. In your first-year physics course, you probably learned about the angular momentum of an object involved in circular motion.

FIGURE 5.5
Circular Motion and Angular Momentum

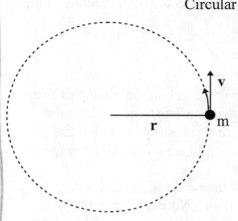

When an object moves in a circle, its velocity vector is always tangent to the circle. Thus, the angle between the radius of the circle and the velocity is 90°. Since the magnitude of the cross product can be given by Equation (1.9), we know that the magnitude of the angular momentum can be calculated as:

$$L = r \cdot p \cdot \sin(90) = r \cdot p$$

Since the translational momentum of an object is $m \cdot v$, the magnitude of the angular momentum in this situation is:

$$L = m \cdot v \cdot r$$

Most likely, the equation you learned for angular momentum in your first-year course is the one at the bottom of the figure. Now you see that this equation is really just a special case of the more general equation for angular momentum, Equation (5.10).

Before I go any further, let me make sure you remember how to use the **right hand rule**. In the figure above, we know that the magnitude of the angular momentum vector is $m \cdot v \cdot r$, but what is its direction? That is determined by the right hand rule. Stick the fingers of your right hand in the direction of **r**, and then curl them along the arc of the angle between **v** and **r**. Your thumb then points in the direction of the angular momentum. Thus, the angular momentum vector has a magnitude of $m \cdot v \cdot r$ and a direction that is coming out of the plane of the paper, perpendicular to both **r** and **v**.

Why is the direction of the angular momentum important? Well, like translational momentum (**p**), angular momentum (**L**) is conserved when no external torques are acting on the system. Not surprisingly, this is called **the conservation of angular momentum**.

Conservation of angular momentum - In the absence of external torques, the angular momentum of a system cannot change.

Now remember, since angular momentum is a vector, in order for it to be conserved, *neither* the magnitude *nor* the direction can change. To see the consequences of this, perform the following experiment.

EXPERIMENT 5.3
The Direction of the Angular Momentum Vector

Supplies

- The front wheel from a bicycle.
- A helper
- A chair or stool that spins around (optional)

Introduction - The direction of the angular momentum vector is hard to visualize, but it is quite easy to feel, given the right conditions.

Procedure:

1. Take the wheel and hold it with both hands. You should be able to hold onto the part that attaches to the bicycle. Grab it with one hand on the part that attaches to one side of the bicycle and the other hand on the part that attaches to the other side. If you are holding it properly, the wheel should be able to spin freely on its axle, and the wheel will be between your arms.
2. Make sure that the wheel is not spinning and turn it so that the wheel is parallel to the floor.
3. Next, turn the wheel so that it is now perpendicular to the floor. Note how easy that was.
4. Next, turn the wheel so that it is once again parallel to the floor and have your helper start spinning the wheel as fast as he can. **Be careful here. If you lose your grip on the wheel, someone could get hurt!**
5. Once the wheel is spinning, have your helper stand back and once again, try to turn the wheel so that it is perpendicular to the floor. Note how much harder it is to turn the wheel.
6. (Steps 6 - 8 are optional. You should read them even if you do not do them, however.) Sit on a chair that spins, lifting your feet up off of the floor so that the chair will spin easily. Make sure the chair and the wheel are not moving.
7. Once again, hold the wheel so that it is parallel to the floor and have your helper start spinning the wheel as fast as he can. **Be careful here. If you lose your grip on the wheel, someone could get hurt!**
8. With your feet still off of the floor, turn the wheel upside down so that it is once again parallel to the floor but spinning in the opposite direction. What happens?
9. Clean everything up, including putting the wheel back on the bicycle.

Did you notice how much more difficult it was to turn the tire while the wheel was spinning? What causes the difficulty? Well, when the tire is spinning, it has angular momentum. What is the direction of the angular momentum? It depends on the way that the tire is spinning. Point the fingers of your right hand from the center of the wheel out and then curl your fingers in the direction that the wheel spins. Your thumb points in the direction of the angular momentum, perpendicular to the wheel. When you turned the wheel, however, the direction of the angular momentum changes to stay perpendicular to the wheel. That goes *against* the conservation of angular momentum. Thus, to turn the wheel, you need to exert a torque. Without the wheel spinning, there is no angular momentum, so turning the wheel is easy. With the wheel spinning, a torque is necessary in order to change the direction of the angular momentum vector. The faster the wheel is spinning, the greater the magnitude of the angular momentum, so the greater the torque required to turn the wheel.

If you did the optional part of the experiment (you should have at least read it), the chair should have started spinning when you turned the wheel. Why? Well, with your feet off of the ground, you could no longer apply a torque to the system. Thus, when the wheel turned, angular momentum had to be conserved. In order to conserve angular momentum, your chair had to start spinning in order to offset the change induced by turning the wheel. Depending on the friction involved, this might not have been a great effect, because friction applies a torque to the chair. Nevertheless, in a well-oiled chair, you can really start spinning this way!

Okay, so the direction of the angular momentum is important, but so is the magnitude. You learned one equation to calculate the magnitude of the angular momentum. For an object moving in a circle, the angular momentum can be calculated as:

$$L = m \cdot v \cdot r \tag{5.11}$$

As we already showed, this equation is really a special case. A more general form of the equation is given by:

$$L = I \cdot \omega \tag{5.12}$$

This equation is applicable to any body that is rotating around a fixed axis. Study the following example to see how to use the concept of angular momentum conservation in analyzing physical situations.

EXAMPLE 5.6

A person (m = 75 kg) stands at the edge of a merry-go-round (a uniform disk, M = 150.0 kg, r = 1.80 m). As the merry-go-round spins freely, the person walks towards the center of the merry-go-round. If the merry-go-round starts out spinning with one revolution every 3.00 seconds, what will its angular velocity be when the person is only 0.500 m from the center?

In this problem, there are two things involved in rotational motion: the merry-go-round and the person. The total angular momentum, then, is:

$$L_{tot} = L_{merry-go-round} + L_{person} = (I_{merry-go-round}) \cdot \omega_{merry-go-round} + (I_{person}) \cdot \omega_{person}$$

The merry-go-round is a disk that is spinning around its central axis. According to Figure 5.4, then, it has a moment of inertia of $\frac{1}{2} \cdot M \cdot r^2$. The person is an object that moves in a circle. Thus, the person's moment of inertia is $M \cdot r^2$, according to Figure 5.4. What about the angular velocity? Well, both the merry-go-round and the person make one revolution every 3.00 seconds. In one revolution, the merry-go-round sweeps out an angle of 2π radians. Thus, the angular velocity is:

$$\omega = \frac{\Delta \theta}{\Delta t} = \frac{2\pi \text{ rad}}{3.00 \text{ sec}} = 2.09 \frac{\text{rad}}{\text{sec}}$$

At the beginning, the man is at the edge of the merry-go-round, so the radius of his motion is the same as the radius of the merry-go-round. The angular momentum is:

at the beginning when the man is standing still.

$$L_{tot} = (\frac{1}{2} \cdot M \cdot r^2) \cdot (2.09 \frac{rad}{sec}) + (m \cdot r^2) \cdot (2.09 \frac{rad}{sec})$$

$$L_{tot} = \frac{1}{2} \cdot (150.0 \text{ kg}) \cdot (1.80 \text{ m})^2 \cdot (2.09 \frac{rad}{sec}) + (75.0 \text{ kg}) \cdot (1.80 \text{ m})^2 \cdot (2.09 \frac{rad}{sec}) = 1016 \frac{kg \cdot m^2}{sec}$$

Once again, the radian unit gets dropped. Now, when the man starts walking, his moment of inertia changes because the radius of his motion changes. That would change the angular momentum, which is not allowed. Thus, the angular velocity changes to compensate. We can calculate how the angular velocity changes by making sure that angular momentum is conserved:

$$L_{tot} = (\frac{1}{2} \cdot M \cdot r^2) \cdot (\omega) + (m \cdot r^2) \cdot (\omega)$$

$$1016 \frac{kg \cdot m^2}{sec} = \frac{1}{2} \cdot (150.0 \text{ kg}) \cdot (1.80 \text{ m})^2 \cdot (\omega) + (75.0 \text{ kg}) \cdot (0.500 \text{ m})^2 \cdot (\omega)$$

$$\omega = \frac{1016 \frac{kg \cdot m^2}{sec}}{\frac{1}{2} \cdot (150.0 \text{ kg}) \cdot (1.80 \text{ m})^2 + (75.0 \text{ kg}) \cdot (0.500 \text{ m})^2} = 3.88 \frac{rads}{sec}$$

Notice that the merry-go-round speeds up from 2.09 rad/sec to 3.88 rad/sec. When the man walks to the center, the total moment of inertia decreases, so the angular velocity must increase so as to keep the angular momentum constant.

Make sure you understand these concepts by solving the following "on your own" problems.

ON YOUR OWN

5.9 A figure skater is spinning on the tip of her skates with her arms folded over her chest. She then stretches her arms out until she is holding them parallel to the ice, fully extended. Ignoring friction, what would happen to the speed at which she is spinning? What would happen if she brought her arms back in again and folded them across her chest?

5.10 Consider the situation discussed in the experiment. A person sits on a chair that is free to spin. The person and the chair form roughly a cylinder which can spin on its central axis. The mass of this "cylinder" is 85.0 kg, and the radius is 15.0 cm. Assume that the person and chair are sitting still. The person holds a wheel as was done in the experiment and has a friend spin the wheel (treat it as a hoop with M = 5.00 kg and r = 13.0 cm) while it is parallel to the ground. If the wheel is rotating at 10.0 revolutions each second, at what angular velocity will the person and chair start spinning if the wheel is turned upside down so that it is parallel to the ground but spinning in the opposite direction?

ANSWERS TO THE ON YOUR OWN PROBLEMS

5.1 a. The raft is uniform, so its center of mass is the very center of the raft. If the raft is 15.0 meters long, that means the center of mass is in the middle of the raft, 7.50 meters from the edge. The man, on the other hand, is 2.50 meters from the edge. In essence, then, we have two masses, 5.00 m from each other, as shown below:

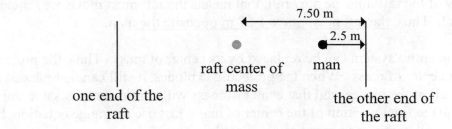

From the right end of the raft, then, the center of mass can be calculated as:

$$x_{cm} = \frac{m_1 \cdot x_1 + m_2 \cdot x_2 + m_3 \cdot x_3 \dots m_n \cdot x_n}{m_1 + m_2 + m_3 \dots m_n} = \frac{(150.0 \text{ kg}) \cdot (7.50 \text{ m}) + (85.0 \text{ kg}) \cdot (2.50 \text{ m})}{150.0 \text{ kg} + 85.0 \text{ kg}} = 5.69 \text{ m}$$

The center of mass of the system is <u>the middle of the raft, 5.69 m from the end that the man is standing near.</u>

b. Think about the situation here. There are no external forces acting on the man/raft system. As a result, momentum is conserved. Initially, the raft and man are motionless, so the momentum is zero. As the man walks, he gains momentum. In order to conserve momentum, the raft will have to move in the other direction.

The problem says that the man walks towards the opposite end so that he ends up 2.5 m from that end. That means he walks a total of 10.0 m. He does this in some time interval, which we will call "t." Thus, his average velocity is 10.0 m/t, resulting in an average momentum of:

$$p_{man} = (85.0 \text{ kg}) \cdot \frac{10.0 \text{ m}}{t}$$

In order to conserve momentum, then, the momentum of the raft must be the opposite. Thus:

$$m_{raft} \cdot v_{raft} = -(85.0 \text{ kg}) \cdot \frac{10.0 \text{ m}}{t}$$

$$(150.0 \text{ kg}) \cdot v_{raft} = -(85.0 \text{ kg}) \cdot \frac{10.0 \text{ m}}{t}$$

$$v_{raft} = -\frac{(85.0 \text{ kg})}{(150.0 \text{ kg})} \cdot \frac{10.0 \text{ m}}{t} = -\frac{5.67 \text{ m}}{t}$$

Since the velocity of the raft must be 5.67 m/t, that means the raft must move 5.67 meters in the same time interval. Thus, the raft must move 5.67 m opposite the man.

5.2 Remember, an entire system can be replaced by its center of mass. Thus, the projectile can be replaced by its center of mass. When the projectile explodes, it still can be replaced by the center of mass of all of the pieces, and that center of mass will continue on its same trajectory. Thus, to determine the final position of the center of mass, just use the range equation, because the center of mass will continue to move as a projectile:

$$R = \frac{(v_o^2) \cdot \sin(2\theta)}{g}$$

$$R = 1380 \text{ m}$$

The center of mass, then, will end up 1380 m from the point at which the projectile was fired.

5.3 In order for the system to not move, the sum of the torques must be zero, and the sum of the forces must be zero. Let's start with the sum of the torques. We can choose any axis of rotation, but the most reasonable one is the elbow. When we do that, the force exerted by the humerus (F_h) disappears, because the distance from the axis is zero. If we define clockwise motion as positive, the sum of the torques becomes:

$$(15.0 \text{ N}) \cdot (38.0 \text{ cm}) - [F_b \cdot \sin(105.0)] \cdot (3.50 \text{ cm}) = 0$$

$$F_b = 169 \text{ N}$$

Notice that the angle I used was 105.0°. That's because the angle is given relative to the vertical. However, that's not the proper definition. The angle must be defined from the horizontal. If the angle relative to the vertical is 90.0°, the angle relative to the horizontal is 90.0° + 15.0°, or 105.0°. Thus, the biceps pull with a force of 169 N at an angle of 105.0° relative to the horizontal.

To get the force that the humerus must exert, we have to sum up the forces in both dimensions. Starting with the horizontal, I will call the horizontal component of the humerus' force F_{hx}. The ball's weight exerts only a vertical force. Thus, we just have to look at the horizontal component of the biceps' force. Now remember, if we use the angles defined properly, then they take care of the signs for us. Thus, I can just add the horizontal component of

F_b, because the properly-defined angle will give you the proper sign. Alternatively, you can use the reference angle ($75.0°$ – the angle from the nearest horizontal) and put the sign in yourself. Since we already have the properly-defined angle, I will use it:

$$F_{hx} \; + \; (169 \text{ N}) \cdot \cos(105.0) = 0$$

$$F_{hx} = 43.7 \text{ N}$$

That's the x-component of the force. To get the y-component, we sum up the forces in the y-dimension:

$$(169 \text{ N}) \cdot \sin(105.0) \; - \; F_{hy} \; - \; 15.0 \text{ N} \; = \; 0$$

$$F_{hy} \; = \; -148 \text{ N}$$

These two components then lead us to <u>a magnitude of 154 N and a direction of 286.5° relative to the positive horizontal</u>.

5.4 Remember, the moment of inertia tells you how much the object resists changes in rotational motion. The more the object resists, the less angular acceleration there will be for the same magnitude of torque. According to Figure 5.4, a hoop that spins about its central axis has a moment of inertia of $M \cdot R^2$. However, when it spins about its diameter, it has a moment of inertia of $\frac{1}{2} \cdot M \cdot R^2$. That means the moment of inertia is *least* when it rotates about its diameter, so <u>the angular acceleration will be greatest when it rotates about its diameter</u>.

5.5 Once we take the pulley into account, the tension of the string on each side of the pulley is different. As a result, the tension that pulls to the right on m_1 (T_1) is different than the tension which pulls up on m_2. If we ignore friction, the only force acting on m_1 is T_1. If we define motion to the right as positive, we get:

only force
$$T_1 \; = \; m_1 \cdot a$$

On mass two, only gravity and T_2 operate. Now, since we defined m_1 moving to the right as positive, that means m_2 moving down is positive. Thus:

2 forces $\Sigma F = ma$
$$m_2 \cdot g \; - \; T_2 \; = \; m_2 \cdot a$$

$$T_2 \; = \; m_2 \cdot g \; - \; m_2 \cdot a$$

When we consider the rotational motion of the pulley, we know that the sum of the torques is equal to the moment of inertia ($\frac{1}{2} \cdot M \cdot R^2$) times the angular acceleration (a/R). Thus, we have the equation:

bcuz of direction of torque
$$T_2 \cdot R - T_1 \cdot R = (\frac{1}{2} \cdot M \cdot R^2) \cdot (\frac{a}{R})$$
Forces   Same as ma

202   Advanced Physics in Creation

Notice that I am using the direction definitions to give me the signs of the torque. Since motion to the right (and down) is positive, T_2 is pulling positively on the pulley and T_1 is pulling negatively on the pulley. If we substitute the equations for T_1 and T_2 that we derived above, we get:

$$(m_2 \cdot g - m_2 \cdot a) \cdot R - (m_1 \cdot a) \cdot R = (\frac{1}{2} \cdot M \cdot R^2) \cdot (\frac{a}{R})$$

$$a = \frac{m_2 \cdot g}{(m_1 + m_2 + \frac{1}{2} \cdot M)}$$

$$a = 4.84 \ \frac{m}{sec^2}$$

Without considering the pulley, the acceleration would have been 4.91m/sec². Now that we have the acceleration, we can get the tensions from the equations above. T_1 = 96.8 N, and T_2 = 99.4 N. The angular acceleration is given by the translational acceleration divided by R, or 48.4 rad/sec².

5.6 Since the angular acceleration of the cylinder will determine the acceleration of the masses, the masses must each have the same acceleration, which we will call "a." This acceleration is the result of two forces working against each other: gravity and the tension in each string. The tension in the string connected to m_1 will be called T_1, and the tension in the string connected to m_2 will be called T_2. Summing up the forces on m_1, calling downward motion negative, gives us:

$$T_1 - m_1 \cdot g = m_1 \cdot a$$

$$T_1 = m_1 \cdot a + m_1 \cdot g$$

Summing up the forces on m_2 gives us:

$$T_2 - m_2 \cdot g = m_2 \cdot a$$

$$T_2 = m_2 \cdot a + m_2 \cdot g$$

That's two equations with three unknowns. However, we can get a third equation from the rotation of the cylinder. The sum of the torques is equal to the moment of inertia ($\frac{1}{2} \cdot M \cdot R^2$) times the angular acceleration (a/R). Thus, we have the equation:

Tension pulls down
$$-T_1 \cdot R - T_2 \cdot R = (\frac{1}{2} \cdot M \cdot R^2) \cdot (\frac{a}{R})$$

Since both tensions pull down on the cylinder, they are negative tensions. If we substitute the equations we already have for those tensions, we will reduce this equation to only one unknown:

$$-(m_1 \cdot a + m_1 \cdot g) \cdot R - (m_2 \cdot a + m_2 \cdot g) \cdot R = (\frac{1}{2} \cdot M \cdot R^2) \cdot (\frac{a}{R})$$

$$a = \frac{-m_1 \cdot g - m_2 \cdot g}{(m_1 + m_2 + \frac{1}{2} \cdot M)}$$

5.7 The best way to get the angular acceleration is to determine the acceleration and then divide by R. The acceleration, according to the equation above, works out to –8.69 m/sec². The negative just means that the masses are accelerating downward. When we divide by R (0.150 m), we get an angular acceleration of -57.9 rad/sec². Once again, the negative sign gives direction. The cylinder rotates clockwise so that the masses fall down.

5.8 a. Think about the energy involved. All three objects start with no kinetic energy and the same potential energy ($M \cdot g \cdot h$). When they get to the bottom, they will each have translational kinetic energy ($\frac{1}{2} \cdot M \cdot v^2$) because they are moving from one point to another. However, they will also have rotational kinetic energy ($\frac{1}{2} \cdot I \cdot \omega^2$). Since they all start with the same total energy, they will all end with the same total energy. However, since the moments of inertia are different, some will have *more* of that energy as rotational kinetic energy, leaving *less* for translational kinetic energy. The one with the least translational kinetic energy will travel slowest. A sphere rotating on its central axis has a moment of inertia of $(2/5) \cdot M \cdot R^2$; a disk rotating that way has a moment of inertia of $\frac{1}{2} \cdot M \cdot R^2$; and a hoop rotating that way has a moment of inertia of $M \cdot R^2$. Thus, the hoop has the highest moment of inertia. This means more energy is needed for the rotational motion, so it has the least translational kinetic energy. In the same way, the sphere has the lowest moment of inertia, so less energy is needed to get it rotating. Thus, it will have the greatest translational kinetic energy. As a result, the hoop will reach the bottom last, while the sphere reaches the bottom first.

b. Remember, we start with a potential energy of $M \cdot g \cdot h$. At the bottom of the ramp, all of that energy is converted to kinetic energy of $\frac{1}{2} \cdot M \cdot v^2 + \frac{1}{2} \cdot I \cdot \omega^2$. We know that $I = M \cdot R^2$ for the hoop and $\omega = \frac{v}{R}$. Thus,

$$M \cdot g \cdot h = \frac{1}{2} \cdot M \cdot v^2 + \frac{1}{2} \cdot I \cdot \omega^2$$

$$M \cdot g \cdot h = \frac{1}{2} \cdot M \cdot v^2 + \frac{1}{2} \cdot (M \cdot R^2) \cdot (\frac{v}{R})^2$$

$$v = \sqrt{g \cdot h} = \sqrt{(9.81 \frac{m}{\sec^2}) \cdot (1.00 \text{ m})} = \underline{3.13 \frac{m}{\sec}}$$

c. In this problem, we assume the sphere, disk, and hoop roll. If there were no friction, they would simply slide, because there would be nothing to provide a torque. After all, gravity works on the center of mass, so it supplies no torque to the objects. Only the friction resulting from the contact of the objects with the ramp generates a torque. Thus, in order for the objects to roll, friction must exist.

5.9 Think about the moments of inertia you have seen so far. They all depend on R^2. Thus, the larger the radius, the larger the moment of inertia. When the skater has her arms tucked into her chest, she has a certain average radius. When she stretches her arms out, that average radius increases. Thus, her moment of inertia increases. If angular momentum ($I \cdot \omega$) must be conserved, then as the moment of inertia increases, the angular acceleration must decrease. As a result, when she stretches out her arms, she will start spinning more slowly. When she pulls them back in, she will start spinning at her original speed.

5.10 The wheel is a hoop. Thus, we can calculate its angular momentum:

$$L = I \cdot \omega = (M \cdot R^2) \cdot \omega$$

We know M and R, and we have what we need to calculate ω. The wheel makes 10.0 revolutions per second. Each revolution sweeps out an angle of 2π radians. Thus, the wheel sweeps out 62.8 radians every second. Thus, the angular velocity is 62.8rad/sec. Now we can determine L:

$$L = (5.00 \text{ kg}) \cdot (0.130 \text{ m})^2 \cdot (62.8 \frac{\text{rad}}{\sec}) = 5.31 \frac{\text{kg} \cdot \text{m}}{\sec^2}$$

Now think about direction. If the wheel is spinning one way, the right hand rule will have the angular momentum pointing directly up. If it is spinning the other way, it will be directly down. When the wheel is flipped over, the direction changes. If it was pointing up before, it points down after. If it pointed down before, it points up after. Suppose it was pointing up before the wheel was flipped. That means $L = +5.31$ kg·m/sec^2 When the wheel is flipped, $L = -5.31$ kg·m/sec^2 (if up is a positive direction then down must be negative). To conserve angular momentum, then, the student on the chair will have to start spinning. In order to keep the angular momentum the same, the student must spin so that he or she has an angular momentum of 10.62 kg·m/sec^2 so that the total angular momentum is 10.62 kg·m/sec^2 + -5.31 kg·m/sec^2, which is 5.31 kg·m/sec^2. Well, now that we know what the student's angular momentum must be, we can determine the student's angular velocity:

$$L = I \cdot \omega = (\tfrac{1}{2} \cdot M \cdot R^2) \cdot \omega$$

$$10.62 \ \frac{\text{kg} \cdot \text{m}}{\text{sec}^2} = \frac{1}{2} \cdot (85.0 \ \text{kg}) \cdot (0.150 \ \text{m})^2 \cdot \omega$$

$$\omega = \underline{11.1 \ \frac{\text{rad}}{\text{sec}}}$$

REVIEW QUESTIONS FOR MODULE #5

1. Imagine two cars approaching one another in opposite directions. The first car is twice as massive as the second car. They move so that the center of mass of the two-car system stays in exactly the same place. What will happen when they collide?

2. For the situation discussed in problem 1, what is the speed of the more massive car relative to that of the lighter car?

3. Is it possible for a system to be in static rotational equilibrium but not be in static translational equilibrium?

4. Suppose a sphere is rolling without slipping down a ramp under the influence of only gravity and is not losing any energy to friction. Is the sphere in dynamic translational equilibrium? Why or why not? Is it in dynamic rotational equilibrium? Why or why not?

5. An object is acted on by only one force. Is it possible for the object to be in any kind of rotational equilibrium? Why or why not?

6. A hollow sphere and a solid sphere each of the same mass are exposed to the same torque. Which will experience the greater angular acceleration?

7. Think about a disk spinning about its central axis at a constant angular velocity. Is it possible for the disk to be experiencing a torque?

8. Imagine that two pennies are sitting on the disk in question #7. Suppose the first penny is close to the center of the disk and the second penny is near the edge of the disk. Compare the angular velocities (ω) of the two pennies. Compare the velocities (v) of the two pennies.

9. In the situation described in question #8, suppose the penny that is near the center of the disk begins to slide so that it moves towards the edge of the disk. What will happen to the angular velocity of the disk?

10. Two identical thin rods are given the same amount of rotational kinetic energy. The first rod spins about a perpendicular axis which passes through its center while the second spins about a perpendicular axis which passes through one of its ends. If the angular velocity of the second rod is ω, what is the angular velocity of the first rod?

PRACTICE PROBLEMS FOR MODULE #5

1. An equilateral triangle is formed by three uniform meter sticks. One of the meter sticks is metal. The other two meter sticks are wooden, and each has a mass that is half that of the metal meter stick. Where is the center of mass of this system relative to the metal meter stick?

2. A uniform, 2.50 m rod (m = 50.0 kg) is attached to a wall at one end. The other end is attached to a cable that attaches to the wall. The cable makes an angle of 30.0° relative to the rod, and the rod is perpendicular to the wall. If a 100.0 kg mass hangs from the center of the rod, what is the tension on the string? What force does the wall apply to the end of the rod?

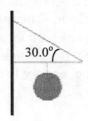

3. A pendulum is constructed of a string (length = 55.0 cm) attached to a bob (m = 50.0 g). The bob is pulled so that the string makes a 25.0° angle relative to its hanging position (dashed line).

a. What is the maximum torque experienced by the bob?
b. What will be the bob's angular acceleration when it experiences the maximum torque?
c. What is the minimum torque experienced by the bob?

4. A piano mover hears that a block-and-tackle system can be used to make lifting heavy objects easier. He constructs the block-and-tackle system shown to the right to lift a grand piano (m = 200.0 kg).

a. If the inner radius of the large pulley is 0.250 meters and the outer radius is 1.00 m, what force (F) will the man need to exert in order to pull the grand piano up at a constant rate?
b. How could the man change the setup to actually make his job easier?

5. A 10.0 kg mass slides down a frictionless ramp as shown to the right. Its acceleration is 3.75 m/sec^2. The mass is attached to a string which is wound around a wheel which spins as the mass falls. If the ramp makes a 25.0° angle with the ground, what is the mass of the wheel? Treat the wheel as a disk rotating about its central axis.

6. A child's top (m = 250.0 g) is a solid sphere (r = 6.00 cm) with a string tied around its center. When the string is pulled, the top spins. Suppose a child pulls in the string with a force of 55.0 N. What would the angular acceleration of the top be?

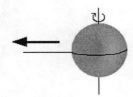

7. Suppose the top in problem #6 was spinning at 5.0 revolutions per second when the string was completely pulled away. What is the angular momentum of the top? Based on the drawing in problem #6, include the direction of the angular momentum.

8. Consider an Atwood's machine. The heavy mass ($m_2 = 25.0$ kg) is held 2.45 m above the ground, and the lighter mass ($m_1 = 10.0$ kg) sits on the floor. The mass is then released and begins to fall. If the pulley has a mass of 5.00 kg and a radius of 75.0 cm, what will be the speed of the heavy mass the instant before it hits the ground? Ignore the mass of the string, energy loss due to friction, and air resistance.

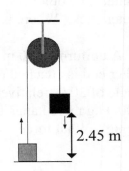

2.45 m

9. A ball is held on an incline at a height of 75.0 cm. It is then released so that it rolls down the incline without slipping. At the bottom of the incline is a loop which the ball rolls around. If the loop is 50.0 cm high at its highest point, what is the speed of the ball at that point?

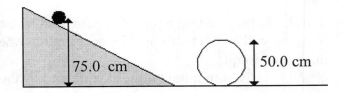

75.0 cm   50.0 cm

10. A large disk ($m = 25.0$ kg, $r = 1.00$ m) is spinning about its central axis at a rate of 10.0 revolutions per minute. A student drops a ball of clay ($m = 2.50$ kg) on the disk as it spins. The ball sticks on the disk at a radius of 0.750 m from the center. Ignoring friction and assuming that there are no net torques acting on the system, how many revolutions per minute will the disk make after the clay has been dropped?

Module #6: Oscillations and Waves

Introduction

In the previous module, you learned a lot about rotational motion. I now want to extend that subject into a discussion of **oscillations**. Wait a minute. What do oscillations have to do with rotational motion? Well, consider an object moving in a circle with a constant speed. That's a form of rotational motion, right? What happens if I project that rotational motion into one dimension? Look at the figure below.

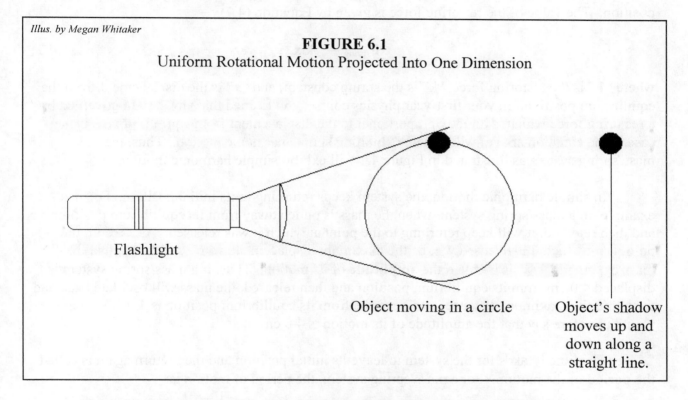

Illus. by Megan Whitaker

FIGURE 6.1
Uniform Rotational Motion Projected Into One Dimension

Flashlight

Object moving in a circle

Object's shadow moves up and down along a straight line.

If the object is moving along its circular path at constant speed (obviously *not* constant velocity), it will always take the object the same amount of time to make a full circle. If you project that motion into one dimension, when the object starts out at the top of the circle, it will be at the top of the one-dimensional projection. When it reaches the top of the circle again, it will reach the top of the one-dimensional projection again. Thus, it will travel down to the bottom of the one-dimensional projection and then back up to the top. It will always take the same amount of time to make this trip, because the object always takes the same amount of time to make one trip around the circle. You should recognize the kind of motion that occurs in one dimension. It is called **simple harmonic motion**, and you learned a lot about that kind of motion in your first-year physics course.

In this module, I want to start with simple harmonic motion, but I don't want to spend a lot of time on it because, well, it's…simple. Thus, I want to run through a real quick review of it and add some more concepts. After that, I want to move on to a general discussion of waves, which represent, of course, another type of oscillation.

The Mass/Spring System

In your first-year course, you learned about the mass/spring system as an example of simple harmonic motion. In Module #4, I discussed two aspects of such a system. First, I discussed how the spring generates a **restoring force** when it is stretched beyond its equilibrium position. The value of the restoring force is given by Equation (4.7):

$$\mathbf{F}_{spring} = -k \cdot \mathbf{x} \tag{4.7}$$

where "$\mathbf{F}$" is the restoring force, "k" is the spring constant, and "$\mathbf{x}$" is the displacement from the equilibrium position. In your first-year physics course, you learned that any system governed by a restoring force which is directly proportional to the displacement from equilibrium (as is the case in the equation above) will end up exhibiting simple harmonic motion. Thus, the mass/spring system as illustrated in Figure 4.1 will exhibit simple harmonic motion.

In simple harmonic motion, the system keeps returning to its initial position. For example, in a mass/spring system, when the mass is pulled away from its equilibrium position and then released, it will keep returning to the point at which it was released. As a result, the point from which it is released will be the maximum displacement from equilibrium that the mass experiences. This is called the **amplitude** of its motion. Thus, if a mass/spring system is displaced 4.0 cm from its equilibrium position and then released, the mass will oscillate back and forth, but the maximum distance it will ever be from its equilibrium position is 4.0 cm. We would therefore say that the amplitude of its motion is 4.0 cm.

The time it takes for the system to leave its initial position and then return again is called the **period** of the motion. For a mass/spring system, the period of motion is:

$$T = 2\pi\sqrt{\frac{m}{k}} \tag{6.1}$$

In this equation, "T" represents the period of the motion, "m" is the mass of the spring, and "k" is the spring constant. Notice that the period of motion is *not* dependent on the initial displacement from equilibrium. Whether the mass is pulled only a small distance from its equilibrium position or a large distance, the time it takes for the mass to return to the point at which it was released is unaffected.

Although it is common to discuss simple harmonic motion in terms of period, some physicists prefer to discuss it in terms of **frequency**. Frequency is a measure of how many times each second the system returns to its original configuration. If you think about it, frequency (f) is, in fact, just the inverse of the period.

$$f = \frac{1}{T} \tag{6.2}$$

After all, if a mass/spring system returns to the point at which it was released every 0.25 seconds, it will return to its original configuration 4.0 times every second. Thus, the period of the mass/spring system is 0.25 seconds, but the frequency is $\frac{1}{0.25 \text{ sec}} = 4.0 \, \frac{1}{\text{sec}}$. The unit "$\frac{1}{\text{sec}}$" is usually referred to as "Hertz," which is abbreviated "Hz." The frequency unit is called "Hertz" in honor of Heinrich Rudolf Hertz, a German physicist who demonstrated that electricity can be transmitted in electromagnetic waves. As you will see in the next module, electromagnetic waves are really just light waves. Hertz's research led to the development of the wireless telegraph, radio, and (eventually) television.

In Module #4, I also reminded you that as a spring is displaced from equilibrium, it stores up potential energy according to the equation:

$$U_{spring} = \frac{1}{2} \cdot k \cdot x^2 \tag{4.8}$$

where "U_{spring}" is the potential energy of the spring, "k" is the spring constant, and "x" is the distance that the system is pulled away from equilibrium. As the mass/spring system oscillates, then, its potential and kinetic energy continually change. As the mass moves away from its equilibrium position, it gains potential energy and loses kinetic energy. As the mass moves towards its equilibrium position, it gains kinetic energy and loses potential energy.

Now that I have done a quick review of the mass/spring system, I want to analyze a situation that is perhaps a little more complex than what you saw in your first-year course.

EXAMPLE 6.1

A 15.0 kg mass is attached to two springs as shown below. The system is arranged so that neither spring is stretched when the mass is at rest in the position shown in the figure. The spring constant of the first spring is 157 N/m, and the spring constant of the second spring is 234 N/m. If the mass is displaced 15.0 cm from the position shown below, what is the amplitude and frequency of its motion? Ignore friction.

Illus. by Megan Whitaker

k = 157 N/m   k = 234 N/m

The key to understanding any mass/spring system is knowing the spring constant. In this case, we have two springs that are both pulling on the mass. How does that affect things? Well,

---

the basis of simple harmonic motion is Equation (4.7). Any system that has a force which behaves as Equation (4.7) dictates will exhibit simple harmonic motion. Thus, let's see whether or not this system really does conform to Equation (4.7). Consider the forces on the mass. When the mass is sitting as shown in the figure, neither spring is stretched. Thus, there are no forces acting on the object (at least not in the horizontal dimension), and the object is in its equilibrium position. Once the mass is displaced, however, there will be *two* forces acting on the mass. Let's suppose we displace the mass to the right of its equilibrium position. If that happens, the spring on the left will be stretched and thus will pull back on the mass. As a result, it will exert a force that attempts to move the mass to the left. The spring on the right, however, will be compressed. Thus, it will push the mass away, which is also a force to the left. The sum of the forces on the mass, then, are shown in the figure below:

$$F = (234\ \frac{N}{m}) \cdot x$$

$$F = (157\ \frac{N}{m}) \cdot x$$

What is the sum of the forces? Well, both forces are pointed in the same direction, so we can just add them:

$$F_{tot} = (234\ \frac{N}{m}) \cdot x + (157\ \frac{N}{m}) \cdot x$$

$$F_{tot} = (391\ \frac{N}{m}) \cdot x$$

In the end, then, the two springs simply combine as if they were one stronger spring. Thus, this mass/spring system is really the same as a mass/spring system in which the mass is connected to only one spring whose spring constant is 391 N/m. As a result, the frequency is:

$$f = \frac{1}{T} = \frac{1}{2\pi}\sqrt{\frac{k}{m}} = \frac{1}{2\pi}\sqrt{\frac{(391\ \frac{N}{m})}{15.0\ kg}} = \frac{1}{2\pi}\sqrt{\frac{(391\ \frac{kg \cdot m}{sec^2}}{15.0\ kg}} = 0.813\ \frac{1}{sec} = \underline{0.813\ Hz}$$

Notice how the units work out. Since a Newton is a (kg·m)/sec^2, the mass and distance units cancel, leaving 1/sec^2, which turns into 1/sec when you take the square root. That's the same as Hz. What's the amplitude of the motion? The mass is originally displaced 15.0 cm from its equilibrium position. Thus, <u>its amplitude is 15.0 cm</u>.

The mass/spring system in the example, then, will simply oscillate back and forth. It will travel 15.0 cm to the left of its equilibrium position, then it will reverse course and travel to the right until it reaches 15.0 cm right of its equilibrium position, which is the point from which it was released. It will make 0.813 of these trips each second.

ON YOUR OWN

6.1 A mass/spring system is constructed with three springs and a 20.0 kg mass as shown to the right. When it is sitting as shown, none of the springs are stretched or compressed. It is then displaced 10.0 cm to the right and released. What is the period of its motion? What is the amplitude of its motion? What is its maximum speed and where does it occur? Ignore friction.

6.2 A mass/spring system is constructed with a 15.0 kg mass attached to a single spring. It is set up horizontally as shown in section A of the figure to the right. When displaced from equilibrium, it oscillates with a frequency of 1.25 Hz. The system is then hung vertically as shown in section B of the figure. When the system is hung vertically, how far will the spring be stretched when the mass is at its new equilibrium position?

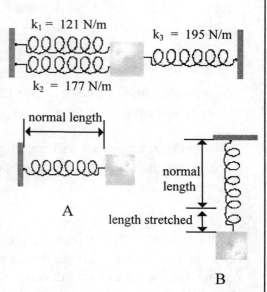

A Detailed Description of the Mass/Spring System

Although it is nice to know the period of motion in a mass/spring system [Equation (6.1)] as well as the energy of the system [from energy conservation and Equation (4.8)], it would be nice to know some other aspects of the system as well. For example, what are the position and velocity of the mass at any given time? In linear motion, I can determine the position and velocity of an object at any time using Equations (2.3) - (2.5). Can I do that in simple harmonic motion? Yes, I can, but the equations are more complicated. To understand where we get the equations, study the following figure.

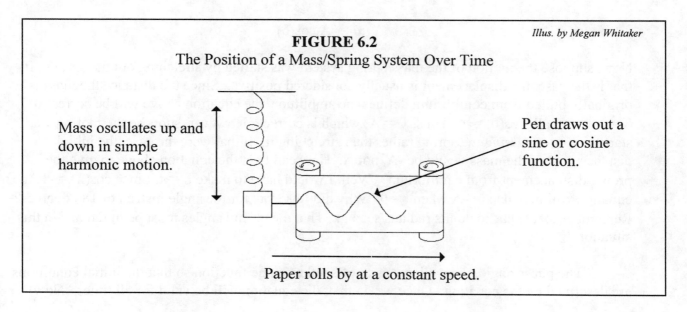

FIGURE 6.2
The Position of a Mass/Spring System Over Time
Illus. by Megan Whitaker

Mass oscillates up and down in simple harmonic motion.

Pen draws out a sine or cosine function.

Paper rolls by at a constant speed.

Notice the pattern that the mass draws on the recording paper. What does it look like? It looks like a *sine or cosine curve*. Remember, the only difference between a sine curve and a cosine curve is 90 degrees. If 90 degrees ($\frac{\pi}{2}$) is added to the argument of a sine function, it becomes a cosine function:

$$\sin(\theta + \tfrac{\pi}{2}) = \cos(\theta) \tag{6.3}$$

As a result, either a sine or cosine function can be used to predict the displacement of the mass from equilibrium at any time.

For reasons that will become apparent later, I will use a cosine function to describe the displacement of a mass in a mass/spring system.

$$\mathbf{x} = A\cdot\cos(\omega\cdot t + \delta) \tag{6.4}$$

In this equation, "A" represents the amplitude of the mass's motion. What is the amplitude? It is the maximum displacement from equilibrium. As you should recall from potential energy arguments, the maximum distance the mass will move from equilibrium is equal to the distance to which the mass was pulled to initiate the motion. The term "ω" is called the **angular frequency** of the motion, and it is given by the following equation:

$$\omega = \frac{2\pi}{T} \tag{6.5}$$

The units of ω are radians/sec.

Finally, the term "δ" is called the **phase angle** of the motion. What is the phase angle? It is a constant that helps us "line up" the cosine function with the motion of the mass. What do I mean by that? Well, look what happens to Equation (6.4) when t = 0:

$$\mathbf{x} = A\cdot\cos(\delta)$$

Now, suppose the motion of the mass/spring system was started by stretching out the spring. If that is the case, the displacement is usually considered positive. Since the distance the mass is originally pulled from equilibrium defines the amplitude, the equation above will be correct if $\delta = 0$. After all, cos(0) = 1. Thus, $\mathbf{x} = A$, which is correct. However, suppose the motion was started by *compressing* the spring rather than stretching it. If that were the case, the initial displacement of the mass would be -A, not A. How can I get the equation above to give the proper displacement from equilibrium? Well, I would have to make $\delta = \pi$. Since cos(π) = -1, the equation will give us $\mathbf{x} = -A$ when t = 0. Why did I use "π" for the angle instead of 180 degrees? Remember that ω has the units radians/second. That means my angles must be in radians in this situation.

The phase angle, then, allows us to offset the cosine function so that the initial conditions are described by the equation. Once we do that, the equation will be valid for all times. Now please note that t = 0 can be defined at any time. The most reasonable definition of t = 0 is the instant that I release the mass. If that is the case, δ will be 0 or π depending on whether I compressed or stretched the spring. However, t = 0 need not be defined in the most reasonable way. For example, I could stretch the spring, release the mass, and then define t = 0 as the time at which the mass passes some arbitrary mark that I have made on the floor. Thus, the phase angle can be any value between 0 and 2π, depending on how t = 0 is defined.

How do we determine the phase angle? That's easy. Since the phase angle is supposed to line up the cosine function so that it is consistent with our initial condition, all we have to do is determine the initial condition and solve for δ. Thus:

$$\delta = \cos^{-1}\left(\frac{x_o}{A}\right) \qquad (6.6)$$

where x_o is the displacement from equilibrium at t = 0. Now you should see why I chose cosine to describe the position of the mass rather than sine. For most cases involving a mass/spring system, t = 0 will be defined as the moment in which the mass is released. If that is the case, then x_o = A and δ is 0. Thus, the cosine function is the most reasonable function to use when describing the position of the mass in a mass/spring system. However, sine can be used as well. The only difference will be the value of δ.

Now, if all of this is a bit too abstract for you, the following example should help clear things up.

EXAMPLE 6.2

A mass/spring system is composed of a 10.0 kg mass and a spring whose spring constant is 151 N/m. The mass is displaced -50.0 cm from equilibrium and then released. The experimenter examines the motion for a moment and then defines t = 0 as the instant that the mass passes through its equilibrium position. What is the displacement of the mass at t = 15.0 seconds?

Before we were given Equation (6.4), the only positions we knew in a mass/spring system were the points at which the velocity of the mass was 0 (that occurs at the maximum distance from equilibrium), and the point at which the speed of the mass was greatest (which occurs at the equilibrium position). With Equation (6.4), we can determine the position of the mass at *any* time. First, however, we must set up the equation. To do that, we need to know what A, ω, and δ are.

Figuring out the amplitude (A) of the motion is easy. The mass is displaced -50.0 cm away from equilibrium in order to get the motion started. As you already know, the energy of the situation forbids the mass from traveling any farther than 50.0 cm from equilibrium. That means the amplitude of the motion is 50.0 cm. What about the angular frequency (ω)? Well, ω is given by Equation (6.5). This equation, however, contains the period of the motion. The period is given by Equation (6.1). Thus, the angular frequency is:

$$\omega = \frac{2\pi}{T} = \frac{2\pi}{2\pi\sqrt{\frac{m}{k}}} = \sqrt{\frac{k}{m}} = \sqrt{\frac{151\,\frac{N}{m}}{10.0\;kg}} = \sqrt{\frac{151\,\frac{kg\cdot m}{sec^2}}{10.0\;kg}} = 3.89\,\frac{rad}{sec}$$

Notice how the units worked out here. Once you substitute in the definition of the Newton, everything in the units cancels except $1/sec^2$. When you take the square root, you get seconds. Where did the radians come from? Remember back to the previous module. Since radian is a dimensionless unit, it can be added to or taken from the units as needed. In this case, we need it, because without the radian, we would not know the unit for angle in Equation (6.4).

We now know A and ω. There is only one thing more that we need: δ. To figure that out, we use Equation (6.6). Time zero is defined as the time at which the mass reaches its equilibrium position. Thus, x_0 is zero, because x is the displacement from equilibrium:

$$\delta = \cos^{-1}\left(\frac{x_o}{A}\right) = \cos^{-1}\left(\frac{0}{A}\right) = \cos^{-1}(0) = \frac{\pi}{2}$$

Now we have the complete equation:

$$x = A\cdot\cos(\omega t + \delta)$$

$$x = (50.0\;cm)\cdot\cos\left((3.89\,\frac{rad}{sec})\cdot t + \frac{\pi}{2}\right)$$

That equation gives us the displacement from equilibrium at any time, t. Thus, to answer the question, we just plug 15.0 sec in for t:

$$x = (50.0\;cm)\cdot\cos\left((3.89\,\frac{rad}{sec})\cdot(15.0\,sec) + \frac{\pi}{2}\right) = (50.0\;cm)\cdot\cos(58.4\;rads + 1.57\;rads) = -47.6\,cm$$

The mass, then, is -47.6 cm from its equilibrium position. Usually, a negative displacement means the spring is compressed. However, the sign convention was not mentioned in the problem. Before you move on, make sure you can solve the equation above on your calculator. Remember, the angles are in *radians*, not degrees. Thus, you must change the mode on your calculator so that it knows the angles are in radians.

You might think (or hope) that we are done with describing the motion of a mass in a mass/spring system. However, we aren't quite done yet. You see, not only can we determine the position of the mass at any time, we can also determine its velocity and acceleration! It turns out that the formulas for velocity and acceleration are very similar to the one we have already discussed:

$$\mathbf{v} = -\omega A \cdot \sin(\omega t + \delta) \qquad (6.7)$$

$$\mathbf{a} = -\omega^2 A \cdot \cos(\omega t + \delta) \qquad (6.8)$$

In these equations, A, ω, and δ are defined exactly as they are for Equation (6.4). If you take calculus, you will eventually learn that Equation (6.7) is simply the **derivative** of Equation (6.4), since velocity is just the derivative of position. In the same way, Equation (6.8) is the derivative of Equation (6.7), since acceleration is the derivative of velocity. For right now, however, you do not need to know that.

Since these equations are so similar to Equation (6.4), I am not going to run through an example of how to use them. After all, the real difficulty in using these equations is in determining A, ω, and δ, and that is the same for all equations. Instead, I want to spend some time discussing how these equations interplay with one another. In Figure 6.3, I have plotted the position (thin black line), velocity (thicker, dark gray line), and acceleration (thickest, light gray line) for a mass/spring system composed of a 100.0 kg mass and a spring whose spring constant is 225 N/m. This mass/spring system was displaced 50.0 cm from equilibrium and released at time = 0. The resulting equations are shown and graphed in the figure below.

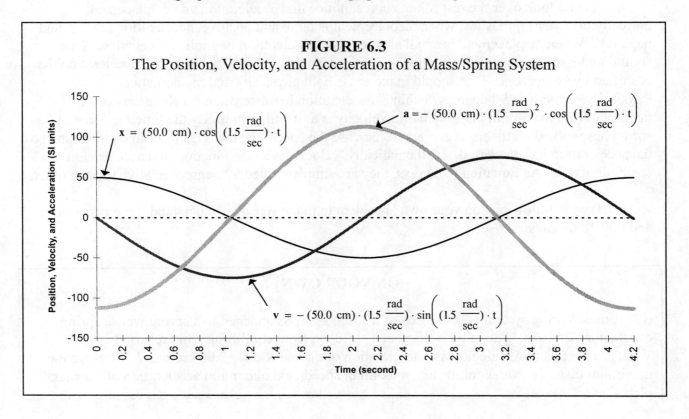

FIGURE 6.3
The Position, Velocity, and Acceleration of a Mass/Spring System

First, let's look at t = 0. At that point, the displacement is 50.0 cm. That makes sense, since I told you that the mass was displaced 50.0 cm and released at t = 0. At that point the velocity is zero. That makes sense as well. The instant that the mass is released, the velocity is zero. What about the acceleration? The acceleration is negative, because the mass will be accelerated opposite of the direction in which it was displaced. Also, notice that the acceleration has its most negative value at t = 0. That should also make sense. At t = 0, it is at its maximum displacement, and since the force is directly proportional to the displacement, the maximum displacement results in the maximum force, which provides the maximum acceleration.

Now look what happens as time progresses. The displacement decreases. That should make sense, because the mass begins moving towards its equilibrium position. The velocity becomes more negative, indicating that the speed of the mass is increasing, and that the mass is traveling away from the initial displacement. The acceleration, in turn, is getting less negative because, as the displacement from equilibrium decreases, the acceleration towards equilibrium decreases.

Notice the situation when the displacement from equilibrium is zero, which occurs at just over 1.0 seconds. At that point, the velocity is at its largest negative value. Once again, that makes sense, since the mass has been accelerating from the moment it was displaced. Once it passes equilibrium, the spring will start to accelerate it in the opposite direction, which will slow it down. Thus, the mass's maximum speed occurs at the equilibrium position. Notice also that the acceleration at the equilibrium position is zero. That makes sense, since the spring exerts no force when the mass is at equilibrium.

As you look over the rest of the curves, notice that acceleration and displacement basically behave as opposites: when displacement is large and positive, acceleration is large and negative. When displacement is small and positive, acceleration is small and negative. That should make sense, given Equation (4.7). Notice also that velocity behaves like acceleration that is shifted by 90 degrees. That should make sense both physically and mathematically. Physically, velocity is 90 degrees "behind" acceleration because when acceleration is at its maximum (the maximum displacement), velocity is at its minimum. By the time the force of the spring has worked on the mass enough to increase the speed, the mass is closer to equilibrium, so the acceleration has decreased. Mathematically, velocity is a sine function, but acceleration is a cosine function. As Equation (6.3) says, they are simply shifted 90 degrees relative to each other.

Try the following "on your own" problem to make sure you understand these equations and how to use them.

ON YOUR OWN

6.3 A mass/spring system is composed of a 150.0 kg mass attached to a spring whose spring constant is 225 N/m. The mass is displaced -15.0 cm from equilibrium and released at t = 0. What are the position, velocity, and acceleration of the mass at t = 3.00 seconds? What are the maximum distance from equilibrium, maximum speed, and maximum acceleration of the mass?

The Pendulum

In your first-year course, you should have also been given an introduction to the pendulum. As illustrated below, when a mass is hung on a string and displaced from its equilibrium position, the mass swings back and forth. This is called a pendulum.

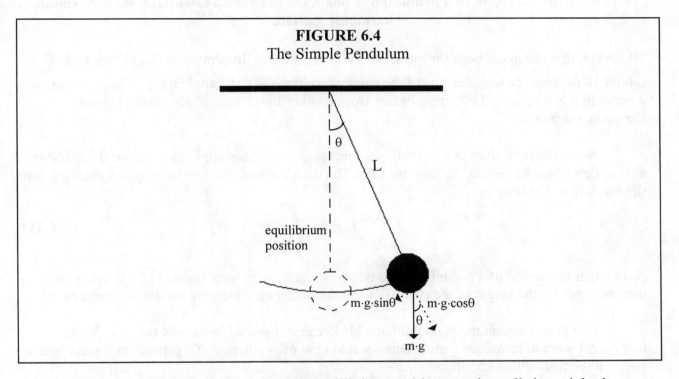

FIGURE 6.4
The Simple Pendulum

When the mass is displaced from its equilibrium position, gravity pulls it straight down. As illustrated in the figure, that gravitational force can be split into two components: one that pulls directly against the string ($m \cdot g \cdot \cos\theta$) and one that pulls perpendicular to the string ($m \cdot g \cdot \sin\theta$). Since the component which pulls perpendicular to the string is pointed back towards the equilibrium position, it is a *restoring force*.

$$F_{restoring} = -m \cdot g \cdot \sin\theta \qquad (6.9)$$

The negative sign simply indicates that the force is opposite the direction of the displacement.

When an angle is small, the sine of that angle is approximately equal to the value of the angle (in radians). Mathematically, then, we can say:

For small θ, $\sin\theta \approx \theta$

Let us now assume that the angle of displacement in a pendulum is small enough for the approximation above to be valid. If that is the case, Equation (6.9) becomes:

$$F_{restoring} = -(m \cdot g) \cdot \theta \qquad (6.10)$$

Notice the structure of this equation. For a given pendulum on a given planet, m·g is a constant. The angle, θ, is a measure of the displacement from equilibrium. Thus, *the restoring force in this case is directly proportional to the displacement from equilibrium.* What does this tell us? It tells us:

When the displacement in a pendulum is small, the pendulum essentially exhibits simple harmonic motion.

Of course, this statement begs the question, "What is small?" In general, when the angle is $\frac{\pi}{10}$ (about 18 degrees) or less, the sine of the angle is within 2% of the angle itself. Thus, as long as a pendulum is displaced 18 degrees or less from equilibrium, it essentially exhibits simple harmonic motion.

Since the pendulum is essentially moving with simple harmonic motion, we should be able to determine its period. Indeed, we can. The derivation of the formula requires calculus, but the result is rather simple:

$$T = 2\pi \cdot \sqrt{\frac{L}{g}} \tag{6.11}$$

Notice that the period of a pendulum does not depend on the mass at the end of the string. It depends only on the length of the string (L) and the planet on which the pendulum operates (g).

I've gone through the pendulum quickly because it should be review for you. Now, however, I want to introduce a more complicated kind of pendulum. To get started, I want you to perform the following experiment.

EXPERIMENT 6.1
The Simple Pendulum and the Physical Pendulum

Supplies:

- Thread
- A piece of wood like you used in Experiment 4.1. If you still have that piece of wood, it will work well.
- A thin nail that is at least ½ of an inch long
- A drill or a nail that is much thicker than the nail listed above
- Hammer
- A few washers or nuts
- A wooden ruler that is about 30 centimeters (1 foot) long. Make sure that it's okay to put a hole in this ruler. That's part of the experiment.
- A few heavy books
- Stopwatch

<u>Introduction</u> - This experiment demonstrates that the amount of mass on the end of a simple pendulum does not affect the period of the pendulum. It also introduces a physical pendulum.

<u>Procedure:</u>

1. Take the piece of wood and hammer a nail into the edge of the board, just like you did in Experiment 4.1. If you have that piece of wood with the nails still in it, just pull out or hammer down one of the nails and use the other one.
2. Place the piece of wood on the edge of a table or cabinet and lay the books on top of the wood to anchor it. The nail should be sticking way out past the edge of the table or cabinet.
3. Cut a piece of string so that it is about twice as long as the ruler. Tie a single washer to one end, but leave plenty of extra string on that end so that you can tie more washers to it later.
4. Tie the other end of the string to the nail. You need to tie it so that the distance from the nail to the center of the washer is the full length of the ruler.
5. Let the washer hang straight down. You now have a simple pendulum whose length is the same as that of the ruler.
6. Displace the pendulum a small angle (less than 18 degrees) away from equilibrium and then release. The moment you release, start the watch.
7. You want to count ten periods and then stop the watch. Thus, the washer must come back to the same point from which you released it 10 times.
8. Take the time it took for the pendulum to complete 10 periods and divide by 10. That is the period of the pendulum.
9. Since you know the length of the pendulum (the length of the ruler), you can use Equation (6.11) and the acceleration due to gravity to determine the period of the pendulum. Make sure your units are consistent!
10. Compare the period you measured in Step #8 to the period predicted in Step #9. If they are different (to the significant figures allowed), the measured period is probably a bit larger. That's because air resistance slows the pendulum down with each swing.
11. Now add another washer to the pendulum and repeat Steps #7 and #8.
12. Add another washer and repeat Steps #7 and #8 again.
13. Add one more washer and repeat Steps #7 and #8 again.
14. Compare the periods measured in Step #8 with those measured in Steps #11-#13.
15. Take the string off of the nail.
16. Now you want to make a pendulum out of your ruler. To do that, drill a hole in the ruler. The hole needs to be in the middle of the ruler as close to one end as possible without splitting the ruler. If you do not have (or are not allowed to use) a drill, you can use a thicker nail to make the hole. Just make sure the hole is large enough so that the thin nail which is on the board will easily fit inside.
17. Slip the nail on the board through the hole in the ruler so that the ruler hangs from the nail. You now have a physical pendulum.
18. Displace the physical pendulum a small angle from equilibrium and let it swing. Once again, measure the time it takes to complete 10 periods. Divide your measurement by ten, and you will get the period of the physical pendulum.
19. Compare the period you measured in Step #18 to the one you measured in Step #8.
20. Clean everything up.

What happened in the experiment? You should have found that the periods measured in Steps #8, and Steps #11-13 were essentially the same. They will not be exactly the same because of experimental error. However, they should be close (within 5% or so). You might have noticed a slight decrease in the period as you tied on more washers. If so, that's because the greater mass was not as strongly affected by air resistance as was the lighter mass. If you think your periods have a lot of variation to them, think about how you changed the mass. Between Step #8 and Step #13, you quadrupled the mass. However, the period changed very little compared to that. This demonstrates that the period of a simple pendulum is independent of the mass used.

Now let's move on to the second part of the experiment. How did the period of the physical pendulum compare to that of the simple pendulum? It should have been significantly less (about 15 - 20%). Why? Well, think of the type of motion the pendulum is exhibiting. Not only is it essentially moving as a simple harmonic oscillator, but it is also exhibiting *rotational motion*. After all, the ruler experiences a torque (from gravity) which causes it to rotate about a fixed point (the nail). Sure, the ruler does not make complete rotations around the nail, but it is still rotating with the nail as its axis of rotation.

What governs the resistance of a body to changes in its rotational motion? The *moment of inertia*. Well, the moment of inertia of a ruler is significantly different than that of a mass on a string. Thus, a pendulum formed by a ruler is different from that of a pendulum formed by a mass on a string. That's why a mass on a string is called a **simple pendulum**, while a pendulum formed from an extended body (like a ruler) is called a **physical pendulum**.

FIGURE 6.5
A Physical Pendulum

A physical pendulum is an extended body that is displaced from equilibrium (dashed vertical line) and swings back and forth around a fixed point.

As long as the angle of displacement (θ) is small, a physical pendulum exhibits simple harmonic motion.

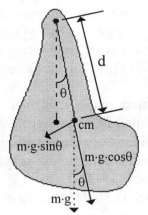

In this situation, the important factors are the distance between the fixed point and the center of mass (d), the mass of the body, and the moment of inertia of the body.

Now it turns out that Equation (6.11) is actually a special case of a more general equation which gives the period of *any* pendulum, whether it is simple or physical:

$$T = 2\pi \cdot \sqrt{\frac{I}{m \cdot g \cdot d}} \qquad (6.12)$$

In this equation, "I" is the moment of inertia; "m" is the mass of the pendulum; "g" is the acceleration due to gravity; and "d" is the distance from the fixed point to the center of mass.

Notice first that for a simple pendulum, Equation (6.12) becomes equation (6.11). After all, for a mass that rotates around a fixed point, the moment of inertia is $m \cdot r^2$. In a simple pendulum, $r = L$. Thus, $I = mL^2$. In addition, the center of mass of a simple pendulum is the center of the mass. Thus, $d = L$. If I put those expressions into Equation (6.12), I get:

$$T = 2\pi \cdot \sqrt{\frac{I}{m \cdot g \cdot d}} = 2\pi \cdot \sqrt{\frac{\cancel{m}L^{\cancel{2}}}{\cancel{m} \cdot g \cdot \cancel{L}}} = 2\pi \cdot \sqrt{\frac{L}{g}}$$

Equation (6.12), then, is the general equation for a pendulum. For a simple pendulum, Equation (6.12) reduces to Equation (6.11). For a physical pendulum, however, one must use Equation (6.12).

Well, in the second part of the experiment, you had a physical pendulum. If you used a standard, 12.00-inch ruler, the moment of inertia (see Figure 5.4) is given by $I = \frac{1}{3} \cdot M \cdot L^2$, where $L = 30.48$ cm. Now, it turns out that this is a bit of an approximation. This equation is for a *rod* rotating about one end. The ruler is more of a plank. Nevertheless, the approximation is actually quite good. The other parameter we need to determine is d, the distance from the fixed point to the center of mass. Well, the center of mass of the ruler is the center of the ruler, which is 6.00 inches, or ½·L.

$$T = 2\pi \cdot \sqrt{\frac{I}{m \cdot g \cdot d}} = 2\pi \cdot \sqrt{\frac{\frac{1}{3} \cdot \cancel{m}L^{\cancel{2}}}{\cancel{m} \cdot g \cdot \frac{1}{2} \cdot \cancel{L}}} = 2\pi \cdot \sqrt{\frac{2 \cdot L}{3 \cdot g}} = 2\pi \cdot \sqrt{\frac{2 \cdot (0.3048 \, \cancel{m})}{3 \cdot (9.81 \, \frac{\cancel{m}}{sec^2})}} = 0.904 \text{ sec}$$

What was the period of your physical pendulum? It should have been something around 0.90 seconds, if you used a standard, 12-inch ruler. A physical pendulum, then, behaves much like a simple pendulum. However, you just have to use a more general equation to calculate its period.

ON YOUR OWN

6.4 A nail is driven through the edge of a uniform hoop and into a wall. The hoop is then displaced a small angle from equilibrium and released so that it swings back and forth. Its period is 0.754 seconds. What is the radius of the hoop? (The moment of inertia of a hoop rotating about a point on its edge is $I = 2 \cdot M \cdot R^2$.)

Transverse and Longitudinal Waves

Since I've been discussing simple harmonic motion, it only seems natural to move from that into a discussion of waves. After all, simple harmonic motion involves an object oscillating back and forth about a fixed point in space. Waves also involve such oscillations. However, in the case of a wave, the *entire medium* oscillates. Consider, for example, what happens when you drop a stone into a lake. Waves move away from where the stone was dropped, but the water itself doesn't move away from the stone. Only the *oscillations* of the water move away from the stone. Thus, the waves oscillate the medium (water) but do not propagate it. The waves themselves do propagate, however, since they move farther and farther from the point at which the stone was dropped.

Before you become more familiar with the behavior of waves, you need to learn the terminology associated with them. First of all, there are two basic types of waves: **transverse waves** and **longitudinal waves**.

Transverse wave - A wave whose propagation is perpendicular to its oscillation

Longitudinal wave - A wave whose propagation is parallel to its oscillation

These waves and their distinguishing characteristics are illustrated in the diagram below.

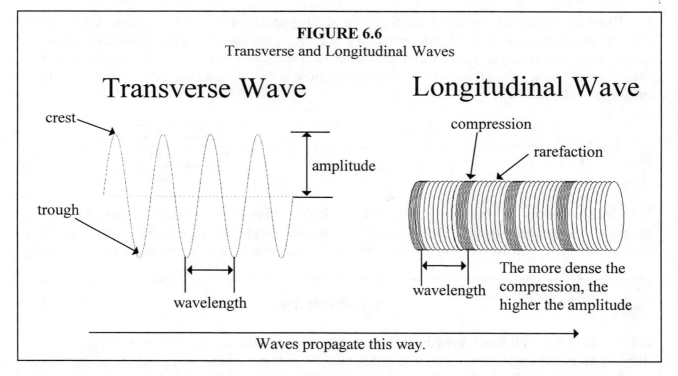

FIGURE 6.6
Transverse and Longitudinal Waves

The first thing I want you to notice is the direction that the waves propagate. They move to the right. The transverse wave (illustrated on the left) oscillates up and down. Thus, the oscillation is perpendicular to the propagation. The longitudinal wave oscillates left and right.

Thus, the propagation is parallel to the oscillation. That's the fundamental difference between these types of waves. The waves on water, then, are transverse waves. Sound waves, on the other hand, are longitudinal waves.

In the transverse wave, the "top" of the wave is called the **crest**, while the "bottom" of the wave is called the **trough**. The size of the wave is measured by the **amplitude**, which is the distance from zero to the crest of the wave. It is also equal to the distance from zero to the trough of the wave. Another important property of a wave is its **wavelength**, which is determined by the distance between the crests, which is also the same as the distance between the troughs.

In a longitudinal wave, the medium "bunches up" more than it normally would at one point. That is analogous to the crest of a transverse wave and is typically called a **compression**. The **rarefaction** is the area in which the medium is "stretched out" more than it normally would be. The amplitude of the longitudinal wave is determined by how "bunched up" the compression is. The more dense the compression, the larger the amplitude. The wavelength is determined by the distance between the centers of the compressions, which is the same as the distance between the centers of the rarefactions.

Another fundamental description of a wave is its **frequency**. The frequency of a wave tells you how many crests (or compressions if it is a longitudinal wave) pass by a given point in a second. The frequency is related to the speed of the wave and its wavelength according to the formula:

$$f = \frac{v}{\lambda}$$
(6.13)

where "f" is the frequency, "v" is the speed of propagation for the waves, and "λ" is the wavelength of the wave. Notice how the units work out. The standard unit for speed is meters per second, and the standard unit for wavelength is meters. Thus, when speed is divided by wavelength, the result is 1/sec, which is Hertz.

Now that you know the terminology of waves, I want you to perform an experiment that will help you get some experience with waves and how they behave.

EXPERIMENT 6.2
Wave motion and Standing Waves

Supplies:

- Slinky® (A metal one works best, but you can use a plastic one.)
- A person to help you
- Table with a smooth surface that will not get scratched up

<u>Introduction</u> - This experiment will give you some experience with the propagation of transverse and longitudinal waves. It will also give you some experience with wave interference and standing waves, which will be discussed in upcoming sections of this module.

<u>Procedure</u>:

1. Hand one end of the slinky to your helper and take the other end yourself.
2. Stand so that you and your helper are 3.5 to 4.0 meters apart from one another and the Slinky is stretched out in between both of you.
3. Have your helper hold his or her end still.
4. Generate a wave on the slinky by raising your end up and then bringing it down quickly. Notice how the wave travels down the Slinky, reflects off of the end that is being held still, and travels back towards you. This is a transverse wave because the wave moves from you to your helper and back (horizontally), but the Slinky oscillates up and down (vertically). Notice that the Slinky does not move horizontally. Only the wave does. Thus, the Slinky is the medium for the wave. The wave you created is called a **mechanical wave**, because it was the result of the mechanical motion of your arm.
5. Allow the Slinky to become reasonably still again. Once again, generate a wave on the Slinky by raising your end up and then bringing it down quickly. Make sure your helper continues to hold his end still. This time, notice *how* the wave bounces off of your helper. When the crest of the wave hits your helper, it bounces back as a trough. That means the wave is **inverted** when it is reflected.
6. Allow the Slinky to become reasonably still again. Now, start creating many waves by moving your end up and down at a constant rate. Make sure that your helper holds his or her end still.
7. Notice that the waves you are creating begin overlapping with each other and creating different patterns. This is called **wave interference**. Since waves move the Slinky up and down, if the waves overlap, they will affect one another. If a trough of one wave, for example, overlaps with the crest of another, the trough and crest will cancel each other out.
8. Let the Slinky settle again. Now, have your helper move his or her end up and down while you do the same. You are now both generating waves which are interfering with each other. If you both move your ends up and down at the right frequency, you can eventually make the Slinky look like this:

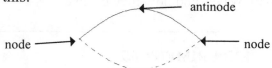

When this happens, the waves are interfering with each other in just the right way so that the entire Slinky is either moving up or moving down. This is called a **standing wave**. This particular standing wave is called the **fundamental frequency** (also called the **first harmonic**) of the Slinky. The point on the Slinky that experiences the greatest oscillation amplitude is called the **antinode**, while the points which experience no oscillation at all are called **nodes**. In this situation, then, there are two nodes and one antinode.

9. Now speed up the frequency at which you both move the slinky up and down. Once again, if you both start moving your ends up and down with exactly the right frequency, you will make

the Slinky look like this:

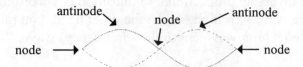

This is another standing wave, and it is typically called the **second harmonic**. Notice that in this standing wave, there are three nodes and two antinodes. Compare the frequency with which you needed to shake the Slinky in this step to the frequency in the previous step.

10. If you can do it, try and form a standing wave with three antinodes and 4 nodes. This is the **third harmonic**, and it would look like this:

Compare the frequency with which you needed to shake the Slinky in this step to the frequencies in the previous two steps.

11. Thank your helper. He or she can leave now. For the next part of the experiment, find a clear tabletop that you will not scratch with the Slinky.

12. Place the Slinky on the tabletop.

13. Stretch it out so that it is about three-quarters of a meter long.

14. Hold one end still and push the other end in and out once. Notice what happens. A portion of the spring compresses (forming the compression) while the portion behind stretches out (forming the rarefaction). The compressed area moves to the end that is being held still. It then bounces off and comes back. This is a longitudinal wave traveling down the Slinky. It will not travel nearly as well as the transverse waves did, since there is a lot of friction between the Slinky and the table.

15. Continue to hold one end still and begin moving the other end back and forth rapidly. See if you can set up a standing wave so that the compression areas do not move. This will be much harder because friction reduces the waves so much. Nevertheless, you should at least be able to see something that is close to a standing wave.

16. Put the Slinky away.

The Propagation of Waves

Now that you have had some experience with how waves travel in a medium, I want to spend some time studying this phenomenon in detail. I will concentrate on transverse waves, because they are easier to picture. However, we could do the same with longitudinal waves if we wanted.

Let's start with the first thing you noticed in your experiment. When you generated a wave on the Slinky, it traveled to your helper and then reflected off of the end that your helper was holding. What determined the frequency and wavelength of the wave? You did. If you raised your hand and lowered it quickly, you made a wave with a short wavelength. Since frequency and wavelength are inversely proportional to one another according to Equation (6.13), that means the frequency of the wave was high. If, on the other hand, you raised and lowered your hand slowly, you generated a long wavelength (low frequency) wave.

Frequency and wavelength are not the only characteristics of a wave, however. Amplitude is another. What determined the amplitude of the wave you generated? Once again, you did. If you raised your hand high, you generated a wave with a large amplitude. If you raised your hand not far from where it was originally, you generated a wave with a small amplitude.

The last important characteristic of a wave is its speed. What determined the speed of the wave? Believe it or not, you had nothing to do with that. You affected only the amplitude, wavelength, and frequency. *The physical characteristics of the Slinky determined the speed.* The best way to understand this is to consider a wave traveling along a string. Look at the forces which are at play:

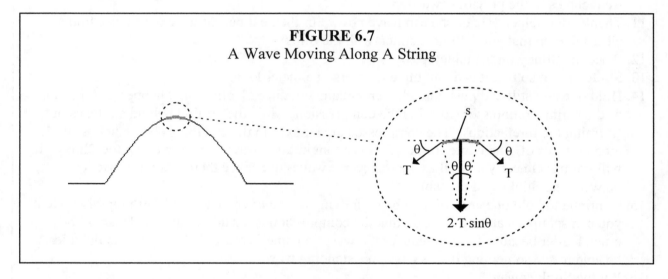

FIGURE 6.7
A Wave Moving Along A String

If I take a small section of the wave (the gray section at the top) and look at the forces acting on it, what forces exist? Ignoring gravity, the only force is the tension in the string (T). It is trying to straighten the string out, so it is pulling down on the crest of the wave from both sides. Now, if we split these tensions into horizontal (T·cosθ) and vertical (T·sinθ), the horizontal components are equal but opposite. Thus, they cancel. However, the vertical components point in the same direction. Thus, they add to give the thick arrow, which is 2·T·sinθ. Since θ is small, however, sinθ ≈ θ, so the total force acting on the crest of the wave is 2·T·θ.

Where is the force pointed? It is pointed directly to the center of a circle whose arc length is "s." What kind of force is that? That's a *centripetal force*, which you learned about in your first-year physics course. Thus, the small portion of the wave (the arc noted as "s") is in circular motion with the centripetal force equal to 2·T·θ. As you learned in your first-year physics course:

$$F_c = \frac{m \cdot v^2}{r} \tag{6.14}$$

where "m" is the mass of the object in circular motion, "v" is its speed, and "r" is the radius of the circle. I can set that expression for centripetal force equal to $2 \cdot T \cdot \theta$, which is the *value* of the force, to get:

$$2 \cdot T \cdot \theta = \frac{m \cdot v^2}{r} \tag{6.15}$$

As you should remember from geometry, the length of an arc (s) is equal to the radius of the circle (r) times the angle subtended by the arc (θ). Since the arc in Figure 6.6 subtends an angle of $2 \cdot \theta$, we could say:

$$r = \frac{s}{2 \cdot \theta} \tag{6.16}$$

Substituting Equation (6.16) into Equation (6.15):

$$2 \cdot T \cdot \theta = \frac{m \cdot v^2 \cdot 2 \cdot \theta}{s} \tag{6.17}$$

Now I want to make one abbreviation. I will call the mass of the arc length (m) divided by the length of the arc (s) to be the **linear mass density** (μ) of the string. Mathematically:

$$\mu = \frac{m}{s} \tag{6.18}$$

If I substitute this definition into Equation (6.17) and then solve for v, I get:

$$\boxed{v = \sqrt{\frac{T}{\mu}}} \tag{6.19}$$

Notice what this equation tells us. It tells us that the speed of a wave on a stretched string depends only on the tension in the string and the linear mass density (mass divided by length) of the string.

Now I realize that you were not using a string in your experiment. You were using a Slinky. I had you use a Slinky because its linear mass density, combined with the tension it develops when stretched, makes it perfect to observe the kinds of waves you can generate using your hands. Nevertheless, the conclusions we drew here are essentially the same for a Slinky.

Before we move on to understanding how waves travel along a medium and interfere with one another, I want you to make sure you can use Equation (6.19).

EXAMPLE 6.3

A string is stretched with a tension of 25.0 N. What is the speed of a wave on the string if it is 45.0 cm long and has a mass of 17.5 grams?

This is a straightforward application of Equation (6.19). However, we need to keep our units consistent. Since the tension is given in Newtons, the length must be in meters and the mass in kilograms.

$$v = \sqrt{\dfrac{25.0\ \text{N}}{\dfrac{0.0175\ \text{kg}}{0.450\ \text{m}}}} = \sqrt{\dfrac{25.0\ \dfrac{\text{kg}\cdot\text{m}}{\text{sec}^2}}{0.0389\ \dfrac{\text{kg}}{\text{m}}}} = \sqrt{\dfrac{25.0\ \text{m}^2}{0.0389\ \text{sec}^2}} = \underline{25.4\ \dfrac{\text{m}}{\text{sec}}}$$

Notice how the units work out. When you substitute the definition of the Newton into the equation, kilograms cancel and you are left with m^2/sec^2 under the square root sign. When you take the square root, then, you get the unit for speed, m/sec.

ON YOUR OWN

6.5 A string (m = 50.0 g, length = 1.0 m) is stretched over a pulley and suspends a mass of 2.5 kg. What is the speed of a wave on the string?

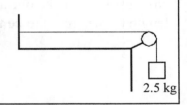

2.5 kg

A Mathematical Description of a Harmonic Wave

Now you know all that you need to know to describe any wave: wavelength, amplitude, and speed. I did not include frequency in that list because if you know the wavelength and speed, you can determine the frequency with Equation (6.13). I now want to show you an equation which will allow you to use those parameters to describe any **harmonic wave**.

Harmonic wave - A wave that has a sinusoidal shape

Of course, the transverse waves we have been studying so far have a sinusoidal shape, so this is simply a definition for the waves you studied in the experiment. Not surprisingly, the equation that describes a harmonic wave contains a sine function:

$$y = A \cdot \sin\left[\frac{2\pi}{\lambda} \cdot (vt \pm x)\right] \tag{6.20}$$

In this equation, "A" is the amplitude of the wave, "λ" is the wavelength, "v" is the speed, and "t" is time. In addition, the "y" term is the vertical position of the medium. In other words, it tells you how high or low the medium rises or falls as the wave passes by. The "x" term is the horizontal position of the wave. This equation, then, allows you to calculate the vertical position of the medium given the time and the horizontal position along the medium. What good is that? I will tell you in a moment. First, however, I have to tell you what the "±" means. In this equation, there could be either a positive or a negative sign at that point. The sign tells you the *direction* of the wave's propagation.

If there is a *negative* sign in Equation (6.20), the wave is traveling in the *positive* x direction. If there is a *positive* sign in Equation (6.20), the wave moves in the *negative* x direction.

Okay, then. We now have an equation that tells us the vertical position of the medium when we are given the time and the position along the medium. What possible good does that do us? Well, first I want you to think about a physical situation. Suppose you dropped a stone in a still lake and watched the surface of the lake. What would you see? You would see waves traveling away from the stone. Unlike the waves on the Slinky in the experiment, these waves would not reflect off of a boundary for a long time, because the lake is large. Thus, in the area that you can see, the waves would just pass by, oscillating the water.

Now suppose you were to take pictures of these waves as they went by. You would have snapshots in time, wouldn't you? Those snapshots might look something like this:

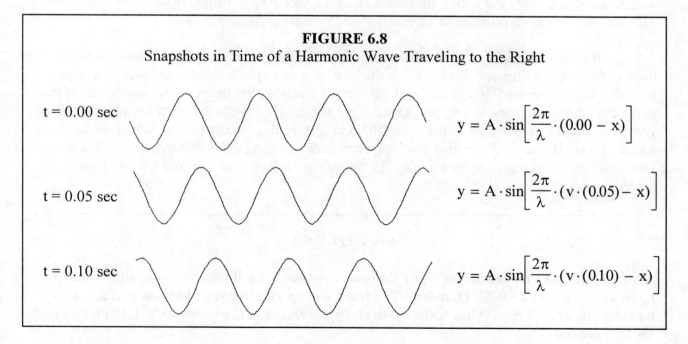

FIGURE 6.8
Snapshots in Time of a Harmonic Wave Traveling to the Right

t = 0.00 sec

$$y = A \cdot \sin\left[\frac{2\pi}{\lambda} \cdot (0.00 - x)\right]$$

t = 0.05 sec

$$y = A \cdot \sin\left[\frac{2\pi}{\lambda} \cdot (v \cdot (0.05) - x)\right]$$

t = 0.10 sec

$$y = A \cdot \sin\left[\frac{2\pi}{\lambda} \cdot (v \cdot (0.10) - x)\right]$$

Notice that although the three snapshots look similar, they are not identical. Why? Because the waves are *traveling away from the stone*. Where is the stone? Well, the stone is to the left of the figure. How do I know that? Look at the wave equations listed to the right. They contain a negative sign in the sine function. What does that tell you? The waves are moving in the positive-x direction, which is to the right. Since they are moving to the right, then motion to the right is away from the stone, and the stone is therefore left of the figure. In the end, then, for a given value of time, this equation produces a "snapshot" of the medium, showing you the oscillations throughout the medium.

Of course, that's not the only way to use this equation. Instead, suppose you watched the same situation (a stone dropped in a lake) but you were not looking at the waves from the side. Suppose you were in the water wearing a snorkeling mask and your eyes were right at the water level. Suppose further that you could not move and thus were forced to view the waves as they hit your mask. What would you see? You would see the water moving up and down on your mask. That scenario is still governed by Equation (6.20), but the value for position (x) does not vary. As time goes on, however, the waves move the water up and down the face of your mask because Equation (6.20) is a sine function in which the time (t) varies. Thus, the waves move the water up and down according to Equation (6.20) where x is constant and t varies.

Make sure you understand the difference between these two situations. In the first situation, t is constant because you are taking snapshots in time. Each snapshot represents one moment in time. However, since you are holding time constant, you can look at the entire medium, and you see the waves frozen in time. When you look at the waves in the next snapshot, they are still frozen, but they have shifted position. Thus, you are holding time (t) constant and allowing position (x) to vary. In the second situation, you are holding position (x) constant because you can only see the water at the spot where you are standing. However, time varies, because you are not taking snapshots. Instead, you are just watching while time goes on. Thus, in that situation, position (x) is constant and time (t) varies.

Of course, in real life, both things vary, right? What Equation (6.20) allows you to do, then, is to choose a time and a position on the lake. For example, suppose you wanted to know how the water behaved 50.0 cm east of the stone 1.0 seconds after the stone was dropped. If you know the amplitude, wavelength, and speed of the wave, you could use Equation (6.20) to tell you the vertical displacement of the water 50.0 cm east of the stone at 1.0 seconds after the stone was dropped. If you think about it, that's a pretty amazing thing to be able to predict! Make sure you understand this equation by studying the following example and working the "on your own" problem after it.

EXAMPLE 6.4

A harmonic wave travels to the right along a rope that has a linear mass density of 0.310 kg/m and is under 25.0 N of tension. The wave has an amplitude of 10.0 cm and a wavelength of 50.0 cm. What is the vertical displacement of the rope at x = 1.10 meters and t = 1.00 seconds?

To answer the question, we have to determine the equation for the harmonic wave. That's pretty easy, however. We were given A (0.100 m in standard units) and λ (0.500 m). We can also calculate v, because we know the tension and the linear mass density of the rope:

$$v = \sqrt{\frac{25.0 \text{ N}}{0.310 \frac{\text{kg}}{\text{m}}}} = 8.98 \frac{\text{m}}{\text{sec}}$$

Now we can set up the equation, realizing that since the wave moves to the right, we must put a negative sign in the equation:

$$y = (0.100 \text{ m}) \cdot \sin\left[\frac{2\pi}{(0.500 \text{ m})} \cdot ([8.98 \frac{\text{m}}{\text{sec}}] \cdot t - x)\right]$$

Now we can answer the question. All we have to do is put t = 1.00 sec and x = 1.10 m into the equation:

$$y = (0.100 \text{ m}) \cdot \sin\left[\frac{2\pi}{(0.500 \text{ m})} \cdot ([8.98 \frac{\text{m}}{\text{sec}}] \cdot [1.00 \text{ sec}] - 1.10 \text{ m})\right] = -0.0998 \text{ m}$$

If you were to look at the point 1.10 m to the right of the origin at a time of 1.00 seconds after the wave began, you would see that the rope would be displaced 9.98 cm *downwards*. Please note that to get the proper answer, your calculator *must* be in radians.

ON YOUR OWN

6.6 A harmonic wave moving to the left is generated on a rope. The speed of the wave is 2.00 m/sec, and the wavelength is 32.1 cm. At t = 2.00 seconds and 1.25 m to the right of the origin, the wave displaces the rope 3.44 cm downwards. What is the amplitude of the wave?

Reflection and Superposition of Waves

Now it is time to learn about how waves reflect off of boundaries and how they can interfere with one another. In Experiment 6.2, what happened to the wave you generated once it reached your helper? It reflected back to you. When it reflected however, it was inverted. Why was the wave inverted? Well, think about the forces at play. Before the wave reached your helper, the only force your helper had to overcome was the force due to gravity. When the wave hit your helper, in order to hold the Slinky still, your helper had to exert more force to counteract the force that was trying to lift the Slinky up. Thus, your helper exerted a force *opposite* to the oscillation of the wave. That inverted the wave. When waves reflect off of stationary objects, then, they are inverted.

Let's suppose that your helper was not holding the Slinky still but that the end was free to move up and down. Suppose you attached a ring to the Slinky and then slid the ring onto a pole. Then, when the wave hit the end of the Slinky, there would be no force opposing it. The ring would rise and then fall again with the wave. Since there would be no force opposing the wave, the wave would still be reflected, but in this scenario, it would not be inverted. The right side of Figure 6.9 illustrates this effect.

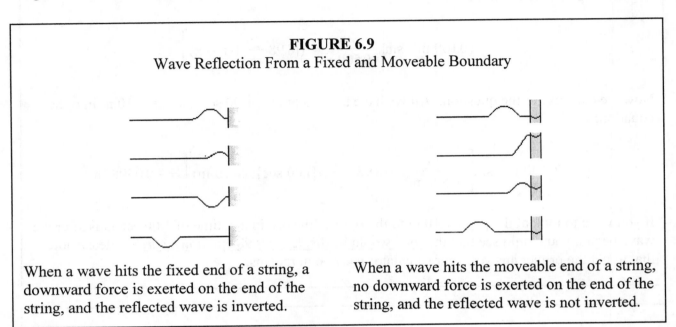

FIGURE 6.9
Wave Reflection From a Fixed and Moveable Boundary

When a wave hits the fixed end of a string, a downward force is exerted on the end of the string, and the reflected wave is inverted.

When a wave hits the moveable end of a string, no downward force is exerted on the end of the string, and the reflected wave is not inverted.

This leads to an important rule :

When waves reflect off of a stationary boundary, they are inverted. However, when they are reflected from a boundary free to move without restriction, they are not inverted.

The two cases discussed above are not the only possibilities when it comes to wave reflection. Suppose the boundary is moveable but another medium is on the other side of the boundary. What happens then? For example, consider a string which has a relatively small linear mass density connected to a rope that has a relatively large linear mass density. If you were to stretch such a system out and generate a wave on the string, what would happen? Well, when the wave reached the boundary between the two, part of the wave would be reflected and part of it would be transmitted along the rope. Thus, one wave would suddenly become two waves. As you might expect, each wave would end up having a smaller amplitude than the original wave, but you would still have two waves when before there was only one.

If the wave began in the string and then reached the rope, the reflected wave that traveled back along the string would be inverted. You might expect that, because the more dense rope would work something like a stationary end. Thus, the wave would reflect inverted, much like it would from a stationary end. If the wave started in the rope, however, and then reached the string, the portion of the wave reflected back along the rope would *not* be inverted, because the lighter string would act more like a boundary which is free to move without restriction. These two scenarios lead to the following picture.

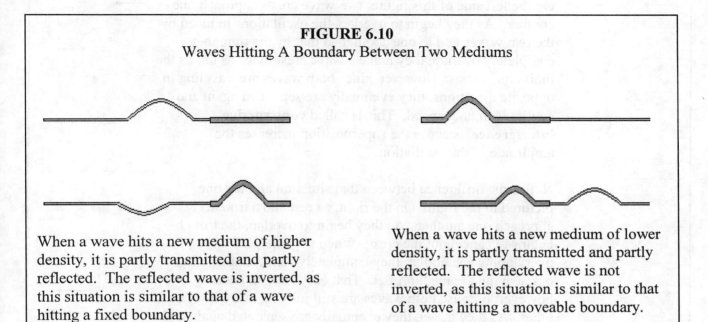

FIGURE 6.10
Waves Hitting A Boundary Between Two Mediums

When a wave hits a new medium of higher density, it is partly transmitted and partly reflected. The reflected wave is inverted, as this situation is similar to that of a wave hitting a fixed boundary.

When a wave hits a new medium of lower density, it is partly transmitted and partly reflected. The reflected wave is not inverted, as this situation is similar to that of a wave hitting a moveable boundary.

This leads to another important principle:

When a wave meets a boundary between two mediums, part of the wave will be transmitted into the new medium, but part will be reflected back into the old medium. If the speed of the wave in the new medium is less than it is in the old medium, the reflected wave will be inverted. If the speed of the wave in the new medium is greater than it is in the old medium, the reflected wave will not be inverted.

How did I get speed to become a part of this rule? Think about it. Equation (6.19) tells us that the higher the linear mass density of the medium, the lower the speed of the wave in the medium. Thus, if a wave is traveling from a medium of low linear mass density (like the string) to a medium of high linear mass density (like the rope), the wave will travel more slowly in the new medium. Thus, the reflected wave will be inverted. If the wave travels from a medium of high linear mass density (the rope) to a medium of low linear mass density (the string), the wave will travel more quickly in the new medium, and the reflected wave will not be inverted.

Why do we care how waves are reflected off of boundaries? Because waves can interfere with each other. You noticed that in Experiment 6.2. When you made several waves, the reflected waves overlapped with each other (we call this the **superposition of waves**) to form different patterns. Figure 6.11 illustrates how two waves can interfere with each other as they travel through a medium.

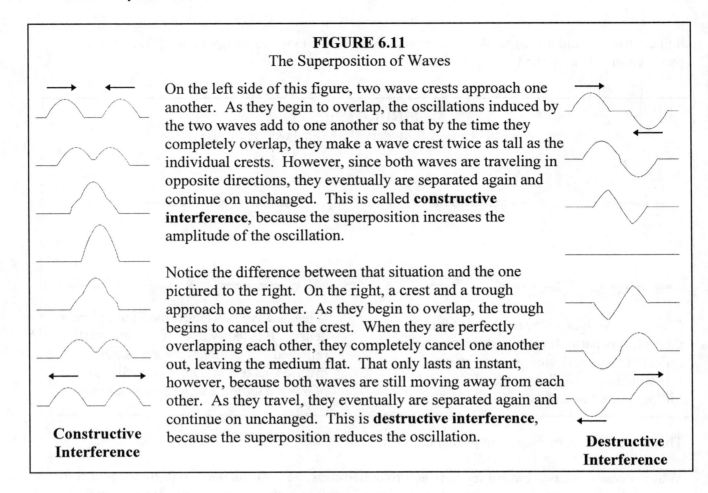

FIGURE 6.11
The Superposition of Waves

On the left side of this figure, two wave crests approach one another. As they begin to overlap, the oscillations induced by the two waves add to one another so that by the time they completely overlap, they make a wave crest twice as tall as the individual crests. However, since both waves are traveling in opposite directions, they eventually are separated again and continue on unchanged. This is called **constructive interference**, because the superposition increases the amplitude of the oscillation.

Notice the difference between that situation and the one pictured to the right. On the right, a crest and a trough approach one another. As they begin to overlap, the trough begins to cancel out the crest. When they are perfectly overlapping each other, they completely cancel one another out, leaving the medium flat. That only lasts an instant, however, because both waves are still moving away from each other. As they travel, they eventually are separated again and continue on unchanged. This is **destructive interference**, because the superposition reduces the oscillation.

Constructive Interference

Destructive Interference

You saw both constructive and destructive interference in your experiment. When you produced standing waves on the Slinky, you were oscillating the Slinky at just the right frequency so that the waves you produced interfered with the waves your helper produced to form a wave pattern that oscillated but did not move along the Slinky. You will learn more about standing waves in the next section.

ON YOUR OWN

6.7 A wave travels along a string whose linear mass density is 0.050 kg/m at a speed of 3.00 m/sec. Another string whose linear mass density is 0.100 kg/m is connected to the first string. Both strings have the same tension. When the wave encounters the second string, what will the speed of the transmitted wave be? What will the speed of the reflected wave be? Will the reflected wave be inverted?

6.8 Two waves approach one another. The first has an amplitude of 15.0 cm and the second has an amplitude of 5.0 cm. What is the minimum and maximum displacement experienced by the medium once the superposition begins?

Standing Waves

As you saw in your experiment, standing waves can be produced when waves in a medium interfere with each other in just the right way. When you shook the Slinky at a low frequency, you and your helper made waves of long wavelength. They interfered with one another to produce the fundamental (or first) harmonic. When you shook at a higher frequency, you ended up making waves of shorter wavelength that interfered with one another to produce the second and perhaps third harmonics. However, realize that had you varied the frequency with which you shook (and hence the wavelength of the waves), those standing waves would have disappeared. After all, if the waves were not of just the right wavelength, they would not have been able to completely fit on the Slinky.

Consider, for example, a string of length "L." If it is attached to a wall and stretched out, it would look like this:

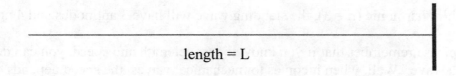

length = L

If the free end of the string was vibrated at just the right frequency so that a standing wave of the fundamental harmonic was produced, it would look like this:

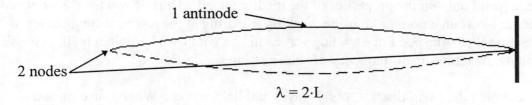

1 antinode

2 nodes

$\lambda = 2 \cdot L$

Notice that in the fundamental harmonic, only one crest or trough of the wave is visible. What does that mean? Well, it takes two crests (or two troughs) to make a wavelength. Thus, the wavelength of this wave must be twice the length of the string. In order to produce a standing wave of the fundamental harmonic, then, you must produce a wave whose wavelength is twice the length of the string.

The second harmonic would look like this:

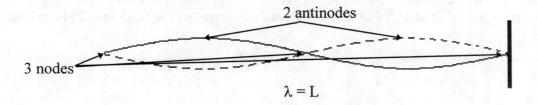

2 antinodes

3 nodes

$\lambda = L$

If you continue this kind of reasoning, you can develop a simple relationship between the length of the string and the wavelength of the standing wave:

$$\lambda = \frac{2L}{n} \qquad \text{where } n = 1,2,3... \qquad (6.21)$$

A string of length "L," then, can support a standing wave of any wavelength given by Equation (6.21). If n = 1, that standing wave is called the fundamental (sometimes called the "first") harmonic.

Notice also that there is a relationship between "n" and the number of nodes and antinodes.

There will be "n" antinodes in a standing wave and n+1 nodes.

Thus, in the third harmonic (n = 3), the standing wave will have 3 antinodes and 4 nodes.

Now please remember that if you know the wavelength and speed, you can determine the frequency of a wave. Well, when it comes to mechanical waves, the speed depends only on the medium. Thus, the length, tension, and linear mass density of the string determine both the wavelength *and* the frequency of the standing waves on the string. The frequencies of the standing waves in a medium are often called the **resonant frequencies** of the medium, because the frequencies depend only on the properties of the medium itself. Thus, if you have a stretched string that is under a certain amount of tension, shaking the string at the resonant frequencies of the string will set up the corresponding standing wave. In "on your own" problem 6.10, you will calculate the fundamental resonant frequency of such a string.

In the next module, I will discuss sound waves and light waves. When I discuss sound waves in particular, you will see the practical consequences of standing waves and resonant frequencies. For right now, however, I just want to make sure you understand the basics.

ON YOUR OWN

6.9 A string of length 15.0 cm is stretched between two supports. A standing wave is developed. The standing wave has a total of 4 antinodes. What is the wavelength of this wave?

6.10 A string of length 25.0 cm is stretched between two supports with a tension of 50.0 N. The mass of the string is 7.50 grams. What is the resonant frequency of the fundamental harmonic of this string?

ANSWERS TO THE ON YOUR OWN PROBLEMS

6.1 To determine things like the period, we need to know the effective force constant of all of those springs. To do that, we think of the forces involved. If the mass is displaced to the right, the first spring exerts a force of $k_1 \cdot x$ to the left, because it is trying to pull the mass back to equilibrium position. The second spring exerts a force of $k_2 \cdot x$ to the left, because it is trying to pull the mass back to its equilibrium position. The third spring exerts a force of $k_3 \cdot x$ *also to the left*, because it is trying to push the mass back to its equilibrium position. The total force, then, is:

$$F_t = k_1 \cdot x + k_2 \cdot x + k_3 \cdot x = (k_1 + k_2 + k_3) \cdot x$$

and that force is directed opposite of the displacement. Thus, this is simple harmonic motion with an effect spring constant of $k_1 + k_2 + k_3$. Now we can use our simple harmonic motion equations:

$$T = 2\pi \sqrt{\frac{m}{k}} = 2\pi \sqrt{\frac{(20.0 \text{ kg})}{493 \ \frac{N}{m}}} = 2\pi \sqrt{\frac{(20.0 \text{ kg})}{493 \ \frac{kg \cdot m}{sec^2}}} = 1.27 \text{ sec}$$

The period, then, is 1.27 seconds. The amplitude is easy. It was displaced 10.0 cm from the equilibrium position, so its amplitude is 10.0 cm. To determine its maximum speed, we have to determine the energy. When displaced, the energy of the mass is potential:

$$U_{spring} = \frac{1}{2} \cdot k \cdot x^2$$

The mass will be at its maximum speed when all of that energy is converted to kinetic. Thus:

$$\frac{1}{2} \cdot k \cdot x^2 = \frac{1}{2} \cdot m \cdot v_{max}^2$$

$$(493 \ \frac{N}{m})(0.100 \text{ m})^2 = (20.0 \text{ kg}) \cdot v_{max}^2$$

$$v_{max} = \sqrt{\frac{(493 \ \frac{kg \cdot m}{sec^2}}{m}) \cdot (0.0100 \text{ m}^2)}{20.0 \text{ kg}}} = 0.496 \ \frac{m}{sec}$$

This maximum speed will occur when the mass is at its equilibrium position, because at that point, there will be no potential energy and therefore all of the energy will be kinetic.

6.2 If we know the frequency, we can calculate the spring constant:

$$f = \frac{1}{T} = \frac{1}{2\pi}\sqrt{\frac{k}{m}}$$

$$1.25\,\frac{1}{sec} = \frac{1}{2\pi}\sqrt{\frac{k}{(15.0\ kg)}}$$

$$k = (2\pi \cdot 1.25\,\frac{1}{sec})^2 \cdot (15.0\ kg) = 925\,\frac{kg}{sec^2} = 925\,\frac{N}{m}$$

The units work because a N/m is the same as a kg/sec^2. Now that we have the spring constant, all we have to do is think of the force involved when the mass hangs from the spring. When that happens, the mass is pulled by gravity with a force of m·g downwards. When the spring pulls back with an equal but opposite force (m·g upwards), the mass will come to rest. That will be the final position of the mass. We can calculate that position with Hooke's Law:

$$\mathbf{F} = -\,k \cdot \mathbf{x}$$

$$(15.0\ kg) \cdot (9.81\,\frac{m}{sec^2}) = -(925\,\frac{N}{m}) \cdot \mathbf{x}$$

$$\mathbf{x} = -\,0.159\ m$$

The spring will be stretched 15.9 cm. Make sure you understand the signs in this equation. Hooke's law calculates the *spring's* force. Thus, the **F** in the equation refers to the force exerted by the spring, which is an upward (positive) force. That's why the force is positive. The **x** is negative because the mass is displaced downwards.

6.3 With Equation (6.4), we can determine the position of the mass at any time. First, however, we must set up the equation. To do that, we need to know what A, ω, and δ are.

Figuring out the amplitude (A) of the motion is easy. The mass is displaced -15.0 cm away from equilibrium in order to get the motion started. That means the amplitude of the motion is 15.0 cm. What about the angular frequency (ω)? Well, ω is given by Equation (6.5). This equation, however, contains the period of the motion. The period is given by Equation (6.1). Thus, the angular frequency is:

$$\omega = \frac{2\pi}{T} = \frac{2\pi}{2\pi\sqrt{\frac{m}{k}}} = \sqrt{\frac{k}{m}} = \sqrt{\frac{225\,\frac{N}{m}}{150.0\,kg}} = \sqrt{\frac{225\,\frac{kg\cdot m}{sec^2}}{150.0\,kg}} = 1.22\,\frac{rad}{sec}$$

Where did the radians come from? Remember back to the previous module. Since radian is a dimensionless unit, it can be added to or taken from the units as needed. In this case, we need it, because without the radian, we would not know the unit for angle in Equation (6.4).

We now know A and ω. There is only one thing more that we need: δ. To figure that out, we use Equation (6.6). Time zero is defined as the time at which the mass is released. Thus, $\mathbf{x_o}$ is -15.0 cm, because **x** is the displacement from equilibrium:

$$\delta = \cos^{-1}\left(\frac{\mathbf{x_o}}{A}\right) = \cos^{-1}\left(\frac{-15.0\,cm}{15.0\,cm}\right) = \cos^{-1}(-1) = \pi$$

Now we have the complete equation:

$$\mathbf{x} = A \cdot \cos(\omega t + \delta)$$

$$\mathbf{x} = (15.0\,cm) \cdot \cos\left((1.22\,\frac{rad}{sec}) \cdot t + \pi\right) = (15.0\,cm) \cdot \cos\left((1.22\,\frac{rad}{sec}) \cdot (3.00\,sec) + \pi\right) = 13.0\,cm$$

The mass, then, is <u>13.0 cm from equilibrium</u>, which is the opposite side compared to where the mass started.

Since we know ω, A, and δ, we also know equations for velocity and acceleration:

$$\mathbf{v} = -\omega A \cdot \sin(\omega t + \delta) = -(1.22\,\frac{rad}{sec}) \cdot (15.0\,cm) \cdot \sin\left((1.22\,\frac{rad}{sec}) \cdot (3.00\,sec) + \pi\right) = \underline{-9.07\,\frac{cm}{sec}}$$

$$\mathbf{a} = -\omega^2 A \cdot \cos(\omega t + \delta) = -(1.22\,\frac{rad}{sec})^2 \cdot (15.0\,cm) \cdot \cos\left((1.22\,\frac{rad}{sec}) \cdot (3.00\,sec) + \pi\right) = \underline{-19.4\,\frac{cm}{sec^2}}$$

The negative signs simply mean that velocity and acceleration are directed opposite of the displacement.

The maximum distance from equilibrium is easy. It was displaced -15.0 cm from the equilibrium position, so <u>its maximum distance from equilibrium is 15.0 cm</u>. The maximum acceleration will occur where the maximum force is exerted on the mass. That occurs when the mass is the farthest away from equilibrium. We can calculate the force:

$$F = -k \cdot x$$

$$F = -(225 \frac{N}{m}) \cdot (-0.150 \text{ m})$$

$$F = 33.8 \text{ N}$$

Now we can use Newton's Second Law to determine the acceleration:

$$F = m \cdot a$$

$$33.8 \text{ N} = (150.0 \text{ kg}) \cdot a$$

$$a = 0.225 \frac{m}{sec^2}$$

Since the acceleration is positive and the displacement is negative, <u>the maximum acceleration will be 0.225 m/sec^2 opposite of the displacement</u>.

You can actually calculate the maximum acceleration another way. You know the formula for acceleration at any time:

$$a = -\omega^2 A \cdot \cos(\omega t + \delta)$$

When will this be at its maximum? It will be at its maximum when the cosine equals ±1. After all, cosine varies from +1 to -1. Thus, the maximum acceleration will occur when cosine is at its maximum. Thus:

$$a_{max} = -\omega^2 \cdot A = -(1.22 \frac{rads}{sec})^2 \cdot (0.150 \text{ m}) = -0.223 \frac{m}{sec^2}$$

The numbers are not identical because of the rounding in the calculation of ω. Note that in order to get the units in m/sec, I had to report A in meters rather than cm.

To determine its maximum speed, we can solve the way we did it in problem 6.1, or we can use the equation for velocity at any time:

$$v = -\omega A \cdot \sin(\omega t + \delta)$$

This will reach its maximum when sine equals ±1. Thus:

$$v_{max} = -\omega \cdot A = -(1.22\ \frac{rads}{sec}) \cdot (0.150\ m) = -0.183\ \frac{m}{sec^2}$$

Once again, the negative just means opposite of displacement. Thus, <u>the maximum speed is 0.183 m/sec opposite of the displacement</u>.

6.4 According to Equation (6.12), the period of a physical pendulum depends on the moment of inertia. Since we have an equation for the moment of inertia, we can stick that into Equation (6.12) and solve for R:

$$T = 2\pi \cdot \sqrt{\frac{I}{m \cdot g \cdot d}}$$

$$0.754\ sec = 2\pi \cdot \sqrt{\frac{2 \cdot \cancel{m} \cdot r^2}{\cancel{m} \cdot (9.81\ \frac{m}{sec^2}) \cdot d}}$$

Wait a minute. We have a problem. What is "d"? The definition of "d" is the distance from the axis of rotation to the center of mass of the hoop. What is that? The nail is stuck through the edge of the hoop, so the distance from the nail to the center of the hoop (which is the center of mass) is the radius!

$$0.754\ sec = 2\pi \cdot \sqrt{\frac{2 \cdot \cancel{m} \cdot r^2}{\cancel{m} \cdot (9.81\ \frac{m}{sec^2}) \cdot \cancel{r}}}$$

$$r = \frac{(0.754\ \cancel{sec})^2 \cdot (9.81\ \frac{m}{\cancel{sec^2}})}{(2\pi)^2 \cdot 2} = \underline{0.0706\ m}$$

6.5 Using what you have learned in the past about Newton's Laws, you can quickly determine that the tension in the string is given by:

$$T = m \cdot g = (2.5\ kg) \cdot (9.81\ \frac{m}{sec^2}) = 25N$$

Now that you know the tension, the speed is a simple application of Equation (6.19).

$$v = \sqrt{\frac{25\ N}{\frac{0.0500\ kg}{1.0\ m}}} = \sqrt{\frac{25\ \frac{kg \cdot m}{sec^2}}{0.050\ \frac{kg}{m}}} = \sqrt{\frac{25\ m^2}{0.050\ sec^2}} = \underline{22\ \frac{m}{sec}}$$

6.6 Since we know the speed of the wave and the wavelength, we can get most of the equation:

$$y = A \cdot \sin\left[\frac{2\pi}{(0.321 \text{ m})} \cdot ([2.00 \frac{\text{m}}{\text{sec}}] \cdot t + x)\right]$$

I used the plus sign because the wave is moving to the left (the negative x direction). Since this equation tells us the vertical displacement of the medium for any time and position, we can put that information in and solve for A:

$$-0.0344 \text{ m} = A \cdot \sin\left[\frac{2\pi}{(0.321 \text{ m})} \cdot ([2.00 \frac{\text{m}}{\text{sec}}] \cdot [2.00 \text{ sec}] + 1.25 \text{ m})\right]$$

$$A = \frac{-0.0344 \text{ m}}{\sin\left[\frac{2\pi}{(0.321 \text{ m})} \cdot ([2.00 \frac{\text{m}}{\text{sec}}] \cdot (2.00 \text{ sec}) + 1.25 \text{ m})\right]} = -0.0436 \text{ m}$$

The negative just means that the medium is displaced downwards. Thus, the amplitude is <u>0.0436 m</u>.

6.7 To figure out the speed of the wave in the second string, we need to figure out the tension. We can do that from the speed of the wave in the first string:

$$v = \sqrt{\frac{T}{\mu}}$$

$$3.00 \frac{\text{m}}{\text{sec}} = \sqrt{\frac{T}{0.050 \frac{\text{kg}}{\text{m}}}}$$

$$T = (3.00 \frac{\text{m}}{\text{sec}})^2 \cdot (0.050 \frac{\text{kg}}{\text{m}}) = 0.45 \frac{\text{kg} \cdot \text{m}}{\text{sec}^2} = 0.45 \text{ N}$$

Now we can figure out the speed in the second string:

$$v = \sqrt{\frac{T}{\mu}}$$

$$v = \sqrt{\dfrac{(0.45\ \text{N})}{0.100\ \dfrac{\text{kg}}{\text{m}}}} = 2.1\ \dfrac{\text{m}}{\text{sec}}$$

The transmitted wave will have a speed of 2.1 m/sec. The reflected wave will have the same speed as the original wave, 3.00 m/sec. Remember, the speed of a wave on a string depends only on the tension and the linear mass density of the string. The reflected wave will be inverted, because it encountered a medium in which it moved more slowly than the medium it was originally in.

6.8 The waves will both destructively and constructively interfere with one another, depending on the overlap. As they approach each other and continue moving, all possible overlaps will eventually happen. When the waves constructively interfere, the medium will experience the greatest oscillation, which will be the sum of the two amplitudes. The least displacement of a medium in *any* wave is zero. Thus, the greatest displacement will be 20.0 cm and the least displacement will be 0 cm.

6.9 When there are 4 antinodes, n = 4. Thus, the wavelength is:

$$\lambda = \frac{2L}{n} = \frac{2 \cdot (15.0\ \text{cm})}{4} = \underline{7.50\ \text{cm}}$$

6.10 The wavelength is easy to calculate:

$$\lambda = \frac{2L}{n} = \frac{2 \cdot (25.0\ \text{cm})}{1} = 50.0\ \text{cm}$$

That's not the answer, though. We want to know the resonant frequency. To find that, we can use Equation (6.13). However, to use that equation, I need to know the speed, which I can get from Equation (6.19):

$$v = \sqrt{\frac{T}{\mu}} = \sqrt{\frac{50.0\ \text{N}}{\dfrac{0.00750\ \text{kg}}{0.25\ \text{m}}}} = 40.8\ \frac{\text{m}}{\text{sec}}$$

Now we can get the frequency:

$$f = \frac{v}{\lambda} = \frac{40.8\ \dfrac{\text{m}}{\text{sec}}}{0.500\ \text{m}} = 81.6\ \frac{1}{\text{sec}} = \underline{81.6\ \text{Hz}}$$

REVIEW QUESTIONS FOR MODULE #6

1. Two mass/spring systems are investigated. The spring constant is the same for each spring, but the mass of the second system is twice that of the first system. They are both displaced the same distance from equilibrium and then released. Compare the following in both systems: total energy, maximum kinetic energy, maximum speed, maximum displacement. Ignore friction.

2. Suppose the two mass/spring systems above were oscillating on a rough surface so that friction was an important consideration. Both systems would eventually stop oscillating. Which would travel the shortest total distance before stopping?

3. A mass/spring system oscillates with an amplitude of A. What is the total distance traveled by the mass in a time equal to the period of the system? A pendulum is displaced by an angle of θ and then released. What is the total angle swept out by the pendulum in a time equal to the period of the system?

4. Potential energy can be negative in many systems. Can the potential energy in a mass/spring system ever be negative? Why or why not?

5. A simple pendulum is hung in an elevator, and its period is measured when the elevator is stationary. Compare that period to the period measured when:

a. The elevator travels upward at a constant velocity
b. The elevator accelerates upward
c. The elevator cable is cut and the elevator is in free fall

6. The motion of two pendulums is studied. They have identical lengths and gravitational acceleration is (obviously) identical for both. Nevertheless, the periods are different. How can you explain this?

7. The speed of waves moving along a stretched spring is measured. If the researcher wanted to double the speed of the waves in the same string, by what factor would the tension of the string need to be changed?

8. The end of a stretched rope is oscillated at a certain frequency in order to create waves. If the frequency is suddenly doubled, what happens to the wavelength of the waves? What happens to the speed of the waves?

9. A wave on a string encounters a new string. The reflected portion of the wave is inverted compared to the original wave. Compare the linear mass densities of the strings.

10. A stretched rope experiences no oscillations despite the fact that it is being oscillated at each end. What is happening?

PRACTICE PROBLEMS FOR MODULE #6

1. A mass/spring system (m = 15.0 kg) is constructed as shown to the right. The first spring has a force constant of 112 N/m, while the second spring has a force constant of 235 N/m. When the mass is displaced from equilibrium and released, what is the period of the motion? (HINT: The springs will stretch different distances when a force is applied to the mass.)

$k = 112$ N/m $m = 15.0$ kg

$k = 235$ N/m

2. A mass/spring system is set in simple harmonic motion. What fraction of the system's energy is kinetic when the mass is one-half of its maximum distance from equilibrium?

3. The displacement of a mass/spring system from its equilibrium position follows this equation:

$$x = (10.0 \text{ cm}) \cdot \cos\left[(11.5 \frac{\text{rad}}{\text{sec}}) \cdot t + \frac{\pi}{2} \right]$$

a. What is the amplitude of the motion?
b. What is the period of the motion?
c. If the block has a mass of 4.5 kg, what is the spring constant?
d. What was the definition of time = 0 for this system?
e. What is the velocity of the block at t = 5.00 seconds?

4. For the mass/spring system in problem #3, what are the maximum speed and acceleration of the block? Where do they occur?

5. A mass/spring system (mass = M, k = K) is set in simple harmonic motion on a frictionless surface with an amplitude of A. When the block is halfway between equilibrium and its maximum distance from equilibrium, a block (mass = ¼·M) is added on top of the first mass. Please note that this is a perfectly inelastic collision.

a. What is the ratio of the frequency of oscillation before the block was added to the frequency after the block was added?
b. What is the ratio of the amplitude before the block was added to the amplitude after the block was added?
c. Suppose the extra block was added when the mass was at A rather than ½·A. Would that change either of the previous two answers? Why or why not?

6. What is the ratio of the period of a simple pendulum of length L to a pendulum made of a uniform rod of length L that pivots on one end? (The moment of inertia of a rod pivoting on one end is $I = \frac{1}{3} \cdot M \cdot L^2$.)

7. A rope (length = 4.00 m, mass = 0.750 kg) is stretched with a tension of 85.0 N. A wave (λ = 45.0 cm) travels down it. What is the frequency of the wave?

8. A wave travels along a string according to the following equation:

$$y = (0.111 \text{ m}) \cdot \sin\left[\frac{2\pi}{(0.350 \text{ m})} \cdot ([35.0 \frac{\text{m}}{\text{sec}}] \cdot t + x)\right]$$

a. If motion to the right is positive, which way is the wave propagating?
b. What is the amplitude of the wave?
c. If the tension in the string is 341 N, what is the linear mass density of the string?

9. The speed of a wave traveling down a stretched rope (length = 5.50 m) is measured to be 45.0 m/sec. What is the frequency of a standing wave on that rope if the wave has 4 nodes?

10. A rope ($\mu = 0.350$ kg/m) is stretched between two fixed points with a tension of 45.0 N. An experimenter notices that the rope has a fundamental resonant frequency of 1.13 Hz. How long is the rope?

Module #7: Sound and Light

Introduction

In the previous module, you learned a lot about waves in general. Now I want to discuss the two kinds of waves you experience every day: sound waves and light waves. Sound waves are probably the easiest to understand, so I will start with them. Then, I will move into a discussion of light and optics.

Sound Waves

As I mentioned briefly in the previous module, and as you should remember from your first-year physics course, sound waves are longitudinal waves. They can travel in many different mediums, but when we hear sound, it is because the waves are traveling in air. When a guitar player plucks a string on the guitar, it begins vibrating at its resonant frequencies, which is determined by the length of the vibrating part of the string, the tension in the string, and the linear mass density of the string. We hear that as sound because as the string vibrates, it pushes the molecules in the air back and forth, making compressions and rarefactions of the molecules in the air. This sets up a longitudinal wave, which then travels to our ears. The mechanisms in our ears pick up those vibrations and convert them to signals sent to our brains, and our brains then interpret those signals as sound.

Although longitudinal waves are different from the transverse waves that I have discussed up to this point, the major concepts and equations still apply. For example, standing longitudinal waves can be set up under certain conditions, and Equation (6.13), the relationship between frequency and wavelength, applies as well. At the same time, however, some of the equations you used in the previous module do not apply here because those equations were based on the physical characteristics of the medium involved. For example, the equation that tells us the velocity of waves on a string [Equation (6.19)] obviously will not apply to *sound* waves, because sound waves oscillate the air, not a string.

Don't get confused here. When a guitar player plucks a string on the guitar, the standing wave set up on the string *does* obey Equation (6.19). However, *that wave* is *not* a sound wave. It is a standing wave on a string. Now, that wave *produces* a sound wave, as I discussed above. However, if the guitar were strummed in a vacuum, the string would still vibrate at its fundamental frequency, but *there would be no sound*, because there would not be any air to push back and forth and thus no longitudinal wave.

When discussing sound, we usually refer to the frequency as **pitch**. The higher the frequency of the sound wave, the higher the pitch. Typically, for example, women speak and sing at a higher pitch than men. This is because women typically have shorter vocal cords than men. Thus, the vocal cords support standing waves of shorter wavelength, which correspond to higher frequency. When the cords vibrate, then, they push air back and forth at a higher frequency, and as a result, women speak and sing at a higher pitch than do men.

Now as you already know, the frequency of a wave is related to its wavelength by the speed of the wave [Equation (6.13)]. Thus, if we know the pitch of a sound wave as well as its speed, we can determine the wavelength. What is the speed of sound? Not surprisingly, it depends on the medium that is transmitting the sound. In general, the speed of sound is given by:

$$v = \sqrt{\frac{\kappa}{\rho}} \tag{7.1}$$

where "v" is the speed, and ρ is the density of the medium. The variable "κ" (the Greek letter "kappa") is the **bulk modulus** of the medium. The bulk modulus is a measure of how easy it is to compress the medium. If the medium is easily compressed, its bulk modulus is low; if the medium is hard to compress, its bulk modulus is high.

Equation (7.1) is not all that useful because the bulk modulus of a medium depends on lots of things. Thus, you have to have many tables in order to use this equation properly. However, there is one thing that you can learn from this equation. In general, the compressibility of a gas is lower than that of a liquid, which is, in turn, lower than that of a solid. Thus, the speed of sound in gas is lower than the speed of sound in a liquid, which is lower than the speed of sound in a solid. This is an important point:

Sound waves travel slower in gas than they do in liquid. They also travel slower in liquid than they do in solid.

Since the speed of a sound wave changes when it changes the medium through which it travels, it is important to note that the *frequency* does not. If a sound wave is traveling in air and then suddenly hits the water, the wave will travel more quickly in the water, but it will have the same frequency as the wave that was traveling in the air. However, its *wavelength* will change.

Since we mostly deal with sound waves traveling through air, it would be nice to have Equation (7.1) evaluated for the specific medium of air. Well, it turns out that both the bulk modulus as well as the density of air depend on the temperature. When this effect is taken into account, the **speed of sound in air** is given by the equation:

$$v = (331.5 + 0.606 \cdot T) \, \frac{m}{sec} \tag{7.2}$$

where "v" is the speed of sound in air, and "T" is the temperature. In order for this equation to work, *the temperature must be expressed in degrees Celsius*. When using this equation, use the temperature in degrees Celsius but just put it into the equation as a number with no unit. If you do that, then the equation is defined so that the speed comes out in m/sec.

Okay, we know about the frequency and speed of sound. What's left? Well, if the frequency of a sound wave is determined by pitch, what determines the loudness of the sound? That is determined by the amplitude of the wave. The tighter the compressions in the sound wave, the louder the sound. It turns out to be a bit easier to measure the **intensity** of a sound wave than it is to measure the amplitude, so we will discuss intensity rather than amplitude.

Intensity of a sound wave - The rate at which sound energy flows through a given area

The intensity of a wave is proportional to the square of its amplitude. Thus, discussing the intensity of a wave is similar to discussing its amplitude. Since the intensity of a sound wave is defined as the energy per unit area, the unit for intensity is Watts (W) per meter squared.

Given that definition of the intensity of a sound wave, physicists use the **bel scale** to measure the loudness of a wave:

$$B = 10 \cdot \log\left(\frac{I}{I_o}\right) \qquad (7.3)$$

In this equation, "B" is the loudness (measured in bels), "I" is the intensity of the sound (in Watts/m^2), and I_o is the intensity of sound which is just at the threshold of human hearing ($I_o = 1.0 \times 10^{-12}$ W/m^2).

Believe it or not, you have heard of this scale before. However, since the bel is a large unit, we typically speak in terms of the **decibel (dB)**, which is one-tenth of a bel. Normal conversation, for example, typically takes place at a loudness of 40 dB. What does that mean? Well, look at Equation (7.1). When the intensity of the sound waves is equal to I_o, the loudness of the sound is 0 bels. Now, since the equation involves taking a log of a ratio, we say that the loudness scale is a **logarithmic scale**. That means an increase in 1 bel is an increase of a factor of 10 in intensity. Thus, a 1 bel sound wave is ten times as intense as a 0 bel sound wave, but a 2 bel sound wave is 100 times as intense as a sound wave at the threshold of hearing. Well, 40 dB is 4 bels, so normal conversation involves sound waves which are 10,000 times more intense than the sound waves that are at the threshold of human hearing.

The table below lists the loudness of common sounds in decibels.

TABLE 7.1
The Loudness of Some Common Sounds

Sound	Decibels	Sound	Decibels
Soft Whisper	20	Gasoline-Powered Mower	95
Normal Conversation	40	Typical Rock Concert	115
Busy Traffic	70	Physical Pain To Ears	120
Pneumatic Drill	80	Physical Damage to Ears	130

Of course, you have to realize that these sound levels depend on *where* you are relative to the sound. After all, as you travel away from the source of a sound, the loudness of the sound decreases. Why? Well, as the sound wave travels, it spreads out in a spherical wave front whose surface area is proportional to the square of the distance traveled. This means:

The intensity of a sound wave is inversely proportional to the square of the distance that the sound wave travels.

Suppose you are standing next to a gasoline-powered mower and do not like the loud noise. If you increase the distance between you and the mower by a factor of 10, the intensity of the wave will decrease by a factor of 10^2, or 100. That corresponds to a drop of 2 bels. Thus, the noise level from the mower will drop from 95 dB to 75 dB.

To give you a little experience with sound waves, perform the following experiment.

EXPERIMENT 7.1
Sound Waves in a Bottle and the "Bottle Paradox"

Supplies:

- Two identical empty glass bottles
- Water
- Vinegar (Any kind)
- Baking soda
- A butter knife
- A funnel
- Paper towels
- A countertop or desktop

Introduction - This experiment will help you learn about the relationship between wavelength and pitch of a sound wave, how the bulk modulus of the medium affects the speed of sound, and why the pitch of a sound depends on *what* is actually vibrating.

Procedure:

1. Take a glass bottle and place your lower lip on the edge of the bottle's opening. Then, blow into the bottle. With a bit of practice, you should eventually hear a nice sound coming from the bottle. That sound is the result of a longitudinal standing wave that you are producing in the air inside the bottle.
2. Next, put the bottle on a countertop or desktop and strike it gently with the knife. You should hear a sound that is markedly different in pitch than the sound you heard in Step #1. Why is it different? In this step, the *glass bottle* is the thing that is vibrating. Those vibrations then push air back and forth, making a sound wave. Thus, you are not making the air vibrate initially. Instead, you are making the glass bottle vibrate, which then makes the air vibrate. This is the reason that the sounds are different.
3. Fill the other bottle one-third of the way full with water. Now, blow into this bottle the same way you did in Step #1.
4. Blow into the bottle that is still empty. Notice the difference in the pitch. The pitch of the bottle one-third full of water should be *higher* than the pitch of the empty bottle. Why? The bottle with water has less air in it. The distance from your mouth to the end of the air in the

bottle is lower than it is in the empty bottle. As a result, the standing wave you can produce in the bottle with water has a *smaller wavelength* than does the wave in the empty bottle. As a result, the wave in the bottle with water has a *higher frequency*. Thus, it makes a higher-pitched sound.

5. Put both bottles on the countertop or desktop.

6. Hit each bottle with the knife again. Now which one produces the higher-pitched sound? The *empty bottle* produces the higher-pitched sound here. Why? In this case, the bottle with the water can support the longer wavelength, because of the water you added. Thus, it produces a *lower* frequency. This is often called the "Bottle Paradox," because the bottle with water produces a higher pitch when blown and a lower one when struck.

7. Leaving the bottle with water in it alone, fill the other bottle two-thirds with water and repeat Steps 3-6. Once again, you should hear that the bottle with the higher level of water produces a higher pitch when blown and a lower pitch when struck.

8. Empty both bottles.

9. Fill each bottle one-third full of vinegar.

10. Put about a teaspoon of baking soda into one of the two bottles. You will see a reaction occurring, because the acetic acid in the baking soda is reacting with the sodium bicarbonate in the baking soda to make carbon dioxide gas. Allow the solution in the bottle to settle. This will take a while.

11. Once the solution in the bottle has settled, wipe the tops of both bottles with paper towels to get rid of any vinegar that may be on the lips of the bottles.

12. Blow into the bottle that contains just vinegar in order to remind yourself of the pitch it produces. Try not to inhale while your mouth is over the bottle, as vinegar fumes are nasty.

13. Blow into the bottle to which you added baking soda. Note the difference in pitch.

14. Blow into that bottle several times. Note that the pitch changes until eventually, it sounds like the other bottle. Why did this happen? The bottle to which you added baking soda was no longer full of air. It was full of the carbon dioxide produced in the reaction. The bulk modulus of carbon dioxide is lower than that of air. Thus, the speed of sound in the carbon dioxide is lower than the speed of sound in air. For a given wavelength (determined by the water level), then, the bottle with carbon dioxide will produce a lower pitch. Why did the pitch change as you kept blowing? Well, as you blew, the carbon dioxide in the bottle was replaced by the mixture of gases you exhaled, which is close to that of air. Thus, the pitch increased until it sounded essentially like the pitch from the other bottle.

ON YOUR OWN

7.1 An amplifier increases the loudness of a sound by increasing the amplitude and thus the intensity of the sound wave. A certain amplifier increases the loudness of a sound from 30 dB to 100 dB. By what factor did the amplifier increase the intensity of the sound wave?

7.2 Suppose you were to heat up an empty bottle to about 90 °C and cool down an identical bottle to about 5 °C. Then, suppose you blew on each bottle like you did in Experiment 7.1. Would the pitch of the sounds produced be the same? If not, which bottle would produce the lower pitch?

<u>Standing Sound Waves</u>

Just as the superposition of waves on a string can produce standing waves, the superposition of sound waves can also produce standing waves. In your experiment, you set up standing waves in the bottle that you blew into. When you blew into the bottle, you compressed some of the air, which left spaces in which the air was "spread out." In other words, you created compressions and rarefactions. Those, of course, constituted a sound wave, which traveled to the bottom of the bottle (or the surface of the water) and then bounced back. Since the length of air in which the waves could travel was fixed, a standing wave developed.

If you were to picture a tube in which sound waves traveled, it would probably look something like this:

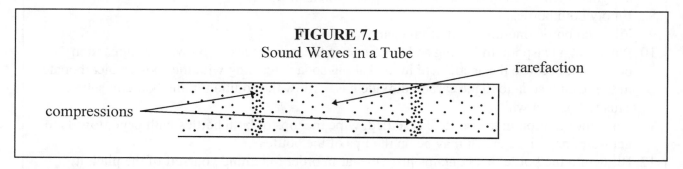

FIGURE 7.1
Sound Waves in a Tube

Although that's the proper way to picture a sound wave, it is a difficult way to understand how to determine the wavelength of standing waves that can get set up in a tube. Thus, although sound waves are really longitudinal (as shown above), I will draw them as transverse just for the purpose of illustrating the kinds of standing waves which can develop.

Think for a moment about the bottles you used in the experiment. They were open on one end and closed on the other. This tells you something about the standing waves you were able to set up in the bottle. After all, there is no way that the air could vibrate past the closed end of the bottle. Thus, the end of the bottle (or the level of the water, which was the end of the air available to the sound wave) must be a *node* of the standing sound wave. However, the open end of the bottle was where the vibrations originated. The vibrations, then, were strongest at that point. Thus, the open end of the bottle was an *antinode* in the experiment. In other words, there was always either a compression or rarefaction at the open end of the bottle. If you think about that situation using a transverse wave, you get the following picture:

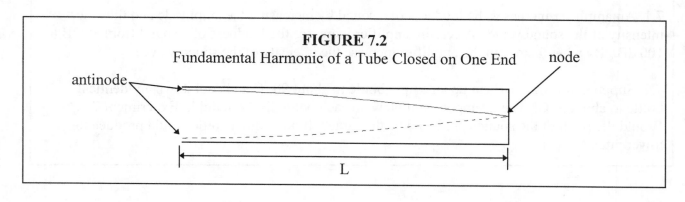

FIGURE 7.2
Fundamental Harmonic of a Tube Closed on One End

Notice that since the node is on one end of the tube and the antinode is on the other end, the length of the tube (L) holds only one-fourth of the wave. Thus, the wavelength is 4·L. Of course, this is just the first (or fundamental) harmonic. Other standing waves can be produced. However, no matter what standing wave is produced, the closed end of the tube must be a node, and the open end must be an antinode. Let's think, then, about the next possible harmonic. If the open end must be an antinode, the next possible harmonic is:

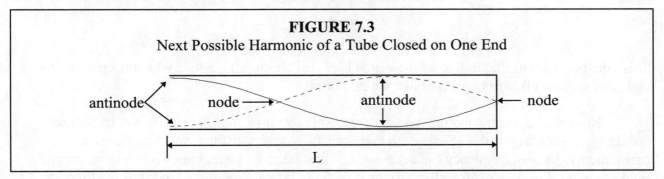

FIGURE 7.3
Next Possible Harmonic of a Tube Closed on One End

antinode   node   antinode   node

L

In this case, then, the wavelength is $\frac{4}{3}$·L. Thus, the fact that the closed end *must* be a node and the open end *must* be an antinode restricts the standing waves that a tube which is closed on one end can support. Notice that the fundamental standing wave is 4·L and the next harmonic has a wavelength of $\frac{4}{3}$·L. You might think that a standing wave with a wavelength of 2·L could be set up in the tube. However, it cannot, because there is no way to fit a wave with that wavelength in the tube and have the closed end as a node and the open end as an antinode. In the end, then, **for a tube closed on one end, the possible standing sound waves are**:

$$\lambda = \frac{4 \cdot L}{n} \qquad n = 1, 3, 5, \dots \qquad (7.4)$$

Notice that "n" cannot be any integer. It must be an *odd* integer. This is because of the restriction that the closed end must be a node and the open end must be an antinode. As a result, we say that a tube which is closed on one end can only accept the *odd* harmonics.

Of course, there is another kind of tube that can support a standing wave. Think, for example, of a flute. A flute is a tube that is open on both ends. Because of that, the standing waves are different than those produced in a tube that is closed on one end. After all, an open end must have an antinode. Thus, in a tube that is open on both ends, there is an antinode on each side of the tube.

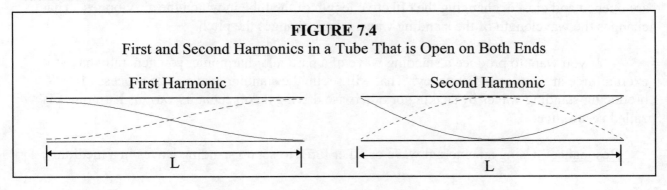

FIGURE 7.4
First and Second Harmonics in a Tube That is Open on Both Ends

First Harmonic   Second Harmonic

L   L

Notice, then, that the first (fundamental) harmonic has a wavelength of 2·L. After all, one end of the tube has a crest while the other end has a trough. That's half of a wave. Thus, the wavelength is 2·L. The second harmonic has a wavelength of L, because the entire wave (crest to crest or trough to trough) is inside the tube. If you were to continue mapping out wavelengths, you would find that **a tube which is open on both ends has the following standing waves**:

$$\lambda = \frac{2 \cdot L}{n} \qquad n = 1,2,3,... \qquad (7.5)$$

This equation tells us that unlike a tube which is closed on one end, a tube which is open on both ends can support all harmonics (not just the odd ones).

Now please understand that when a person blows into a flute, several of the harmonics are set up as standing waves. Since each harmonic has its own distinct wavelength, each harmonic has its own frequency (pitch) as well. Thus, when a person blows into a flute, several pitches are produced. However, the harmonic with the largest amplitude (and thus the loudest volume) is the fundamental (first) harmonic. The other harmonics are there, each producing its own pitch, but because they mix so well with the sound of the first harmonic, and because they are softer than the first harmonic, they cannot be distinguished as separate notes. Thus, the harmonics "add" to the fundamental harmonic to make what is generally called the **timbre** (tam' ber) of the instrument. This is what typically separates the sound of one instrument from the sound of another. If each instrument always played only the fundamental harmonic of a given note, they would all sound the same.

This is true of all instruments, including your voice. When a guitar string is plucked, for example, several harmonics are set up on the guitar string. Thus, several different sound wave frequencies are formed. Once again, however, the fundamental harmonic is the loudest, so that's the pitch you hear. The other harmonics just add to form the timbre of the instrument.

How does an instrument vary the pitches it produces? Well, in the case of a guitar string, the player "tunes" the guitar by varying the tension of each string. The strings, since they have different linear mass densities and different tensions, support different standing waves and thus play different notes. However, the guitar player is certainly not limited to those notes. He or she can pinch a string against the fret board of the guitar. This reduces the length of the string, changing the wavelength of the standing wave, which in turn changes the pitch, making a new note. All instruments work on this principle. Wind instruments (like the flute) have holes that are opened and closed, changing the effective length of the tube in which the air vibrates. That changes the wavelength of the standing wave, which changes the pitch.

If you want to produce a standing wave of a particular harmonic, you generally have to exert a force at the proper frequency. That will set up the standing wave. The process of producing standing waves by shaking or otherwise driving an object at its various harmonics is called **resonance**.

<u>Resonance</u> - Using an external wave or other force to set up standing waves in a medium

When you shook the Slinky at just the right frequencies, you set up standing waves. That's an example of resonance. You were the outside force shaking the medium, which was the Slinky. You shook the Slinky at just the right frequency, and you were able to produce one of three harmonics.

Resonance has all sorts of interesting consequences. Have you ever seen video footage of a singer breaking a glass by singing at a very high pitch? The singer does this with resonance. The sound waves she produces do not have enough energy to break the glass. However, if she sings at just the right frequency, her sound waves will hit the glass at one of its harmonics. When that happens, a standing wave develops in the glass. In this case, an external wave (the singer's sound wave) sets up standing waves in a medium (the glass). The waves in the glass grow in amplitude as the standing wave gets established and, eventually, the violence of the oscillations from the standing waves in the glass actually breaks the glass. The singer could yell at the glass all day and nothing would happen. However, if she uses the right resonant frequency, she will set up a standing wave in the glass which will result in the glass breaking.

This can happen in other situations as well. For example, a **tuning fork** is a metal object shaped a bit like a fork with two prongs. When you strike the tuning fork, it begins shaking at its fundamental harmonic, producing a nice, clear tone. By varying the physical characteristics of the fork, you can vary the pitch of the sound wave produced. If you were to use a tuning fork whose fundamental harmonic corresponded to the *second harmonic* of a guitar string, striking the fork and bringing it near the guitar string would set up a standing wave on the guitar string that corresponded to the string's second harmonic. This is an example of resonance because, once again, an outside wave (the sound waves produced by the tuning fork) set up a standing wave in a medium (the guitar string).

Resonance can also lead to problems. For example, consider a bridge. A bridge is a long "ribbon" of material stretched between two points. Thus, in some ways, it behaves like a string stretched between two points. As a result, it can support standing waves. Thus, the surface of the bridge can, if driven at just the right frequencies, begin oscillating as a wave. Of course, that would be a bad thing, but in fact, it has happened before!

In 1940, the **Tacoma Narrows Bridge** (a bridge in Tacoma, Washington) collapsed because the wind applied forces to the bridge at one of its resonant frequencies. As a result, standing waves were produced, and the bridge began to oscillate. The oscillations eventually became large enough to destroy the bridge. Only a dog lost its life in the disaster, but had the bridge been occupied at the time, it could have been a real tragedy. If you have a hard time believing that such a thing can happen, you can view a video of this very bridge and its standing waves at

http://www.camerashoptacoma.com/narrows.asp

It turns out that *every* object can support standing waves, so every object has resonant frequencies that can destroy it. Engineers now make sure that the resonant frequencies of the structures they build are outside the range of day-to-day experience so that disasters like the

Tacoma Narrows Bridge do not happen again. Before this was done, however, at least *11 bridges* around the world were destroyed by resonance.

EXAMPLE 7.1

If an organ pipe is closed on one end and is 33.0 cm long, what is its fundamental frequency at 24.0 °C?

Since the pipe is closed on one end, we use Equation (7.4) to determine its wavelength:

$$\lambda = \frac{4 \cdot L}{1} = 4 \cdot (0.330 \text{ m}) = 1.32 \text{ m}$$

We can determine the frequency if we know the speed. For that, we must use Equation (7.2):

$$v = (331.5 + 0.606 \cdot T) \, \frac{\text{m}}{\text{sec}} = (331.5 + 0.606 \cdot [24.0]) \, \frac{\text{m}}{\text{sec}} = 346.0 \, \frac{\text{m}}{\text{sec}}$$

Now we can determine the frequency:

$$f = \frac{v}{\lambda} = \frac{346.0 \, \frac{\text{m}}{\text{sec}}}{1.32 \, \text{m}} = \underline{262 \text{ Hz}}$$

That's the frequency for middle "C."

ON YOUR OWN

7.3 A physics student stretches a string ($\mu = 0.0150$ kg/m) between two points. The student then strikes a "G" tuning fork, which vibrates at 392 Hz. He brings the tuning fork near the string and starts tightening the string. He notes that when the tension of the string reaches 144 N, it begins to vibrate at its second harmonic. How long is the string? (You need to use Equation (6.19) and Equation (6.21) to solve this problem).

7.4 A physics student makes two tubes: one that is closed on one end and one that is open. What is the ratio of the lengths of the tubes if they produce the same pitch when air oscillates inside?

<u>Beats</u>

Sounds waves can interfere with one another to form standing waves, but they can also interfere with each other in another interesting way. If two sound waves are produced with close but not identical pitch, they can interfere with one another to produce variations in the *volume* of what is heard. Although sound waves are longitudinal, it is easiest to understand how this happens if you use transverse waves to illustrate the effect.

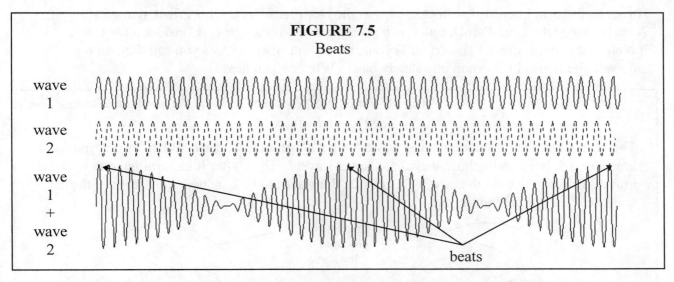

FIGURE 7.5
Beats

Suppose the wave labeled "wave 1" represents the first sound wave, and "wave 2" represents the second sound wave. You have to look very closely, but you can see that they do not have identical wavelengths, and therefore they are of different frequencies. Nevertheless, the frequencies are close to one another. Look what happens when those waves are added together, which is shown at the bottom of the figure. Notice that for a while, the two individual waves constructively interfere. Eventually, however, the second wave gets "out of synch" with the first wave, and the waves begin destructively interfering.

Now think about how this would sound. The overall frequency that a person would hear would be the frequency of the third wave. If you study Figure 7.5, you will notice that the frequency of the third wave is close to the frequency of the other two waves. Thus, the person listening would hear a pitch very close to the pitch of either individual sound wave. However, what the person listening would notice is that the sound varied in *loudness*. Remember, the amplitude of a sound wave determines its volume. Thus, the sound would start out loud, get very soft, get loud again, get soft again, and get loud again. Each time the sound reaches its maximum, we say that a **beat** occurs.

Now notice that the beats themselves occur at a regular frequency as well. It turns out that the frequency can be determined with a very simple equation:

$$f_{beat} = | f_{wave\ 1} - f_{wave2} |$$ (7.6)

The absolute value of the difference in frequencies, then, gives you the frequency of the beats. Note that if the frequencies of the waves are identical, the frequency of beats is zero, indicating that there are no beats. That should make sense, since the very phenomenon of beats is the result of the sound waves having slightly different frequencies.

The Doppler Effect

The fact that the pitch of the sounds you hear is related to the frequency of the sound waves leads to an interesting effect known as the **Doppler effect**. This effect, named after Austrian physicist Christian Doppler, is best explained with a figure. Consider a car that is traveling down the street. The driver is your friend, and when he sees you standing on the sidewalk, he honks his horn in one steady blast. What do you hear?

FIGURE 7.6

Illus. from the MasterClips collection

The Doppler Effect

The horn from a car produces sound waves with a constant frequency. When the car moves, however, the horn emits those waves as the car travels. Thus, after it has emitted one wave, it moves forwards to emit the next. This causes the waves to be bunched up in front of the car and stretched out behind the car.

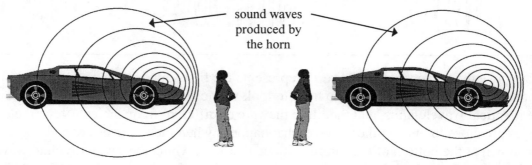

sound waves produced by the horn

Since the sound waves get bunched up in front of the car, the wavelength seems shorter, so the frequency is higher. If the car is heading towards you, then, you will hear a pitch that is higher than the true pitch of the horn.

When the car passes you, the sound waves that reach your ears are the ones traveling behind the car. These sound waves are stretched out, which gives them a longer wavelength and thus a lower frequency. This results in a pitch that is suddenly lower than that of the true pitch.

The Doppler effect, then, is a result of the wave nature of sound. When a sound-emitting object is moving towards you, the crests and troughs of the sound waves get pushed closer to one another. This decreases the wavelength and, therefore, increases the frequency of the sound that your ears hear. This results in a pitch that is higher than the pitch you would hear if the object were stationary. Once the object begins moving away from you, the crests and troughs get pulled farther away from one another. This increases the wavelength and, therefore, decreases the frequency of the sound that hits your ears. As a result, the pitch is lower than what it would be if the object were stationary.

Of course, you can produce the same effect by moving towards or away from a fixed object which is emitting sound waves. If the object is stationary, its sound waves do not get "bunched up" or "stretched out" like those of a moving object. However, if you move towards the object, you will start encountering its sound waves at a high frequency, because the relative velocity between you and the sound waves has decreased. Thus, moving towards an object generates the same Doppler effect that you experience when a moving object moves towards you.

In the same way, if you run away from a stationary object that is emitting a sound, the sound waves will hit you with a *lower* frequency, because the relative velocity between you and the sound waves has decreased. Thus, moving away from a fixed object results in the same Doppler effect that you experience when a moving object is traveling away from you.

The Doppler effect is actually very easy to calculate. It depends only on the true frequency of the sound wave (in other words, the pitch you would hear if neither you nor the source of the sound were moving), the speed of the observer, and the speed of the sound's source:

$$f_{observed} = \left(\frac{v_{sound} \pm v_{observer}}{v_{sound} \pm v_{source}} \right) \cdot f_{true} \qquad (7.7)$$

How do you know when to use pluses and minuses in this equation? Well, all you have to do is reason it out. For example, suppose the source is moving. If it is moving *away from* the observer, you must use a *plus* in the denominator of the equation. After all, when the source moves away from the observer, the frequency observed will be *lower* than the true frequency. The way you will get an observed frequency lower than the true frequency is if the number in the denominator is increased. Thus, you use the plus sign so that the denominator gets bigger. In the same way, suppose the observer is moving away from the source. If that's the case, then once again you expect the observed frequency to be lower than the true frequency, so you would use the *minus* sign in the numerator of the equation so that the numerator (and thus the observed frequency) gets smaller.

EXAMPLE 7.2

A horn emits a sound with a frequency of 355 Hz when the car is at rest. If a car is traveling towards a person on a bicycle and beeps the horn, what frequency will the bicyclist hear? The car is traveling at a speed of 21.0 m/sec, and the bicyclist is traveling towards the car with a speed of 4.2 m/sec. Assume that the speed of sound is 343.0 m/sec.

This is a direct application of Equation (7.7). Since the car is traveling towards the observer, that will increase the horn's frequency. Thus, we must use a minus in the denominator of the equation to make the denominator smaller. Since the observer is moving towards the source, that will also increase the frequency. Thus, we must use a plus sign in the numerator of the equation to make the numerator bigger. The equation, then, is:

$$f_{observed} = \left(\frac{v_{sound} + v_{observer}}{v_{sound} - v_{source}} \right) \cdot f_{true} = \frac{343.0 \frac{m}{sec} + 4.2 \frac{m}{sec}}{343.0 \frac{m}{sec} - 21.0 \frac{m}{sec}} \cdot 355 \text{ Hz} = \underline{383 \text{ Hz}}$$

Now please note that although the Doppler effect is best illustrated with sound waves, it applies to *all waves*. For example, astronomers think that the universe is expanding because they observe that light waves coming from stars is shifted in a way that looks like a Doppler shift. If it is a Doppler shift, it indicates that most stars are moving away from the earth.

ON YOUR OWN

7.5 A train is traveling north at 45.0 m/sec. A man is behind the train in a car. He is also traveling north at 25.0 m/sec. If the train blows its horn (frequency = 411 Hz when the train and observer are both stationary), what is the frequency that the man will hear? (T = 25.0 °C)

Light: Electromagnetic Waves

       In your first-year physics course, you learned about optics. Mostly likely, you learned about reflection, refraction, and how light behaves when it hits mirrors and lenses. While you learned all of that, you probably drew light as a ray: a straight line that travels to a mirror, for example, and then reflects off of the mirror as another straight line. This is the way that Newton pictured light. He thought of light as a stream of particles that traveled in a straight line. However, we now know that light has properties which are best understood if we think of light as a wave. Perform the following experiment to see what I mean.

EXPERIMENT 7.2
Interference of Light Waves

Supplies:
- A comb
- A cardboard tube (A tube from a roll of toilet paper works best. If you have a longer tube, cut it down to the length of a roll of toilet paper.)
- Black construction paper
- Tape
- A flashlight (It needs to be a small flashlight that can fit inside the tube.)
- A dark room

Introduction - As you already know, waves can constructively and destructively interfere with one another. In this experiment, you will see how light can constructively and destructively interfere with itself, indicating that light is a wave.

Procedure:

1. Most combs have teeth that are spaced farther from one another at one end and closer to one another at the other. You want to use the construction paper and tape to cover the entire comb *except for one tooth and the spaces on each side of the tooth*. Use a tooth on the end where the teeth are close together. Your comb should look like the following drawing:

          comb

comb that is mostly covered with black paper -
one tooth and the space on each side is exposed

2. Put the comb covered in paper across the end of the tube. The exposed tooth on the comb should be near the center of the tube opening. Use tape to attach the comb to the tube.

3. If there are any open spaces between the comb and the tube, cover them with black paper and tape. In the end, the only way light should be able to pass through that end of the tube is through the two spaces on either side of the exposed tooth.

4. Take the flashlight and the comb/tube assembly into a dark room. Turn on the flashlight and stick it in the tube.

5. Point the tube to a blank wall and look at the light that comes out. It will probably look a little strange.

6. With the tube still pointing to the wall, tilt the flashlight so that it shines mostly at the side of the tube.

7. Looking at the light cast on the wall, move the flashlight back and forth (and perhaps play with the tilt of the flashlight) until you see several bars of light on the wall.

8. Now remember, there are only two spaces through which the light can travel (the spaces on either side of the exposed tooth). However, you should be able to position the flashlight so that you see *several* bars of light on the wall. How does that happen? You will learn the answer to that question in a moment.

9. Before you finish, play around with the tilt and position of the flashlight to see what kinds of patterns you can make.

10. Clean everything up.

What did you see in the experiment? You saw the **wave nature of light**. Imagine that the flashlight was putting out waves. The waves hit the comb, which has just two slits through which the waves could travel. As the waves began traveling through the slits, eventually, the waves from one slit began to overlap with the waves from the other slit. The result was a pattern of constructive and destructive interference that produced a pattern of light and dark spots on the wall. This situation is depicted in the figure below:

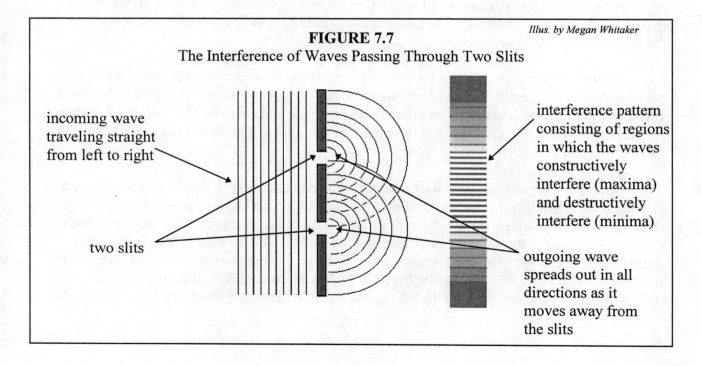

FIGURE 7.7
The Interference of Waves Passing Through Two Slits

Illus. by Megan Whitaker

incoming wave traveling straight from left to right

two slits

interference pattern consisting of regions in which the waves constructively interfere (maxima) and destructively interfere (minima)

outgoing wave spreads out in all directions as it moves away from the slits

This experiment was originally performed by Thomas Young in 1801. He considered it solid evidence that light is, indeed, a wave. That view of light remained unchanged until Einstein came on the scene in the early 1900's. You will learn about what happened then in a later module of this course. Of course, you should already know that light has properties consistent with those of a wave. For example, you should know that the brightness of light is proportional to the amplitude of the light wave, and the wavelength of visible light determines the color of the visible light.

Let's look at the details of what happens in an experiment like the one you performed. First, notice that when the light passes through the slits, the direction of its travel changes. Prior to hitting the slits, the waves were traveling straight from the left side of the figure to the right side of the figure. Once the waves hit the slits, however, they "bent" around the slits and started radiating outwards from the slits. This phenomenon is called **diffraction**, and all waves behave this way when they travel through small openings or encounter obstacles.

<u>Diffraction</u> - The spreading of waves around an obstacle

In the experiment, diffraction makes the two slits act like individual light bulbs whose light radiates in all directions on the other side of the slits. Unlike two individual light sources, however, the light from the two slits is **coherent**, which means that the waves all have the same phase angle.

Now think about this for a moment. If I have two waves that have exactly the same equation (the wavelength, speed, amplitude, and phase angle are all the same), it is easy to determine where constructive and destructive interference will occur. Constructive interference will occur when the light from one slit travels a distance that is λ (or any multiple of λ) farther than the other. When that happens, the wave crests and troughs overlap, making constructive interference. That's where you will see bright spots. When the light from one slit travels $\frac{1}{2} \cdot \lambda$ (or any odd multiple of $\frac{1}{2} \cdot \lambda$), the crests of one wave will line up with the troughs of the other, making destructive interference. The interference pattern seen on the screen, then, depends on the wavelength of light involved.

In your experiment, you used white light, which has a range of wavelengths. As a result, your interference pattern was blurred compared to the interference pattern you would observe if you used light of a particular wavelength. However, your experiment was very close to Young's original experiment. He used sunlight instead of a flashlight, and he used a card rather than the tooth of a comb.

One thing you might be wondering is why you had to tilt the flashlight in order to see an interference pattern like the one pictured above. You might also be wondering why the pattern changed so much when you changed the position and tilt of the flashlight. The answer to both of those question lies in the *phase* of the waves produced. A flashlight bulb produces light that travels in all directions. The light heading away from the flashlight continues on its way, while the light traveling the other way gets reflected off of the shiny coating behind the light bulb and then starts traveling away from the flashlight. As a result, the light that comes from a flashlight contains waves with a mix of phase angles. In order to get a nice, definite interference pattern on the wall, however, you really need to use light waves which are coherent, as discussed above. By tilting the flashlight, you are selecting mostly those light waves which originally traveled away from the flashlight and were not reflected off of the shiny surface. Thus, these waves mostly had the same phase. As you turned the flashlight and played with its position, you began introducing waves with several phase angles, and that changed the interference pattern.

Now of course, if light is a wave, there is a question that must be answered: *What does light oscillate?* After all, a wave must oscillate a medium. Water waves oscillate water. Sound waves oscillate air (or whatever substance through which sound travels). The waves on a guitar string oscillate the string. So what does light oscillate? It does not oscillate air, because it travels through the vacuum of space. Sound cannot travel through space because there is nothing for it to oscillate. Light, however, can, as evidenced by the fact that we see light from stars and light reflected off of planets. The question remains - WHAT does light oscillate?

That question plagued physicists throughout the turn of the century. For a long time, physicists thought that there was a substance called the **ether**, which permeated space, the earth, and anywhere else light traveled. Light travels through space, so the ether must be in space. Light travels through air, so the ether must be in air as well.

In 1887, however, two physicists, A. A. Michelson and E.W. Morley, devised an experiment to measure some physical characteristics of the ether, and to their surprise, the experiment indicated that there probably was no such thing as the ether. Several physicists tried to explain their way around that experiment, but the explanations seemed rather desperate. In the end, the Michelson-Morley experiment threw physicists right back to where they were before: They could not answer a fundamental question: "What does light oscillate?"

In 1873, the great physicist James Clerk Maxwell (a devoted Christian who started every experiment with a prayer) had already derived a series of equations which we today call **Maxwell's Equations**. Although the implications of his equations were not understood until later, they were recognized as important, because the equations described in mathematical detail the relationship between electrical and magnetic phenomena. The equations indicate that electrical and magnetic phenomena are related, and the relationship involves a wave. The equations also predict the speed of that wave, and the speed predicted is equal to the *measured* speed of light. Now please understand how important this is. Maxwell's equations, which unify electrical and magnetic forces into a single **electromagnetic force**, specify that this force is mediated by a wave whose speed is a direct result of the mathematics. That speed is equal to the measured speed of light (2.998×10^8 m/sec), which is typically abbreviated as "c."

What does that tell us? It took physicists a while to realize the implication, but Maxwell's equations tell us that light is an *electromagnetic wave*. What does that mean? Well, remember from your first-year course that when an electric field varies, it produces a magnetic field. For example, as current runs through a wire, a magnetic field is produced because the electrical field varies as the charges in the current move. Also, remember that a changing magnetic field produces a changing electric field. For example, when you vary the magnetic field that passes through a conductor, an electric current is produced. As you learned in your first-year physics course, that's how an electrical power plant produces electricity.

Think about those two facts. Suppose you varied a magnetic field. What would you get? You would get an electric field. Suppose you varied the magnetic field at a certain frequency. The resulting electric field would also vary at that frequency. However, what does a varying electric field produce? A magnetic field. Do you get the picture? A varying magnetic field produces a varying electric field, which produces a varying magnetic field, which produces a varying electric field, and on and on and on. *That's* an electromagnetic wave, and that's what light is.

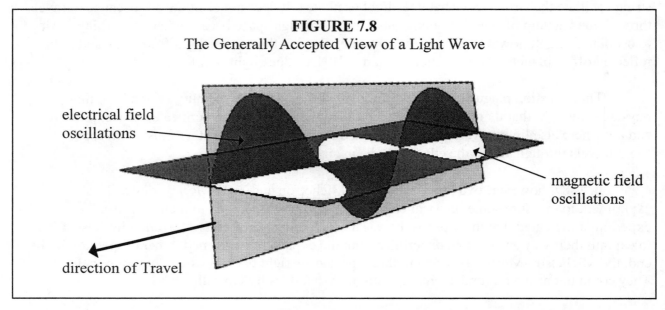

FIGURE 7.8
The Generally Accepted View of a Light Wave

electrical field oscillations

magnetic field oscillations

direction of Travel

Of course, like any other wave, an electromagnetic wave can have a wide range of wavelengths. As a result, there are many wavelengths in the **electromagnetic spectrum**. Thus, the broader term for light is simply "electromagnetic wave," and the light that we can see (visible light) is only a tiny range of the wavelengths (400 - 700 nm) in the electromagnetic spectrum.

FIGURE 7.9
The Electromagnetic Spectrum

WAVELENGTH

10^{-14} m 10^{-12}m 10^{-10} m 10^{-8} m 10^{-6} m 10^{-4} m 10^{-2} m   1 m 10^{2} m 10^{4}m

Gamma Rays		Ultraviolet Rays			Infrared		TV		
			Visible light				Short-wave Radio		
	X-Rays					Microwaves	FM		AM

10^{22} Hz 10^{20} Hz 10^{18} Hz 10^{16} Hz 10^{14} Hz 10^{12} Hz 10^{10} Hz 10^{8} Hz 10^{6} Hz 10^{4} Hz

FREQUENCY

ON YOUR OWN

7.6 A student tries to set up an interference pattern using two tiny light bulbs rather than light hitting two slits. He reasons that diffraction simply makes the slits act like tiny light sources. Will he see an interference pattern? Why or why not?

A Quick Review of Reflection and Refraction

Although light definitely has wave characteristics, a beam of light can still be represented as a ray traveling in a straight line for the purposes of analyzing physical situations. In fact, in your first-year physics course, that's probably how you represented light when you studied optics. During your study of optics, you learned the law of **reflection**:

Law of reflection - The angle of reflection equals the angle of incidence

When light is reflected off of a surface, then, the angle at which it leaves the surface is equal to the angle at which it hits the surface.

In your first-year course, you also should have learned about **refraction**:

Refraction - The process by which a light ray bends when it encounters a new medium

The amount that it bends is governed by **Snell's Law**, which is given by the following equation:

$$n_1 \cdot \sin\theta_1 = n_2 \cdot \sin\theta_2 \qquad (7.8)$$

In this equation, "θ_1" is the angle of the incident light ray relative to a line perpendicular to the surface between the old medium and the new medium, while "θ_2" is the angle of the light relative to that same line once the light is in the new medium. The "n_1" and "n_2" terms represent the **index of refraction** of the old medium and the new medium, respectively. What is the index of refraction of a medium? It is the ratio of the speed of light in a vacuum to the speed of light in the medium.

$$n = \frac{c}{v_{\text{light in medium}}} \qquad (7.9)$$

Remember, the speed of light is a physical constant - a consequence of Maxwell's equations. Those equations also tell us that when light encounters a new medium, its speed changes. The speed of light is highest in a vacuum, so $n \geq 1$.

Let's put all of this together and combine it with what you learned about waves in the previous module. Suppose that light is incident on the surface of a bowl of water. The law of reflection, combined with Snell's Law, leads us to the following picture:

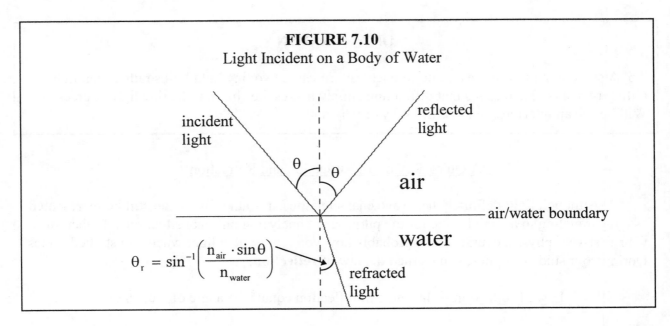

FIGURE 7.10
Light Incident on a Body of Water

Notice what we have here. The light is striking the surface of the water at an angle of θ relative to a line perpendicular to the surface of the water. A portion of the light is reflected and a portion is transmitted. Why? In the previous module, you learned that when a wave encounters a new medium, part of the wave is reflected and part is transmitted into the new medium. Since light has wavelike properties, this happens to light as well. Your own experience tells you this. After all, when you look at the surface of a body of water, you can see your face (thus light is reflected from the surface), but you can also see under the water (so light must travel in and back out of the water as well). The angle of the reflected light ray is equal to the angle of the incident light ray. The angle of the refracted light ray depends on the index of refraction of both mediums, according to Snell's Law. If light moves more slowly in the new medium, the light ray bends *towards* the perpendicular line. If light moves more quickly in the new medium, the light ray will bend *away from* the perpendicular line.

There are a couple of consequences to refraction which are worth discussing. For example, I am sure that somewhere along the line during your education, you shined some visible light on a prism or crystal and saw that the light was separated into several colors. The reason this happens is because of **dispersion**:

Dispersion - The variation in wave speed due to wavelength

Although the speed of light is not related to its wavelength *in a vacuum*, once the light travels through a material medium, its speed is affected by the wavelength. **The higher the energy (the shorter the wavelength), the slower the light travels in a material medium.** Remember, the spectrum of colors in white light can be remembered by thinking about a man named ROY G. BIV. In this acronym, the colors of light are listed in terms of *increasing energy* (decreasing wavelength). Thus, red light has the lowest energy (longest wavelength), while violet light has the highest energy (smallest wavelength) of visible light.

Based on Equation (7.9), then, you can predict that the *index of refraction* of red light is lowest (because its speed is highest), while the *index of refraction* of violet light is the largest. Think about the practical result of this, then. When white light (all wavelengths) enters a piece of glass, the violet light is bent towards the perpendicular more than is the red light. Thus, inside the glass, the light is "spread out," depending on the wavelength. Then, when the light leaves the glass, the violet light is bent away from the perpendicular more than is the red light. Once again, then, the white light gets "spread out," depending on the wavelength. That's why light is separated into its colors when it passes through a prism.

There is another interesting consequence of refraction. Consider the situation in which light passes from a medium whose index of refraction is high into a medium in which the index of refraction is low. If you solve Snell's Law for the light's angle when it enters the new medium, you will find that there are certain angles for which refraction cannot occur. That happens when

$$\sin\theta_1 \geq \frac{n_2}{n_1} \quad \text{(condition for total internal reflection)} \quad (7.10)$$

For these angles, solving Snell's Law tells you that θ_2 is 90° or undefined. What does this mean? It means for any angles given by Equation (7.10), light never enters the new medium. Thus, the light is completely reflected back into the old medium.

If the value of the incidence angle is given by Equation (7.10), *no refraction can occur*. **All of the light will be reflected back into the original medium.**

This phenomenon, called **total internal reflection**, is used in fiber optics to allow light to pass through long fibers without "leaking out" along the way.

Okay, except for the last two topics, the rest of this section should have been review for you. In the next section, we will take these concepts and apply them to mirrors. Once again, that will be partly review for you, but there will be new material as well.

ON YOUR OWN

7.7 Suppose a light ray is traveling in air (n =1.00) and hits a layer of glass, as shown in the figure. The incident angle is 60.0° relative to the perpendicular.

a. Draw five light rays that will result, filling in their angles.
b. If the reflected light is allowed to hit a screen above the glass layers, an interference pattern will be observed. Why?
c. Consider the two light rays that are interfering with one another as they travel to the screen. They each travel a different distance to the screen. If the difference between the distances they travel is Δl, what is the relationship between Δl and λ that will result in destructive interference?

<u>Flat Mirrors</u>

You worked with flat mirrors already in your first-year physics course, so I don't want to spend too much time on them here. However, I do want to point out something about flat mirrors that you may not have noticed. Consider, for example, a man in a tuxedo. He wants to make sure he looks okay before he goes out to his formal dinner. Thus, he wants to see himself in a full-length mirror. How tall must the mirror be in order for the man to see his entire body?

To answer this question, think about *why* the man sees himself. When light strikes his foot, for example, some of it bounces off of his foot and hits the mirror. The light then strikes the mirror and reflects according to the Law of Reflection. Then, the light hits his eyes, and he sees it. Since his brain is used to thinking that light travels in a straight line, it extrapolates the light straight back and sees an image *inside* of the mirror.

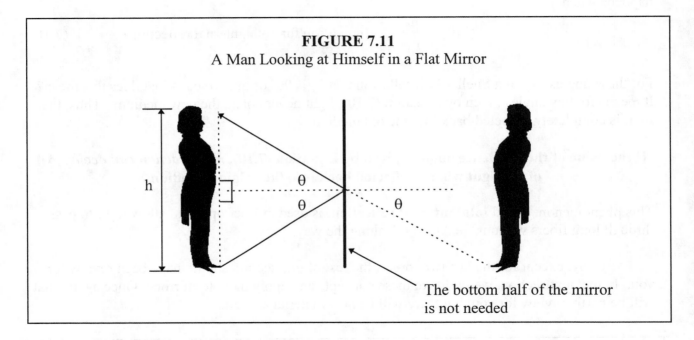

FIGURE 7.11
A Man Looking at Himself in a Flat Mirror

The bottom half of the mirror
is not needed

The man sees his own eyes, his head, etc. in the same manner.

Now let's examine the geometry of the situation. In order to hit his eyes, the light that comes from the man's feet must hit the mirror at just the right angle. Such is the case for him to see any part of his body, but let's concentrate on his feet. The light ray that hits his eyes (essentially the top of his head) must bounce off of the mirror at a specific angle (θ relative to the perpendicular), which also equals the angle of incidence. If I then draw a line (the horizontal dashed line), perpendicular to both the man and the mirror, which hits the mirror at the same point as the light ray hits the mirror, I get two right triangles which share a side. The angle inside each right triangle must be θ. Thus, I have two triangles that have two equal angles (θ and the 90° angle) and one equal side (the side they share). By the angle-side-angle postulate of geometry, the two triangles are identical. Well, notice that the two bases of the triangles add up to the man's height (h). Thus, the base of each triangle is h/2. What does that mean? Since the light from the foot must hit just the very bottom of the mirror, then the mirror need only have a height of h/2 in order for the man to see his full reflection! Any additional mirror is wasted.

I showed you this for two reasons. First, I wanted to make sure you understood that optics does not always give us the results we expect. Most people think that a full-length mirror must be as tall as the person who wants to see himself. That might "make sense," but physics says it is not true. Thus, when dealing with optics, you really have to think through and analyze the situation before jumping to conclusions. The other reason I went through this example is to show you the geometrical reasoning we often must apply in order to analyze an optics situation. You will be expected to do similar reasoning, such as that given in the "on your own" problem below.

ON YOUR OWN

7.8 Suppose the man in Figure 7.11 is standing at a distance "x" from the mirror. How far back in the mirror does he see his reflection?

Curved Mirrors and the Mirror Equation

Remember from your first-year course that the law of reflection leads to an interesting phenomenon when light strikes a curved mirror:

FIGURE 7.12
Light Rays Striking Two Curved Mirrors

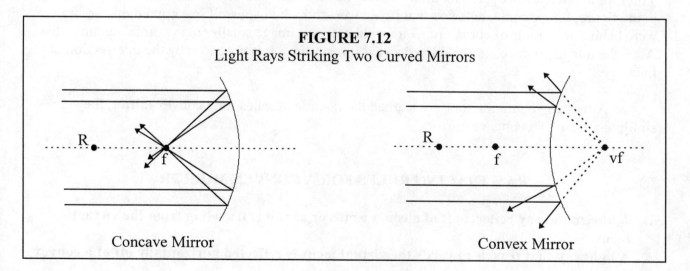

Concave Mirror   Convex Mirror

When light rays which are parallel to the horizontal strike a **concave mirror**, the light rays are focused at the **focal point** (f) of the mirror. The distance from the mirror to that focal point (often called the **focal length**) is equal to half the **radius of curvature** (R) of the mirror. If light strikes a **convex mirror**, the light is reflected back as if it all originated from the focal point on the *other side* of the mirror, which is often called the **virtual focus** (vf) of the mirror.

If you consider the law of reflection and light rays that follow other specific paths, you will find that for concave mirrors, if a light ray travels through the focus, it will be reflected back parallel to the horizontal. Also, light that follows the radius of curvature of the mirror will be reflected straight back along the same line, as the radius of curvature is always perpendicular to the mirror. Thus, if we consider placing an object (such as an arrow) behind the radius of curvature of a concave mirror, the situation would look like this:

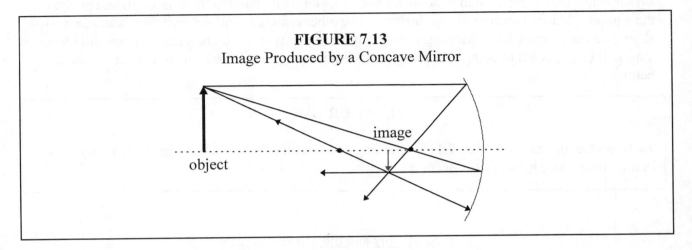

FIGURE 7.13
Image Produced by a Concave Mirror

This should look familiar to you. It is an analytical technique called **ray tracing**, and it allows you to analyze an optical situation to learn about the image formed in mirrors and lenses. You should have learned a lot about ray tracing in your first-year physics course. The ray tracing in the figure, for example, tells you that if you were to look at yourself in a curved mirror and were behind the radius of curvature, you would see your image smaller than normal and inverted. Also, the image produced is considered a **real image**, since it is produced by the intersection of light rays.

Although you might not have learned the ray tracing rules for a convex mirror, they are similar to those of a concave mirror:

RAY TRACING RULES FOR A CONVEX MIRROR

1. **A horizontal ray reflects off of a convex mirror as if it is traveling from the virtual focus.**
2. **A light ray that travels towards the virtual focus is reflected horizontally off of a convex mirror.**
3. **A light ray that is headed towards the radius of curvature of a convex mirror bounces back along exactly the same path.**

If we took the situation depicted above and changed it to a convex mirror, then, the result is illustrated in Figure 7.14.

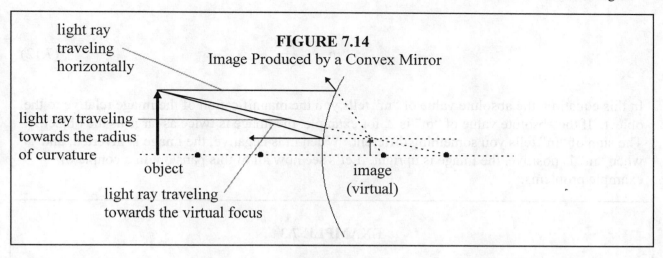

FIGURE 7.14
Image Produced by a Convex Mirror

light ray traveling horizontally

light ray traveling towards the radius of curvature

object

light ray traveling towards the virtual focus

image (virtual)

The image produced by the convex mirror in this example is a **virtual image**, as it is formed by *extrapolating light rays back to their point of intersection*. Note that there is no observable difference between real and virtual images. They look the same. The terms "real" and "virtual" simply denote how the image is formed. Notice also that unlike the image produced in the previous example, this image is **upright** as compared to the object.

Now most of this should be review for you, which is why I went through it so quickly. However, now I want to introduce something new. I want you to see how an equation, reasonably enough called the **mirror equation**, can provide you with even more information than ray tracing does. The mirror equation is:

$$\frac{1}{s_o} + \frac{1}{s_i} = \frac{1}{f}$$

(7.11)

In this equation, "s_o" is the distance from the object to the mirror; "s_i" is the distance from the image produced and the mirror; and "f" is the focal length of the mirror, which is half the radius of curvature.

The mirror equation is a bit more difficult than it first appears, because you have to be aware of certain sign conventions used in the equation:

Sign Conventions for the Mirror Equation

1. The object distance (s_o) is *always* positive.
2. The focal length (f) of a concave mirror is positive; the focal length of a convex mirror is negative.
3. If the image distance (s_i) is positive, it is a real image and is on the same side of the mirror as the object. If the image distance is negative, it is a virtual image on the other side of the mirror.

Before I show you how to use the mirror equation and these sign conventions, I want to show you the **magnification equation**, which tells you how large the image is relative to the object.

$$m = -\frac{s_i}{s_o} \qquad (7.12)$$

In this equation, the absolute value of "m" tells you the magnification of the image relative to the object. If the absolute value of "m" is 2, for example, the image is twice as large as the object. The sign of "m" tells you something different. When m is negative, the image is inverted, and when "m" is positive, the image is upright. Let's see how all of this pans out in a couple of example problems.

EXAMPLE 7.3

An object is placed 10.0 cm from a concave mirror whose radius of curvature is 25.0 cm. On which side of the mirror is the image formed? Is it real or virtual? Is it upright or inverted? What is the magnification?

Do you think I asked enough questions? I want to first solve this with the mirror equation and then show you that ray tracing gives you the same result. Since this is a concave mirror, "f" is positive. Since the focal length is half the radius of curvature, $f = 12.5$ cm. The mirror equation, then, gives us:

$$\frac{1}{s_o} + \frac{1}{s_i} = \frac{1}{f}$$

$$\frac{1}{10.0 \text{ cm}} + \frac{1}{s_i} = \frac{1}{12.5 \text{ cm}}$$

$$s_i = -50.0 \text{ cm}$$

Since the image distance is negative, <u>the image is on the side of the mirror opposite of the object and is virtual</u>. To determine the magnification and whether the image is real or virtual, we must use the magnification equation.

$$m = -\frac{s_i}{s_o} = -\frac{-50.0 \text{ cm}}{10.0 \text{ cm}} = 5.00$$

Thus, <u>the image is upright and five times as large as the object</u>. Now, of course, ray tracing will give you all of that information except the numbers. If we follow the ray tracing rules, we get.

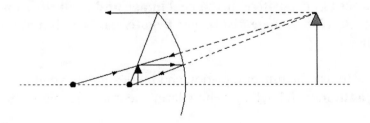

Notice that in this picture, the image is on the opposite side of the mirror relative to the object; it is virtual; it is magnified; and it is upright.

Answer all of the same questions if the situation above used a *convex* mirror instead.

The only mathematical difference between this problem and the one before is the fact that since the mirror is convex, the focal length is negative.

$$\frac{1}{s_o} + \frac{1}{s_i} = \frac{1}{f}$$

$$\frac{1}{10.0 \text{ cm}} + \frac{1}{s_i} = \frac{1}{-12.5 \text{ cm}}$$

$$s_i = -5.56 \text{ cm}$$

This tells us that <u>the image is on the opposite side of the mirror relative to the object and is virtual</u>. The magnification equation gives us:

$$m = -\frac{s_i}{s_o} = -\frac{-5.56 \text{ cm}}{10.0 \text{ cm}} = 0.556$$

This tells us that <u>the image is upright and only 0.556 times as tall as the object</u>. If you went through the ray tracing steps for this situation, you would find that it gives consistent results.

ON YOUR OWN

7.9 An object is placed 15.0 cm from a convex mirror whose radius of curvature is 20.0 cm. What is the magnification of the image relative to the object? Is the image real or virtual? Is it upright or inverted? Repeat the problem for a concave mirror.

<u>Lenses</u>

As you learned in your first-year physics course, the phenomenon of refraction also leads to interesting optical consequences. For example, when light travels through curved glass, it can be bent towards a focal point. In your first-year course, you probably learned how to use ray tracing to determine what an image would look like when viewed through a **converging lens**.

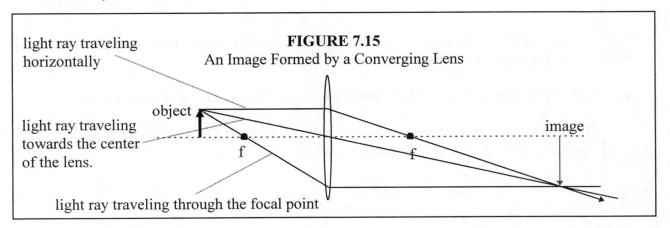

FIGURE 7.15
An Image Formed by a Converging Lens

light ray traveling horizontally

light ray traveling towards the center of the lens.

object

f

f

image

light ray traveling through the focal point

Now remember, light passes through a lens, because it is made of glass. Thus, it is not like a mirror which reflects the light that strikes it. Of course, as you learned previously, *some* light will be reflected whenever it hits a new medium, but in the case of lenses, we are interested in the light that *passes through* the lens. According to the rules you learned in your first-year course, if a light ray travels horizontally, it passes through the focal point on the other side of the converging lens. If a light ray travels through the very center of a lens, it experiences no net deflection. Finally, if a light ray passes through the focal point of a converging lens, it travels horizontally on the other side of the lens.

In your first-year course, you might not have learned that in addition to converging lenses, there are **diverging lenses** as well. Rather than bending light towards the focal point, a diverging lens (as its name implies) bends light *away from* a focal point. The ray tracing rules for a diverging lens are as follows:

RAY TRACING RULES FOR A DIVERGING LENS

1. **A light ray that travels horizontally will be refracted so that it appears to have originated at the focal point.**
2. **A light ray that passes through the center of the lens experiences no net deflection.**
3. **A light ray that travels towards the focal point on the other side of the lens will be refracted so that it travels horizontally.**

Suppose, for example, an object was placed behind the focal point of a diverging lens. The resulting ray tracing diagram would look like this:

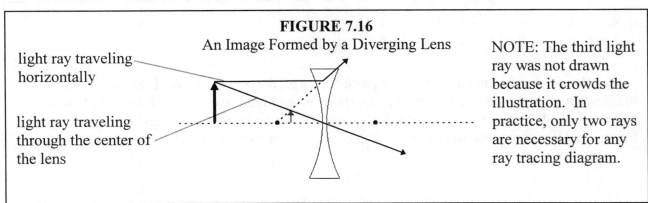

FIGURE 7.16
An Image Formed by a Diverging Lens

light ray traveling horizontally

light ray traveling through the center of the lens

NOTE: The third light ray was not drawn because it crowds the illustration. In practice, only two rays are necessary for any ray tracing diagram.

Notice first the difference between the converging lens and the diverging lens. When each side of the lens is convex, the result is a converging lens. When each side is concave, the result is a diverging lens. Notice also the difference in the images produced. In Figure 7.15, the converging lens produces a real, inverted, and magnified image. The diverging lens in Figure 7.16, however, produces a virtual (even though one ray is real, the other is extrapolated, so this is a virtual image), upright image which is smaller than the object. Also notice that in Figure 7.16, I only drew two of the three light rays. Once you get used to ray tracing, you should probably make that a practice as well. Since ray tracing requires rather precise drawing, it may be hard to get all three rays to intersect properly. However, if you get two rays to intersect, the third ray *must* intersect there as well. Thus, two rays are really enough to determine the image in a ray tracing diagram.

As you might imagine, a mathematical equation can be used to give us the same information that we learn from ray tracing. In fact, we can use *exactly the same* equations that we used for mirrors. The only thing we have to worry about is the sign conventions that we use.

Sign Conventions for Equation (7.11) When Applied to Lenses

1. **The object distance (s$_o$) is *always* positive.**
2. **The focal length (f) of a converging lens is positive; the focal length of a diverging lens is negative.**
3. **If the image distance (s$_i$) is positive, it is a real image and is on the opposite side of the lens as compared to the object. If the image distance is negative, it is a virtual image and is on the same side of the lens as the object.**

Not surprisingly, when we adopt these sign conventions, Equation (7.12) works for lenses as well. If the magnification (m) is negative, the image is inverted. If it is positive, the image is upright. The absolute value of the magnification, of course, tells you the ratio of the size of the image to that of the object.

EXAMPLE 7.4

Consider the converging lens in Figure 7.15. The drawing is consistent with an object being placed 14.0 cm from a lens whose focal length is 10.0 cm. Use Equation (7.11) and Equation (7.12) to determine whether the image is real or virtual, upright or inverted, and what the magnification of the image is relative to the size of the object.

From the ray tracing diagram, we know the answers to all of these questions except the last one. However, it is instructive to see that Equation (7.11) and Equation (7.12) give us the same answers. Since this is a converging lens, "f" is positive. Also, the object's position is positive. Thus:

$$\frac{1}{s_o} + \frac{1}{s_i} = \frac{1}{f}$$

$$\frac{1}{14.0 \text{ cm}} + \frac{1}{s_i} = \frac{1}{10.0 \text{ cm}}$$

$$s_i = 35.0 \text{ cm}$$

Thus, the image is real, because the image distance is positive. Also, it is on the opposite side of the lens as compared to the object, but the question did not ask about that. To determine the answer to the other questions, we must use the magnification equation:

$$m = -\frac{s_i}{s_o} = -\frac{35.0 \text{ cm}}{14.0 \text{ cm}} = -2.50$$

As shown in the ray tracing diagram, then, the image is inverted. The equation tells us that the image is 2.5 times larger than the object.

ON YOUR OWN

7.10 An object is placed 10.0 cm from a diverging lens that has a focal length of 15.0 cm. On what side of the lens is the image produced? Is it real or virtual? Is it upright or inverted? What is the size of the image relative to the object?

Before I finish this module, I want to make it clear what you have been doing with mirrors and lenses. Some students can master ray tracing and the equations associated with mirrors and lenses but still do not grasp the significance of what they are doing. When you look at an object in a mirror or through a lens, *you do not see the object. You see only the image.* Remember, mirrors and lenses reflect and refract light. We can see an object because our eyes receive light that has bounced off of the object and into our eyes. Mirrors reflect the light and *then* it hits our eyes. Thus, the pattern of light that our eyes and brain interpret is not the original pattern of light that is coming off of the object. It is the pattern of light that is coming off of the mirror. Thus, we do not see the object. We see the image formed by the mirror.

The same is true for lenses. When we view an object through a lens, the lens bends the light. Thus, we no longer see the light as it left the object. Instead, we see the light as it is bent through the lens. Thus, we see the image produced by the lens. We do not see the object. This is why glasses help people with poor vision. If we saw both the object and the image when looking through a lens, it would be incredibly confusing, and glasses would not help at all!

ANSWERS TO THE ON YOUR OWN PROBLEMS

7.1 A loudness of 30 dB is 3 bels. A loudness of 100 dB is 10 bels. Thus, the loudness increased by 7 bels. Since each unit (in bels) is equal to a factor of ten increase in intensity, the amplifier increased the intensity of the sound wave by a factor of 10^7.

7.2 The pitches would not be the same. Since the bottles are identical, the *wavelength* is the same in each sound wave. However, the *speed* of a sound wave depends on temperature. The sound will travel more slowly in the cold air. When you look at Equation (6.13), you see that a lower speed will mean a lower frequency and thus a lower pitch. As a result, the cold bottle will produce a lower pitch than will the warm bottle.

7.3 We know that the frequency of this string's second harmonic is 392 Hz, because that's the frequency at which sound waves are hitting the string, and that frequency resonates the second harmonic. Since we know the tension and linear mass density, we can get the speed of the waves in the string with Equation (6.19):

$$v = \sqrt{\frac{T}{\mu}} = \sqrt{\frac{144 \text{ N}}{0.0150 \frac{\text{kg}}{\text{m}}}} = 98.0 \frac{\text{m}}{\text{sec}}$$

Now we can determine the wavelength:

$$f = \frac{v}{\lambda}$$

$$\lambda = \frac{v}{f} = \frac{98.0 \frac{\text{m}}{\text{sec}}}{392 \frac{1}{\text{sec}}} = 0.250 \text{ m}$$

Now we can determine the length of the string. Since this is the second harmonic, n=2.

$$\lambda = \frac{2L}{n}$$

$$0.250 \text{ m} = \frac{2L}{2}$$

$$L = 0.250 \text{ m}$$

7.4 For a tube that is closed on one end, the possible wavelengths are:

$$\lambda = \frac{4 \cdot L}{n} \qquad n = 1, 3, 5, \ldots$$

For a tube open on both ends, the possible wavelengths are:

$$\lambda = \frac{2 \cdot L}{n} \qquad n = 1, 2, 3, \ldots$$

Since most of what you hear is the first harmonic, we can set $n = 1$. Also, since the air is the same temperature in both tubes, the same pitch (frequency) also means the same wavelength. Thus, if we divide these equations:

$$\frac{\lambda_{closed}}{\lambda_{open}} = \frac{\dfrac{4 \cdot L_{closed}}{1}}{\dfrac{2 \cdot L_{open}}{1}}$$

$$1 = \frac{4 \cdot L_{closed}}{2 \cdot L_{open}}$$

$$\frac{L_{closed}}{L_{open}} = \frac{1}{2}$$

The open tube, then, is twice as long as the closed tube.

7.5 The overall equation for the Doppler shift is not so bad as long as we know what signs to use:

$$f_{observed} = \left(\frac{v_{sound} \pm v_{observer}}{v_{sound} \pm v_{source}} \right) \cdot f_{true}$$

In this problem, both the observer and the source are moving. The observer is moving towards the source. Thus, his motion will increase the frequency, so we must add his motion in the numerator of the equation. The source is moving away from the observer, which will decrease the frequency. Thus, we must add the speed of the source in the denominator of the equation. That gives us:

$$f_{observed} = \left(\frac{v_{sound} + v_{observer}}{v_{sound} + v_{source}} \right) \cdot f_{true}$$

To use the equation, however, we need to know the speed of sound:

$$v = (331.5 + 0.606 \cdot T)\ \frac{m}{sec} = 346.7\ \frac{m}{sec}$$

Now we can calculate the observed frequency:

$$f_{observed} = \left(\frac{346.7\ \frac{m}{sec} + 25.0\ \frac{m}{sec}}{346.7\ \frac{m}{sec} + 45.0\ \frac{m}{sec}} \right) \cdot (411\ Hz) = \underline{3.90 \times 10^2\ Hz}$$

Since the observer and source are moving away from each other, the net effect is to reduce the frequency of the horn. Note that if the train and car were moving at the same speed, the observed frequency would be the same as the true frequency, since the source and observer would not be moving relative to one another.

7.6 <u>The student will not see an interference pattern, since the two light bulbs will not produce light waves that are in the same phase relative to one another.</u> Remember, to see the interference, the waves must be coherent.

7.7 The light will be reflected at each boundary, and it will also be refracted. When the light moves into a medium of higher index of refraction, the light will refract towards the perpendicular. When it moves into a medium of lower index of refraction, it will bend away from the perpendicular.

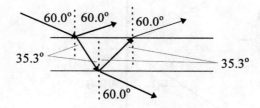

Where did I get the angles? In the reflected rays, the angle of incidence equals the angle of reflection. In the refracted rays, I used Snell's Law. To determine the angle of the first refracted ray:

$$n_1 \cdot \sin\theta_1 = n_2 \cdot \sin\theta_2$$

$$\sin\theta_2 = \frac{n_1 \cdot \sin\theta_1}{n_2} = \frac{(1.00) \cdot \sin(60.0^\circ)}{1.50}$$

$$\theta_2 = 35.3^\circ$$

To determine the angle of the other refracted rays, I could have used Snell's Law, or I could just see that the other refractions are the reverse of the first refraction. Thus, the original angle is reestablished. This could, of course, continue on, since each light ray that hits a boundary is reflected to some degree.

b. <u>An interference pattern will be observed because there are two light sources: the reflection off of the top layer of glass and the reflection off of the bottom layer. These light sources are coherent, so they will produce an interference pattern</u>. Note that the interference pattern will not be as strong as the one you observed in your experiment, since the ray reflected off of the bottom of the glass and then refracted through the top of the glass is less intense than the ray that reflects off of the top of the glass.

c. Remember that a wave will invert when reflected off of a boundary when the wave travels slower in the new medium than in the old medium. Thus, the wave reflected from the top of the glass will be inverted. However, the wave reflecting from the bottom of the glass will *not* be inverted. Thus, everywhere the wave reflected from the top of the glass has a crest, the other wave will have a trough. Thus, to get destructive interference, these waves just have to "line up." As a result, <u>when Δl is any integral multiple of the wavelength, destructive interference will result</u>.

7.8 Looking at the geometry again:

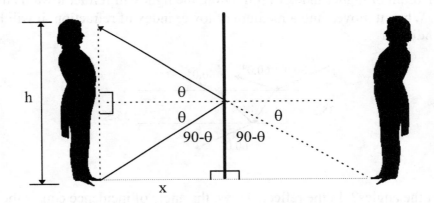

Note the two triangles at the bottom. They each share a side, and they each have two equal angles ($90-\theta$ and the right angle at the bottom of the figure). Thus, by the angle-side-angle postulate, these triangles are identical as well. Thus, since the base of the triangle on the left is length "x," the base of the other triangle must be "x" as well. As a result, <u>the man's image will appear a distance of "x" inside the mirror</u>.

7.9 The focal length (half the radius of curvature) of a convex mirror is negative. Thus:

$$\frac{1}{s_o} + \frac{1}{s_i} = \frac{1}{f}$$

$$\frac{1}{15.0 \text{ cm}} + \frac{1}{s_i} = \frac{1}{-10.0 \text{ cm}}$$

$$s_i = -6.00 \text{ cm}$$

This tells us that <u>the image is virtual</u>. To get the magnification:

$$m = -\frac{s_i}{s_o} = -\frac{-6.00 \text{ cm}}{15.0 \text{ cm}} = 0.400$$

<u>The image is 40.0% of the object's height and is upright</u>.

The only difference for a concave mirror is that the focal length is positive.

$$\frac{1}{s_o} + \frac{1}{s_i} = \frac{1}{f}$$

$$\frac{1}{15.0 \text{ cm}} + \frac{1}{s_i} = \frac{1}{10.0 \text{ cm}}$$

$$s_i = 30.0 \text{ cm}$$

This tells us that <u>the image is real</u>. To get the magnification:

$$m = -\frac{s_i}{s_o} = -\frac{30.0 \text{ cm}}{15.0 \text{ cm}} = -2.00$$

<u>The image is 2.00 times the height of the object and is inverted</u>.

7.10 In a diverging lens, the focal length is negative.

$$\frac{1}{s_o} + \frac{1}{s_i} = \frac{1}{f}$$

$$\frac{1}{10.0 \text{ cm}} + \frac{1}{s_i} = \frac{1}{-15.0 \text{ cm}}$$

$$s_i = -6.00 \text{ cm}$$

Based on the sign conventions for lenses, <u>the image is virtual and is on the same side of the lens as is the object</u>. The magnification equation tells us the rest of what we need to know:

$$m = -\frac{s_i}{s_o} = -\frac{6.00 \text{ cm}}{10.0 \text{ cm}} = 0.600$$

<u>The image is 60.0% the size of the object and is upright.</u>

REVIEW QUESTIONS FOR MODULE #7

1. Imagine a sound wave with a particular wavelength and frequency that is traveling through the air. If it strikes a brick wall, compare the frequency and wavelength of the sound wave that is reflected to that of the original wave. Compare the phase angle of the two waves.

2. Imagine the situation given in question #1, and now consider the portion of the wave that travels into the wall. Compare the frequency and wavelength of the sound wave in the wall to what it was when it was traveling through the air. Compare the phase angle of the two waves as well.

3. When you breathe in a lot of helium (by sucking on a helium balloon, for example), the pitch of your voice goes up substantially. What can you say about the speed of sound in helium as opposed to air?

4. Suppose a singer wants to break a glass using her voice. How could she determine the pitch at which she needs to sing in order to break the glass?

5. A young girl is running away from a mean boy that is chasing her with a frog. As is often the case, the young girl is screaming at a constant pitch and loudness. As they run towards a wall, the boy hears the loudness of the girl's scream vary at a regular frequency. However, the girl is not varying the loudness of her scream. What is happening?

6. Two transparent pieces of plastic are stacked on top of one another, and a beam of light is directed through one layer. The top piece of plastic has an index of refraction equal to 2.5, and the bottom piece has an index of refraction equal to 1.4. If the experimenter wants to observe total internal reflection, should the beam of light originate in the top piece of plastic or the bottom piece of plastic?

7. When you look at something that is underwater, the depth at which you observe it is not the proper depth. Why? Is the observed depth more or less than the proper depth?

8. A typical parlor trick involves placing a coin in a bowl so that a person looking at the bowl cannot see the coin. However, when water is poured into the bowl, the coin becomes visible. Draw a diagram that explains this trick.

9. Suppose you set up a two-slit experiment such as Experiment 7.2. If you looked at the interference pattern produced and then increased the distance between the screen and the slits, what would happen to the distance between the bright lines?

10. The diagram to the right shows where the image appears for a distant object in an eye that is nearsighted. In order for the image to be seen clearly, it should be focused right on the retina. If you were to use glasses to correct this problem, would the glasses be made of converging or diverging lenses?

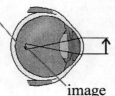

PRACTICE PROBLEMS FOR MODULE #7

1. A man hears music from a car that is about 100 meters away from him. He estimates that he is hearing the music at a loudness of about 40 dB. If someone were unfortunate enough to be standing only 1 meter from the car, how loud would the music be?

2. A bat uses sonar to navigate. Suppose the bat emits a "chirp" and 0.55 seconds later hears the echo from that chirp. How far away is the obstacle that caused the sound wave to bounce back? Assume the temperature is 20.0 °C.

3. A pipe that is open at both ends is 25.0 cm long. What is the fundamental frequency of the pipe when the air is at a temperature of 25.0 °C?

4. Suppose you took a 12.8 cm pipe that is closed on one end and put it next to the pipe in problem #3. If you blew on both so that the air (25.0 °C) began vibrating at the pipes' fundamental frequencies, you would hear beats. At what frequency would you hear the beats?

5. A policeman's radar gun measures the speed of a car by shooting a radar beam (an electromagnetic wave) at the car. When the wave hits the car, it is Doppler shifted by the motion of the car. Thus, when the wave is reflected back to the radar gun, it is Doppler shifted as if the car is a moving source of the wave. If the speed of light is 2.998 x 10^8 m/sec, what is the percentage change in the frequency of the radar beam if a car is traveling at 23.0 m/sec (about 55 miles per hour)? Assume that the policeman using the radar gun is not moving and the car is approaching the policeman.

6. In Young's double-slit experiment, the interference pattern produced had a bright spot on the screen right in the center between the two slits. This is called the "central maximum." How much farther (in terms of λ) did the light from one slit travel as compared to light from the other slit for the bright spot that is right above the central maximum?

7. A fisherman drops his flashlight in a lake. He doesn't realize it for a moment, however, so he keeps traveling in his boat. Eventually he notices that he doesn't have his flashlight anymore. However, he is not worried. He knows that the light was on, and since it is night, he decides that he can see his flashlight shining underwater. However, when he turns around, he does not see the flashlight. He starts heading back the way he came and eventually sees the light shining underneath the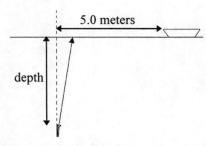
water. Assuming that the flashlight is shining at a slight angle relative to the perpendicular, at what depth in the water (n = 1.4) is the flashlight given the fact that the fisherman must be within 5.0 meters of the flashlight's horizontal position before he sees it?

8. When white light passes through a prism, it is often separated into its colors. In the situation depicted below, which color is on top? Which color is on the bottom?

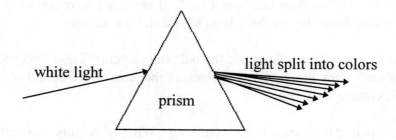

9. An object of height 15 cm is placed 7.5 cm in front of a convex mirror. An image forms 5.0 cm on the opposite side of the mirror. What is the radius of curvature of the mirror? Is the image real or virtual? Is it upright or inverted? What is the size of the image?

10. You want to magnify an object 15.0 cm away using a converging lens. If you want to magnify the object so that it is upright and twice as large, what focal length will you need for the lens?

Module #8: Gravity and Relativity

Introduction

In the past few modules, we have been dealing with different types of periodic motion: rotational motion, simple harmonic oscillation, and waves. There is one more type of periodic motion I want to discuss, and that is the motion of the planets. A study of this motion, of course, leads to a discussion of gravity. Although you learned a lot about gravity and the planets in your first-year course, I do want to introduce you to a couple of new concepts related to the subject. Also, a discussion of light (which we had in the previous module) and a discussion of gravitation (which will take place in this module) easily leads us into a discussion of relativity (which will end this semester of the course).

Kepler's Laws and Gravity

Although you learned Newton's Law of Universal Gravitation in your first-year physics course, you probably did *not* learn what inspired Newton to come up with his law. Newton was able to write his Universal Law of Gravitation by examining the work of **Johannes Kepler**. Kepler was the student of a man named **Tycho Brahe**, an astronomer who collected *volumes* of data regarding the known planets and their positions in the sky. Kepler studied this data intensely, and he eventually was able to distill this data into three basic laws which, reasonably enough, are called **Kepler's Laws**. These laws are best understood in the context of a figure, such as the one given below.

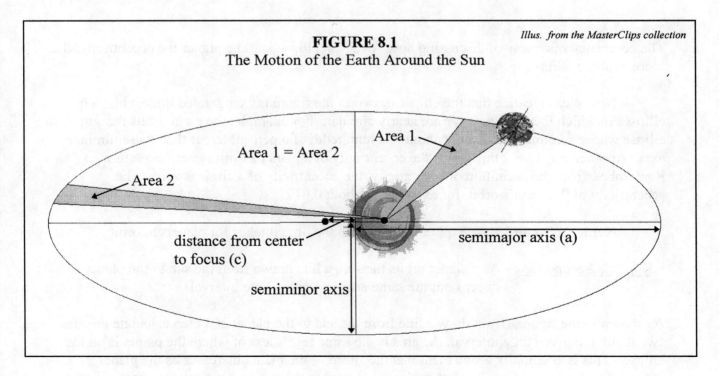

FIGURE 8.1

The Motion of the Earth Around the Sun

Illus. from the MasterClips collection

Area 1

Area 1 = Area 2

Area 2

distance from center to focus (c)

semimajor axis (a)

semiminor axis

The first thing to notice about the figure is that it has the earth orbiting the sun. This went against the established view of the heavens at the time, which held that the earth sat at the center of the solar system and the sun (as well as all of the planets) orbited the earth. Even Tycho Brahe, Kepler's teacher, held to a modified version of this view. Kepler, however, was convinced by the data that the sun was at the center of the solar system and that the planets orbited around it. We know today, of course, that Kepler was right.

Another look at the figure will lead you to **Kepler's First Law**.

Kepler's First Law - The planets move in an elliptical orbit, with the sun at one focus.

Remember from geometry that an ellipse is simply an oval, and it is defined by two foci. An ellipse contains the set of all points in which the sum of the distances between the foci and the point is equal to a given number. When discussing ellipses, mathematicians typically say that the ellipse has a **semimajor axis** (as illustrated in the figure) and a **semiminor axis** (as illustrated in the figure). Mathematicians can also define an ellipse by its **eccentricity**.

Eccentricity - The distance between the center of an ellipse and either focus divided by the
            length of the semimajor axis.

Mathematically, if the distance from the center to a focus is "c" and the length of the semimajor axis is "a," we can say that the eccentricity (e) is given by:

$$e = \frac{c}{a}$$

(8.1)

The eccentricity is a way of discussing how "oval" an ellipse is. The higher the eccentricity, the more oval the ellipse.

Now please realize that the ellipse drawn in the figure is exaggerated quite a bit. The ellipses in which the planets move are nearly circular. For example, the earth orbits the sun in an ellipse whose semimajor axis only about one hundredth of a percent larger than its semiminor axis. Another way to say this is that the eccentricity of a planet's orbit is very close to zero. Remember, from the definition of eccentricity, the eccentricity of a circle is zero. The eccentricity of the earth's orbit, for example, is about 0.017.

Kepler's Second Law explicitly deals with the time it takes for planets to orbit.

Kepler's Second Law - As a planet orbits the sun, a line drawn from the sun to the planet
            sweeps out the same area in a given time interval.

As shown in the figure, if you draw a line from the sun to the planet and then calculate the area swept out in a given time interval, the area is the same regardless of where the planet is on the ellipse. This is essentially a statement that the speed of the planet increases as the planet approaches the sun. After all, when a planet is closer to the sun, it must cover a greater distance around the ellipse in order to sweep out an area that is equal to the area swept out when the planet is far from the sun. Now once again, since the ellipses swept out by the planets are very close to circles, this difference is minor. However, Kepler's Laws also apply to comets whose orbits are ellipses with large eccentricities. The difference in speed for a comet when it is close to the sun compared to when it is far from the sun is significant.

Kepler's Third Law relates the orbits of all of the planets.

Kepler's Third Law - The ratio of the period of the planet's orbit squared to the length of the semimajor axis cubed is the same for all planets.

If we call the planet's orbital period "T" and the length of the semimajor axis "a," we can say:

$$\frac{T^2}{a^3} \text{ is constant for all planets} \tag{8.2}$$

Although Kepler had no idea *why* the planets obeyed his laws, he just knew that all of the observations he and his teacher made were consistent with these laws. Although many religious leaders opposed Kepler's work, Kepler himself (as is the case with most of the great scientists of the past) was a devout Christian. In fact, he once wrote, "I wanted to become a theologian. For a long time, I was restless. Now, however, behold how through my effort God is being celebrated in astronomy." (As quoted in Gerald Holton, *American Journal of Physics* 24 (May 1956): 340-351). This should be a lesson to you. You do not have to be in a full-time church ministry position to serve God. Use the talents that He has given you, and God will be glorified.

Newton showed that Kepler's first two laws indicate that the planets and the sun exert mutual gravitational forces on one another. The gravitational force between a planet and the sun, for example, is proportional to the mass of each object and is inversely proportional to the distance between them squared. Newton suggested that *all bodies* experience a mutual gravitational force with *all other bodies*, so he called it a "universal law" of gravity. Mathematically, **Newton's Universal Law of Gravitation** is expressed as:

$$F = \frac{G \cdot m_1 \cdot m_2}{r^2} \tag{8.3}$$

where "m_1" and "m_2" are the masses of the objects in question, "r" is the distance between the objects, and "G" is the gravitational constant, which is $6.67 \times 10^{-11} \frac{N \cdot m^2}{kg^2}$.

Although you have seen and used this equation before, I want to remind you of a couple of things. First, the gravitational force is *mutual*. In other words, the earth exerts a gravitational force on the moon (given by the equation), and the moon exerts an *equal but opposite* force on the earth (given by the same equation). The same is true for any two objects. A ball falls, for example, because the earth exerts a gravitational force on the ball. In response, the ball exerts an equal but opposite force on the earth. Thus, both the ball and the earth are attracted to one another with an equal force. As the ball falls to the earth, then, the earth also rises to meet the ball. Of course, since the earth is so massive relative to the ball, the earth's acceleration is negligible compared to that of the ball.

The other thing I want to remind you of is how this equation applies to the motion of planets, satellites, and so forth. Remember that for circular motion to occur, a centripetal force must be present. The equation for the centripetal force required for circular motion was given in Module #6:

$$F_c = \frac{m \cdot v^2}{r} \qquad (6.14)$$

Now please understand that centripetal force is not a fundamental force like gravity or the electromagnetic force. Something must *supply* the centripetal force. For example, when you twirl a toy airplane around your head, the tension on the string supplies the centripetal force, and Equation (6.14) tells you the value of that force. Well, the centripetal force that keeps the planets moving in their almost circular orbits is *gravity*. The following example reminds you how we can use the fact that the centripetal force for planets and satellites is supplied by gravity.

EXAMPLE 8.1

Show that Newton's Law of Universal Gravitation actually gives Kepler's Third Law.

Let's assume that the orbit of a planet around the sun is circular. It is not. In reality, it is an ellipse. However, a circle is a special type of ellipse - one in which the eccentricity is zero. Since the eccentricity of a planet's orbit is nearly zero, we can go ahead and make the assumption. For circular motion to occur, there must be a centripetal force, the strength of which is given by Equation (6.14). In this case, gravity supplies the centripetal force, and the strength of the gravitational force is given by Equation (8.3). In the end, then, if I set the gravitational force equation equal to the centripetal force, I get:

$$\frac{m_p \cdot v_p^{\,2}}{r} = \frac{G \cdot m_p \cdot m_s}{r^2}$$

where "m_p" is the mass of the planet; "m_s" is the mass of the sun; "v_p" is the speed of the planet in its orbit; and "r" is the distance from the center of the planet to the center of the sun.

Notice that the mass of the planet cancels because it is on both sides of the equation. Now, let's think about how to calculate "v_p." The planet makes a full orbit once each period (denoted as "T"). In that time, it travels a total distance of $2 \cdot \pi \cdot r$. Thus, the average speed of the planet is:

$$v_p = \frac{2 \cdot \pi \cdot r}{T}$$

If we stick this expression for "v_p" in the equation, we get:

$$\frac{\left(\dfrac{2 \cdot \pi \cdot r}{T}\right)^2}{r} = \frac{G \cdot m_s}{r^2}$$

$$\frac{4 \cdot \pi^2 \cdot r}{T^2} = \frac{G \cdot m_s}{r^2}$$

$$\frac{r^3}{T^2} = \frac{G \cdot m_s}{4 \cdot \pi^2}$$

$$\underline{\frac{T^2}{r^3} = \frac{4 \cdot \pi^2}{G \cdot m_s}}$$

Notice that this equation is a statement of Kepler's Third Law. After all, the left side of the equation is T^2/r^3, and everything on the right side of the equation is the same, regardless of the planet in the solar system. Thus, it tells us that the period squared divided by the radius cubed (the radius of a circle is both the semimajor and the semiminor axis) is the same for all planets in the solar system.

ON YOUR OWN

8.1 Calculate the average speed of the earth in its orbit. Is this speed perfectly constant? If not, when does the earth move at its fastest speed? When does it move at its slowest speed? (mass of the sun = 1.99×10^{30} kg, average radius of earth's orbit = 1.50×10^{11} m)

8.2 A **geosynchronous** orbit is an orbit in which the position of the orbiting body relative to any point on the planet's surface remains the same. At what distance must a satellite orbit the earth so as to maintain a circular, geosynchronous orbit? (mass of the earth = 5.98×10^{24} kg).

Gravity and Extended Bodies

Throughout your first-year physics course, you have made an assumption about gravity. The assumption is correct, but it needs to be pointed out. Up to this point, when you did problems involving the gravitational attraction between two bodies, you treated each body as if all of its mass was concentrated at the center of mass of the object. As you learned in Module #5, this is often a valid assumption, and such is the case with gravity. Even if two objects are touching at their edges, the gravitational force between them can be calculated by assuming that the mass of each object is concentrated in a minuscule point located at the body's center of mass.

However, what happens if you get *inside* a mass. For example, suppose you dug a very deep well and climbed down the well. What would the gravitational force between you and the earth be then? Well, it turns out that the mass which is at a *higher depth* than you will exert *no net gravitational force on you*! Why? Examine the figure below.

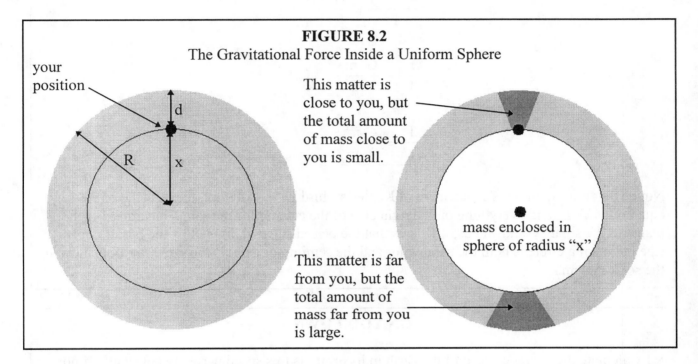

FIGURE 8.2
The Gravitational Force Inside a Uniform Sphere

your position

This matter is close to you, but the total amount of mass close to you is small.

This matter is far from you, but the total amount of mass far from you is large.

mass enclosed in sphere of radius "x"

When you reach a depth of "d" inside the sphere, you can split the mass of the sphere into two parts. There is the mass contained in the sphere of radius "x" and the mass contained in the ring of thickness "d." Note that x + d = R, the entire radius of the sphere. Well, the sphere of radius "x" can be treated as if all of its mass is located in a point at the center of mass. The gravitational attraction you feel from that sphere can then be calculated with Equation (8.3). What about the ring of mass which represents all of the material that is more shallow than your location in the sphere? It exerts *no net gravitational force*. Why? Think about it.

The mass right above your head is very close to you, so it exerts a strong gravitational force. The mass on the far side of the ring is far away and exerts less gravitational force on you. However, there is not a lot of mass near you. Most of the mass is far away. If you work through the geometry, you will find that the *amount* of mass increases by the square of the distance away from you. This tends to increase the gravitational force, since more mass means stronger gravity. However, the gravitational force decreases as the distance squared. Thus, the increase in force caused by the increase in mass is perfectly offset by the decrease in force caused by the increase in distance. As a result, the ring pulls equally in all directions, and the *net* gravitational force is zero. Thus, as far as the gravitational force is concerned, the ring of mass might as well not even be there!

Any extended body, then, can be treated (from a gravitational standpoint) as if all of its mass is concentrated at the center of mass as long as you are outside of the body. If you are inside of a sphere, the only gravitational force you feel is the gravitational force of the mass contained in the sphere of radius "x," where "x" is the distance between you and the center of the sphere.

ON YOUR OWN

8.3 Suppose you were inside a sphere (mass = M) of uniform density. If the radius of the sphere is R, give an equation for the gravitational force that you feel when you are a distance x away from the center of the sphere. Note that since you are in the sphere, x < R. Let m represent your mass. Your equation should be in terms of M, m, R, x, and G.

8.4 Given the fact that the mass of the earth is 5.98×10^{24} kg and its radius is 6.37×10^{6} m, use Equation (8.3) to calculate the acceleration due to gravity at the surface of the earth.

True Weight and Measured Weight

Although you probably don't realize this, there is a difference between your **true weight** and your **measured weight**. When you step on a scale, the scale is supposed to measure your weight. Now remember, your weight is simply a measure of how strongly gravity attracts you towards the center of the earth. However, as long as the earth is spinning on its axis, the weight that the scale measures is not exactly the strength at which you are being pulled to the center of the earth. Why? Well, think about any object that sits on the surface of the earth. The earth is spinning on its axis. Thus, the object is in circular motion about the center of the earth, right? If the object is in circular motion, what does that tell you? It tells you there is a *centripetal force* acting on the object. That force "interferes" with the measurement of the true weight of the object. How? Let's look at the forces which are at play in this situation.

FIGURE 8.3
The Forces at Work on an Object at the Surface of the Earth

Since the object is moving in a circular path (it is rotating with the earth), it must be experiencing a centripetal force:

$F_c = W - F_n$

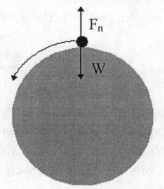

Notice that there are two forces acting on the object: the force due to gravity (W for "weight") and the normal force (F_n). When you weigh something, you are actually measuring F_n, not W, because a scale measures the force with which *it must push* to keep the object from falling. Thus, when you measure the weight of something, you are really measuring F_n. If the earth were not rotating on its axis, these two forces would cancel out exactly so that $F_n = W$. In that situation, the fact that you are measuring F_n instead of W is irrelevant, since they are both equal. However, since the earth is spinning, we know that these two forces *cannot* be equal. If they were equal, there would be no net force acting on the object and, as a result, it could not move in a circle, and it would fly off of the earth.

Since the object does not fly off of the earth, there must be a net force which supplies the centripetal force necessary for the object to move in a circle. Since the only two forces at play are W and F_n, we therefore know that F_n must be slightly weaker than W, so that the net force is pointed towards the center of the earth, which must be the direction of the centripetal force. Thus:

$$F_{centripetal} = W - F_n \tag{8.4}$$

We know an equation for centripetal force. If we plug that equation into the equation above, we get:

$$\frac{m \cdot v^2}{r} = W - F_n$$

Now, at what speed is the object moving? It is moving at the speed of the earth's rotation. Let's assume that the object is sitting on the equator. If that is the case, the object moves a distance of $2 \cdot \pi \cdot r$ in a total time of 24 hours (one day), which we will call "T," the period of the earth's rotation.

$$\frac{m \cdot \left(\dfrac{2 \cdot \pi \cdot r}{T}\right)^2}{r} = W - F_n$$

$$\frac{4 \cdot \pi^2 \cdot m \cdot r}{T^2} = W - F_n$$

Now remember, F_n is the measured weight, and W is the actual weight. Therefore:

$$\text{measured weight} = W - \frac{4 \cdot \pi^2 \cdot m \cdot r}{T^2}$$

How large an effect is this? We can easily calculate it. Let's suppose a "typical" adult male (mass = 75.0 kg) weighs himself. Since the radius of the earth is 6.37×10^6 m, and the period of the earth's rotation (T) is 24 hours (86,400 seconds), we can actually determine the amount that the rotation of the earth takes away from the man's true weight:

$$\text{measured weight} = W - \frac{4 \cdot \pi^2 \cdot (75.0 \text{ kg}) \cdot (6.37 \times 10^6 \text{ m})}{(86{,}400 \text{ sec})^2} = W - 2.64 \text{ N}$$

Since 2.64 N is a tiny force compared to the man's weight, it is a tiny effect. Nevertheless, it does exist.

ON YOUR OWN

8.5 In "on your own" problem 8.4, you calculated the acceleration due to gravity. However, if you were to measure the acceleration due to gravity of an object near the surface of the earth, it would not be precisely equal to your calculation, because of the effects discussed in this section. What would the *measured* gravitational acceleration be? (Derive it. Do not just state it.)

Gravitational Potential Energy

In this course and in your first-year physics course, you dealt with gravitational potential energy quite a bit. When an object is at a height (h) relative to some point, we say that the object has potential energy due to gravity, and that the potential energy is given by:

$$PE = m \cdot g \cdot h \tag{4.4}$$

Although this is an insanely useful equation, you must understand that there is an assumption built into it. What is the assumption? The assumption is *that the object is near the surface of the earth*. Think about it. Suppose I wanted to lift an object of mass "m" vertically through a distance of "h." How much work would I have to do? Well, gravity pulls down on the object with a force equal to m·g, and therefore I must exert a force equal and opposite of that in order to lift the object at a constant velocity. If I lift it a height of "h," I can calculate the work as force times distance, or m·g·h. That work adds directly to the potential energy, so the object gains potential energy equal to m·g·h.

Did you notice the assumption in that reasoning? Since I said that gravity pulls down on the object with a force equal to m·g, I am assuming that the object is near the surface of the earth. After all, the value for "g" assumes that you are near the surface of the earth. If an object is far from the center of the earth, gravity does not pull with a force of m·g, it pulls with a weaker force, because the gravitational force depends on the distance between the object and the center of the earth. This is very important to remember.

Equation (4.4) assumes that the object in question is near the surface of the earth.

Even though most of the physics problems that we analyze are near the surface of the earth, sometimes we want to analyze the motion of satellites, planets, comets, etc., which are far from the earth. Thus, it would be nice to have an equation that calculates gravitational potential energy regardless of how far you are from the earth. It would also be nice to have an equation that tells us the gravitational potential energy associated with *any* two objects. Equation (8.5) does both. For any two objects whose masses are "m_1" and "m_2" that are separated by a distance of "r," the gravitational potential energy is:

$$U_{grav} = -\frac{G \cdot m_1 \cdot m_2}{r} \qquad (8.5)$$

Notice that the potential energy due to gravity is negative. That's important. Remember what a negative potential energy means. It means that the object in question is *bound*. When an object is near enough to the earth to feel its gravity, for example, it is bound to the earth in some way. The moon, for example, is bound to the earth because it is caught in earth's gravitational field. You are bound to the earth because you are caught in its field. Thus, the potential energy due to gravity is *negative*.

This may seem really odd to you, since the equation you have been using for the potential energy due to gravity [Equation (4.4)] up to this point is not negative. That's because the equation assumes we are dealing with things near the surface of the earth that will never leave the surface of the earth. Thus, the fact that they are bound is irrelevant. Also, it assumes that the force due to gravity is constant, which is a good assumption as long as your height relative to the surface of the earth is very small compared to the radius of the earth. However, if you get rid of those assumptions, you must define the gravitational potential energy as negative in order to be consistent with all of the other rules we have drawn up so far.

Notice that there is one similarity between Equations (4.4) and (8.5). They both state that the higher you go, the larger the potential energy. After all, as "h" increases, Equation (4.4) gets larger. Thus, the higher you are, the more gravitational potential energy you have. Equation (8.5) agrees. The larger the distance between the two objects, the smaller the negative number given by the equation. Well, the smaller the negative number, the larger the value of that number.

Equation (8.5) allows us to consider many interesting situations, such as the one given in the example below.

EXAMPLE 8.2

In order for a rocket to leave the earth and head to the moon or another planet, it must essentially "escape" earth's gravitational field. With what minimum speed must a rocket be launched in order to do this? (mass of the earth = 5.98×10^{24} kg, radius of the earth = 6.37×10^6 m)

When a rocket is at the surface of the earth, it has a potential energy given by Equation (8.5). It also has a kinetic energy given by $\frac{1}{2}\cdot m\cdot v^2$. That's its total energy. As the rocket rises, its potential energy increases, because as Equation (8.5) indicates, the farther the rocket gets from earth, the less negative the potential energy becomes. As a result, the kinetic energy decreases. If a rocket were to just lose all of its kinetic energy when it finally has no more potential energy from the earth's gravity, it would just barely escape the earth.

If the rocket has neither potential nor kinetic energy, its total energy is zero. The Law of Conservation of Energy states that the total energy must always be the same. Thus, to get a rocket to leave orbit, the kinetic energy plus the potential energy must equal zero.

$$TE_{before} = TE_{after}$$

$$\frac{1}{2}\cdot m_{rocket}\cdot v^2 - \frac{G\cdot m_{rocket}\cdot m_{earth}}{r_{earth}} = 0$$

$$v = \sqrt{\frac{2\cdot G\cdot m_{earth}}{r_{earth}}} = \sqrt{\frac{2\cdot (6.67\times10^{-11}\frac{N\cdot m^2}{kg^2})\cdot (5.98\times10^{24}\,kg)}{6.37\times10^6\,m}} = 1.12\times10^4\sqrt{\frac{N\cdot m}{kg}} = 1.12\times10^4\frac{m}{sec}$$

Notice how the units work out. A Newton is a $\frac{kg\cdot m}{sec^2}$. When you divide by kg and multiply by m, you get m²/sec², which becomes m/sec when you take the square root. The rocket, then, must attain a speed of at least 1.12x10⁴ m/sec. This number, of course, neglects such inconvenient things as air resistance, so in reality, a rocket must have a higher speed in order to leave the earth's gravitational field. One thing to note here is that when the rocket escapes earth's gravitational field, it has a gravitational potential energy of zero. At that point, the potential is not negative, indicating that the rocket is no longer bound to earth. That's another way of saying that the rocket has escaped earth's gravitational field: its gravitational potential energy with respect to the earth is no longer negative.

Notice that the speed which the rocket needs to escape earth's gravity is not dependent on the mass of the rocket. It is only dependent on the radius and mass of the earth. As a result, *any* object that wants to leave earth's gravitational field must achieve the same minimum speed. Not surprisingly, then, this is called the **escape velocity** for earth.

Escape velocity - The minimum speed necessary for an object to escape the gravitational field of another object

If we have the mass and radius of any planet (or any other object), we can calculate the escape velocity.

Since the escape velocity of any object is not dependent on the physical characteristics of the object, we come to an interesting conclusion. Consider light, for example. It travels with a speed of 2.998×10^8 m/sec. That's a pretty large velocity, so light can escape from earth's gravitational field, the sun's gravitational field, etc. However, it is *possible* that there is some structure in the universe that even light does not have enough velocity to escape the structure's gravitational field. In that case, even light would not be able to leave the structure. What would you call such a structure? Physicists today call it a **black hole**. Theoretically, if a structure in the universe has a large enough mass and a small enough radius (in other words, if its *density* is high enough), even light would not have the velocity necessary to escape the gravitational field. As a result, nothing (including light) can leave it.

Black holes became a theoretical possibility when Einstein's General Theory of Relativity (which we will discuss briefly in the last part of this module) indicated that it was possible for such structures to exist. Of course, the difficulty in finding evidence for them rests in the fact that light cannot escape them. Thus, we cannot *see* them. After all, we see the stars and the planets in our solar system because light comes from them, and we can detect the light in telescopes. Now remember, "light" is a broad term. I don't mean just visible light. Certainly, we can see visible light coming from stars and planets, but stars produce a wide range of wavelengths of light, and special telescopes are used to receive those wavelengths which are not visible to the human eye.

Do black holes exist, then? Well, even though we cannot see them, we can develop indirect evidence for them. For example, the Hubble space telescope has captured events in which light emitted by highly-excited matter seems to be disappearing at a particular point in space. This is consistent with what physicists think would happen at the **event horizon** of a black hole. The event horizon is the point at which light is close enough to the black hole to be caught in its gravitational pull and thus is unable to escape. As a result, you cannot see light coming from any point inside the event horizon. Also, there are several observations of galaxies in which the behavior of the stars close to the center of the galaxy is consistent with the existence of a black hole at the galaxy's center. Thus, there is *indirect* evidence for the existence of such structures. Most astronomers consider the evidence strong enough to say that black holes are real, but sometimes Creation fools us. Thus, there is no way to be completely sure.

ON YOUR OWN

8.6 Calculations indicate that a reasonable radius for a black hole is about 10.0 km. What is the mass necessary for a sphere of radius 10.0 km to be a black hole?

8.7 Suppose you are adjusting the orbit of a satellite (m = 1576 kg), which is orbiting the earth (m = 5.98×10^{24} kg, r = 6.37×10^6 m) 1015 km above its surface. You want to use the satellite's engines to move the satellite into an orbit that is 1505 km above the surface of the earth.

    a. What is the total energy of the satellite before you make the adjustment to the orbit?
    b. What is the total energy of the satellite after you make the adjustment?
    c. How much work did the engines have to do in order to make the adjustment?

With all of the work you have done with gravity between this course and your first-year course, you might think that we understand gravity really well. The fact is, however, there are things about gravity which still remain somewhat of a mystery to us. For example, *why* are two masses attracted to one another? We can write an equation that tells us *how strongly* they are attracted to one another, and we can describe the energy consequences of the attraction, but *why* does the attraction exist? Also, why isn't there gravitational repulsion? The electromagnetic force can be either attractive or repulsive. Why isn't that the case with gravitation? Also, how quickly does this force act? If I suddenly increase the mass of an object by 10 kg, does that *instantaneously* change the force with which it attracts the object that sits on the other side of the room, or does it take time for the effect to "travel" over to that object?

These are all serious questions which theorists have attempted to answer over the years. I want to try to introduce you to what modern physics believes are the answers. A proper discussion of these answers must include a discussion of **Einstein's General Theory of Relativity**. However, the best way to introduce the theory of general relativity is to start with something that is not quite as difficult to understand: **Einstein's Special Theory of Relativity**.

Einstein's Special Theory of Relativity

Back in Module #3, you learned about **inertial reference frames**. You learned that in physics, you really can't say something like, "I am moving and you are standing still." That's impossible to say, because, in fact, you must define motion *relative* to something else. On the other hand, you could say, "I am moving relative to that tree, and you are standing still relative to that tree." Although you can't say for sure whether or not you are moving, you can certainly tell whether or not you are moving relative to that tree. Thus, motion must be stated relative to something else. Using this idea, an inertial reference frame is a reference frame that moves at a constant velocity relative to another inertial reference frame.

Although it is not absolutely true, you learned in Module #3 that we will treat the earth as an inertial reference frame. Thus, anything moving at a constant velocity relative to the earth is an inertial reference frame. An elevator in free fall, for example, is not an inertial reference frame, because it is accelerating relative to the earth. If the elevator is falling at a constant velocity, however, it is an inertial reference frame, since it is moving at a constant velocity relative to the earth. A race car traveling at a constant speed around a circular track is not an inertial reference frame, because its direction (and therefore its velocity) is changing. Thus, it is not moving at a constant velocity relative to the earth. A race car traveling along a straight-away at a constant speed is an inertial reference frame, however, because its speed and direction (and thus its velocity) is not changing with respect to earth.

Now remember what is special about an inertial reference frame. In an inertial reference frame, Newton's Laws of Motion work. In a non-inertial reference frame, they do not necessarily work. When a car is traveling at a constant velocity, for example, boxes on the seat which are sitting still will not begin moving until they are acted on by a force. That's Newton's First Law of Motion. On the other hand, if the car goes around a curve, the boxes might begin moving seemingly of their own accord. That's because once the car goes around the curve, it is no longer an inertial reference frame, and as a result, Newton's First Law is no longer valid in the reference frame of the car.

Okay, then. That's all review from Module #3. Where do we go from here? Well, we said in Module #3 that Newton's Laws work in *any* inertial reference frame. What about the laws of electromagnetism? Will they work in *any* inertial reference frame? That's a no-brainer, right? If Newton's Laws work in any inertial reference frame, the laws of electromagnetism work in any inertial reference frame. That may sound like a simple statement, but the *consequences* of that statement are *profound*. Why? Well, the laws of electromagnetism (Maxwell's equations) state that the speed of light in a vacuum is 2.998×10^8 m/sec, which we usually abbreviate as "c." Since that is a *consequence* of the laws of electromagnetism, and since we want to believe that the laws of electromagnetism work in all inertial reference frames, we must therefore agree that the speed of light is equal to c in all inertial reference frames. Does that sound like a simple statement? It is definitely not!

To illustrate just how profound all of this is, let's imagine a scene in our heads. Suppose you could run at the speed of light. As long as you are running in a straight line and your speed does not change relative to the earth, you are in a inertial reference frame, right? Thus, Newton's Laws work, and the laws of electromagnetism work. Okay, then. Suppose you are holding a mirror while you run. If you look in the mirror, what will you see? Think about it.....

Most people, when confronted with such a situation, will say that you will not see anything in the mirror. After all, you are running at the speed of light. In order to see yourself in the mirror, light must reflect off your face, hit the mirror, and return to your eye. Well, light can strike your face, but can it reach the mirror? After all, you are running with the mirror at the speed of light. The light reflects off of your face at the speed of light. Thus, the light will never hit the mirror, and it will therefore never have a chance to reflect off of the mirror and reach your eyes, right? *WRONG!!!!!!*

Remember, the laws of electromagnetism work in *all* inertial reference frames. Thus, even in your inertial reference frame (running at the speed of light), light travels at a speed of c. Well, in your inertial reference frame, the mirror is not moving. It is staying at the same position relative to you, so it is at rest in your inertial reference frame. Since it is at rest in your inertial reference frame, and since light moves at a speed of c in your inertial reference frame, light will reflect off of your face, hit the mirror, and reach your eyes just as if you are not moving. Whether you stand still relative to the earth, run at 100 m/sec, run at 1,000,000 m/sec, or run at c, light will always reflect off of your face, hit the mirror, and reflect back into your eyes, all with a speed of c. It must, if the laws of electromagnetism are the same in all reference frames.

The situation I discussed above was originally discussed by Einstein in an attempt to explain the reasoning behind his special theory of relativity. Although his theory has some incredible consequences (as we will discuss in a moment), it can really be summed up in one statement that, on the face of it, seems like nothing more than common sense:

<u>Einstein's Special Theory of Relativity</u> - The laws of physics work the same in all inertial reference frames.

This sounds so simple that most people just assume it to be true. Regardless of whether I am stationary relative to the earth or moving at a constant velocity relative to the earth, the laws of physics work the same. If I do experiments while I am stationary, or if I do experiments on a space ship that is moving at a constant velocity relative to earth, the experiments will have exactly the same results, because the laws of physics work in all inertial reference frames.

So far, none of this may surprise you, but I think this next concept will. If the laws of physics are the same in all inertial reference frames, and if the laws of electromagnetism state that the speed of light in a vacuum is c, then you will find that "common sense" will not always describe physical situations.

What do I mean by that? Well, suppose you are standing on a street and far, far away, your friend turns on a flashlight. The light approaches you at a speed of c, right? If you had some device that you could use to measure the speed of light, you would determine that the light is approaching you with a speed of 2.998×10^8 m/sec. Okay, that makes sense. Now, suppose you start running towards your friend, and suppose you could run at one-half the speed of light, 1.499×10^8 m/sec. If you then used the same device to measure the speed at which the light is approaching you, what would you get? Many people think that you would measure that the light is approaching you at 4.497×10^8 m/sec, which is the sum of your speed and the speed of light. However, that is *WRONG!* Remember, the laws of physics must be the same in all inertial reference frames. Thus, the speed of light must be 2.998×10^8 m/sec in all inertial reference frames. This means that *whether you are standing still relative to your friend, or whether you are running at your friend at one-half the speed of light, you will measure that the light is approaching you at exactly 2.998×10^8 m/sec.*

That last statement probably blew you away. After all, if I drive a car at 55 miles per hour east, and another person drives a car at 55 miles per hour west, how quickly are the cars approaching one another? They are approaching one another at 110 miles per hour. That's easy. However, if I am traveling at the speed of light east and light is heading towards me from the east, the light is approaching me at exactly the speed of light. Whether I stand still or move towards the light source, the light will *always* be approaching at exactly 2.998×10^8 m/sec - nothing more and nothing less! That's a direct consequence of the idea that the laws of physics work the same in all inertial reference frames. Since the laws of physics state that light moves at a speed of 2.998×10^8 m/sec in a vacuum, then no matter what inertial reference frame you are in, you will always measure the speed of light to be 2.998×10^8 m/sec.

FIGURE 8.4

Illus. from the MasterClips collection

The Speed of Light is the Same in All Inertial Reference Frames

When you are at rest relative to your friend with the flashlight, you measure the speed of light approaching you at 2.998x10^8 m/sec.

When you are running towards your friend with the flashlight, you *still* measure the speed of light approaching you at 2.998x10^8 m/sec, even if you are running at 2.998x10^8 m/sec!

Let me just mention one more situation and then I will move on. Suppose you are in a car that is initially at rest relative to a friend of yours. You turn on your headlights, and both you and your friend measure the speed of the light from the headlights. You measure the speed of the light as it heads away from you, and he measures the speed of the light as it approaches him. Now, suppose you travel towards him at three-fourths the speed of light. Once again, you flip on your lights and you both measure the speed of the light. What speed will you measure? In your inertial reference frame, the light will be traveling away from you at 2.998x10^8 m/sec. In your friend's inertial reference frame, the light will be moving towards him at 2.998x10^8 m/sec. The speed of the car does not add to the speed of the light for your friend, nor does it take away from the speed of the light for you. Both you and your friend measure the speed of the light to be exactly 2.998x10^8 m/sec.

Now all of this might sound really odd to you, because it goes against your common sense. Remember, however, that common sense is built on your experiences, which are, quite frankly, rather limited. If we want to believe that the laws of physics work the same in all inertial reference frames, then all of the situations I discussed above must be true. Of course, you might just want to give up on the idea that the laws of physics are the same in all inertial reference frames. However, as we will see in the next section, there is strong experimental evidence that Einstein's Special Theory of Relativity is correct. Thus, whether or not we "like" it, it is most likely true.

Time Dilation and Length Contraction

If you are willing to accept what I have told you so far, then you are ready to move on to two of the more profound consequences of Einstein's Special Theory of Relativity: time dilation and length contraction. To understand why special relativity predicts these strange effects, I need to describe another situation to you. Suppose you wanted to measure the speed of light. You could do this by setting up a laser that shoots out a pulse of light and, at the same instant, starts a clock. The light travels to a mirror, reflects straight back, and travels back to the laser. At the instant the light hits the laser, the clock is stopped. The speed of light, then, is twice the distance between the laser and the mirror divided by the time.

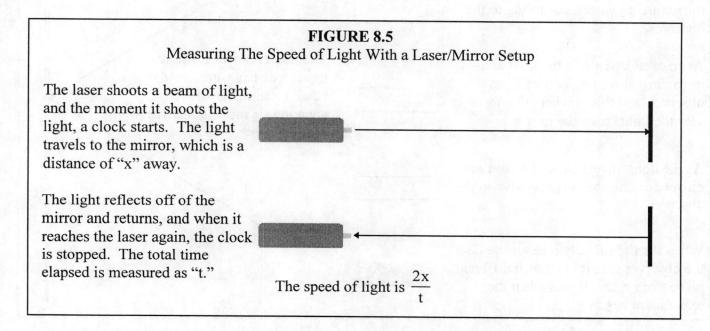

FIGURE 8.5
Measuring The Speed of Light With a Laser/Mirror Setup

The laser shoots a beam of light, and the moment it shoots the light, a clock starts. The light travels to the mirror, which is a distance of "x" away.

The light reflects off of the mirror and returns, and when it reaches the laser again, the clock is stopped. The total time elapsed is measured as "t."

The speed of light is $\dfrac{2x}{t}$

Although the technology used to do this experiment is pretty complicated, the experiment itself is not. If you were to do this experiment in a lab that is stationary relative to earth, you would find that the speed of light is 2.998×10^8 m/sec, just as the laws of physics demand. Okay, now suppose you set up this experiment in a rocket ship moving at very near the speed of light. What would the results of your experiment indicate? Well, once again, it would indicate that the speed of light is 2.998×10^8 m/sec, because the speed of light is the same in all inertial reference frames.

Now let's add a twist. Let's suppose the rocket in which you are doing your experiment is transparent, and let's have an observer at rest relative to the earth watch your experiment through a telescope as you pass by. Suppose you are passing by so that the setup is perpendicular to your velocity. What will the observer see? Figure 8.6 illustrates that.

FIGURE 8.6
What an Observer on Earth Would See if the Experiment in Figure 8.5 were Done While Moving Relative to Earth

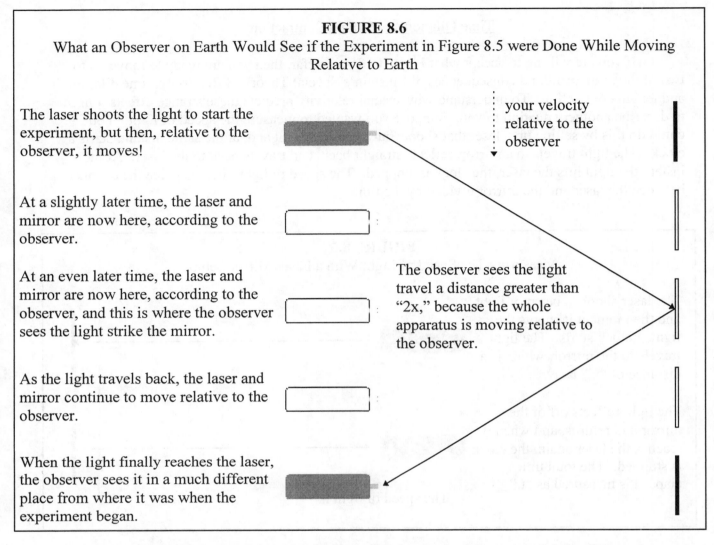

The laser shoots the light to start the experiment, but then, relative to the observer, it moves!

your velocity relative to the observer

At a slightly later time, the laser and mirror are now here, according to the observer.

At an even later time, the laser and mirror are now here, according to the observer, and this is where the observer sees the light strike the mirror.

The observer sees the light travel a distance greater than "2x," because the whole apparatus is moving relative to the observer.

As the light travels back, the laser and mirror continue to move relative to the observer.

When the light finally reaches the laser, the observer sees it in a much different place from where it was when the experiment began.

Now please understand that *you* don't see this happening. In your reference frame, the experiment is stationary. Thus, you see the light shoot straight towards the mirror, hit the mirror, and come straight back. However, that's not what the observer at rest relative to you sees. Since you are moving relative to him, he sees the whole apparatus move. As a result, the light does not travel straight for him. Instead, it travels at a diagonal, because it hits the mirror, which is moving, as far as he can tell. Well, since the light travels diagonally relative to the observer, he sees the light traveling a longer distance than "2x."

Suppose the observer decided to time the light in order to determine its speed. Thus, he starts a clock the instant he sees the laser fire, and he stops the clock the instant he sees the light return to the laser. Then, he takes the distance that he saw the light travel and divides by the time. What does he get for the speed of light? Well, if the laws of physics work the same in all inertial reference frames, *he will also get a speed of 2.998×10^8 m/sec*. Remember, the speed of light is a consequence of the laws of physics. Thus, if the laws of physics are the same in *all* inertial reference frames, then he must get the speed of light demanded by those laws, which is 2.998×10^8 m/sec.

Now wait a minute. The observer on earth sees the light travel a distance *larger* than "2x." How in the world can he determine that the speed of light is 2.998×10^8 m/sec? After all, he will take a number larger than "2x" and divide by the time. How will he come up with 2.998×10^8 m/sec? He will do so because ***the time that he measures will be longer than the time you measure!*** Remember, when *you* do the experiment, you will take "2x" and divide by the time. He will take a number greater than "2x" and divide by time as well. The only way he can get the same answer as you get (which is required if the laws of physics are the same in all inertial reference frames), is if he divides by a *longer* time! This means that he measures a *longer time* than you do. In other words, from his point of view, ***time runs slowly in your reference frame***.

That's the statement which usually makes a student's head spin. After all, you are used to time being the same everywhere. Thus, it is natural for you to assume that no matter what, time marches on the same everywhere. However, we are pretty certain these days that time is *not* the same everywhere. As you will see in a moment, there is a substantial amount of evidence that time does, indeed, vary from one reference frame to another. Thus, even though you are used to thinking about time as a constant, give it up. Physics says that it just isn't so.

Now let me make clear *exactly* what special relativity tells us with regard to time. When you are in a reference frame that is moving relative to someone else, *you do not notice anything unusual in your own reference frame*. Time does not move slowly as far as you are concerned. Indeed, everything is perfectly normal for you. However, if someone who is a rest relative to you looks at your reference frame, he or she observes that time runs slowly in your reference frame. If this person were to see a clock in your space ship, he would see the clock run slower than the clocks in his reference frame. Now remember, nothing is unusual as far as you are concerned. The clocks in your ship are keeping perfect time. However, *someone at rest relative to you sees a much different picture. He sees the clocks running slowly, because, according to him, time is dilated in your reference frame*. Of course, we know of one thing that he sees the same in your reference frame as in his - the speed of light. The speed of light is the same in *all* reference frames.

I know that this is hard to wrap your head around, but experiments do bear this out. Before I discuss these experiments, I want to give you the equation which relates the time in one reference frame to the time in another.

$$t' = t \cdot \sqrt{1 - \left(\frac{v}{c}\right)^2}$$

(8.6)

In this equation, "t'" is the time that is measured *within* the reference frame, and "t" is the time measured by someone at rest relative to that frame. The "v" term is the speed of the reference frame relative to the observer who is measuring a time of "t," and "c" is the speed of light.

One thing I want you to notice about the equation is that when the speed of the reference frame is small compared to c, "t'" essentially equals "t." Consider, for example, a speed of 1,000 m/sec. That sounds fast to you and me, but compared to the speed of light, it is small. When you take 1,000 m/sec and divide by the speed of light, you get 3×10^{-6}. When you square that, you get 9×10^{-12}. Well, $1 - 9 \times 10^{-12}$ is essentially 1, so for speeds with which we are used to dealing, time dilation isn't a factor. Thus, we are not used to experiencing it. However, when the speed of the reference frame becomes comparable to c, we notice the effects. Consider the following example:

EXAMPLE 8.3

A person travels to a distant star on a space ship that moves at a constant velocity of 0.900c relative to earth. If the star is 20.0 light years from earth, how much time will pass on earth before the ship reaches its destination? How much time will pass in the space ship?

A light year is the distance over which light travels in a year. Thus, if the rocket ship could travel at the speed of light (c), 20 years would pass on earth before the space ship reached the star. However, the rocket ship can only travel at 0.900c, so it will take a bit longer. How much longer? Well, if light takes 20 years to travel that far, we can say that the distance is (20 years)·(c). As long as c is expressed in meters per year, then the units work out. We know that the space ship is traveling at 0.900c. Thus, we have the distance and the time:

$$\text{time} = \frac{\text{distance}}{\text{speed}} = \frac{(20.0 \text{ years}) \cdot c}{0.900 \cdot c} = 22.2 \text{ years}$$

That means <u>22.2 years will pass on earth before the space ship gets to the star</u>.

How much time will pass on the ship, however? Since the ship moves relative to the earth, it experiences time differently than those on earth. To find out how differently, we use Equation (8.6). Now remember, t' is the time that is measured in the reference frame, and t is the time measured by someone relative to whom the reference frame is moving. In this case, the earth is stationary relative to the space ship, and the space ship is moving. Thus, we need to solve for t', because we want to know how much time passes in the reference frame. This means that t = 22.2 years, because that's the time measured in the reference frame stationary relative to the space ship.

$$t' = t \cdot \sqrt{1 - \left(\frac{v}{c}\right)^2}$$

$$t' = (22.2 \text{ years}) \cdot \sqrt{1 - \left(\frac{0.900 \cdot c}{c}\right)^2} = 9.68 \text{ years}$$

This means that <u>on the space ship, only 9.68 years pass</u>.

What does this mean? Don't 22.2 years "really" pass on the space ship? *NO!* Only 9.68 years pass. Suppose, for example, a man leaves on the space ship, but his twin stays behind on earth. The man travels to the star and then turns around and travels back. When he gets back to earth, a total of 44.4 years (22.2 years there, 22.2 years back) have passed. Thus, his twin is 44.4 years older. However, on the space ship, only 19.4 years have elapsed. As a result, the man is only 19.4 years older. This means that *his twin is now 25 years older than he is*. That's the way it works!

This gets even a bit more strange. For the person in the space ship, only 9.68 years pass as he travels to the star. Of course, he knows the speed at which he was traveling relative to earth, so he could calculate the distance that he traveled over those 9.68 years. What would he calculate? Well, he knows that he was traveling at 0.900c relative to earth, so he knows that his speed is $(0.900) \cdot (2.998 \times 10^8$ m/sec), or 2.698×10^8 m/sec relative to earth. He also knows that he has been traveling for 9.68 years. Thus, he traveled:

$$(2.698 \times 10^8 \ \frac{m}{sec}) \cdot (9.68 \ \text{years}) \cdot (\frac{31,557,600 \ \text{sec}}{\text{year}}) = 8.24 \times 10^{16} \ m$$

His friends on earth, however, know that the distance from the earth to the star is 20.0 light years, which is:

$$(2.998 \times 10^8 \ \frac{m}{sec}) \cdot (20.0 \ \text{years}) \cdot (\frac{31,557,600 \ \text{sec}}{\text{year}}) = 1.89 \times 10^{17} \ m$$

Wait a minute. That's *longer* than the distance that the man in the space ship calculates. Which one is right? Well, *BOTH ARE RIGHT!*

You see, just as time is not a constant from one reference frame to another, space is not, either. In the space ship's reference frame, the space ship traveled only 8.24×10^{16} m, while those on earth watched the space ship travel 1.89×10^{17} m. Thus, just as time dilates in a reference frame that is moving relative to you, length contracts! Suppose, for example, there was a meter stick on that space ship. To the person on the space ship, it would be exactly 1.000 m long. However, if the space ship were transparent and someone on earth were to look at the meter stick, it would not be 1.000 m long. It would be shorter than that! In fact, length contraction is a bit more complicated because it occurs only in the direction of travel. If the meter stick was perpendicular to the velocity of the space ship, the meter stick would look the same in both reference frames. Nevertheless, if a stationary person were to observe a moving reference frame whose speed is comparable to the speed of light, he would see that time moves slowly and length is contracted in the direction of the velocity! Space and time, then, are not absolutes. They vary from reference frame to reference frame.

Okay, now wait a minute. This is a wild theory. Is there really any evidence to support it? Yes, there is. Firstly, we know that the speed of light is the same in all reference frames. Consider, for example, the fact that we can see stars which are far from us. Because we are orbiting our sun, we are moving relative to the star. Sometimes we are moving away from the star, and sometimes we are moving towards the star. In addition, some stars orbit other stars in what is called a **binary star system**. Sometimes, those stars are traveling towards us, and sometimes they are traveling away from us. Nevertheless, the light from those stars is *always* approaching us at a speed of c, regardless of which way we are moving and regardless of which way the star is moving.

How do we know that? Well, suppose the light approached us more quickly when we moved towards the star or when the star moved towards us. During those times, the light would reach us in a shorter time. However, if this were to happen, when we moved away from the star or the star moved away from us, the light would take longer to reach us. If this were the case, the path of the star would look erratic to us. It would seem to spend less time in the part of its orbit during which it is moving towards us and more time in its orbit when it is moving away from us. However, we do not see that. The orbit is smooth, indicating that light travels towards us at the same speed regardless of our motion relative to the star or the star's motion relative to us.

Okay, so there's evidence for that idea. But there's no evidence for time dilation, right? *WRONG!* Back in the 1950's scientists studied a group of particles called **muons** (myou' ons), which constantly rain down on the earth at a speed of 0.994·c. These muons decay at a fixed rate, and we know that rate for stationary muons. Thus, we know how long a muon will "live" before it decays. However, the muons that are raining down on us at a speed of 0.994c "live" a *lot longer* than stationary muons. How long do they live? They live for *exactly* the length of time predicted by Equation (8.6)! Thus, we know that in their reference frame, time actually does move more slowly than it does for earth, and the dilation is given exactly by Equation (8.6).

Lots of studies like this one have put the concept of time dilation on firm experimental footing. For example, in another classic experiment, two very precise clocks were synchronized and observed over a long period of time. During the entire time that they were at rest relative to one another, they kept *exactly* the same time. Then, one clock was placed in a very high-speed jet and flown around the world a few times. When that clock was compared to the clock that remained on earth, *it was behind by exactly the amount of time predicted by relativity*! This gives us good evidence that time dilation is real, and therefore time is *not* constant. It varies based on the speed of the reference frame.

Now please understand that time dilation and space contraction are real effects that must be taken into account in high-speed situations. For example, in a television, the electrons that make the image on the screen move at about 0.3·c. If the engineers who design televisions do not take length contraction into account, televisions will not focus properly.

ON YOUR OWN

8.8 Consider the experiment described in this section. You are on a space ship traveling at 0.80c east relative to the earth, and you measure the speed of light as described in Figure 8.5. The distance from the laser to the mirror is 10,000.0 m. (It's a *big* space ship!) If an observer on the earth watches your experiment and times how long it takes for the light to travel from the laser to the mirror, what time will he measure?

The Twin Paradox

If I haven't bothered you enough, I want to bother you with one more idea. Remember, I have said (both in Module #3 and this module) that there is no way to tell whether or not a reference frame is really moving. I can say that a reference frame is moving relative to some object, but I cannot say that a reference frame is moving absolutely. Thus, if I am driving a car at 55 miles per hour towards a tree, I could say that I am moving towards the tree and the tree is stationary, but I could just as easily say that I am stationary and the tree is moving towards me. From a physics point of view, both statements are equally correct.

However, if you paid close attention, you should have uncovered something that was not "quite right" about the space ship trip I have been talking about. When the space ship gets back to earth, I told you that the man in the space ship would be younger than the twin. But wait a minute, this seems to indicate that we know which reference frame was moving. After all, if the ship is moving away from the earth at 0.900·c, isn't that equivalent to the space ship standing still and the earth moving away from it at 0.900·c? According to everything we know about physics, it should be. Well, if we look at it that way, the twin that is on the earth is the one that is moving, so time runs slowly in *his* reference frame compared to that of the twin in the space ship, so why isn't the twin on earth younger than the twin on the space ship?

This is called the **twin paradox**, because it seems to break the rule that you cannot determine which twin was moving. If you treat the earth as stationary and the space ship as moving, the twin on the space ship will be younger than the twin on earth when he returns. On the other hand, if you treat the space ship as stationary and the earth as moving away from it, the twin on earth will be younger than the twin on the space ship when the earth returns to the space ship. However, that's not how it works. The twin on the space ship will be the younger one every time. Doesn't that mean we know which twin was moving?

Yes, it does mean we know which twin is moving, but that does not really break any of the rules. You see, in order to get back to earth, the twin on the space ship must *turn around*. Thus, for a while, he is not in an inertial reference frame. The twin on earth never turns around. Thus, he is always in an inertial reference frame. As a result, we *know* that the space ship was the moving reference frame. In inertial reference frames, there is no way to tell which is moving. However, since Newton's Laws of Motion only work in inertial reference frames, as soon as the twin in the space ship turns around, his motion is defined relative to the twin on the earth.

Now let me make this clear, *until the space ship turns around, there is no way of knowing which twin is moving!* If the twin in the space ship were to observe the twin on the earth, the twin on the space ship would think that time is running slowly on earth. If the twin on earth were to observe the twin on the space ship, he would think that time on the space ship was running slowly. Both would think that time was slow *in the other's reference frame*. However, once the space ship turns around, its motion is defined relative to the other twin. On the way back, both twins would still think time was running slowly in the other's reference frame, but when they came together, they would see that compared to the earth, time ran slowly in the space ship, because the twin in the space ship would be younger.

The Famous Equation

I want to conclude my discussion of special relativity by introducing what is probably the most recognized equation in the world:

$$E = mc^2 \tag{8.7}$$

Most people associate this equation with Einstein and relativity, but in actuality, Einstein published his paper on special relativity in 1905, but he did not publish a comprehensive paper on Equation (8.7) for two more years.

What does this equation tell us? It tells us that energy and mass are really just different forms of the same thing. The speed of light is the "conversion factor" between the two. Thus, just as inches and centimeters measure the same physical quantity (length), energy and mass are both measures of the same physical quantity. Just as 2.54 cm/in is the conversion relationship between inches and centimeters, the speed of light squared is the conversion relationship between energy and mass.

If energy and mass are really just different measures of the same thing, is it possible to transform one into the other? Yes. As you should have learned in chemistry, the nucleus of an atom is made up of neutrons and protons. The nucleus of a carbon-12 atom, for example, contains 6 protons and 6 neutrons. If you were to measure the mass of 6 individual protons and 6 individual neutrons, you would find that the total mass is *greater* than the mass of a carbon-12 nucleus. Why? When the protons and neutrons come together, some of the mass is converted to energy which holds the nucleus together. This **binding energy** can be calculated using Equation (8.7). In the same way, a nuclear reactor makes energy by nuclear reactions in which mass is converted to energy via Equation (8.7).

The reverse is possible as well. In a nuclear physics laboratory, a gamma ray of a specific energy can suddenly change into two particles: an electron and a **positron**. A positron has all of the physical characteristics of an electron but has a positive charge rather than a negative charge. In this process, the gamma ray disappears, and the two particles simply appear. The gamma ray, which is just electromagnetic energy, can transform into two particles, each of which are composed of matter. Thus, energy can be converted into mass, and mass can be converted into energy. Equation (8.7) tells you the relationship between the two.

EXAMPLE 8.4

The mass of an electron (and that of a positron) is 9.11×10^{-31} kg. What is the energy of a gamma ray that can produce an electron and a positron?

If a gamma ray produces an electron and a positron, its energy is being converted into mass. The total mass produced is:

total mass = mass of electron+mass of positron = 9.11×10^{-31} kg + 9.11×10^{-31} kg = 1.822×10^{-30} kg

To determine how much energy is required to produce this mass, we just use Equation (8.7):

$$E = m \cdot c^2 = (1.822 \times 10^{-30} \text{ kg}) \cdot (2.998 \times 10^8 \frac{\text{m}}{\text{sec}})^2 = 1.638 \times 10^{-13} \frac{\text{kg} \cdot \text{m}^2}{\text{sec}^2} = \underline{1.638 \times 10^{-13} \text{ J}}$$

That must be the energy of the gamma ray. This doesn't sound like a lot of energy, but not much matter is being created, either. Note how the units work out here. As long as mass is in kg and the speed of light is in m/sec, the energy unit works out to be $\frac{\text{kg} \cdot \text{m}^2}{\text{sec}^2}$, which is the same as a Joule. In the "on your own" problem at the end of this section, you will get a better feel for how much energy exists in even a small amount of matter.

Equation (8.7) not only tells us how much energy is in an amount of matter (or vice-versa), it also leads us to another interesting fact:

Nothing can accelerate to a speed faster than the speed of light in a vacuum.

How does it lead us to this incredible statement? I cannot give you a rigorous explanation, because the mathematics gets a bit tricky, but I can give you a qualitative explanation.

What happens to an object if its mass increases? It gets harder to move, right? In Module #3, you learned about **inertial mass**. This is the idea that mass is really just a measure of an object's inertia. The harder an object is to move, the larger its mass. Likewise, the more massive the object, the harder it is to move. Well, Equation (8.7) tells us that energy and mass are really just the same thing. Thus, when I increase an object's *energy*, the object also becomes harder to move. In other words, adding energy is like adding mass. The more energy an object has, the more inertia it has.

When I accelerate an object, I am adding energy to it. Thus, every time the speed of the object increases, its inertia increases as well. As an object starts moving faster, then, it also becomes harder to move. There is actually an equation which governs all of this, but I do not want to get bogged down in the math at this point. However, the equation tells you that the closer the object's speed gets to c, the more quickly its inertia grows. In the end, the inertia of an object grows without limit as its speed approaches the speed of light. Thus, it is simply impossible to travel at or beyond that speed. In the end, then, the speed of light in a vacuum is the ultimate "speed limit" of the universe. An object cannot travel faster than the speed of light, and information cannot be transmitted faster than the speed of light.

ON YOUR OWN

8.9 On the star ship Enterprise, the crew has access to "replicators," which take energy and covert it into any kind of matter. If Captain Jean-Luc Picard walks up to a replicator and asks it to make Earl Grey Tea, how much energy must the replicator use? The total mass of the tea and the cup from which to drink the tea is 600.0 grams.

Einstein's General Theory of Relativity

Now remember, the whole reason I wanted to tell you about special relativity was to get to a theory about what gravity really is. That's **Einstein's General Theory of Relativity**. Although Einstein did not begin developing this theory as an explanation of gravity, it quickly became one. What Einstein really wanted to do with his general theory of relativity was to generalize the idea that the laws of physics are the same in all inertial reference frames to an idea in which the laws of physics are the same in *all* reference frames, *regardless* of whether or not the reference frame is inertial.

Wait a minute! We *know* that's not the case, right? In a non-inertial reference frame (like a car rounding a curve), things contrary to Newton's Laws (like packages moving on the seats seemingly of their own accord) occur. Thus, how can the laws of physics be the same in all reference frames, even the non-inertial ones? Well, Einstein had the idea that Newton's Laws weren't exactly correct. They were really only special cases of more general laws that worked in all reference frames. Thus, what Einstein really wanted to do was formulate general laws of physics which work in all reference frames, regardless of the acceleration of the frame. How did he do this? He started with the **principle of equivalence**. Consider, for example, this picture, which was taken on the space shuttle:

FIGURE 8.7
Weightlessness on the Space Shuttle

This man is weightless *not* because there is no gravity. That is a common misconception! He is in the space shuttle, which is in orbit around the earth. If there were no gravity, the space shuttle would not stay in orbit.

He is weightless because he is in *free fall*. In orbit, an object is constantly falling towards the earth under the influence of gravity. Since the man's reference frame is falling with him, he does not feel any of the effects of gravity.

As explained in the figure (and in Module #3), the man is definitely being influenced by gravity. During this picture, the space shuttle was in orbit about 300 miles above the surface of the earth. If you were to climb a ladder that high to talk to him, you would weigh 85% of what you weigh on the surface of the earth. Why, then, is he weightless? He is weightless because his reference frame (the shuttle) is in free fall. It is freely falling towards the earth under the influence of earth's gravity. However, because of the shuttle's velocity, which is perpendicular to the acceleration, the shuttle keeps "missing" the earth. As a result, it is in orbit.

Einstein said to consider a reference frame that is freely falling. Objects *inside* the reference frame do not experience any force due to gravity. The reference frame itself does, but the objects inside do not. This reference frame is *equivalent in every way* to a reference frame in deep space that is so far from any star, galaxy, or planet that there is no gravity whatsoever. Thus, we can produce the absence of gravity by simply allowing our reference frame to accelerate at whatever acceleration is produced by gravity. Under those conditions, the people inside the reference frame would have no way of knowing whether or not gravity is really there.

Einstein also said that you could reverse the situation. Suppose, for example, the space shuttle was sitting on the earth. The people in the space shuttle would no longer be weightless. They would "feel" the gravity produced by the earth. However, we could fool the occupants of the space shuttle by taking them into deep space (so far away from any matter so that there really is no gravity) and then have the space shuttle accelerate directly upwards at 9.81 m/sec^2. If we did that, the occupants of the space shuttle would think that there was gravity, because they would weigh what they weighed on earth, and everything would work just as if they were at rest on earth's surface. However, there really is no gravity at all. The shuttle simulates the effect of gravity by accelerating upwards.

Have you ever watched a science fiction movie in which a space station is rotating, and the people on the inside of the space station are walking around as if they are under the influence of gravity? There is no gravity, however. The rotation *simulates* the effect of gravity.

FIGURE 8.8   *Illus. by Megan Whitaker*
The Simulation of Gravity Through Rotation

If the space station is rotating, the floor of the space station must push against a person inside the space station in order to keep that person rotating with the space station. The force with which the floor must push is the centripetal force, which depends on the speed of the rotation, the radius of the rotation, and the mass of the person. The person, however, does not notice this as long as the radius of rotation is large. As a result, the person just feels himself being pushed upwards by the floor. This is exactly what the person experiences when he is on earth, under earth's gravitational influence. This situation is equivalent in every way to being in a gravitational field, but there is no gravity anywhere.

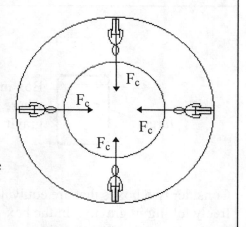

The point of this discussion is simple. We can construct reference frames in which gravity is really there but the objects inside the reference frames behave as if there is no gravity (freely-falling reference frames like the space shuttle). We can also construct reference frames in which there is no gravity, but the objects behave as if there is gravity (the space shuttle accelerating upwards or the rotating space station). These reference frames are equivalent in every way. That's the principle of equivalence.

The principle of equivalence led Einstein to conclude that *gravity is not a force*. He said that if a force were real, it could not be "taken away" by constructing the proper reference frame. The electrical force that attracts positive and negative charges, for example, exists in all frames of reference. You cannot construct a frame of reference in which the objects inside behave as if there is no electrical force. The same can be said for the magnetic force. There is no way to construct a frame of reference in which the objects behave as if there is no magnetic force. However, you can construct a frame of reference in which objects behave as if there is no gravitational force. In the end, then, gravitational force is not a real force. It must be an artifact - something that we interpret as a force but is really not a force.

Although this sounds strange, we actually apply this logic to other situations. Consider the car that rounds a curve. When the car rounds a curve, the packages fly off of the seat, seemingly of their own accord. Some people say that this is because the packages experience a "centrifugal force." However, there is really no such thing as a centrifugal force. The fact that the packages move off of the seat is the result of Newton's First Law of Motion as observed by someone at rest relative to the car. However, people in the car cannot tell that their velocity is changing, so they assume that there is a "centrifugal force" causing the packages to move. The "centrifugal force" is really an artifact, however. It is an artifact of the acceleration of the reference frame.

Einstein said that gravity is another artifact. Since we can construct reference frames in which gravity doesn't seem to exist, then gravity must not be a true force. It must be an artifact of our reference frame and perhaps other reference frames as well. What is this artifact? Well, to understand that, consider another comparison between two reference frames:

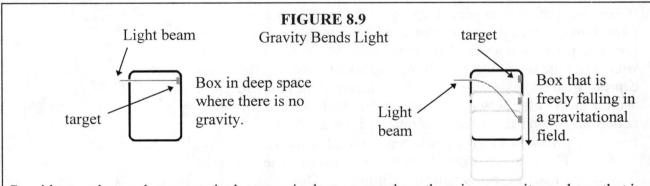

FIGURE 8.9
Gravity Bends Light

Consider two boxes that are equivalent: one in deep space where there is no gravity, and one that is freely falling in gravity. In the box in deep space, light that enters the hole in the box will hit the target. Since the other box is equivalent (as discussed above), light must also hit the target there as well. However, since that box is moving, light must *bend* in order to hit the target!

Remember, the principle of equivalence states that a reference frame (such as the box in Figure 8.9) that is in deep space where no gravity exists is equivalent in every way to a box that is freely falling. If we do an experiment in the first, it must have exactly the same result in the second. So, let's construct a simple experiment. Light is allowed to pass through a hole in the box that is in deep space. It travels straight and hits a target. No problem. However, the experiment must yield the same result in the freely falling box. Thus, light must enter the hole and then hit the target. However, once light enters the hole, it must travel across the box. By that time, the box has fallen a bit. Thus, the light must *curve* in order to still hit the target. This leads us to an amazing fact:

Gravity causes light rays to bend.

Now remember, Newton's Law of Universal Gravitation *does not* predict this. According to Newton, the gravitational force that exists between objects depends on the *mass* of the objects. Light has no mass. Thus, according to Newton, gravity should not affect light. However, it does. If the principle of equivalence is correct, in order for the experiments above to have the same result, light must bend when it is in a gravitational field. What does this tell us about gravity? Well, what can make light bend? You can push or pull on light all day, and you will not have an effect. You can send light through a magnetic or electric field, and you will not be able to bend it. What, then, can bend light?

This is where we can refer back to special relativity. In special relativity, we learned that neither time nor space were absolute. They change depending on the reference frame. However, Einstein constructed a four-dimensional substance called **spacetime** which *is* absolute. The four dimensions of spacetime are the three dimensions of space plus a fourth dimension, which is time. This four-dimensional quantity, spacetime, is the same from reference frame to reference frame.

According to Einstein, the laws of motion could really be boiled down to one statement:

In the absence of external forces, objects travel the straightest possible path in spacetime.

Since light bends in the places we think of as having a gravitational field, Einstein decided that:

Mass and energy cause spacetime to curve.

Thus, what we observe as a "gravitational force" is no force at all. It is simply a consequence that objects want to travel along a straight line in spacetime but that mass curves spacetime. Instead of moving in a straight line, then, the moon moves in an orbit around earth not because it is really attracted to earth, but because it is moving along a straight path in spacetime, but spacetime is curved by the mass of the earth and the moon. As a result, the straight line in spacetime is really an orbit. To try and wrap your brain around this concept, try the following experiment.

EXPERIMENT 8.1
Simulating Curved Spacetime

Supplies:

- A soft seat cushion from a couch (A soft bed will work as well.)

- A bowling ball (A heavy rock will work as well.)
- A marble

Introduction - Einstein's General Theory of Relativity concludes that the gravitational "force" is not really a force at all. It is actually a result of the fact that mass curves spacetime. This experiment will help illustrate such a strange concept.

Procedure:

A. Lay the seat cushion on the floor. If you are using a bed, just stand next to the bed.
B. Find a spot on the cushion which is away from the center of the cushion but relatively flat. Put the marble on that point so that it stays there without rolling.
C. Now lay the bowling ball at the very center of the cushion. Note what happens to the marble.
D. Next, take the bowling ball off of the cushion and smooth it out so that it is reasonably flat again.
E. Roll the marble (slowly) straight across the cushion, but not near the center. Note that it rolls reasonably straight.
F. Put the bowling ball back in the center of the cushion and roll the marble along the same path that you rolled it before, with the same slow speed. Note the path that the marble takes.

Einstein's General Theory of Relativity states that space is not always the way it appears to us. Suppose, for example, that you did not know the world was round. Would you think that it was? Probably not. After all, the earth looks pretty flat all around you. Thus, you would probably think that the earth is flat. We know that this is not the case, though. Despite what it looks like from our vantage point, we know that the earth is round. In the same way, Einstein postulated that although it does not appear to change at all, space actually bends in the presence of an object with mass.

In the first part of your experiment, the seat cushion represents spacetime. With nothing on the seat cushion, it stayed relatively flat. However, when a massive object (the bowling ball) was placed there, the entire seat cushion bent. The bend was greatest in the middle and least around the edges, but nevertheless, the entire seat cushion bent. In response, the marble rolled towards the bowling ball. This is Einstein's picture of gravity. Spacetime (the seat cushion) bends in the presence of mass (the bowling ball). As a result, all objects (the marble) accelerate towards the mass. This makes it look like a force is being applied to the object.

In the second part of your experiment, you watched the marble roll straight across the flat seat cushion. When the bowling ball was once again placed on the seat cushion, the marble did not roll straight. Instead, it rolled in a curved path. According to Einstein, this is why planets orbit the sun. In his theory, the planets are all actually moving in a straight line in spacetime. Because spacetime is so strongly bent by the mass of the sun, however, that straight line is deformed until it becomes a circle. Thus, as far as the planets are concerned, they are traveling in a straight line. Curved spacetime, however, causes that straight line to become a circle.

I know that this is a terribly complicated picture to put in your head. That's why I tried to illustrate it to you with an experiment. However, please note that the experiment is not a true analogy. After all, spacetime is four-dimensional, while the surface of your cushion is two-dimensional. Also, gravity plays a role in this experiment, even though there is no gravity in general relativity. Thus, the experiment was just an attempt to get you to visualize a part of what general relativity states. Here is another visualization:

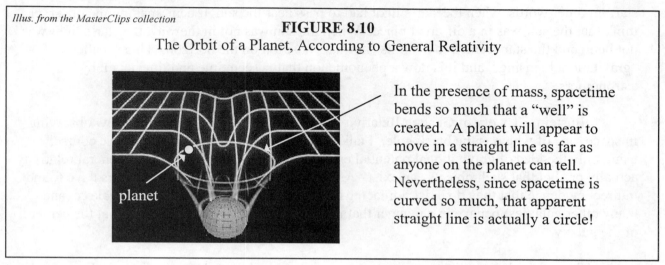

Illus. from the MasterClips collection

FIGURE 8.10
The Orbit of a Planet, According to General Relativity

planet

In the presence of mass, spacetime bends so much that a "well" is created. A planet will appear to move in a straight line as far as anyone on the planet can tell. Nevertheless, since spacetime is curved so much, that apparent straight line is actually a circle!

In Einstein's General Theory of Relativity, then, the laws of physics are the same in all reference frames, regardless of whether or not those reference frames are in uniform motion or being accelerated. However, Newton's Laws of Motion are not really correct. They are approximations of the true laws of motion, which are based on the idea that, in the absence of all forces, objects move in a straight line in spacetime. If we accept this view, then gravity is not a force at all. It is simply a consequence of the fact that mass curves spacetime.

Okay, this is another wild theory. Is there any evidence for it? Yes, there certainly is. Einstein produced one bit of evidence himself. Long before Einstein, astronomers had noticed that Mercury did not obey Newton's Law of Universal Gravitation exactly. Newton's Law of Universal Gravitation predicts that the planets will orbit the sun in ellipses that *never change*. However, over the years, it became apparent that Mercury's orbit does change a bit. The ellipse which defines the orbit actually tilts relative to the other planets, and that tilt changes slightly from year-to-year. This was a puzzle in physics, but since the effect was very small, it was regarded as more of a curiosity than anything else.

Einstein realized that Mercury was a planet on which he could test his theory. The planet Mercury is the planet closest to the sun. Thus, it experiences the sun's gravity more than any other planet. Einstein noted that his theory (which is full of a lot of incredibly complicated math) was essentially equal to Newton's Laws when the gravitational force between objects is weak. That's why Newton's Laws work so well for us. However, as gravity gets stronger, Einstein's equations of general relativity differ from Newton's Laws. When he applied his equations to Mercury, he found out that his equations *predict* Mercury's orbit's tilt. In fact, they predict *exactly* the behavior that Mercury has exhibited over the years.

Over the years, as we have been able to observe situations in space in which large gravitational forces play a role, we have seen more and more experimental confirmations of Einstein's Theory of General Relativity. For example, we have actually observed the bending of light predicted by the equivalence principle. This was first seen by Sir Arthur Eddington, a devout Christian, on May 29, 1919. Eddington was observing stars during a solar eclipse, and he noticed that the positions of the stars were different when the sun was near the line of sight of the star. In other words, when the star's light had to pass near the sun, it bent, making the observer think that the star was in a different place. When the sun was not in the way, the star's light was not bent, and the star seemed to be in its "normal" position on the horizon. This is called "gravitational lensing," and it is now a phenomenon that is seen time and time again by astronomers.

Einstein's Theory of General Relativity predicts many things that we are now observing in space, one of which is the black hole. I talked about black holes previously in the course, using only the idea of gravitational potential energy. However, the equations of general relativity actually predict that such objects can exist. As I mentioned previously, astronomers have found indirect evidence that they do exist. In fact, gases at the center of the Milky Way galaxy (and many other galaxies) behave in a manner that is consistent with a black hole being at the center of the galaxy.

There are other predictions of general relativity which have been confirmed. For example, general relativity predicts that time moves more slowly the more intense the gravity in the area (the more that spacetime is curved). This has been demonstrated experimentally. In fact, if you believe that the earth is thousands of years old instead of billions of years old, you might want to read *Starlight and Time* by Russell Humphreys. This book uses the prediction that curved spacetime slows down the passage of time in order to explain why we can see starlight from billions of light years away even if the earth is only thousands of years old.

Of course, these past 18 pages have contained just a quick glimpse into the fascinating field of relativity. If you want to learn more about special and general relativity, you might want to read *Einstein's Mirror* by Hey, Walters, and Hey. It is an excellent book that deals with both special and general relativity in a non-mathematical way. It takes its title from the situation I gave previously of running at the speed of light with a mirror in your hand.

ON YOUR OWN

8.10 On the surface of the moon, the gravitational acceleration is 1.62 m/sec^2. Suppose I wanted to construct a lab on earth in which all of my experiments would work as if I were on the surface of the moon. Neglecting the absence of an atmosphere on the moon, temperature, etc., what would I have to do to the lab to make this happen? Think about the principle of equivalence.

ANSWERS TO THE ON YOUR OWN PROBLEMS

8.1 Calculating the details of a planet's orbit usually starts by setting the centripetal force required to keep the planet in circular motion equal to the gravitational force, which is actually supplying the centripetal force:

$$\frac{m_p \cdot v_p^2}{r} = \frac{G \cdot m_p \cdot m_s}{r^2}$$

$$v_p = \sqrt{\frac{G \cdot m_s}{r}} = \sqrt{\frac{(6.67 \times 10^{-11}\ \frac{N \cdot m^2}{kg^2}) \cdot (1.99 \times 10^{30}\ kg)}{1.50 \times 10^{11}\ m}} = \sqrt{8.85 \times 10^8\ \frac{N \cdot m}{kg}} = 2.97 \times 10^4\ \frac{m}{sec}$$

Note how the units work out. A Newton is a $\frac{kg \cdot m}{sec^2}$ (you can remember that from F = m·a). When you take that unit, multiply by meters and divide by kilograms, you get m^2/sec^2. When you take the square root, you get m/sec. Thus, the average speed of the earth in its orbit is 2.97×10^4 m/sec.

This is the average speed, but it is <u>not constant. The earth moves faster when it is close to the sun and slower when it is far from the sun</u>. You can figure that out either with Kepler's Second Law or from your knowledge of centripetal force. In Kepler's Second law, the planet sweeps out equal areas in equal times. Well, when the earth is far from the sun, it must move more slowly to sweep out an equal area than when it is close to the sun (see Figure 8.1). From a centripetal force point of view, the higher the centripetal force, the higher the speed (see Equation 6.14). When the earth is closest to the sun, the gravitational force (which supplies the centripetal force) is higher, so the speed is higher as well.

8.2 Since the orbit is geosynchronous, we know the speed. How do we know the speed? Well, the satellite must stay in the same spot relative to the earth at all times. The only way it can do this is to have an orbital period of 24 hours. That way, it will orbit at the same speed that the earth is rotating. Well, in a single orbit, the satellite moves a distance equal to the circumference of the orbit, or $2 \cdot \pi \cdot r$. It does so in 24 hours, so the speed is $2 \cdot \pi \cdot r$ divided by 24 hours, which is 86,400 seconds.

$$\frac{m_{sat} \cdot v_{sat}^2}{r} = \frac{G \cdot m_{sat} \cdot m_e}{r^2}$$

$$\frac{m_{sat} \cdot \left(\dfrac{2 \cdot \pi \cdot r}{86{,}400 \text{ sec}}\right)^2}{r} = \frac{G \cdot m_{sat} \cdot m_e}{r^2}$$

$$r^3 = \frac{G \cdot m_e \cdot (86{,}400 \text{ sec})^2}{4 \cdot \pi^2} = \frac{(6.67 \times 10^{-11} \frac{N \cdot m^2}{kg^2}) \cdot (5.98 \times 10^{24} \text{ kg}) \cdot (86{,}400 \text{ sec})^2}{4 \cdot \pi^2}$$

$$r = 4.23 \times 10^7 \text{ meters}$$

Please note that this is the distance from the center of the earth, not the surface of the earth, because "r" in the universal law of gravitation refers to the distance between the center-of-mass of each object.

Notice how the units work out. Remembering that a Newton is a $\frac{kg \cdot m}{sec^2}$, when you multiply by m^2 and sec^2 and then divide by kg, you have m^3. When you take the cube root, you get meters.

8.3 Remember, when you are inside a sphere, the ring above you pulls at you equally from all directions. In the end then, you feel no net gravitational force from the ring above you. In addition, the mass below you can be replaced with a single dot at the center-of-mass. Thus, the distance between you and that dot is just "x," and since the sphere is uniform, the mass is simply the density times the volume. What is the density? Well, the mass is M and the volume is $(4/3) \cdot \pi \cdot R^3$:

$$\text{density} = \frac{M}{V} = \frac{M}{\frac{4}{3} \cdot \pi \cdot R^3}$$

Since the volume of a sphere of radius x is $(4/3) \cdot \pi \cdot x^3$, the mass at any value of x is simply the density (above) times the volume:

$$\text{mass} = \rho \cdot V = \left(\frac{M}{\frac{4}{3} \cdot \pi \cdot R^3}\right) \cdot \left(\frac{4}{3} \cdot \pi \cdot x^3\right) = M \cdot \frac{x^3}{R^3}$$

That's the mass of the sphere underneath you. You know the distance between you and the center-of-mass (x). Thus, if you are inside a sphere of uniform density the gravitational force is:

$$F = \frac{G \cdot m_1 \cdot m_2}{r^2}$$

$$F = \frac{G \cdot \left(M \cdot \dfrac{x^3}{R^3} \right) \cdot m}{x^2}$$

$$\underline{F = \frac{G \cdot M \cdot m}{R^3} \cdot x}$$

Since G, M, m, and R do not change no matter where you are in the sphere, you see that the gravitational force you experience while you are in the sphere increases linearly with the distance from the center of the sphere. Of course, once you get out of the sphere, this equation does not work any more, because the mass no longer increases as you move farther away. Thus, the gravitational force is then just given by Newton's Universal Law of Gravitation.

8.4 When you are sitting on the surface of the earth, the earth can be replaced by a point of mass right at the center. Your distance from that mass is just the radius of the earth, which was given. The gravitational force on an object of mass m, then, is:

$$F = \frac{G \cdot m_e \cdot m}{r^2}$$

$$F = \frac{(6.67 \times 10^{-11} \; \frac{N \cdot m^2}{kg^2}) \cdot (5.98 \times 10^{24} \; kg) \cdot m}{(6.37 \times 10^{6} \; m)^2} = (9.83 \; \frac{m}{sec^2}) \cdot m$$

$$F = m \cdot (9.83 \; \frac{m}{sec^2})$$

This takes the form F = m·a, so the acceleration due to gravity is $\underline{9.83 \; m/sec^2}$. Note that this is a bit higher than the $9.81 \; m/sec^2$ we normally use. You will see why in the next section.

8.5 Now we will take our answer to 8.4 and take earth's rotation into account. The measured weight is given by:

$$\text{measured weight} = W - \frac{4 \cdot \pi^2 \cdot m \cdot r}{T^2}$$

Well, measured weight would be mass times the measured g ($g_{measured}$), while true weight (W) would be mass times the true g (g_{true}).

$$m \cdot g_{measured} = m \cdot g_{true} - \frac{4 \cdot \pi^2 \cdot m \cdot r}{T^2}$$

$$g_{measured} = g_{true} - \frac{4 \cdot \pi^2 \cdot r}{T^2}$$

$$g_{measured} = 9.83 \frac{m}{sec^2} - \frac{4 \cdot \pi^2 \cdot (6.37x10^6 \ m)}{(86,400 \ sec)^2} = \underline{9.80 \frac{m}{sec^2}}$$

Notice that this is not quite the 9.81 m/sec^2 that we use, either. That's because the earth is not a perfect sphere, and 9.81 represents the best average over the entire planet.

8.6 In order for something to be a black hole, its escape velocity must be greater than that of light.

$$TE_{before} = TE_{after}$$

$$\frac{1}{2} \cdot m \cdot (2.998x10^8 \ \frac{m}{sec})^2 - \frac{G \cdot m \cdot m_{black \ hole}}{1.000x10^4 \ m} = 0$$

$$m_{black \ hole} = \frac{(2.998x10^8 \ \frac{m}{sec})^2 \cdot (1.000x10^4 \ m)}{2 \cdot (6.67x10^{-11} \ \frac{N \cdot m^2}{kg^3})} = 6.74x10^{30} \ \frac{kg^2 \cdot m}{N \cdot sec^2} = \underline{6.74x10^{30} \ kg}$$

Note that this is just slightly more mass than that of our sun. Thus, if our sun were shrunk from its current radius (6.96x10^8 m) to just under 10.0 km, it would be a black hole.

8.7 a. We can use Equation (8.5) to calculate the satellite's potential energy. Note that the distance given, however is not r! It is the distance from the surface of the earth. In the equation, r is the distance between the center-of-masses. Thus, we must add the radius of the earth to the distance given.

$$U_{grav} = -\frac{G \cdot m_1 \cdot m_2}{r} = -\frac{(6.67x10^{-11} \ \frac{N \cdot m^2}{kg^2}) \cdot (5.98x10^{24} \ kg) \cdot (1576 \ kg)}{6.37x10^6 \ m + 1.015x10^6 \ m} = -8.51x10^{10} \ J$$

That's the potential energy. What is the kinetic energy? To get that, we need to learn the speed. We can determine that by setting the centripetal force equal to the gravitational force:

$$\frac{m_{sat} \cdot v_{sat}^2}{r} = \frac{G \cdot m_{sat} \cdot m_e}{r^2}$$

$$v_{sat} = \sqrt{\frac{G \cdot m_e}{r}} = \sqrt{\frac{(6.67\times10^{-11} \ \frac{N \cdot m^2}{kg^2}) \cdot (5.98\times10^{24} \ kg)}{6.37\times10^6 \ m + 1.015\times10^6 \ m}} = 7.35\times10^3 \ \frac{m}{sec}$$

Now we can determine the kinetic energy:

$$KE = \frac{1}{2} \cdot m \cdot v^2 = \frac{1}{2} \cdot (1576 \ kg) \cdot (7350 \ \frac{m}{sec})^2 = 4.26\times10^{10} \ J$$

The total energy, then, is:

$$TE = PE + KE = -8.51\times10^{10} \ J + 4.26\times10^{10} \ J = \underline{-4.25\times10^{10} \ J}$$

Why is the total energy negative? Remember, the satellite is bound to the earth, and negative energies generally represent a bound system.

b. We have to do all of this nonsense again for the new orbit:

$$U_{grav} = -\frac{G \cdot m_1 \cdot m_2}{r} = -\frac{(6.67\times10^{-11} \ \frac{N \cdot m^2}{kg^2}) \cdot (5.98\times10^{24} \ kg) \cdot (1576 \ kg)}{6.37\times10^6 \ m + 1.505\times10^6 \ m} = -7.98\times10^{10} \ J$$

$$\frac{m_{sat} \cdot v_{sat}^2}{r} = \frac{G \cdot m_{sat} \cdot m_e}{r^2}$$

$$v_p = \sqrt{\frac{G \cdot m_e}{r}} = \sqrt{\frac{(6.67\times10^{-11} \ \frac{N \cdot m^2}{kg^2}) \cdot (5.98\times10^{24} \ kg)}{6.37\times10^6 \ m + 1.505\times10^6 \ m}} = 7.11\times10^3 \ \frac{m}{sec}$$

Now we can determine the kinetic energy:

$$KE = \frac{1}{2} \cdot m \cdot v^2 = \frac{1}{2} \cdot (1576 \ kg) \cdot (7110 \ \frac{m}{sec})^2 = 3.98\times10^{10} \ J$$

The total energy, then, is:

$$TE = PE + KE = -7.98\times10^{10} \ J + 3.98\times10^{10} \ J = \underline{-4.00\times10^{10} \ J}$$

c. Look at what happened. The satellite did have a total energy of -4.25×10^{10} J. After the orbit switch, it has an energy of -4.00×10^{10} J. The total energy *increased* (got less negative) by 2.5×10^{9} J. How can that happen? The only way that can happen is if you *work* on the satellite with that much energy. Thus, the engines did 2.5×10^{9} J of work on the satellite.

8.8 First, we have to determine the time that *you* measure. If the distance is 10,000.0 m, and the speed of light is 2.998×10^{8} m/sec, you measure:

$$x = v_o \cdot t$$

$$t = \frac{x}{v_o} = \frac{10,000.0 \; \cancel{m}}{2.998 \times 10^{8} \; \dfrac{\cancel{m}}{sec}} = 3.336 \times 10^{-5} \; sec$$

That's t' (the time in the reference frame). Your friend measures t:

$$3.336 \times 10^{-5} = t \cdot \sqrt{1 - \left(\frac{0.80 \cdot \cancel{c}}{\cancel{c}}\right)^{2}}$$

$$t = 5.6 \times 10^{-5} \; sec$$

While only 3.336×10^{-5} seconds pass in your reference frame, 5.6×10^{-5} sec pass in your friend's reference frame.

8.9 This is a straightforward application of Equation (8.7). You just have to make the units work by putting mass in kg.

$$E = mc^{2} = (0.6000 \; kg) \cdot (2.998 \times 10^{8} \; \frac{m}{sec})^{2} = 5.393 \times 10^{16} \; J$$

That's a *lot* of energy. It is the same amount of energy that a 100 Watt light bulb uses if the light bulb burns for 17 *million* years!

8.10 The principle of equivalence says that all I have to do is construct a reference frame in which things accelerate downwards at 1.62 m/sec^{2}. As you learned in Module #3, when a reference frame is falling, the acceleration of the reference frame subtracts from the acceleration due to gravity. Near the surface of the earth, the acceleration due to gravity is 9.81 m/sec^{2}. Thus, if I do experiments in a lab that is falling with an acceleration of 8.19 m/sec^{2}, the net acceleration for objects falling inside the lab is 9.81 m/sec^{2} - 8.19 m/sec^{2}, which is 1.62 m/sec^{2}. That will be just like the surface of the moon (neglecting the lack of an atmosphere, the lower temperature, etc.).

REVIEW QUESTIONS FOR MODULE #8

1. An object of mass m has a weight of w at the surface of the earth. If it is raised to an altitude that is equal to the radius of the earth, what is its mass and weight?

2. Two objects are placed a distance x apart from one another. The first is 16 times more massive than the second. The force exerted by the first mass on the second mass is called F, and the force exerted by the second mass on the first mass is called f. What is the mathematical relationship between F and f?

3. Suppose you wanted to place a third object in between the two objects described above. Where would you put the third object so that there would be no net gravitational pull on it?

4. Suppose a new planet was discovered whose mass is 1/10 that of earth and whose radius is 1/5 that of earth. What is the gravitational acceleration at the surface of that planet?

5. The distance from Mercury to the center of the sun is 0.387 times that of earth. How long does it take for Mercury to orbit the sun?

6. Suppose you had a way of measuring the speed at which the earth is traveling in its orbit. How could you use it to tell when the earth was farthest from and closest to the sun?

7. An object is placed inside a hollow sphere of mass M. What is the gravitational force exerted on it by the sphere? If the mass is moved around within the sphere, how will the gravitational force change?

8. Suppose you are in a space ship traveling at 0.8c. Another space ship approaches yours, also traveling at 0.8c. Are the space ships approaching each other at 1.6c? Why or why not?

9. Consider the two space ships discussed above. If the first were to turn on a light and shine it at the second, at what speed would the light be approaching the second space ship? At what speed would the light be traveling away from the first?

10. If you ask a physicist how many different types of force there are in Creation, he or she would say three: the electroweak force, the strong nuclear force, and the gravitational force. If Einstein's General Theory of Relativity is true, how many different types of force are there in Creation?

PRACTICE PROBLEMS FOR MODULE #8

$$(G = 6.67 \times 10^{-11} \frac{N \cdot m^2}{kg^2}, c = 2.998 \times 10^8 \text{ m/sec})$$

1. A satellite is orbiting the earth at a radius of R and has a kinetic energy of KE. If the satellite moves to an orbit whose radius is $3 \cdot R$, what is the new kinetic energy in terms of KE?

2. A satellite is orbiting Neptune with a radius of R and an orbital period of T. What is the mass of Neptune in terms of R, T, and G? This is one way to measure the mass of a planet, since R and T are observable from earth and G is a constant.

3. Mars has a mass of 6.42×10^{23} kg and a radius of 3.37×10^6 m. If a rock is dropped from a height of 5.51×10^6 m from the surface of the planet, at what speed will the rock be traveling when it hits the planet's surface? Ignore any resistive forces.

4. Two masses (m_1 and m_2) are in deep space, at rest a distance R apart. They are not being acted on by any other forces, and they start to move under their mutual gravitational attraction. In terms of G, m_1, and m_2, and R, what is the acceleration of each mass when they are a distance R/2 from one another?

5. An astronomer observes indirect evidence for the existence of a black hole. Based on the behavior of the substances around this black hole, the astronomer estimates that the mass of the black hole is 5.67×10^{35} kg. What is the radius of the black hole?

6. A satellite of earth ($m_e = 5.98 \times 10^{24}$ kg) orbits the earth once every 12.0 hours. What is the radius of the satellite's orbit?

7. If you wanted to increase the radius of the satellite (m = 1123 kg) in problem #6 by 25.0%, how much energy would be required?

8. A space ship leaves earth traveling at $0.999 \cdot c$. It is headed to a location that is 677 light years from earth, as reckoned by observers on earth. How much time will pass on the ship before it reaches the location? How far will the people in the ship have traveled?

9. A 1,000.0 megawatt coal-burning power plant burns about 4 million tons of coal each year. A nuclear power plant, however, uses the conversion of matter into energy in order to produce electricity. Assuming that the nuclear power plant is 100% efficient, how much mass would it consume each year? (Remember, Watt is a power unit, and P = Work/time).

10. Suppose you had a spherical space station whose radius is 3500.0 m. To provide the same gravitational effects as the surface of the earth, at what speed (in m/sec) must the space station rotate?

Module #9: Heat

Introduction

Throughout the course of your physics education, you have used the concepts of energy and work quite a bit. In this module, we will take an in-depth look at one type of energy: **thermal energy**.

Thermal energy - The kinetic energy in the random motion of molecules or atoms in a system

For example, when you touch a piece of metal that is glowing red, it burns you. Why? The atoms in the metal are vibrating back and forth at a very fast rate. This motion, of course, is indicative of a large amount of kinetic energy. That rapid atomic motion is an example of thermal energy. When you touch the metal, the atoms begin colliding with your skin, transferring a lot of that energy. Your cells cannot handle all of that energy, so they die. The result is a burn.

Thermal energy, then, is simply the energy associated with the motion of the molecules or atoms that make up an object or a system. The thermal energy in the glowing metal is not what burned you, however. What burned you was the fact that the energy was *transferred* to you. That's what we call **heat**.

Heat - Energy that is transferred as a consequence of temperature differences

When you touched the metal, the atoms in the metal transferred energy to your skin. The energy transfer happened because the molecules which make up your skin were moving much more slowly than the atoms in the metal. Thus, energy flowed from the metal to your skin, and we call that heat.

Now, what about this thing called **temperature**? In our everyday language, most people say that temperature is a measure of heat. That is simply not true, however.

Temperature - A measure of the concentration of thermal energy in a system

Remember, heat is energy that is being transferred. Temperature does not measure that. Instead, it is essentially a measure of how quickly the molecules or atoms in a system are moving around. The faster they are moving around, the higher the temperature. In the situation we have been discussing, your skin had a lower temperature than the glowing piece of metal, because the molecules in your skin were not moving nearly as quickly as the atoms in the metal. You need to keep these definitions straight if you are to understand the rest of this module.

Please note one thing about this module. If you had a good chemistry course, much of this module might be review for you. However, some of it will be new as well. It would be best for you to study the entire module rather than trying to skip around. If you study the entire module, the topics you have covered already will become fresh in your mind again, and you won't run the risk of missing any new topics.

Temperature Scales

We all know that in order to measure temperature we use a thermometer. But how does a thermometer work? A thermometer makes use of the fact that substances tend to expand as they get warmer. We will look into that in more detail later on in this module. A typical thermometer consists of a substance (usually mercury or alcohol) that is contained in a column of glass. As the substance gets warmer, it begins to expand. Since the only way it can expand is in the upward direction, it begins to move up the glass column. The height that it moves up the column is directly related to the temperature.

Now that we know how temperature is measured, we need to know what units are used in the measurement. The temperature unit that you are probably most familiar with is **Fahrenheit** (abbreviated as ^{o}F).   Although this is a very common temperature unit, it is not used by physicists. Instead, physicists usually use one of two temperature units: **Celsius** (^{o}C) or **Kelvin** (K). These units all rely on definition. Remember, when we use a thermometer, we are measuring temperature indirectly. As a result, we can define any temperature scale that we want. The only thing we know for sure is that as the temperature increases, the concentration of thermal energy in the system increases.

We can define all of these temperature scales in terms of the boiling and freezing of water. In the Fahrenheit scale, water freezes at 32.0 ^{o}F and boils (under normal atmospheric pressure) at 212.0 ^{o}F. In the Celsius scale, water freezes at 0.0 ^{o}C and boils (under normal atmospheric pressure) at 100.0 ^{o}C. Finally, in the Kelvin scale, water freezes at 273.15 K and boils (under normal atmospheric pressure) at 373.15 K.

Why do we define temperature scales in this way? Well, temperature scales are linear. Since two points define a line, if you have two points, you can define a temperature scale. The boiling and freezing of water are typically used as reference points because both processes are easy to observe in the course of normal activities.

Interestingly enough, the Celsius and Fahrenheit scales are based on definition. Thus, the two reference points given are exact and therefore contain an infinite number of significant figures. However, this is not the case for the Kelvin temperature scale. The Kelvin temperature scale is considered an **absolute temperature scale**, because we cannot reach a temperature of 0 K. We can get arbitrarily close to it, but we can never reach it. The lowest temperature achieved as of 5/2001, for example, was 0.00000001 K. Well, the absolute temperature scale was defined based on experiment, so as a result, it has experimental error associated with the measurement. Thus, the reference points given above for the Kelvin scale do not have an infinite number of significant figures.

We can convert between these three temperature scales using the following two equations:

$$^{o}C = \frac{5}{9}(^{o}F - 32.00)$$

(9.1)

$$K = {}^{\circ}C + 273.15 \tag{9.2}$$

These equations are probably familiar to you already. If not, they are easy to use, and as a result, I will not give you any example problems using them. However, I will expect you to be able to use them in problems, so be sure you remember them by solving the following "on your own" problem.

ON YOUR OWN

9.1 What is the Fahrenheit equivalent of 0.00 K?

<u>Temperature Changes Due to Heat</u>

Now remember, heat is energy that is transferred. It is not a measure of how "hot" or "cold" something is. It is simply a quantity of energy that has been transferred from one system to another. When energy is transferred, several things can happen. In the next few sections, I will deal with the various things that happen as a result of energy transfer, or heat. We will start with the most obvious:

When energy is transferred, temperature *may* change.

Note the word "may" in the sentence. If I transfer energy from one object to another, the temperature of each object may change, or something else may happen. In the next section, you will learn about something else that can happen instead of a temperature change. In this section, however, we will concentrate on how temperature changes as a result of heat.

If energy is transferred from one object to another object, one object must lose energy while the other object gains energy. Since temperature is a measure of the thermal energy in a substance, then it is possible that when energy is transferred, the temperature of both objects will change. If that happens, the amount of energy transferred can be related to the change in temperature by the following equation:

$$q = m \cdot c \cdot \Delta T \tag{9.3}$$

In this equation, "q" is the heat (the amount of energy transferred), "m" is the mass of the object that is gaining or losing energy, "c" is the **specific heat capacity** (sometimes referred to as the "specific heat") of the object, and "ΔT" is the *change in temperature* of the substance, which can be given by:

$$\Delta T = T_{final} - T_{initial} \tag{9.4}$$

Notice, then, that this equation clearly shows us that temperature is not a measure of heat. Since heat is energy that is being transferred, the *change in temperature* can be *related* to heat, but temperature is definitely not a measure of heat.

Before I go over how to use this equation, I want to spend a few moments discussing specific heat capacity.

Specific heat capacity - The amount of heat necessary to raise the temperature of 1.0 gram of a substance by 1.0 °C

In other words, specific heat capacity tells how easy it is to warm up a substance. For example, if I put a metal plate on the burner of a stove and I put a wooden plate on another burner of the stove, which one do you think would get hot faster? As long as the wood did not catch on fire, the metal plate would get much hotter much faster. This is because the metal plate has a lower specific heat capacity than the wood. Since metals have low heat capacities, then even a small amount of heat changes the temperature significantly. On the other hand, wood has a relatively large specific heat capacity. This means that it takes a lot of heat to make even a small change in the temperature of the wood.

Each substance has its own, unique specific heat capacity. Table 9.1 lists some common substances and their heat capacities.

TABLE 9.1
Specific Heat Capacities of Common Substances

Substance	Specific Heat Capacity $\left(\dfrac{J}{g \cdot {}^\circ C}\right)$
Copper	0.382
Iron	0.452
Aluminum	0.900
Glass	0.837

Notice the units on specific heat capacity: energy divided by grams divided by °C. If you look at Equation (9.3), you will see that these units allow the equation to work out so that "q" is in Joules. This makes sense, since the Joule is an energy unit. Now look at the numbers in the table. Based on the numbers, if I add the same amount of energy to equal masses of each of the substances listed, copper will experience the greatest change in temperature; iron will experience the second largest change in temperature; glass will experience less of a change in temperature than iron; and aluminum will experience the smallest change in temperature. You need not memorize any of these heat capacities, but there is one that I will require you to memorize:

The specific heat capacity of water in its liquid phase is 4.19 J/(g·°C)

You must memorize this because water is so common in Creation that you need to know many of its physical properties, and specific heat capacity is one of them.

Now that you understand specific heat capacity, it is time to see how we can use Equation (9.3) to analyze physical situations. Consider the following example:

EXAMPLE 9.1

A piece of copper and a piece of glass have exactly the same mass (45.0 g) and are at the same temperature (25.0 °C). If both absorb the same amount of energy (450.0 J), what will be the final temperature of each?

If you look at Equation (9.3), we have q (450.0 J), c (we can get the c for both from Table 9.1), and m. Thus, we can solve for ΔT:

$$q_{copper} = m_{copper} \cdot c_{copper} \cdot \Delta T_{copper}$$

$$450.0 \text{ J} = (45.0 \text{ g}) \cdot (0.382 \frac{J}{g \cdot ^\circ C}) \cdot \Delta T_{copper}$$

$$\Delta T_{copper} = \frac{450.0 \text{ J}}{(45.0 \text{ g}) \cdot (0.382 \frac{J}{g \cdot ^\circ C})} = 26.2 \ ^\circ C$$

Of course, the problem did not ask for the change in temperature. It asked for the final temperature. For copper:

$$\Delta T = T_{final} - T_{initial}$$

$$26.2 \ ^\circ C = T_{final} - 25.0 \ ^\circ C$$

$$\underline{T_{final} = 51.2 \ ^\circ C}$$

If you do the same kind of calculation for the glass, you will find <u>the final temperature of the glass is 36.9 °C</u>. Note that this answer is exactly what we would expect from the heat capacities. Since glass has a higher specific heat capacity than copper, its temperature does not rise as high for the same amount of energy absorbed.

Although we learned something from the analysis given in the example, it was not all that useful. After all, how many situations will come up in which you know exactly how much energy is absorbed or released from an object? However, now that you know the basics of how to use the formula, you can start applying it to more detailed situations. For example, suppose you took a hot piece of metal and dropped it into some cold water. What would happen? You know the basic answer to this question. The metal would begin to lose energy, lowering its temperature. The water would gain that energy, raising its temperature. When will this end? It will end when the two objects have the same temperature. This is called **thermal equilibrium**. Since the objects have the same temperature, there will be no net energy transfer. Energy will still be transferred from the metal to the water, but an equal amount of energy will be transferred from the water back to the metal. Thus, since there is no net energy transfer, there will be no temperature changes, and the metal and water will stay at the same temperature. Equation (9.3) allows us to determine what the temperature of thermal equilibrium will be.

EXAMPLE 9.2

A piece of iron (m = 50.0 g) at 100.0 °C is dropped into an insulated cup that contains 200.0 g of water at 24.0 °C. Once thermal equilibrium is reached, what will be the temperature of both the water and the metal?

We know that the metal will lose energy and the water will gain energy, right? We also know that all of the energy lost by the metal will be gained by the water. Thus, the q of the water will be equal (in some way) to the q of the metal. However, we have to be careful about this. The water *gains* energy, but the metal *loses* energy. If you look at Equations (9.3) and (9.4), when a substance loses energy, its ΔT is negative. That means its q is negative as well. This makes sense, since a negative q would imply a loss of energy. In this case, then, the metal's q is negative (it loses energy) and the water's q is positive (it gains energy). If the metal loses 50 J, for example, it will have a q = -50 J. However, the water will gain that 50 J, so its q = +50 J. In the end, then, the q of the metal will equal the *negative* of the q of the water:

$$q_{metal} = -q_{water}$$

Since we have an equation for q, Equation (9.3), we can plug that equation into the equation above. To make the math easier, I will also insert the equation for ΔT, Equation (9.4) into Equation (9.3):

$$m_{metal} \cdot c_{metal} \cdot (T_{final} - T_{metal\_initial}) = -m_{water} \cdot c_{water} \cdot (T_{final} - T_{water\_initial})$$

Note that T_{final} is the same for both the water and the metal. Why? Remember, thermal equilibrium is reached. Thus, at the end, the metal and the water have the same temperature. Now we can plug in our numbers, and the only thing we don't know is T_{final}:

$$(50.0 \text{ g}) \cdot (0.452 \frac{J}{g \cdot °C}) \cdot (T_{final} - 100.0 \text{ °C}) = -(200.0 \text{ g}) \cdot (4.19 \frac{J}{g \cdot °C}) \cdot (T_{final} - 24.0 \text{ °C})$$

$$(22.6 \frac{J}{°C} + 838 \frac{J}{°C}) \cdot T_{final} = 2260 \text{ J} + 20,100 \text{ J}$$

$$T_{final} = \frac{22,400 \text{ J}}{861 \frac{J}{°C}} = \underline{26.0 \text{ °C}}$$

Notice, then, that even though the metal was 76.0 °C hotter than the water, the water's temperature increased only 2.0 °C. This is due to the mass of the water in this example and the large specific heat capacity of water.

ON YOUR OWN

9.2 A sample of unknown metal (m = 150.0 g) at 95.0 °C is dropped into an insulated cup that contains 300.0 g of water at 25.0 °C. Thermal equilibrium is achieved at 27.4 °C. What is the specific heat capacity of the metal?

Phase Changes Due to Heat

Although the temperature of an object might increase if it absorbs energy (or decrease if it releases energy), that's not the only thing that can happen. If an object gains or loses energy, it might also experience a **phase change**. As you know, matter has three basic phases: solid, liquid, and gas. As you add energy, the solid phase gives way to the liquid phase (we call that melting), and the liquid phase eventually gives way to the gas phase (we call that evaporating). Alternatively, if I remove energy, the gas phase gives way to the liquid phase (we call that condensing), and the liquid phase eventually gives way to the solid phase (we call that freezing). Thus, when energy is released or absorbed, the result might be a change in phase.

EXPERIMENT 9.1
The Energy Associated With a Phase Change

Supplies:

- Table salt
- Water
- Three Styrofoam coffee cups
- Thermometer (It needs to read temperatures from -10 °C to 100° C.)
- Freezer
- Stove
- Pot in which to boil water
- One-quarter cup measuring cup
- Empty ice cube tray

Introduction - A phase change requires energy, as illustrated in this experiment.

Procedure:

1. Fill one of the Styrofoam cups ¾ of the way with water and dissolve as much salt as possible into the water. If there is left-over salt at the bottom of the cup, don't worry about it.
2. Measure out ¼ of a cup of water, and pour it into as many ice cube depressions in the ice cube tray as are necessary to accept all of the water in the measuring cup.
3. Put both the ice cube tray and the cup of salt water into the freezer, and leave them there until the water in the ice cube tray freezes. The salt water in the cup should not freeze, because by adding salt, you have reduced the freezing point of the water. This is called **freezing point depression**, and you should have learned about it when you took chemistry.

4. Place the thermometer in the freezer as well, so that it can measure the temperature of the freezer.
5. When the water in the ice cube tray is nearly frozen, boil at least 2 cups of water in the pot.
6. Nest one coffee cup into the other. You now have a **calorimeter**, which is something else you should have learned about in chemistry.
7. Read the temperature on the thermometer and remove it from the freezer.
8. Take the salt water out of the freezer and quickly measure out ¼ of a cup of it. Pour that into the coffee cup calorimeter.
9. Place the thermometer in the cup so that the bulb is immersed in the salt water.
10. Quickly measure out ¼ cup of boiling water and pour the hot water into the coffee cup calorimeter.
11. Stir the solution with the thermometer and read the temperature occasionally. After a while the temperature should level out. Read that as the final temperature.
12. Dump out the solution in the coffee cup calorimeter and rinse it out.
13. If you took the pot of water off of the stove, put it back on, because you will need boiling water again right away.
14. Take the ice cube tray out of the freezer and remove the cubes that have been made from the ¼ cup of water.
15. Place the ice cubes into the coffee cup calorimeter and put the thermometer in again.
16. Once again, quickly measure out ¼ cup of boiling water and dump it in the calorimeter.
17. Once again, stir with your thermometer and continue to read the thermometer until the temperature levels out. Record the final temperature.
18. Clean everything up.

What happened in the experiment? Well, in the first part of the experiment, energy was transferred from the hot water to the cold water (heat). This warmed the cold water and cooled the warm water until thermal equilibrium was achieved. Since the boiling water was approximately 100 $^\circ$C (depending on atmospheric pressure), and since the mass of cold water was about the same as the mass of warm water (because of the salt, the mass of the cold water was a bit higher), the final temperature should have been the midpoint between the temperature of the cold water and 100.0 $^\circ$C. Because your experiment was not perfect (energy leaked into the surroundings), and because the cold water was more massive than the hot water, the final temperature was probably lower than the midpoint.

In the second part of your experiment, the final temperature should have been *significantly* lower than the final temperature in the first part of the experiment. In fact, your final temperature might have ended up being very near 0 $^\circ$C. Why? After all, the ice was less massive than the cold salt water, since it had no salt in it. Nevertheless, more energy was transferred from the hot water to the ice than was transferred from the hot water to the cold salt water. The reason is simple. In order to melt ice, you need to supply more energy than what is required to raise its temperature. Once the ice's temperature was raised to the melting point, additional energy had to be added in order to actually melt the ice. If additional energy was not required to make the phase change, the final temperature in the second part of the experiment would have been nearly equal to the final temperature in the first part of the experiment.

This brings me to another important point. Energy was being transferred from the hot water to the ice, but once the ice reached its melting point (0 °C), it did not warm up while the ice was melting. That's because the energy it was receiving was dedicated solely to melting the ice and thus could not be used to raise its temperature. This means:

During a phase change, the temperature of the substance does not increase while energy is added or decrease while energy is removed.

This happens with all phase changes. For example, suppose you take some water and begin heating it on the stove. The temperature of the water will increase, because energy is being transferred from the burner to the water. Eventually, the water will reach 100.0 °C and begin to boil. However, *while the water is boiling, the temperature will not continue to increase*! It will remain at a constant 100.0 °C.

Why does the temperature stay constant during a phase change? As the experiment showed, it takes energy to go from solid to liquid and from liquid to gas. In order to go from solid to liquid, for example, the atoms that make up the substance must break away from a rigid arrangement in which they can only vibrate back and forth. Once they break away from this rigid arrangement, they can move around somewhat freely. In order to break out, however, they need energy. In the same way, molecules in the liquid state stay relatively near each other because they are attracted to one another. To get into the gas phase, those molecules must pull far apart from one another. It takes energy to overcome the attraction that they have for one another, so it takes energy to go from the liquid phase to the gas phase.

In the same way, when a substance changes from gas to liquid, it must release energy. After all, the molecules or atoms that make up the substance are traveling around freely while in the gas phase. When they come together to form a liquid, they must move more slowly, because they feel the effects of their mutual attraction. Thus, they must lose a lot of kinetic energy to go from the gas phase to the liquid phase. As a result, energy is released. When going from the liquid phase to the solid phase, the molecules must lose a lot of kinetic energy once again, because they must go from being able to move around to being arranged in a rigid structure which only allows for vibration. Thus, they must lose kinetic energy and, once again, energy is released.

When you are warming a substance up, once it begins to melt or evaporate, all of the energy you are supplying goes towards the phase change. As a result, temperature cannot increase during the phase change. In the same way, while you are cooling a substance down, during the time it is freezing or condensing, the temperature cannot change because any energy you are taking away from the substance is being released as a result of the phase change. Once again, then, the temperature cannot decrease.

How much energy is required to produce a phase change? Not surprisingly, it depends on the substance involved and the mass. The equation is as follows:

$$q = m \cdot L \qquad\qquad (9.5)$$

where "q" is the heat required to make the transition, "m" is the mass of the substance, and "L" is called the **latent heat of transformation**. This is unique for every substance as well as for each phase change. Typically, the "L" for freezing (or melting) is called the **latent heat of fusion**, while the "L" for evaporating (or condensing) is called the **latent heat of vaporization**. The latent heat of fusion for water, for example, is 334 J/g. This means that for every gram of ice at 0.0 °C, 334 J must be added to turn it into liquid water at 0.0 °C. The latent heat of vaporization for water is 2,260 J/g, which means it takes 2,260 J to change one gram of liquid water at 100.0 °C to one gram of gaseous water (water vapor) at 100.0 °C.

In order to boil water, then, it is not enough to just warm it up to 100.0 °C. You must also supply enough energy to actually make the phase change occur. Study the following example to see what I mean.

EXAMPLE 9.3

How much energy must be added to 150.0 g of water at 25.0 °C in order to completely boil the water away? ($L_{vaporization}$ = 2260 J/g for water)

To get the water boiling to begin with, we must raise its temperature to 100.0 C. To calculate the heat for that, we must refer to Equations (9.3) and (9.4).

$$q = m \cdot c \cdot \Delta T = (150.0 \text{ g}) \cdot \left(4.19 \frac{J}{g \cdot °C}\right) \cdot (100.0 \text{ }°C - 25.0 \text{ }°C) = 47,100 \text{ J}$$

That's not enough, however. We must now supply the energy for the phase change:

$$q = m \cdot L = (150.0 \text{ g}) \cdot \left(2,260 \frac{J}{g}\right) = 339,000 \text{ J}$$

Notice that the energy required to cause the phase change is significantly higher than the energy required to warm the water. The total energy required, then, is the sum of these energies.

$$q_{total} = q_{heating} + q_{vaporization} = 47,100 \text{ J} + 339,000 \text{ J} = \underline{386,000 \text{ J}}$$

ON YOUR OWN

9.3 How much energy does it take to completely evaporate 50.0 g of water if the water starts out as ice at a temperature of -11.0 °C? [The specific heat capacity of ice = 2.02 J/(g·°C), $L_{vaporization}$ = 2260 J/g for water, L_{fusion} = 334 J/g for water]

Before I leave this section, I want to introduce a term that is more common in chemistry but nevertheless is often used by physicists. The study of the relationship between heat and temperature is often called **calorimetry**. Experiment 9.1, for example, is often called a "calorimetry experiment," because it studies the transfer of heat from the hot water to the ice and relates that to the temperature of the overall solution. The setup you used (coffee cups and a thermometer) is often called a **calorimeter**. Where do these terms come from? Another unit for energy is the **calorie** (abbreviated as "cal"). This unit, common in chemistry, is defined as the amount of energy required to warm up one gram of water one degree Celsius. Please note that this unit is different from the *food* calorie (usually abbreviated as "Cal"). It takes 1,000 cals to make one Cal.

Volume and Length Changes as a Result of Heat

As you probably learned in elementary school, substances expand when they are heated and contract when they are cooled. In other words, when a steel beam used in construction is warm, it is longer than when it is cool. From a molecular standpoint, we can understand that. As a solid is warmed, its molecules vibrate more energetically. This stretches out the solid. When a solid is cooled, its molecules vibrate less energetically, shrinking the solid. In the same way, when liquids and gases are heated, the molecules have more energy, so they overcome more of their mutual attraction, and thus they can range farther from one another. As they are cooled, they do not have as much energy to overcome their mutual attraction and must therefore stay closer to one another.

In physics, we can actually predict the amount that substances will expand or contract as a result of heat. Consider, for example, a steel beam such as one that is used in construction. When the beam gets hot, its length increases. The formula which describes this increase in length is surprisingly simple:

$$\Delta L = \alpha \cdot L_0 \cdot \Delta T \tag{9.6}$$

In this equation, "ΔL" is the change in length, L_0 is the length before the temperature changed, "ΔT" is the change in the temperature, and "α" is the **coefficient of linear expansion** of the substance. This coefficient is different for every substance, because every substance has a unique molecular or atomic makeup. The coefficient of linear expansion for steel, for example, is 1.2×10^{-5} $1/^{\circ}C$.

Notice how this equation works. If the temperature rises, ΔT is positive. The coefficient of linear expansion for most substances is positive, so when temperature rises, ΔL is positive. Thus, as the temperature rises, things get longer. If the temperature decreases, ΔT is negative, and therefore ΔL is negative. This means that as the temperature decreases, things get shorter.

Of course, when the temperature changes, the length is not the only thing that changes. The width and the height of an object changes as well. This changes the *volume* of the object, as given by the following equation:

$$\Delta V = \beta \cdot V_0 \cdot \Delta T \tag{9.7}$$

where "ΔV" is the change in volume, "V_o" is the volume before the temperature changed, "ΔT" is the change in temperature, and "β" is the **coefficient of volume expansion**, which once again is unique for each substance.

The coefficient of volume expansion for most substances is positive, so when temperature increases (ΔT is positive), volume increases (ΔV is positive). When temperature decreases, volume decreases. Interestingly enough, there is a relationship between α and β for solids:

$$\beta \approx 3 \cdot \alpha \text{ for most solids}$$

This relationship ought to make sense. After all, when a solid expands, it expands in three dimensions: length, width, and height. Thus, the coefficient of volume expansion is three times that of length expansion.

EXPERIMENT 9.2
Measuring the Coefficient of Volume Expansion for a Gas

Supplies:

- A round balloon (the bigger the better - but it must fit in your freezer)
- Thermometer
- Thread
- Scissors
- Meter stick
- Tape

Introduction - The coefficients discussed in this section are typically measured by experiment. You will conduct such an experiment to measure the coefficient of volume expansion for the air that you exhale.

Procedure

1. Blow up the balloon so that it is mostly spherical.
2. Wrap the thread around the middle of the balloon so that it is the length of the balloon's circumference. Cut it so that it is exactly the length of the circumference.
3. Tape the thread to the balloon in a few spots so that it stays exactly where you measured the circumference. Since the balloon is not perfectly spherical, the circumference changes from place to place. You will be basing your measurement on the *difference* between the circumference now and once the balloon is cold. Thus, you want to make sure you are measuring the circumference at the same place both times.
4. Put the balloon in the freezer.
5. Read the temperature of the room from the thermometer and put it in the freezer as well.
6. Wait for at least an hour.
7. Open the freezer and quickly read the temperature.

8. Take out the thermometer and close the freezer again. Wait a few minutes. Opening the freezer actually increased the temperature in the freezer, so you are letting the freezer get back to its original temperature.

9. Now open the freezer and grab the balloon. Even though you are wasting energy, it is best to stand there with the door open and the balloon as much in the freezer as possible. Quickly wrap the thread around the balloon. Notice that the ends of the thread overlap now, because the balloon's volume (and thus the circumference) has decreased. Grab one end of the thread at the point where the other end touches it as the thread is wrapped around the balloon. The distance from the place where you have grabbed the thread to the end is the amount by which the circumference decreased.

10. Use the meter stick to measure the length from the point where you grabbed the thread to the end. Then, use the meter stick to measure the length of the thread. That is the original circumference of the balloon.

11. Take the length of the thread and subtract the distance from where you grabbed the thread to the end. That number is the circumference of the balloon once the balloon was cold.

12. Since circumference $= 2 \cdot \pi \cdot r$, you can use the two circumferences you measured to determine the radius of the balloon at room temperature and the radius of the balloon at the freezer's temperature.

13. Since $V = \frac{4}{3} \cdot \pi \cdot r^3$ for a sphere, you can now calculate the volume of the balloon at room temperature and the volume of the balloon at freezer temperature. This isn't 100% correct, since the balloon is not a sphere, but it is not a bad estimate.

14. Now take the volume of the balloon at freezer temperature and subtract from it the volume of the balloon at room temperature. That's ΔV. The number will be negative, since the volume decreased from room temperature to freezer temperature.

15. Next, take the freezer temperature and subtract from it the room temperature. That's ΔT. Once again, it will be negative, since the temperature decreased.

16. Since we are considering the original situation to be that of room temperature, the volume of the balloon at room temperature is V_o.

17. You now have everything in Equation (9.7) except for β, so you can solve for it.

18. The actual value of β for most gases at normal atmospheric pressure and the temperatures with which you were working is 0.00366. How close was yours?

ON YOUR OWN

9.4 There is at least one substance for which the coefficient of volume expansion is negative. What is that substance and around what temperature is the coefficient of volume expansion negative?

9.5 A steel beam used in the construction of a bridge is cut to a length of 50.00 m at 25.0 °C. What is the length of the beam on a hot day (T = 40.0 °C)? ($\alpha = 1.2 \times 10^{-5}$ 1/°C)

The Behavior of Gases

Most of the physical situations we have studied in both this course and your first-year course have dealt with solid objects: automobiles, rocks, etc. However, I want to spend some time on gases now, since the behavior of gases best illustrates several important concepts in a field called **thermodynamics**, which I will cover in the next module.

To begin with, I need to review with you something that you learned if you took chemistry. In chemistry, you should have learned about the **kinetic theory of matter**. I have spoken about it briefly in the past few pages, but I really want to focus on it now. In the kinetic theory of matter, the molecules or atoms which make up a substance are constantly moving in a random way. In solids, the atoms or molecules vibrate back and forth in random directions. In liquids, the molecules or atoms move around in random directions, but they stay relatively close to one another. In gases, the molecules or atoms also move in random directions, but they are far from one another. Figure 9.1 illustrates this idea.

FIGURE 9.1
Random Atomic Motion in the Three Phases of Matter

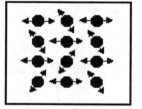

In the solid phase, atoms (or molecules) vibrate back and forth in random directions.

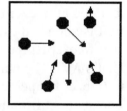

In the liquid phase, atoms (or molecules) move about freely, colliding with one another and the walls of their container

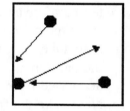

In the gas phase, atoms (or molecules) move about faster than in the liquid phase. They are also much farther apart.

In chemistry, you should have learned that the motion of the atoms or molecules in a substance is, in fact, the fundamental difference between the phases. Water, for example, is water whether it is ice, liquid water, or water vapor. The only real difference is the motion of the water molecules and how far apart they are from one another.

The liquid state can be rather messy to deal with because the molecules are moving around, but they are also still close enough to one another to feel their mutual attraction. The force of this attraction makes the physics a little hard to model. However, gases are convenient to study, because the molecules (or atoms) are so far apart from one another that they do not really feel any attraction from the other molecules (or atoms). As a result, we can treat a gas as a collection of individual atoms or molecules which do not really interact with one another. Although this is an approximation, it is actually a pretty good approximation for most gases near room temperature and normal atmospheric pressure. Nevertheless, it is an approximation. We call this kind of behavior "ideal" behavior, so a gas that behaves as a bunch of individual atoms or molecules which do not interact with one another in any way is called an **ideal gas**. In this course, we will assume that all gases are ideal gases.

Since an ideal gas behaves in such a simple manner, we really need only four characteristics in order to describe an ideal gas: pressure, volume, temperature, and quantity. If we know these four characteristics, we know everything that we need to know for an ideal gas. Notice one thing that is missing there: the *identity* of the gas. Is the gas hydrogen, oxygen, water vapor, or what? If the gas is ideal, it doesn't matter. In the world of ideal gases, hydrogen behaves just like oxygen, which behaves just like water vapor. In the end, then, the identity of an ideal gas is not relevant. We only need to know its pressure, volume, temperature, and the quantity of atoms or molecules. That's it.

Since these four characteristics are all that we need in order to model the behavior of an ideal gas, it is important that you understand each of them. You already understand the concept of volume, and we have discussed the concept of temperature in this module. What about pressure, however? What is pressure?

Remember that the atoms or molecules of a gas are moving around at high speeds (you will calculate those speeds later on in this module). As they move around, they will eventually crash into the wall of the container which holds them. That crash will result in a force that is exerted on the wall. In accordance with Newton's Third Law, when a molecule (or atom) exerts a force on the wall, the wall will exert an equal but opposite force on the molecule (or atom). The pressure of a gas is related to the force that the gas molecules (or atoms) exert on the container:

$$P = \frac{F}{A} \tag{9.8}$$

In this equation, "P" is the pressure, "F" is the force exerted, and "A" is the area.

As you should have learned in your first-year physics course, the standard unit of pressure (as you can see from the equation) is Newtons/meter^2, which is called the **Pascal (Pa)** in honor of the great Christian philosopher/mathematician/scientist Blaise Pascal. Although the Pascal is the standard unit for pressure, there are other units as well. The **atm** is a unit of pressure that references the normal pressure of earth's atmosphere. A pressure of 1.0 atm (101.3 kPa) is the pressure exerted by earth's atmosphere on an object at sea level. The unit **mmHg**, which is often called the **torr**, measures the height of a column of mercury in a barometer. There are 133 Pascals in 1.00 mmHg.

As you can see from the equation, pressure is just a measure of force exerted per unit area. Have you ever wondered why a sharp knife cuts better than a dull knife? The answer is really a result of pressure. The area on the edge of a sharp knife is significantly smaller than the area on the edge of a dull knife. Thus, for a given amount of force exerted by the user of the knife, a sharp knife applies more pressure to the object being cut. As a result, a sharp knife cuts better. The effect of area in Equation (9.8) is quite significant. As you should have learned in your first-year course, for example, a woman in high heel shoes exerts more pressure on the ground than does an elephant, because the area over which the woman's weight is distributed is so small compared to that of an elephant. If you want to walk on snow, you use snow shoes, which distributes your weight over a large area, reducing the pressure that you exert on the surface of the snow.

What about the last characteristic of a gas: quantity? How do we measure the quantity of a gas? Well, the quantity of a gas is best expressed in terms of **moles**. This is a term with which you should be intimately familiar if you took chemistry. A mole is a collective pronoun which refers to a certain number of molecules. Just as the term "dozen" means "12," the term "mole" means "6.02×10^{23}." This number is called **Avogadro's Number**, in honor of Amedeo Avogadro. Although it is a huge number, don't let that throw you. It is just a number that is equivalent to saying "mole." If I have two pennies, I could say that I have a *couple* of pennies. If I have 12 pennies, I could say that I have a *dozen* pennies. If I have 6.02×10^{23} pennies, I could say that I have 1 *mole* of pennies. In the same way, if I say that I have 1 mole of gas molecules, I know that I have 6.02×10^{23} gas molecules. If I have 2 moles of gas molecules, I have 12.04×10^{23} gas molecules. If I have 1.5 moles of gas molecules, I have 9.03×10^{23} molecules. The term "mole," then, simply refers to a certain number of molecules.

Okay, you know each of the four characteristics that describe an ideal gas. Now you can learn how they relate to one another. The **ideal gas law** relates them in the following way:

$$PV = nRT \qquad (9.9)$$

where "P" is the pressure of the gas, "V" is the volume, "n" is the number of moles of gas, "T" is the temperature, and "R" is a fundamental constant in Creation called the **ideal gas constant**. The two most popular values of the ideal gas constant are:

$$R = 0.0821 \ \frac{L \cdot atm}{mole \cdot K} \ \text{ or } \ 8.31 \ \frac{J}{mole \cdot K}$$

Please understand that the only difference between these two numbers is the units. If you are using standard units (m^3 for volume, Pa for pressure, moles for n, and Kelvin for temperature), you will use the second number (8.31) for R. If you measure volume in liters, pressure in atm, quantity in moles, and temperature in Kelvin, you will use the first number (0.0821).

Before I give you an example of how to use the ideal gas law, I want you to see a couple of consequences of the law. Consider, for example, blowing up a balloon. Why does the size of the balloon increase when you blow it up? Well, look at the ideal gas law. While you are standing in a room, the temperature stays pretty constant, as does the pressure. Thus, P and T are constants. R is also a constant. Thus, the only variables in Equation (9.9) for this situation are V and n. When you blow into a balloon, you are adding gas to the balloon. Thus, you are increasing n. As Equation (9.9) predicts, then, as n increases, V will have to increase; therefore, the balloon expands. Why did the balloon shrink when you put it in the freezer in Experiment 9.2? Well, in that case, the quantity (n) and pressure (P) were constant, as was the ideal gas constant (R). As a result, the only two variables in Equation (9.9) for that situation were V and T. As the equation predicts, when T goes down, V will go down. So, the balloon got smaller. Let's see how all of this works in an example problem.

EXAMPLE 9.4

Standard temperature and pressure (STP) is defined as T = 273.15 K and P = 101.3 kPa (normal atmospheric pressure). How much volume does 1.00 mole of gas occupy at STP?

In this problem, we know the pressure (1.013×10^5 Pa), the temperature (273.15 K), and the number of moles (1.00 moles). We also know R. Since our units are all standard, we will need to use 8.31 J/(mole·K) as the value of R.

$$PV = nRT$$

$$V = \frac{nRT}{P} = \frac{(1.00 \ \cancel{\text{mole}}) \cdot (8.31 \ \frac{J}{\cancel{\text{mole} \cdot K}}) \cdot (273.15 \ \cancel{K})}{1.013 \times 10^5 \ \text{Pa}} = 0.0224 \ \frac{J}{Pa} = 0.0224 \ \frac{N \cdot m}{\frac{N}{m^2}} = 0.0224 \ m^3$$

Notice how the units work out. Since a Joule is a N·m (from W = F·d) and a Pa is a N/m² (from P = F/A), the volume works out to the standard volume unit, m^3. When using the ideal gas law, the units work out as long as you use the units that are consistent with the value of R, as listed on the previous page. Thus, 1.00 mole of gas occupies 0.0224 m³ at STP. Of course, you are probably not used to working with m^3 as a unit for volume. The liter unit is probably more familiar to you. Since 1 m³ = 1,000 L, this is equivalent to saying that at STP, one mole of gas occupies 22.4 L of volume.

Notice that the results of this calculation are independent of the type of gas. As long as the gas behaves ideally, 6.02×10^{23} molecules of the gas (1.00 mole), will occupy 0.0224 m³ of volume. Thus, whether you have 6.02×10^{23} molecules of hydrogen gas, 6.02×10^{23} molecules of oxygen gas, or 6.02×10^{23} molecules of ammonia gas, they will all occupy 0.0224 m³ at STP.

ON YOUR OWN

9.6 A gas is contained in a spherical balloon at atmospheric pressure (P = 101.3 kPa). If the balloon has a radius of 10.0 cm, what is the average force exerted by the gas molecules as they strike the balloon? (The surface area of a sphere is $4\pi r^2$.)

9.7 If the temperature of the situation described in problem 9.6 is 25.00 °C, how many moles of gas are contained in the balloon? How many *molecules* of gas are contained in the balloon? (The volume of a sphere is given by $\frac{4}{3}\pi r^3$.)

The Speed of Gas Molecules

Now that you know about the ideal gas law, I want to manipulate it so that I can teach you a bit about how quickly gas molecules move. Remember, the fundamental difference between solids, liquids, and gases is the motion of the molecules. In solids, the molecules can only vibrate back and forth. In liquids, the molecules move relatively freely, but they stay rather close to one another. In gases, the molecules move very quickly and stay far from one another. Thus, the speed at which the molecules move is an important quantity to consider.

The first thing I want to do is simple. I just want to define a different physical constant. This one is called **Boltzmann's constant** in honor of Ludwig Boltzmann, an Austrian physicist who did much to explain the laws of thermodynamics on a molecular level.

$$k = \frac{R}{N_A} = 1.38 \times 10^{-23} \frac{J}{K}$$

Unlike the ideal gas constant, you do not have to memorize this one. It will be provided on the test. The Boltzmann constant is simply the ideal gas constant divided by Avogadro's number (6.02×10^{23}). Remember, that is the number of molecules in a mole. Why do I define this constant? You will see in a while. For now, just accept the definition.

Now I want to put that constant into the ideal gas law. Remember that the ideal gas law contains a variable called "n," which is the number of moles of the gas. Well, if I take the number of molecules in a sample (N) and divide by Avogadro's number (N_A), I get the number of moles. After all, if I take the number of doughnuts I have and divide by 12 (the number of doughnuts in a dozen), I determine how many dozen doughnuts I have. In the same way, if I take the number of molecules and divide by 6.02×10^{23} (the number of molecules in a mole), I will get the number of moles. I can put that into the ideal gas law:

$$PV = nRT$$

$$n = \frac{N}{N_A}$$

$$PV = \frac{N}{N_A}RT$$

$$PV = NkT \qquad\qquad (9.10)$$

Equation (9.10), is simply a restatement of the ideal gas law using N and k instead of n and R.

Once again, don't worry about why I did this yet. That will come later. Now let's switch gears a bit and think about the individual molecules in a gas. Consider a single molecule of gas that is housed in a cubic container. Each side of the container has a length of d, and let's assume for simplicity that the molecule is moving horizontally. Eventually, it will strike the container. When that happens, it will bounce straight back. The situation can be visualized with the following figure:

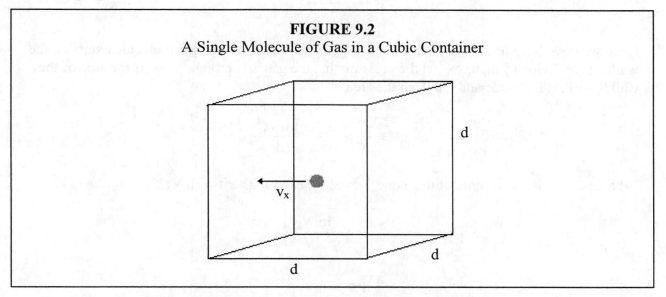

FIGURE 9.2
A Single Molecule of Gas in a Cubic Container

Well, remember that force is proportional to impulse [Equation (4.12)], and impulse is defined as the change in momentum [Equation (4.13)]. Thus, if we want to learn about the force, let's think about how the momentum changes. If the molecule is initially traveling at a velocity of v_x, when it hits the wall and bounces directly back, it will have a velocity of $-v_x$. If it has a mass of m, then, the change in momentum will be:

$$\Delta p = m \cdot (-v_x) - mv_x = -2m \cdot v_x$$

According to what we learned in Module #4, the change in momentum is equal to the impulse ($F \cdot \Delta t$). That means:

$$-F \cdot \Delta t = -2m \cdot v_x$$

$$F \cdot \Delta t = 2m \cdot v_x$$

Where did the negative sign on the force come from? The force exerted on the molecule must be in the negative direction, because the molecule's velocity changes in that direction.

Now let's think about the time interval, Δt. The molecule's speed is v. It will make a collision with the wall, travel across to the other side of the cube, make a collision with that wall, and then travel back to hit the first wall again. It will travel a total distance of 2d during that time. Since we know distance and speed, we can use them to calculate Δt:

$$F \cdot \left(\frac{2d}{v_x} \right) = 2m \cdot v_x$$

$$F = \frac{m \cdot v_x^2}{d}$$

Look what we have now. We have an equation for the force that the gas molecule exerts on the wall. If we divide by area, we get the pressure that the gas is exerting. What is the area of the wall? Well, it is d wide and d tall, so the area is d^2.

$$P = \frac{F}{A} = \frac{F}{d^2} = \frac{m \cdot v_x^2}{d^3}$$

What is d^3? It is the volume of the cube. Thus, we can replace it with V:

$$P = \frac{m \cdot v_x^2}{V}$$

$$PV = m \cdot v_x^2$$

This gives us a relationship between the pressure, volume, mass, and speed of a single gas molecule in a cube. Now let's make this a bit more realistic. First, you never have just one gas molecule. There are several gas molecules in any container of gas, so let's say there are N gas molecules. As we will see later, they do not all move at exactly the same speed, so rather than using v_x^2, we will use $\overline{v_x^2}$ to denote the *average* of the speeds squared.

$$P = \frac{m \cdot v_x^2}{V}$$

$$PV = N \cdot m \cdot \overline{v_x^2}$$

We still have one more piece of realism to inject into this analysis. The gas molecules can travel in any dimension, but we are considering only the horizontal dimension here. There is no preferred direction for the gas molecules to travel, so they can have an x-component to their velocity, a y-component, and a z-component. Well, since all dimensions are equivalent, the *average* of the total speed squared will simply be three times the average of the speed squared in each dimension.

$$\overline{v^2} = 3 \cdot \overline{v_x^2}$$

$$\overline{v_x^2} = \frac{1}{3} \cdot \overline{v^2}$$

Substituting this into our equation, we get:

$$PV = N \cdot m \cdot \frac{1}{3} \cdot \overline{v^2}$$

Okay, were almost done. Let's go back to Equation (9.10). According to that equation, $PV = NkT$. Well, let's substitute NkT for PV in the equation above. Also, let's group the m and $\overline{v^2}$ term together with a ½:

$$\cancel{N}kT = \cancel{N} \cdot \frac{1}{3} \cdot m \cdot \overline{v^2}$$

$$kT = \frac{2}{3} (\frac{1}{2} \cdot m \cdot \overline{v^2})$$

$$\boxed{\overline{KE} = \frac{3}{2} \cdot kT} \qquad (9.11)$$

Notice what we have in Equation (9.11). We have an expression for the *average* kinetic energy *per molecule* in our sample of gas. Notice also what the equation says. Since 3/2 and k are both constants, it tells us that the temperature of the gas is directly proportional to the average kinetic energy of the gas molecules. Of course, I told you that already:

Temperature is not a measure of heat, it is a measure of the average kinetic energy of the molecules in a substance.

Equation (9.11) just demonstrates this fact with mathematical rigor, for a gas.

I want to take this equation one step further. Let's go back to an earlier form of the equation and use it to solve for $\overline{v^2}$:

$$kT = \frac{2}{3} (\frac{1}{2} \cdot m \cdot \overline{v^2})$$

$$\boxed{\overline{v^2} = \frac{3kT}{m}} \qquad (9.12)$$

This is another important equation, as it allows us to calculate the average speed of a molecule in a sample of gas.

Before I show you an example of how to use the two important equations we derived in this section, I want to mention something that you should have learned if you took chemistry. The mass of a molecule is (obviously) quite small. Thus, it is expressed in the **atomic mass unit**, which is abbreviated amu. The atomic mass unit tells you how many grams it takes to make a mole of molecules. In other words, the mass of an NH_3 molecule is 17.0 amu, which is also expressed as 17.0 g/mole. This means that a mole of NH_3 molecules has a mass of 17.0 grams. We can use that to determine the mass of an individual molecule. After all if a mole (6.02×10^{23}) of these molecules has a mass of 17.0 grams, an individual molecule has the following mass:

$$\text{mass of one molecule of } NH_3 = \frac{17.0 \text{ g}}{6.02 \times 10^{23}} = 2.82 \times 10^{-23} \text{ g}$$

In other words:

The mass in grams per mole (or amu) divided by Avogadro's number (6.02×10^{23}) equals the mass of an individual molecule.

This is an important thing to remember.

EXAMPLE 9.5

A 2.00-mole sample of nitrogen gas has a total kinetic energy of 7,427 J. What is the temperature of the sample?

Remember, temperature is a measure of the average kinetic energy of the gas molecules. Thus, we can use Equation (9.11) to determine the temperature. However, remember that this equation is applicable to a *single* molecule. This sample has 2 moles, or $2 \times (6.02 \times 10^{23})$ molecules. Thus, let's first determine the average kinetic energy per molecule:

$$\overline{KE} = \frac{7,427 \text{ J}}{2 \times (6.02 \times 10^{23})} = 6.17 \times 10^{-21} \text{ J}$$

Now we can use Equation (9.11):

$$\overline{KE} = \frac{3}{2} \cdot kT$$

$$6.17 \times 10^{-21} \text{ J} = \frac{3}{2} \cdot (1.38 \times 10^{-23} \frac{J}{K}) \cdot T$$

$$T = 298 \text{ K}$$

The temperature of the gas is 298 K (or 25 °C), which is essentially room temperature.

If the mass of nitrogen molecules is 28.0 grams per mole, what is the average speed of the gas molecules in this sample?

For this, we use Equation (9.12), but we first must determine the mass of an individual molecule of nitrogen. To get that, we divide grams per mole by Avogadro's number:

$$\text{mass of one molecule of nitrogen} = \frac{28.0 \text{ g}}{6.02\text{x}10^{23}} = 4.65\text{x}10^{-23} \text{ g} = 4.65\text{x}10^{-26} \text{ kg}$$

Note that we must get the mass in kg, as the unit for k has Joules in it, which is defined based on kg. Remember, if you are dealing with standard units (like the Joule), keep all of your measurements in standard units (like kg for mass). Now we can use Equation (9.12):

$$\overline{v^2} = \frac{3kT}{m}$$

$$\overline{v^2} = \frac{3\cdot(1.38\text{x}10^{-23}\,\frac{J}{K})\cdot(298\text{ K})}{4.65\text{x}10^{-26} \text{ kg}}$$

$$\overline{v} = \sqrt{\frac{3\cdot(1.38\text{x}10^{-23}\,\frac{\frac{kg\cdot m^2}{sec^2}}{K})\cdot(298\text{ K})}{4.65\text{x}10^{-26} \text{ kg}}} = 515\,\frac{m}{sec}$$

Notice how the units work out. When you substitute the definition of the Joule, everything cancels except for m²/sec². When you take the square root, you get m/sec. Thus, the average speed of a nitrogen molecule at room temperature is 515 m/sec, which is about 1,150 miles per hour!

In the example above, I was able to calculate the *average* speed of nitrogen atoms in a sample of nitrogen at room temperature. However, it is important to note that not every molecule has this speed. Some molecules move faster than this, while others move slower. In other words, there is a *distribution* of speeds with a sample of gas molecules. This distribution, often called a **Maxwell-Boltzmann distribution** after the two scientists (James Clerk Maxwell and Ludwig Boltzmann) who were instrumental in describing it, is shown below for two different temperatures.

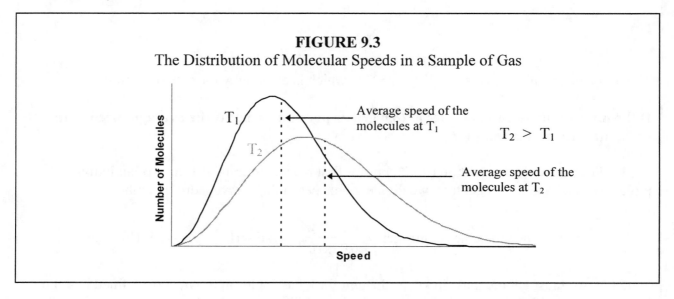

FIGURE 9.3
The Distribution of Molecular Speeds in a Sample of Gas

In the figure, I am plotting the number of gas molecules versus the speed of those molecules. Both curves deal with the same sample of gas, so the total number of gas molecules represented by each curve is the same. Notice what happens to the distribution when temperature is increased. At the lower temperature, the average speed of the molecules is lower [as per Equation (9.12)], and the "tail" of the distribution that extends to high molecular speeds falls off at a faster rate. As the temperature increases, the average speed gets higher, and the tail that extends to the higher molecular speeds does not fall off as quickly. Thus, the higher the temperature, the higher the average speed of the molecules in the gas, and the larger the number of molecules that possess really high speeds.

ON YOUR OWN

9.8 The average kinetic energy of a mole of gas is 3,123 J. If the average speed of the gas molecules is 512 m/sec, what is the temperature? What is the mass of one of the molecules? You can give your answer in kg or kg per mole, whichever you prefer.

9.9 Which of the following graphs best depicts the distribution of speeds among the gas molecules in the sample discussed above?

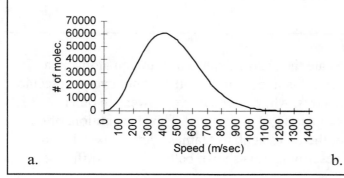

a.

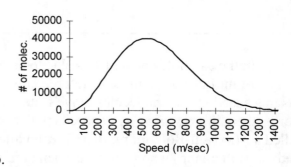

b.

Heat Transfer in Gases

In an earlier section of this module, I discussed heat transfer in substances, and I gave you Equation (9.3), which allows you to calculate the amount of heat absorbed or released by a substance. At the time, I led you to believe that Equation (9.3) applies to all substances, but it does not. It applies only to liquids and solids. Why? Well, think about the difference between a liquid and a gas or a solid and a gas. When a liquid or solid is heated, it expands, right? When a gas is heated, it will expand *if the container that contains the gas can expand*. If you warm up a gas in a balloon, the balloon will, indeed, allow the gas to expand. However, what if you warmed up a gas that was contained in a thick, metal container? The container will expand a bit, but it will not expand nearly as much as the gas would like to expand. Thus, the gas will be constrained.

If you think about it, whether or not a gas is allowed to expand as it is warmed will affect the temperature of the gas. If a gas is allowed to expand as it is warmed, some of the energy that it absorbs will be used to expand the gas. After all, for the gas to expand, it must push outwards. That's work, and work requires energy. Thus, if the gas is allowed to expand while it is warmed, its temperature will not increase as rapidly as when it is not allowed to expand. Thus, the relationship between heat and temperature for a gas depends on the *way* that the gas is warmed.

In this course, we will discuss two ways in which a gas can be warmed. First, a gas can be warmed under **constant pressure**. What does this mean? Well, if the pressure is constant, it means that the pressure does not change. This means that the *volume of the container expands with the gas*. Why? Think about the definition of pressure. Pressure is the force exerted by the molecules as they strike the container divided by the surface area of the container. Well, as the temperature increases, the average speed of the molecules increases, so the force with which they strike the wall increases. If pressure is going to stay the same, then, the container must expand so that its surface area increases. The other way that we will consider warming a gas is under conditions of **constant volume**. Under these conditions, pressure will increase as the gas is warmed, since the average speed of the molecules (and hence the force with which they strike the container) increases but the surface area of the container does not.

Although a gas has unique considerations when it is absorbing or releasing heat, the equations that govern these considerations are remarkably similar to those which govern a liquid or solid:

$$\text{For constant pressure: } q = n \cdot C_p \cdot \Delta T \tag{9.13}$$

$$\text{For constant volume: } q = n \cdot C_v \cdot \Delta T \tag{9.14}$$

In these equations, "q" is the heat, "n" is the number of moles of gas, "ΔT" is the change in temperature, C_v is the **molar heat capacity at constant volume**, and C_p is **the molar heat capacity at constant pressure**.

For each gas, the molar heat capacity at constant volume is different than the molar heat capacity at constant pressure. However, these two quantities are related to one another. For the same gas:

$$C_p = C_v + R \qquad (9.15)$$

Now remember, "R" is a constant. Thus, this equation tells us that the molar heat capacity at constant pressure (C_p) will always be greater than the molar heat capacity at constant volume (C_v). This should make sense to you. Remember what heat capacity tells you. It tells you how hard it is to warm up a substance. The higher the heat capacity, the more energy it takes to make a given change in temperature. Well, when pressure is constant, the gas can expand. Thus, some of the energy you put into the gas will go into the work done by the expansion. As a result, less will be available to raise the temperature of a gas. Therefore, it takes more energy to make a given temperature change when the pressure is constant as compared to when the volume is constant. That's just another way of saying that C_p is greater than C_v.

Equation (9.15), then, allows us to do calorimetry (the study of the relationship between heat and temperature) with gases. The main difference is that in doing calorimetry on gases, we must specify whether the gas is kept at constant volume or constant pressure. Please note that we will use Equations (9.13) - (9.15) heavily in the next module, so you need to make sure that you can use them!

EXAMPLE 9.6

A sample of gas that contains 2.00 moles at 45.0 °C is held at constant volume while 565 Joules are transferred to the gas. What is the final temperature of the gas? What would the final temperature of the gas be if the gas were held at constant pressure rather than constant volume? (C_v = 20.8 J/[mole·K])

The gas is being held at a constant volume, so first, we use Equation (9.14):

$$q = n \cdot C_v \cdot \Delta T$$

$$565 \text{ J} = (2.00 \text{ moles}) \cdot (20.8 \frac{J}{mole \cdot K}) \cdot \Delta T$$

$$\Delta T = 13.6 \text{ K}$$

Since one converts from Celsius to Kelvin by simply adding 273.15, the ΔT is also 13.6 °C. After all, to get ΔT, you subtract the initial temperature from the final temperature. The 273.15, then, cancels out. Thus, ΔT is also 13.6 °C. This means the final temperature is <u>58.6 °C</u>.

Next, we need to determine the final temperature of the gas if its pressure were held constant. For that, we need C_p, which we get from Equation (9.15):

$$C_p = C_v + R = 20.8 \frac{J}{mole \cdot K} + 8.31 \frac{J}{mole \cdot K} = 29.1 \frac{J}{mole \cdot K}$$

Now we can use Equation (9.13):

$$q = n \cdot C_p \cdot \Delta T$$

$$565 \text{ J} = (2.00 \text{ moles}) \cdot (29.1 \frac{J}{mole \cdot K}) \cdot \Delta T$$

$$\Delta T = 9.71 \text{ K}$$

Once again, that's the same as $\Delta T = 9.71\ ^\circ C$, so the final temperature is 54.7 $^\circ$C. Note that this final temperature is lower. That's because, as I have been saying, some of the energy was used for the work required to expand the gas. As a result, the temperature will not rise as high as it would if the volume were held constant.

ON YOUR OWN

9.10 A 4.50-mole gas absorbs 1000.0 J of energy while the pressure is held constant. As a result, its temperature increases by 21.5 $^\circ$C. What is its molar heat capacity *at constant volume*?

ANSWERS TO THE ON YOUR OWN PROBLEMS

9.1 To convert to Fahrenheit, we must first get to Celsius:

$$K = {}^{\circ}C + 273.15$$

$${}^{\circ}C = K - 273.15 = 0.00 - 273.15 = -273.15$$

Now we can convert to ${}^{\circ}F$:

$${}^{\circ}C = \frac{5}{9}({}^{\circ}F - 32.00)$$

$${}^{\circ}F = \frac{9}{5} \cdot ({}^{\circ}C) + 32.0 = \frac{9}{5} \cdot (-273.15) + 32.00 = \underline{-459.67 \ {}^{\circ}F}$$

9.2 In this problem, the metal loses energy while the water gains energy. Thus:

$$q_{metal} = -q_{water}$$

Equations (9.3) and (9.4) can be put together in the equation above:

$$(150.0 \text{ g}) \cdot (c) \cdot (27.4 \ {}^{\circ}C - 95.0 \ {}^{\circ}C) = -(300.0 \text{ g}) \cdot (4.19 \ \frac{J}{g \cdot {}^{\circ}C}) \cdot (27.4 \ {}^{\circ}C - 25.0 \ {}^{\circ}C)$$

$$c = \frac{-3.0 \text{x} 10^3 \text{ J}}{(150.0 \text{ g}) \cdot (-67.6 \ {}^{\circ}C)} = \underline{0.30 \ \frac{J}{g \cdot {}^{\circ}C}}$$

9.3 To evaporate all that is in the ice cube, we must first warm the ice cube to $0.0 \ {}^{\circ}C$:

$$q = m \cdot c \cdot \Delta T = (50.0 \text{ g}) \cdot (2.02 \ \frac{J}{g {}^{\circ}C}) \cdot (0.0 \ {}^{\circ}C - -11.0 \ {}^{\circ}C) = 1,110 \text{ J}$$

Now that the ice is at $0.0 \ {}^{\circ}C$, it can melt. However, it will not melt until the proper amount of energy is added:

$$q = m \cdot L = (50.0 \text{ g}) \cdot (334 \ \frac{J}{g}) = 16,700 \text{ J}$$

Now we have to take the liquid water and warm it up to the boiling point:

$$q = m \cdot c \cdot \Delta T = (50.0 \text{ g}) \cdot (4.19 \frac{J}{g \cdot °C}) \cdot (100.0 \text{ °C} - 0.0 \text{ °C}) = 2.10 \times 10^4 \text{ J}$$

Now that the water can boil, we just have to add the energy required to evaporate it:

$$q = m \cdot L = (50.0 \text{ g}) \cdot (2,260 \frac{J}{g}) = 113,000 \text{ J}$$

The sum of all of the energies calculated above represents the total amount of energy needed:
$$q_{tot} = 1,110 \text{ J} + 16,700 \text{ J} + 2.10 \times 10^4 \text{ J} + 113,000 \text{ J} = \underline{152,000 \text{ J}}$$

9.4 Water is less dense in its solid form than its liquid form. That's why ice floats on water. Since solid water is less dense than liquid water, <u>the coefficient of volume expansion for water is negative at temperatures near the freezing point of water</u>. It turns out that the coefficient of volume expansion for water is negative from about 0 °C to about 4 °C.

9.5 This is a straightforward application of Equation (9.6):

$$\Delta L = \alpha \cdot L_o \cdot \Delta T = (1.2 \times 10^{-5} \frac{1}{°C}) \cdot (50.00 \text{ m}) \cdot (40.0 \text{ °C} - 25.0 \text{ °C}) = 0.0090 \text{ m}$$

That, of course, is just the CHANGE in the length. The new length, therefore, is <u>50.01 m</u>. Notice that this is not a huge difference. Nevertheless, the board is longer on the warmer day.

9.6 To determine the average force, we can use Equation (9.8) if we know the area over which the force is exerted. This can be calculated from the surface area equation:

$$A = 4 \pi r^2 = 4\pi(0.100 \text{ m})^2 = 0.126 \text{ m}^2$$

To get the units to work out, we must use standard units, so $P = 1.013 \times 10^5$ Pa:

$$P = \frac{F}{A}$$

$$F = P \cdot A = (1.013 \times 10^5 \text{ Pa}) \cdot (0.126 \text{ m}^2) = (1.013 \times 10^5 \frac{N}{m^2}) \cdot (0.126 \text{ m}^2) = \underline{12,800 \text{ N}}$$

That's a LOT of force!

9.7 To determine the number of moles, we will need the ideal gas law. To use that equation, however, we will need to calculate the volume:

$$V = \frac{4}{3}\pi r^3 = \frac{4}{3}\pi(0.100 \text{ m})^3 = 0.00419 \text{ m}^3$$

That's the standard unit for volume. Now we need to get temperature into K:

$$K = {}^\circ C + 273.15 = 25.00 + 273.15 = 298.15 \text{ K}$$

Now we are all set:

$$PV = nRT$$

$$n = \frac{PV}{RT} = \frac{(1.013 \times 10^5 \text{ Pa})\cdot(0.00419 \text{ m}^3)}{(8.31 \frac{J}{\text{mole}\cdot\cancel{K}})\cdot(298.15 \cancel{K})} = 0.171 \frac{Pa\cdot m^3 \cdot \text{mole}}{J} = 0.171 \frac{\frac{\cancel{N}}{\cancel{m^2}}\cdot \cancel{m^3} \cdot \text{mole}}{\cancel{N}\cdot \cancel{m}} = \underline{0.171 \text{ moles}}$$

That's only one answer, however. The mean guy who wrote this problem also wants number of molecules. Well, 1 mole contains 6.02×10^{23} molecules. Thus:

$$\text{\# molecules} = (0.171 \cancel{\text{moles}})\cdot(\frac{6.02\times10^{23} \text{ molecules}}{1 \cancel{\text{mole}}}) = \underline{1.03\times10^{23} \text{ molecules}}$$

9.8 The first part of the problem is a straightforward application of Equation (9.11). However, we must understand that this equation uses the kinetic energy *per molecule*. This sample has one mole, which has 6.02×10^{23} molecules. Thus, the kinetic energy per molecule is:

$$KE = \frac{3,123 \text{ J}}{6.02\times10^{23}} = 5.19\times10^{-21} \text{ J}$$

We can relate *that* to the temperature:

$$\overline{KE} = \frac{3}{2}\cdot kT$$

$$T = \frac{2\cdot\overline{KE}}{3\cdot k} = \frac{2\cdot(5.19\times10^{-21} \cancel{J})}{3\cdot(1.38\times10^{-23} \frac{\cancel{J}}{K})} = \underline{251 \text{ K}}$$

Now we need to calculate the mass. You could either use the definition of kinetic energy ($KE = \frac{1}{2}\cdot mv^2$), or you can use Equation (9.12). I will use the latter:

$$\overline{v^2} = \frac{3kT}{m}$$

$$m = \frac{3kT}{\overline{v^2}} = \frac{3 \cdot (1.38 \times 10^{-23}\, \frac{J}{K}) \cdot (251\, K)}{(512\, \frac{m}{sec})^2} = 3.96 \times 10^{-26}\, \frac{J}{m^2/sec^2} = 3.96 \times 10^{-26}\, \frac{\frac{kg \cdot m^2}{sec^2}}{m^2/sec^2} = \underline{3.96 \times 10^{-26}\, kg}$$

9.9 If you look at Figure 9.3, the average speed is to the right of the peak in the graph, since the graph is not symmetric. The average speed here is 512 m/sec. In graph (b), 512 is on the peak or just to the left of the peak. On <u>graph (a)</u>, 512 is to the right of the peak.

9.10 We can get the molar heat capacity at constant pressure rather easily:

$$q = n \cdot C_p \cdot \Delta T$$

$$C_p = \frac{q}{n \cdot \Delta T} = \frac{(1000.0\, J)}{(4.50\, moles) \cdot (21.5\, K)} = 10.3\, \frac{J}{mole \cdot K}$$

Note that I put Kelvin in the unit instead of degrees Celsius. Remember, when dealing with ΔT, Kelvin and Celsius are the same.

That's not the answer, however. The mean guy who wrote this problem wants the molar heat capacity at constant *volume*:

$$C_p = C_v + R$$

$$C_v = C_p - R = 10.3\, \frac{J}{mole \cdot K} - 8.31\, \frac{J}{mole \cdot K} = \underline{2.0\, \frac{J}{mole \cdot K}}$$

REVIEW QUESTIONS FOR MODULE #9

1. When a gas is held at a constant volume, the pressure it exerts increases with increasing temperature. Why?

2. A chemist puts a flame under a container which holds a substance the chemist wants to study. The chemist graphs the temperature of the substance as a function of the time it is exposed to the flame. The chemist gets the graph shown to the right. The flame burned steadily the entire time so that the rate of heat transfer to the substance was constant throughout the experiment. What happened from t = 10.0 minutes to t = 15.0 minutes?

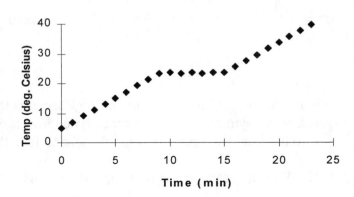

3. Consider a sample of liquid water. Suppose you cooled it down to 0.0 °C but kept it from freezing by gently stirring it. Then, suppose you stopped stirring and carefully measured the temperature of the water's surroundings as the water froze. Would the temperature of the surroundings increase, decrease, or remain the same as the water froze?

4. In which phase (solid, liquid, gas) does a substance exert the least amount of pressure?

5. A gas exerts a given amount of pressure on its cubic container. Suppose the length of each side of the cube was decreased by a factor of 2. If the temperature of the gas and the amount of gas does not change, what is the change in pressure?

6. If you have 50.0×10^{25} molecules of gas, how many moles of gas do you have?

7. The temperature of a sample of gas increases by a factor of 2. By what factor does the average speed of the gas molecules increase?

8. In the situation described above, by what factor does the pressure increase if the volume and amount of gas are not allowed to change?

9. You have a certain amount of energy that you can transfer to a sample of gas. If you want the temperature of the gas to change as little as possible, should you keep the gas at constant volume or constant pressure?

10. The two graphs below depict the distribution of molecular speeds for the same sample of gas. Which graph represents the gas at a higher temperature?

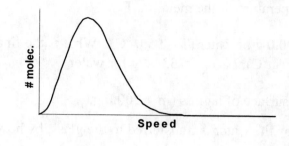

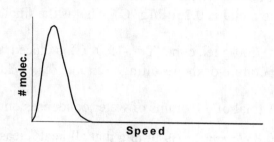

a.

b.

PRACTICE PROBLEMS FOR MODULE #9

1. A 50.0-g chunk of metal initially at 75.0 °F absorbs 350.0 Joules. If the specific heat capacity of the metal is 0.250 J/(g·°C), what is the final temperature of the metal in °F?

2. A 75.0-g ice cube (T = -15.0 °C) is placed in 300.0 g of water (T = 95.0 °C). What is the final temperature of the resulting mixture? (c_{ice} = 2.02 J/(g·°C), L_{fusion} = 334 J/g for water)

3. A total of 5.0 grams of water condenses on the surface of a glass (m = 200.0 g, $c = 0.837 \dfrac{J}{g \cdot °C}$). Assuming that all heat released by the water is transferred to the glass, by how many degrees Celsius does the temperature of the glass increase? (L_{vap} = 2,260 J/g)

4. A metal cube initially at 25.0 °C is heated to 100.0 °C. As a result, its volume increases by 2.00%. What is the approximate coefficient of linear expansion (α) of the metal?

5. A 1.00 mole sample of a gas is held at atmospheric pressure (101.3 kPa) and heated from 25.0 °C to 50.0 °C. What was the volume of the gas at 25.0 °C? What is the volume of the gas at 50.0 °C?

6. What is the coefficient of volume expansion for the gas in the problem above?

7. Suppose the gas in problem #5 was held in a container that had a pressure-release valve. This valve allows gas to escape so as to maintain both a constant volume (the volume the gas occupied at 25.0 °C) and a constant pressure (101.3 kPa). How many *molecules* will be left in the container once the temperature reaches 50.0 °C?

8. A 1.00 mole sample of gas is held at constant pressure while 1,678 J of energy are taken out of the gas. What is the change in the temperature of the gas? (C_v = 20.8 J/[mole·K])

9. A 4.50 mole sample of gas has a mass of 319.5 grams. If it is held at a temperature of 50.0 °C, what is the average speed of the molecules?

10. A physicist examines the volume of a metal plank and notices that when the temperature increases by 10 °C, the volume of the plank increases by a factor of 1.000006. What is the approximate coefficient of linear expansion for the metal?

Module #10: Thermodynamics

Introduction

In the previous module, you learned about heat, temperature, and the behavior of ideal gases. I now want to bring all of this together in a discussion of **thermodynamics**. What is thermodynamics? Well, think about how we can transfer energy from one object to another. So far, you have learned two ways that this can happen: work and heat. When force acts over a distance, work is done, and that work changes the energy of the object that is being worked on. For example, when you push a box, it begins to move. You have done work (exerted a force over a distance) and, as a result, the kinetic energy of the box changes. The other way energy can be transferred is via heat. When a hot object is placed in thermal contact with a cold object, energy is transferred from the hot object to the cold object. Thermodynamics is the study of the effects of energy transfers involving *both* work and heat.

The First Three Laws of Thermodynamics

The field of thermodynamics is built on three basic laws. Although the laws sound quite simple at first glance, they are deeply profound. Let's start with the simplest of these laws: the **Zeroth Law of Thermodynamics**.

The Zeroth Law of Thermodynamics - If object A is in thermal equilibrium with object C, and if object B is in thermal equilibrium with object C, objects A and B are in thermal equilibrium with each other.

The first thing you might be wondering is why we call this the "zeroth" law of thermodynamics. Well, this law was added to the list of the laws of thermodynamics later as a means of "cleaning up" some problems with the overall framework of thermodynamics. Since it is considered the most fundamental of the laws, it should come first. However, the First Law of Thermodynamics had already been written, so it was decided that this should be called the "zeroth" law.

What does the law say? It says that when two objects are each in thermal equilibrium with a third object, they are also in thermal equilibrium with each other. As is typical with the laws of thermodynamics, this sounds simple, but it tells us something very important:

When two objects of different temperature are placed in thermal contact, energy will flow from the hot object to the cold object.

Of course, you *knew* that already, but it is a fundamental postulate of thermodynamics. If the Zeroth Law of Thermodynamics is true, then thermal equilibrium can only be reached by the objects coming to the same temperature.

The **First Law of Thermodynamics** is also something with which you are already familiar.

<u>The First Law of Thermodynamics</u>- Energy cannot be created or destroyed. It can only change form.

What this law tells us is that God only made so much energy for the entire universe. This energy is used to do all of the work that has to get done in order for the universe to exist. Since humans are not as smart or powerful as God, there is no way that we can make or destroy energy. Now remember, based on special relativity, mass is a form of energy. Thus, the term "energy" in the First Law of Thermodynamics really refers to the sum of the mass and energy in the universe.

When we study this law in more detail in the next section, we will develop a mathematical expression which describes it. However, for right now, I want to make sure you understand its conceptual meaning. When you use energy arguments to solve a motion problem, you are really using the First Law of Thermodynamics. A rock on top of a cliff, for example, has a lot of potential energy and no kinetic energy. If it falls off of the cliff, its potential energy gets converted to kinetic energy, and the rock accelerates. This is an example of the First Law of Thermodynamics. The rock doesn't "create energy" to make its acceleration possible. The work done by gravity simply converts potential energy into kinetic energy. Thus, energy is not made, it simply changes form. The First Law of Thermodynamics simply extends this principle to all forms of energy.

The **Second Law of Thermodynamics** will be familiar to you if you have taken a good chemistry course. Before you can review that law, however, you must first review the fascinating subject of **entropy**:

<u>Entropy</u> - A measure of the disorder that exists in any system

Since entropy is a measurement, it must have units. These units are always an energy unit divided by both moles and Kelvin. Thus the standard unit for entropy is $\frac{\text{Joules}}{\text{mole} \cdot \text{K}}$.

Now it might sound odd to you that we can measure disorder, but it turns out that disorder is one of the most fundamental things we can learn about a system. For example, suppose you have a priceless vase sitting on a shelf somewhere. Suppose further that something happens which causes the vase to fall onto the floor and shatter into a million pieces. Which situation, do you think, represents more disorder? Clearly, when the vase is shattered, it is more disordered than when it was sitting on the shelf in one piece. Thus, we would say that while the vase was sitting on the shelf, it was in a state of low entropy, because it was not very disordered. However, when the vase shatters, it moves into a state of high entropy, because now it is very disordered.

Although you can imagine a vase falling from a shelf and shattering into a million pieces, can you ever imagine the reverse process happening? Can you imagine a situation where a shattered vase spontaneously rearranges itself into a whole vase again? Of course not! Even though you know that this will never happen, do you know why? The reason that this cannot happen is because of the **Second Law of Thermodynamics**:

<u>The Second Law of Thermodynamics</u> - The entropy of the universe must always either increase or remain the same. It can never decrease.

Think, for a moment, about how this law would apply to our vase. If the shattered vase were to spontaneously rearrange itself into a whole vase again, it would be going from a high entropy state to a low entropy state. This would mean that the entropy of the universe would decrease. This would violate the Second Law of Thermodynamics.

It turns out that the Second Law of Thermodynamics has quite a few implications. For example, have you ever wondered why a ball that is sitting at rest on the floor cannot spontaneously start moving? Of course, Newton's First Law (the law of inertia) says that it can't, but why not? After all, the ball just needs energy to move. Suppose the floor was a bit warmer than the ball. Heat would flow into the ball, right? Suppose the ball somehow converted that heat into kinetic energy. The ball would then begin to roll. This process would be consistent with the Zeroth Law of Thermodynamics (heat flows from the warm floor to the cooler ball) and the First Law of Thermodynamics (the kinetic energy is not created, it is transformed from thermal energy).

Why, then, will this not happen? The answer is that this would lead to a universe which is more ordered. Remember, thermal energy is the kinetic energy contained in the random motion of the molecules or atoms which make up a substance. That is a very disordered form of energy, as it is resulting in random motion. If the ball converts that energy into kinetic energy for rolling, the energy is suddenly more ordered. As a result, entropy would decrease. That's why a ball cannot just absorb energy from the floor and convert it into kinetic energy of rolling. The entropy of the universe would decrease, violating the Second Law of Thermodynamics.

Now, even though the ball cannot convert thermal energy into kinetic energy of rolling, such a process *can* happen, if it is done properly. After all, that's what a gasoline-powered automobile does. It ignites gasoline, and the thermal energy from the resulting combustion causes expansion in the engine's cylinders. The motion of the pistons in the cylinders is then used to turn the wheels of the automobile. Thus, thermal energy from combustion is converted into kinetic energy of rolling. This can happen, however, because it *does not* violate the Second Law of Thermodynamics.

How in the world is this possible? Why does it contradict the Second Law of Thermodynamics for a ball sitting on a floor to convert thermal energy to kinetic energy of rolling when an automobile doing the same thing *does not* contradict the Second Law of Thermodynamics? The answer is simple. The Second Law of Thermodynamics constrains only one thing: *the total entropy of the universe*. It says *nothing* about the total entropy of a single object or even a single system. It says only that the total entropy *of the universe* must always stay the same or increase. In the case of the ball converting thermal energy into kinetic energy of rolling, the total entropy of the universe (the ball, the floor, and all of their surroundings) would decrease. However, in an automobile engine, the total entropy of the universe (the engine, the gasoline, the combustion products, and all of their surroundings) actually *increases*.

When the gasoline is ignited, a lot of thermal energy is released. This thermal energy is absorbed by the engine, the air around the engine, the engine coolant, etc., increasing their temperature. When temperature increases, entropy increases, because there is more thermal energy, and thermal energy is the most disordered form of energy. Thus, the entropy of all of these things increases. In addition, if you took chemistry, you know that the entropy of the products in a combustion reaction (carbon dioxide and water vapor) is higher than the entropy of the reactants (the gasoline and oxygen in this case). As a result, the entropy of the chemicals increases as well. Thus, entropy is increasing across the board.

Well, it turns out that only a certain amount of thermal energy in an automobile engine actually gets converted to kinetic energy of rolling. The rest of it stays as thermal energy, and that's one reason engines get hot and must be cooled with coolant and a fan. The other reason, of course, is friction, but friction does not play a role in this discussion. Well, if much of the energy from the combustion of gasoline stays as thermal energy and only a certain amount is converted to kinetic energy of rolling, the total entropy of the universe will still increase. A small amount of the energy from combustion will become more ordered (the part that went into rolling energy), but the rest will get more disordered, and the net effect is that the *total* entropy will still increase.

It turns out that this very condition puts a constraint on the efficiency of a car engine, or any engine that uses thermal energy as its energy source. Since the total entropy of the universe must always increase, only a certain fraction of thermal energy can be converted into a more ordered form of kinetic energy. As a result, an engine can only be so efficient. It is impossible for an engine to be 100% efficient in converting thermal energy into directed motion, because if that were to happen, the universe would become more ordered. As you will learn in a later section of this module, the previous sentence is actually an alternative way of expressing the Second Law of Thermodynamics.

Before I leave this section, I must make one point that you should have learned in chemistry. The Second Law of Thermodynamics *does not* forbid the process of evolution. You might think that it does, since evolution states that random chemicals produced a high-ordered life form, and that this life form eventually gave rise to more ordered and complex life forms. However, the second law does not forbid this happening, as long as the production of the new order also produces enough disorder so that the total entropy of the universe remains constant or increases. In other words, if evolutionists could produce a mechanism by which the increase in order which results from evolution of an organism is accompanied by an offsetting decrease in order of the organism's surroundings, evolution could be consistent with the second law. Of course, evolutionists cannot produce such a mechanism, and I doubt that one exists. Nevertheless, the main point is that the Second Law of Thermodynamics does not forbid evolution. It merely puts constraints on the mechanism by which it could happen.

ON YOUR OWN

10.1   When water freezes, it experiences a large decrease in its entropy. How can this happen, in light of the Second Law of Thermodynamics?

A More Detailed Look at the First Law of Thermodynamics

Now that you have an introduction into the three main laws of thermodynamics, I want to look at both the first law and the second law in more detail. Let's start with the first law, and let's start our more detailed look at the first law by giving it a mathematical definition.

$$\Delta U = q - W \tag{10.1}$$

In this equation, "ΔU" represents the change in the internal energy of the system. What is the internal energy of the system? In Equation (9.11), we determined the relationship between the average kinetic energy per molecule in a sample of gas and the temperature. Well, the internal energy is just the sum of all of the kinetic energies of all of the gas molecules. In other words, the internal energy of a gas is proportional to its temperature. If the internal energy of a gas increases, its temperature increases. If the internal energy of a gas decreases, its temperature decreases.

The "q" term in Equation (10.1) is, as always, heat. If the system absorbs heat, q is positive. If it gives up heat, q is negative. Finally, "W" represents work. If work is done on the system, W is negative. If the system does work on its surroundings, then W is positive. What do I mean by this? Suppose you took a balloon that was full of air and squished it. If you did that, you would be working on the system, and W would be negative if we were analyzing the gas in the balloon. If, on the other hand, you warmed the balloon and it expanded, it would be doing work on the surroundings (pushing air out of the way), so W would be positive if you were analyzing the gas in the balloon.

The best way I can illustrate how to use the First Law of Thermodynamics as given by Equation (10.1) is to analyze a system of gas molecules. As I discussed in the previous module, gas systems are a bit easier to analyze than liquid or solid systems, as the molecules (or atoms) which make up gas systems are far from one another, and, as such, we can ignore the attraction that they feel for one another. With that in mind, let's consider the work involved in changing the volume of an ideal gas. Suppose we put a gas in a cylinder whose top is a piston which can move up and down and then watch the gas as it expands:

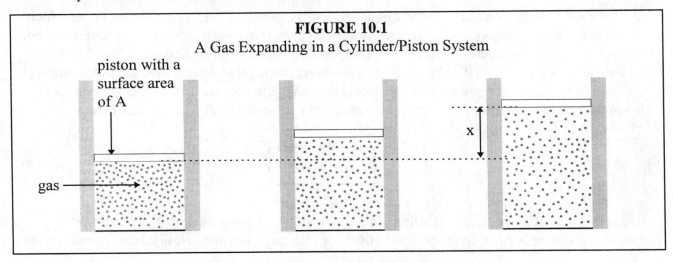

FIGURE 10.1
A Gas Expanding in a Cylinder/Piston System

piston with a surface area of A

x

gas

In thermodynamics, it is very important to identify the **system** as well as the **surroundings**. In general, the system is whatever you happen to be studying, and the surroundings are essentially everything else that can be affected by the system. In this example, then, the system is the gas itself. The surroundings are the cylinder, the piston, and the air surrounding the outside of the cylinder and piston.

In the situation we are analyzing, the system (the gas) is doing work. After all, it is moving the piston. It must exert a force in order to do that, so the gas is exerting a force against the piston, and since the piston is moving, the force is being exerted over a distance. Thus, work is done. How much work is done? Well, back in Module #4, we learned that

$$W = F \cdot x \cdot \cos\theta \qquad (4.1)$$

Remember, θ is the angle between the force and the displacement. The gas pushed in the same direction that the piston moves, so $\theta = 0$.

$$W = F \cdot x \qquad (10.2)$$

Now let's think about the force that the gas is exerting. In order to move the piston, the gas must overcome whatever force is pushing down on the piston. The force of gravity is pushing the piston down, but we will actually ignore that, because the piston is not very massive. There is another force pushing down on the piston that is substantially larger than the gravitational force. What is that force? It is the force that results from the *air pressure* which is pushing against the cylinder/piston arrangement. Remember, pressure is the result of force, and since there is air surrounding the cylinder and piston, there is air pressure. That pressure, of course, is given by:

$$P = \frac{F}{A} \qquad (9.8)$$

We can rearrange this equation to solve for force, and we can put the resulting expression into Equation (10.2) to get:

$$W = P \cdot A \cdot x \qquad (10.3)$$

Now let's think about what this equation means. The "A" represents the area over which the air pressure is being exerted. Air pressure is being exerted over the entire cylinder/piston, but the only thing we are interested in is the piston, because that's what is moving. Thus, "A" is the surface area of the piston. The "x" in this equation represents the distance that the piston moves up. So, what does A·x represent? It represents the change in volume that the gas experiences when the piston moves up. We can call the change in volume "ΔV." This tells us that:

$$\boxed{W = P \cdot \Delta V} \qquad (10.4)$$

This is an important equation. It tells us that the work which a gas does as it expands under constant pressure is equal to the pressure times the change in volume. Notice how the units work out in this equation. Pressure has the units N/m^2, and volume has the units m^3. When I multiply those units together, I get N·m, which is the same as a Joule.

I want you to notice something else about this equation. In this equation, the value of work can be positive or negative. If the gas expands, the final volume is greater than the initial volume, and ΔV is positive. As a result, work is positive. If the gas contracts, the final volume is smaller than the initial volume, and ΔV is negative. That makes work negative. What does this mean? Well, when work is positive, we know that the *system* did the work on the surroundings. When the gas in Figure 10.1 expands, for example, it (the system) must work on the piston (the surroundings). However, if the gas in Figure 10.1 were to contract, the gas would not be doing the work. Instead, the surroundings (the piston) would be doing work on the system (the gas). This is actually a very important distinction in thermodynamics.

When work is positive, the system does work on the surroundings. When work is negative, the surroundings do work on the system.

Now that you know a bit more about how to calculate the work done by (or on) a gas, let's try using the knowledge you gained in the previous module with this new information in an application of the First Law of Thermodynamics.

EXAMPLE 10.1

A 1.50 mole sample of gas is contained in a cylinder/piston system such as the one shown in Figure 10.1. It starts out at a pressure of 156 kPa and a volume of 0.0151 m^3 and then expands to a volume of 0.0251 m^3 while the pressure stays constant. What is the change in the internal energy of the gas? [The C$_p$ of an ideal gas is 20.8 J/(mole·K).]

According to the First Law of Thermodynamics, $\Delta U = q - W$. Thus, to get the change in internal energy (ΔU), we need to determine q and W. How do we do that? Well, we have equations from the previous module [Equations (9.13) - (9.14)] that allow us to calculate heat absorbed or released by a gas (q), and Equation (10.4) allows us to calculate work (W). Let's start with the latter, as it is easiest to calculate.

$$W = P \cdot \Delta V = (1.56 \times 10^5 \text{ Pa}) \cdot (0.0251 \text{ m}^3 - 0.0151 \text{ m}^3) = 1560 \text{ J}$$

Notice that we first had to convert kPa to Pa to keep everything in standard units. In addition, notice that the work is positive. That means the *system* (the gas) did work. That should make sense. The gas expanded. That means it had to push up on the piston, and that means the gas did work.

Now we have to determine q. We will use Equation (9.13) since pressure stays constant:

$$q = n \cdot C_p \cdot \Delta T$$

Now wait a minute. To get q, we need ΔT. There are no temperatures given in the problem. However, we can *calculate* the temperatures using the ideal gas law! Notice that the problem gives us the pressure, the volume, and the number of moles. Thus, the ideal gas law can give us the temperature at each point.

At the beginning of the problem, P = 1.56×10^5 Pa, V = 0.0151 m^3, and n = 1.50 moles.

$$PV = nRT$$

$$T = \frac{PV}{nR} = \frac{(1.56 \times 10^5 \ \cancel{Pa}) \cdot (0.0151 \ \cancel{m^3})}{(1.50 \ \cancel{moles}) \cdot (8.31 \ \frac{\cancel{Pa} \cdot \cancel{m^3}}{\cancel{mole} \cdot K})} = 189 \text{ K}$$

Thus, the initial temperature is 189 K. What is the final temperature? Well, at the end, P = 1.56×10^5 Pa, V = 0.0251 m^3, and n = 1.50 moles.

$$PV = nRT$$

$$T = \frac{PV}{nR} = \frac{(1.56 \times 10^5 \ \cancel{Pa}) \cdot (0.0251 \ \cancel{m^3})}{(1.50 \ \cancel{moles}) \cdot (8.31 \ \frac{\cancel{Pa} \cdot \cancel{m^3}}{\cancel{mole} \cdot K})} = 314 \text{ K}$$

Now we can finally calculate q:

$$q = n \cdot C_p \cdot \Delta T = (1.50 \ \cancel{moles}) \cdot (20.8 \ \frac{J}{\cancel{mole} \cdot \cancel{K}}) \cdot (314 \ \cancel{K} - 189 \ \cancel{K}) = 3.90 \times 10^3 \text{ J}$$

Notice that q is positive. That means the system (the gas) absorbed energy. That should make sense, since the temperature increased. Now that we have q and W, determining ΔU is a snap:

$$\Delta U = q - W = 3.90 \text{x} 10^3 \text{ J} - 1560 \text{ J} = \underline{2340 \text{ J}}$$

Now before you go on to the next section of this module, I want to make sure you understand the significance of what was calculated in the example problem. First, think about what was calculated. Using easy-to-measure data such as pressure, volume, and number of moles, we can calculate a very detailed quantity: the change in the internal energy of the gas. That's pretty amazing. The First Law of Thermodynamics is like having an "energy meter" in the gas, because it can be used to track how the energy of the gas changes. Second, think about what the answer tells us. In order to change the temperature of the gas from 189 K to 314 K, the gas needed to absorb 3900 J of energy. However, the gas did not keep *all* of that energy in the form of thermal energy. Because the gas expanded, *some* of that energy went into work. Thus, the change in internal energy of the gas was not 3900 J, it was 2340 J. The difference (1560 J) is the energy it "cost" for the gas to expand.

ON YOUR OWN

10.2 A 2.50-mole sample of gas is compressed under a constant pressure. It begins with a volume of 0.0514 m^3 and ends with a volume of 0.0201 m^3. If the compression causes the internal energy of the gas to drop by 2570 J, what is the pressure? [C_p = 20.8 J/(mole·K)]

10.3 A gas is in a cylinder/piston system. The system is connected to a heater which allows a person to add heat gently in a very controlled way. The gas expands at a constant temperature. If the work done is 2,020 J, how much heat was added to the gas?

A More General Way to Calculate Work

Although Equation (10.4) is useful, it is also very limited. Think about a big assumption we made in deriving it. We assumed that the pressure was constant while the gas expanded. Although that is true in *many* cases (such as when you blow up a balloon), it is not always the case. Sometimes, pressure can vary as a gas expands. There is a more general way of expressing the work done by a gas. This process involves studying a **P-V diagram**, which is illustrated in Figure 10.2:

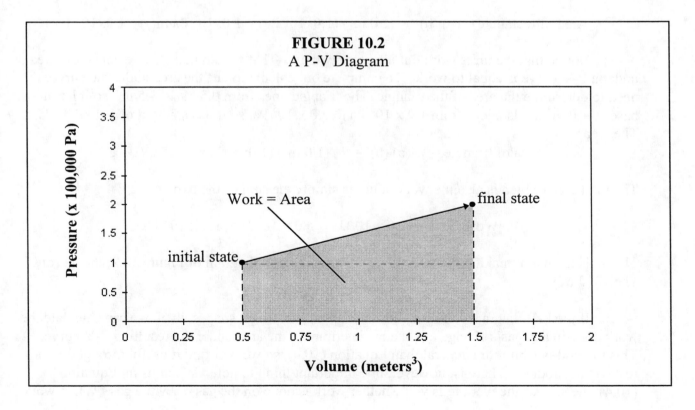

FIGURE 10.2
A P-V Diagram

In this figure, we plot the pressure and volume of a gas as it changes. In this graph, there are only two points. The gas starts out at a pressure of 1.0×10^5 Pa and a volume of 0.5 m^3 and ends up at a pressure of 2.0×10^5 Pa and a volume of 1.5 m^3. Thus, the gas expanded, but it did not expand under constant pressure, because the final pressure is different from the initial pressure. The arrow between the two points illustrates how the pressure and volume changed as the gas went from its initial to its final state.

It turns out that the work done by the gas in this expansion can be calculated by finding the area underneath the arrow on this P-V diagram. This is a general result:

The area beneath a P-V curve is equal to the work done when a gas changes states.

When you take calculus, you will learn that a *definite integral* is the means by which the area under any curve can be calculated. However, for right now, you can use geometry to calculate the area under a curve as long as the "curve" is simple, such as the one shown above.

How do we calculate the area under the curve in Figure 10.2? We do the same thing that we did when we were finding the area under velocity versus time diagrams in Module #2: We split the area under the curve up into simple geometrical shapes whose areas we know how to calculate. In Figure 10.2, for example, I have taken the area under the arrow and divided it into two regions: a triangle (above the dashed, gray line) and a rectangle (below the dashed gray line). The rectangle goes from 0.5 m^3 to 1.5 m^3, so it has a base of 1.0 m^3. It also goes from 0 to 1.0×10^5 Pa, so it has a height of 1.0×10^5 Pa. Its area, then, is:

Area of rectangle = (b)·(h) = (1.0 m^3)·(1.0×10^5 Pa) = 1.0×10^5 Pa·m^3 = 1.0×10^5 J

Notice that the units work out into energy units. That should make sense, since the area under a P-V curve is equal to work. To complete our calculation of the area under the curve, we need to determine the area of the triangle. The triangle goes from 0.5 m^3 to 1.5 m^3, so it has a base of 1.0 m^3. It also goes from 1.0 x 10^5 Pa to 2.0 x 10^5 Pa, so it has a height of 1.0 x 10^5 Pa. The area is:

Area of triangle = ½·(b)·(h) = ½·(1.0 m^3)·(1.0×10^5 Pa) = 5.0×10^4 J

The total area (which is also the work done) is simply the sum of the two:

Work done = 1.0 x 10^5 J + 5.0 x 10^4 J = 1.5 x 10^5 J

This tells us that in making the transition shown in the P-V diagram of Figure 10.2, the gas did 1.5×10^5 J of work.

If the P-V diagram can be split into simple geometrical shapes, then, we can calculate the work done in any gas's change of state by determining the area under the resulting P-V curve. This method is a bit more general than Equation (10.4), so we will find it useful throughout the rest of this module. There is, however, one important thing to note. When using Equation (10.4), the sign of the work tells you whether work is done on the gas or by the gas. When work is positive, it is done by the gas. When work is negative, it is done on the gas. When using the area under the curve method, you must *determine* the sign of the work. In Figure 10.2, the gas expanded, because it went from 0.5 m^3 to 1.5 m^3. Thus, work was done by the gas and it is therefore positive. Had the gas contracted, however, we would still have gotten a positive area for the work done. Thus, *we would have had to add the negative sign* in order to indicate that work was done on the gas. You will see how that works in the following "on your own" problem.

ON YOUR OWN

10.4 Two samples of gas are compressed in different ways. The first is compressed from 0.40 m^3 to 0.20 m^3 at a constant pressure of 1.50x10^5 Pa as shown by the dashed arrow in the figure to the right. The second is compressed from 0.40 m^3 to 0.20 m^3 while the pressure increases to 2.5x10^5 Pa. Then, the gas is cooled so that the pressure is decreases to 1.5x10^5 Pa while the volume does not change. This process is shown with the two solid arrows in the figure to the right. As a result, both gases have the same initial and final conditions. Calculate the work in each case.

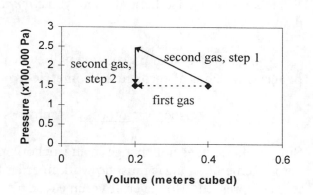

A Few Terms Related To The First Law of Thermodynamics

Now that you know how to calculate work in terms of a P-V diagram, I want to really dig deep into the First Law of Thermodynamics. To do that, I need to define and discuss some terms first. Let's start with the term **isobaric process**.

Isobaric process - A process which occurs at constant pressure

When you use Equation (10.4), for example, the gas must be undergoing *isobaric compression* or *isobaric expansion*, because Equation (10.4) is only applicable to processes which occur at constant pressure. In "on your own" problem 10.4, the first gas underwent an *isobaric compression*, since its pressure did not change while it was being compressed.

The next term I want you to learn is **isothermal process**.

Isothermal process - A process which occurs at constant temperature

When a gas changes pressure, volume, or both but experiences no change in temperature, it is undergoing an *isothermal process*. Now it is important to point out that isothermal processes often *require* heat to be added or taken away from the gas. That might sound odd to you, since you naturally assume that if a substance absorbs heat, its temperature will increase. However, as I have tried to stress, that's not necessarily true. If a gas expands, it must do work, and that takes energy. If you add just the amount of heat necessary for the gas to work to do its expansion, there will be no energy "left over" to increase the temperature of the gas.

In fact, that's the heart of the First Law of Thermodynamics. Remember, temperature is a measure of a system's internal energy. If I add just enough heat (q) to supply the work for expansion (W), then the change in internal energy (ΔU) is q - W, which is zero. Thus, even though heat is added to the gas, its internal energy (and thus its temperature) does not change. When a process is isothermal, then, you *cannot* conclude that q = 0. Instead, you must conclude that $\Delta U = 0$.

Another kind of process we will be dealing with is the **isochoric** (eye soh kor' ik) **process**, which is also called an **isometric process**.

Isochoric process - A process which occurs at constant volume

Since volume does not change in an isochoric process, the work done during such a process is zero. Remember, a gas must do work in order to expand. Alternatively, work is done on a gas if it is compressed. However, if volume doesn't change, no work needs to be done, and W = 0.

The last process you need to learn about is the **adiabatic** (aye' die uh ba' tik) **process**.

Adiabatic process - A process in which no heat is transferred between the system and the surroundings

Based on the definition, then, we can conclude that in an adiabatic process q = 0, because heat cannot flow into or out of the system. Now once again, you must be careful here. Many students want to conclude that since q = 0, ΔT also must equal 0. That is simply not true. Adiabatic processes are not usually isothermal. Consider, for example, the following experiment.

EXPERIMENT 10.1
Adiabatic Compression and Expansion

Supplies:

- A large plastic bottle with a lid (You need to be able to see into the bottle, so remove any labels that might be on the bottle.)
- A thermometer that fits comfortably inside the bottle (The thermometer needs to read slightly above and below room temperature. It must also fit into the bottle easily, because you will be compressing the bottle.)
- Water
- A match

Introduction - In this experiment, you will be observing adiabatic compression and expansion in two different ways. You will see that an adiabatic process is not necessarily isothermal.

Procedure:

1. Open the plastic bottle and dump out any contents.
2. Place the thermometer into the bottle.
3. Screw the lid onto the bottle tightly so that the seal is airtight.
4. Watch the thermometer for a few moments. It might raise or lower slightly until it equilibrates.
5. When the thermometer is reading a constant temperature, squeeze the bottle hard so that the gas inside is compressed. Keep your eye on the thermometer and continue to squeeze.
6. As long as your system is airtight, you should notice a change in the thermometer as you squeeze. Once you have noted the change, release the bottle so that it expands back to it original size.
7. Note the change in the thermometer when you release the bottle.
8. Open the bottle and remove the thermometer.
9. Add some water to the bottle so that about one-tenth of the volume is water.
10. Light the match and then drop it into the bottle so that it hits the water and goes out.
11. Immediately put the lid back on the bottle and screw it tightly so that the seal is airtight.
12. Once again, squeeze the bottle hard and hold it for a second.
13. Release the bottle so that it expands to it initial size. Note what happens.

In the experiment, you were dealing with an adiabatic process. Since the temperature of the bottle contents was roughly the same as the temperature of the surroundings, and since plastic is an insulator, little if any heat was transferred from the gas inside the bottle to the surroundings, or vice-versa. Thus, $q \approx 0$ in this experiment. Nevertheless, in the first part of the experiment, you saw that ΔT was *not* equal to zero. Why? Think about the First Law of Thermodynamics.

When you compressed the air inside the bottle, you did work on the air, right? As a result, $W < 0$. Remember, when work is done on the gas, the work is negative. Also, since the process was adiabatic, $q = 0$. Thus, $\Delta U = - W$ according to the First Law of Thermodynamics. Well, if $W < 0$ and $q = 0$, then $\Delta U > 0$. In other words, when you worked on the gas, the internal energy of the gas increased. That's why the temperature in the bottle increased when you squeezed the bottle. Now, of course, the increase was small (probably about 1-2 degrees Celsius), because the amount of work you did was small. Had you been able to compress the gas to an even smaller volume, the increase in temperature would have been greater.

When you released the bottle and allowed the air inside it to expand, you should have seen the temperature drop. After all, when the gas expands, $W > 0$. Since $q = 0$, the first law says $\Delta U < 0$, which means the temperature must decrease. In other words, since heat was not being added ($q=0$), and since the air inside the bottle had to do work, the energy for that work had to come from the air's internal energy. As a result, the internal energy and thus the temperature decreased. Because the thermometer takes time to respond, however, that effect might not have been as noticeable, so that's why I had you do the second part of the experiment.

In the second part of the experiment, you squeezed the bottle while it had some water in it. This heated up the water, causing it to evaporate. When you released the bottle, the air cooled back down. As the air cooled, it could not hold as much water vapor as it did when it was warmer. Thus, the water vapor had to condense out of the air, and that's why the bottle clouded up when you released it. The water vapor that had been put into the air by the higher temperature had to condense back out, so it formed a cloud inside the bottle.

Why did I have you use the match? If you ever studied weather, you probably learned that in order for a cloud to form, there must be something onto which the water can condense. The match put small particles of smoke into the bottle. The water then could condense onto those smoke particles, forming a cloud. Most clouds in Creation form around small particles in the atmosphere, like the smoke particles left by the match in your experiment. We call these particles "cloud condensation nuclei," because they form the "center" of water condensation, which forms clouds.

At some point in your education, you probably learned that the higher you go, the cooler it gets. Some mountains, for example, are so high that their tops are covered in snow even during the summer. Although this is a fact that most elementary school students know, few people understand *why* this is the case. Think of the atmosphere as a large sphere. The larger the radius, the larger the volume. Thus, as air rises in the atmosphere, it must expand. To expand, it must do work, and since there is no source from which the air can absorb heat, the energy to do the work comes from the internal energy of the gas. As a result, the air cools. Thus, the temperature gets lower the higher you climb in altitude because of adiabatic expansion.

Just to make sure you understand how important adiabatic processes are, I want to discuss one more example. Have you ever wondered how a refrigerator actually cools things down? The answer is surprising: it does so with adiabatic expansion. Examine Figure 10.3.

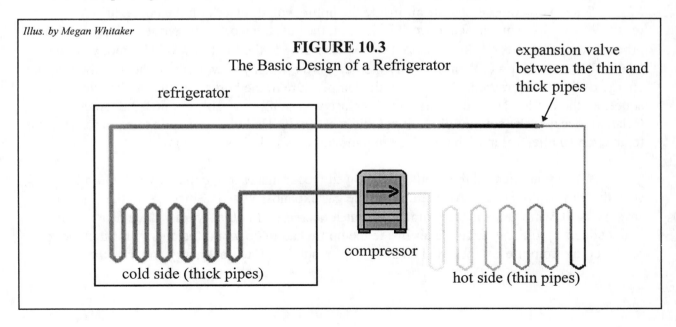

Illus. by Megan Whitaker

FIGURE 10.3
The Basic Design of a Refrigerator

expansion valve between the thin and thick pipes

refrigerator

compressor

cold side (thick pipes)

hot side (thin pipes)

The "functional unit" of a refrigerator is composed of pipes, a compressor, and a gas. First, the gas is compressed by the compressor. This is mostly adiabatic, so the gas's temperature increases substantially. The gas then travels through several twists and turns of the pipes where it exchanges most of its heat with the surroundings. This takes place outside of the refrigerator, typically behind it.

Once the gas has traveled through the twists and turns of pipes outside of the refrigerator, it encounters an expansion valve. In this area, the volume that the gas can occupy increases, so the gas expands. Once again, this is essentially an adiabatic process, so as the gas expands, it cools. The cold gas then travels through a series of twists and turns which are *inside* the refrigerator. This is what cools the inside of the refrigerator. When the gas gets back to the compressor, the process starts all over again. A refrigerator, then, just uses adiabatic expansion to produce a "cold side" and adiabatic compression to produce a "hot side." The outside of the refrigerator is the hot side, and the inside is the cool side, and that's what keeps your milk from spoiling!

Before we leave this section, I want to summarize these terms and how they relate to the First Law of Thermodynamics by showing you a table. You need to know the information contained in Table 10.1. Although you can choose to just memorize the table, I would rather that you look at the table and think through the definitions so that the table *makes sense* to you.

TABLE 10.1
Thermodynamics Terms and Their Relationship to the First Law

Term	First Law Implications
Isothermal	$\Delta U = 0$
Isochoric (isometric)	$W = 0$
Isobaric	P is constant, so Equation (10.4) can be used to calculate W
Adiabatic	$q = 0$

ON YOUR OWN

10.5 a. In an isothermal process, what is the relationship between q and W?
b. In a isochoric process, what is the relationship between ΔU and q?
c. In an adiabatic process, what is the relationship between ΔU and W?
d. In an isobaric process, what is the relationship between ΔU, q, P, and ΔV?

Cyclic Processes and The First Law of Thermodynamics

Now I want to put together everything you have been learning in a discussion of cyclic processes. Consider, for example, the following P-V diagram.

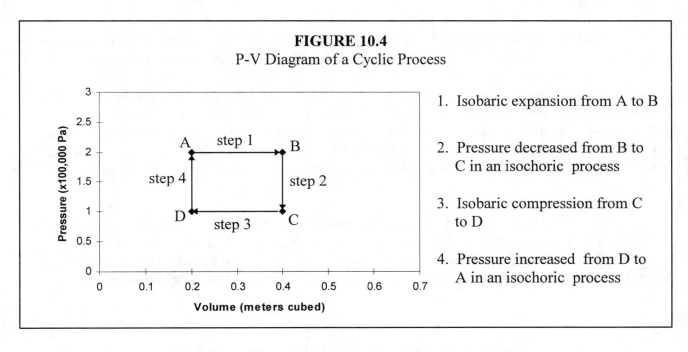

FIGURE 10.4
P-V Diagram of a Cyclic Process

1. Isobaric expansion from A to B

2. Pressure decreased from B to C in an isochoric process

3. Isobaric compression from C to D

4. Pressure increased from D to A in an isochoric process

This P-V diagram illustrates a four-step process in which a gas starts out at a certain pressure and volume (point A on the diagram) and ends up at the same pressure and volume by the end of the process. Not surprisingly, then, this is called a **cyclic process**. There are many different kinds of cyclic processes, so the illustration above represents one of many. We will discuss a few more in the remainder of this module. In this particular cyclic process, the gas is first expanded. We can see that, because in going from A to B, the gas's volume increases. The expansion is *isobaric*, because pressure stays constant at 2.0×10^5 Pa. In step 2, the gas's pressure decreases, but it does so in an isochoric fashion, because the volume stays constant at 0.40 m^3. The gas is then compressed in step 3, which is an isobaric process, and the pressure is then increased in step 4, which is isochoric.

Cyclic processes are quite common. As discussed in the previous section, for example, a refrigerator uses cyclic expansion and compression of a gas to produce a hot side and a cold side. One thing that is very important to remember about cyclic processes is that the gas returns to the same state at which it started. Since that's the case, the internal energy of the gas must be the same at the end of the cyclic process as it was at the beginning.

In a cyclic process, $\Delta U = 0$ over a complete cycle.

This, of course, should make sense. The ideal gas law tells us that $PV = nRT$. In a cyclic process, P and V are the same at the end of the cycle as they were at the beginning. Assuming no gas was lost, n is also the same, and R is a constant. Well, if P, V, n, and R are all the same at the beginning and end, then T must be the same as well, which tells you that the internal energy is the same. Let's see how all of this works out in an example problem.

EXAMPLE 10.2

A 1.50-mole sample of ideal gas undergoes the cyclic process shown in Figure 10.4. Calculate the work done and the heat exchanged in each step as well as one full cycle. (C_p = 20.8 J/mole·K).

Reading from the graph, the gas starts out at a pressure of 2.0×10^5 Pa and a volume of 0.20 m^3. It then expands in an isobaric process to a volume of 0.40 m^3. Calculating the work done is easy, since the process is isobaric:

$$W = P \cdot \Delta V = (2.0 \times 10^5 \text{ Pa}) \cdot (0.40 \text{ m}^3 - 0.20 \text{ m}^3) = 4.0 \times 10^4 \text{ J}$$

Notice that the work is positive. That means the gas did work.

Now we have to determine q. We will use Equation (9.11) since pressure stays constant:

$$q = n \cdot C_p \cdot \Delta T$$

To get ΔT, we must use the ideal gas law. At the beginning of the problem, P = 2.0×10^5 Pa, V = 0.20 m^3, and n = 1.50 moles.

$$PV = nRT$$

$$T = \frac{PV}{nR} = \frac{(2.0 \times 10^5 \text{ Pa}) \cdot (0.20 \text{ m}^3)}{(1.50 \text{ moles}) \cdot (8.31 \frac{\text{Pa} \cdot \text{m}^3}{\text{mole} \cdot \text{K}})} = 3200 \text{ K}$$

At the end, P = 2.0×10^5 Pa, V = 0.40 m^3, and n = 1.50 moles.

$$PV = nRT$$

$$T = \frac{PV}{nR} = \frac{(2.0 \times 10^5 \text{ Pa}) \cdot (0.4 \text{ m}^3)}{(1.50 \text{ moles}) \cdot (8.31 \frac{\text{Pa} \cdot \text{m}^3}{\text{mole} \cdot \text{K}})} = 6400 \text{ K}$$

Now we can calculate q.

$$q = n \cdot C_p \cdot \Delta T = (1.50 \text{ moles}) \cdot (20.8 \frac{\text{J}}{\text{mole} \cdot \text{K}}) \cdot (6400 \text{ K} - 3200 \text{ K}) = 1.0 \times 10^5 \text{ J}$$

For step 2, we can immediately conclude that W = 0. This is a vertical line, and there is no area under a vertical line. Since the work done is the area under the P-V curve, the work done in step 2 is zero. The value for q, however, is not zero. We will have to calculate that. Realize, of course, that we cannot use C_p here, because pressure is changing. However, we can use C_v, but we will have to determine it first:

$$C_p = C_v + R$$

$$C_v = C_p - R = 20.8 \frac{J}{mole \cdot K} - 8.31 \frac{J}{mole \cdot K} = 12.5 \frac{J}{mole \cdot K}$$

I will not go through the ideal gas law calculation again. However, if you did it, you would find that at the beginning of step 2, T = 640 K, and at the end of step 2, T = 320 K. Thus:

$$q = n \cdot C_v \cdot \Delta T = (1.50 \, \text{moles}) \cdot (12.5 \, \frac{J}{mole \cdot K}) \cdot (3200 \, K - 6400 \, K) = -6.0 \times 10^4 \, J$$

Notice that q is negative. That tells us that the gas cooled down. This should make sense, since the pressure of the gas decreased but the volume did not. The only way a gas's pressure can decrease when the volume stays constant is if the gas cools down.

We can calculate the work and heat of steps 3 and 4 in the same way. I will not go through the actual calculations, but the work in step 3 is calculated with Equation (10.4) again, and it turns out to be -2.0×10^4 J. The work is negative because the gas was compressed; thus, work was done on the gas. The heat is calculated by determining the initial and final temperature with the ideal gas law and then calculating q using C_p, because the process is isobaric. The heat is -5.0×10^4 J. Once again, q is negative because the gas cools down.

In the last step, no work is done, because the line is vertical and thus there is no area under it. Once again, if we calculate the temperature at the beginning and end of the process, we can use C_v to determine q. The value for q works out to 3.0×10^4 J. It is positive because the gas warmed up. Now let's look at all of the steps:

1. W = 4.0×10^4 J, q = 1.0×10^5 J
2. W = 0, q = -6.0×10^4 J
3. W = -2.0×10^4 J, q = -5.0×10^4 J
4. W = 0, q = 3.0×10^4 J

Notice what happens when we calculate the *total* work done and heat exchanged. The total work done is 2.0×10^4 J, and the total heat exchanged is 2.0×10^4 J. Notice, then, that in this process q = W for one cycle. This makes sense. After all, $\Delta U = q - W$, and we know that for one full cycle, $\Delta U = 0$. Thus, q must equal W in a cyclic process. Interestingly enough, if you calculate the area enclosed by the square, you will get 2.0×10^4 J. This is a general result.

The work done in one full cycle is the area enclosed by that cycle on a P-V diagram.

Now don't get lost in all of the math of the example and miss what you are *learning* here. In a cyclic process, the gas ends up in the same state as it started. Thus, the internal energy does not change, meaning that $\Delta U = 0$. However, *work and heat do not equal zero at the end of the cycle*. This is very significant. In this process, heat was absorbed (q was positive) and the gas did work (W was positive). Thus, in this cyclic process, heat was *converted* to work! In the end, however, the gas was back to its original state, so that another cycle could start and more heat could be converted to work.

I want to go over one more cyclic process with you.

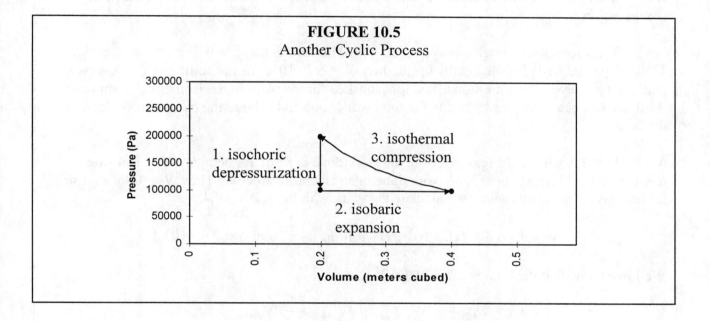

FIGURE 10.5
Another Cyclic Process

This cyclic process is composed of only three steps: an isochoric process that lowers the pressure, an isobaric expansion, and then an isothermal compression. Notice the shape of the isothermal path. It turns out that all isothermal processes have that curved shape, because in an isothermal process, T is constant. Since n and R are also constant, the ideal gas law becomes:

$$PV = \text{constant}$$

$$P = \frac{\text{constant}}{V}$$

On a P-V diagram, an isothermal process will have the shape of a y = 1/x graph.

Now remember, since this is a cyclic process, we know that ΔU equals 0. This means that for the entire process, q = W. This is important, because it would be nice to know q and W for each step as well as the entire cycle. However, we cannot calculate W for the isothermal compression. After all, it is not isobaric, so we cannot use Equation (10.4), and we cannot split the area underneath the curve into nice, recognizable geometric shapes because of the curved nature of the line. However, using the First Law of Thermodynamics and the fact that $\Delta U = 0$ for a cyclic process, we can determine the work done in the isothermal compression if we know something about the heat transferred. Study the following example to see what I mean.

EXAMPLE 10.3

A 1.0 mole sample of an ideal gas is taken through the cyclic process shown in Figure 10.5. If q = -9.0x10³ J for one complete cycle, what is the work done during the isothermal compression?

We know that through one cycle, $\Delta U = 0$. This means that q = W for the entire cycle. Thus, if q = -9.0x10³ J for the entire cycle, then W = -9.0x10³ J for the entire cycle. However, that's not quite what the question asked for. It asked for the work of the isothermal compression. Well, we can calculate that by taking the total work done and subtracting out the work done in the other steps.

In the isochoric depressurization, the work done is zero. Remember, there is no area under a vertical line, so there is no work done in an isochoric process. Thus, W = 0 for that step. In the isobaric expansion, we can calculate the work with Equation (10.4):

$$W = P \cdot \Delta V = (1.0 \times 10^5 \text{ Pa}) \cdot (0.40 \text{ m}^3 - 0.20 \text{ m}^3) = 2.0 \times 10^4 \text{ J}$$

Well, we know that the total work is -9.0x10³ J, so:

$$W_{total} = W_{isochoric} + W_{isobaric} + W_{isothermal}$$

$$-9.0\text{x}10^3 \text{ J} = 0 + 2.0\text{x}10^4 \text{ J} + W_{isothermal}$$

$$W_{isothermal} = -11,000 \text{ J}$$

The work in the isothermal step, then, is -11,000 J. The negative sign means that the surroundings worked on the gas, which makes sense, since the gas was compressed.

ON YOUR OWN

10.6 Given the P-V diagram to the right, calculate the total work done and total heat exchanged in one cycle.

10.7 In the P-V diagram to the right, what would happen to the values of W and q if the cycle were done in reverse? In other words, what would happen if the arrows were pointing opposite of the way they are pointing now?

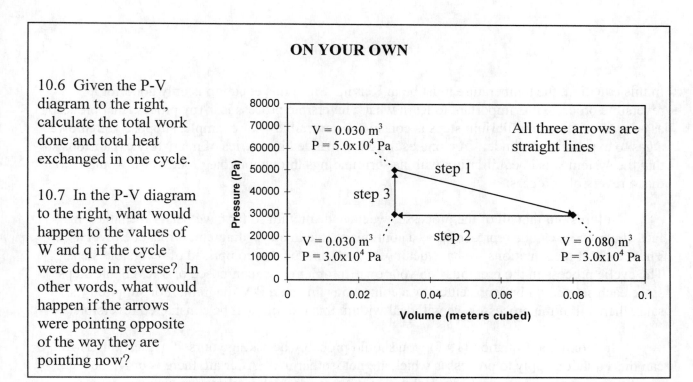

The Second Law of Thermodynamics

Now that you have had a thorough introduction to the First Law of Thermodynamics, it is time to draw our attention to the Second Law of Thermodynamics. As stated in a previous section, the Second Law of Thermodynamics states that the entropy of the universe must either increase or stay the same; it can never decrease. To understand the Second Law better, then, we need to learn more about entropy.

As you already know, entropy is a measure of the disorder in the system. For some strange reason, physicists and chemists use the letter "S" to represent entropy. As a result, we use "ΔS" to represent the change in entropy. A restatement of the Second Law of Thermodynamics, then, is:

$$\Delta S_{universe} \geq 0 \qquad (10.5)$$

Well, since the universe can be split into the system which we are studying and all of its surroundings, we can actually be a bit more specific:

$$\Delta S_{system} + \Delta S_{surroundings} \geq 0 \qquad (10.6)$$

Now, of course, the big question is how can we determine ΔS? Well, it turns out that for **reversible processes**, ΔS is pretty easy to calculate.

$$\Delta S_{rev} = \frac{q}{T} \tag{10.7}$$

In this equation, the temperature must be in Kelvin. Since this equation is only good for a reversible process, it is important to learn what a reversible process is. Any process that proceeds as a series of slow, equilibrium steps is considered reversible. For example, suppose you allowed a gas to expand in a cylinder. As long as the gas expanded in a series of many tiny expansions so that the system was in equilibrium with its surroundings throughout the process, we would call that a reversible process.

It turns out that all of the processes we have dealt with so far have been reversible. In fact, if a process can be represented as a continuous line in a P-V diagram, it must be reversible. Thus, each of the situations we have dealt with so far have been comprised of reversible steps. The cyclic process in the previous "on your own" problem was composed of 3 reversible steps, since each step could be represented by a continuous line on a P-V diagram. For simplicity's sake, then, all of the processes we will deal with in this module will be considered reversible.

In looking at Equation (10.7), you should probably be asking yourself a question. How can this equation apply to processes which are not isothermal? After all, there is only one temperature in the equation. If we deal with a process in which temperature changes, what temperature do we use? Well, if we were doing a calculus-based physics course, we could do a definite integral on this equation, splitting the process into an infinite number of tiny steps, each of which has its own temperature. However, we are not doing a calculus-based physics course. Thus, we will assume that the temperature varies fairly linearly in the processes we deal with. As a result, we can simply use the *average* temperature for the process.

See how we use Equation (10.7) by studying the following example.

EXAMPLE 10.4

A 50.0-g cube of ice is at -5.00 °C. What is the ΔS of the ice cube if it is melted at 0.00 °C? What is the *minimum* ΔS of the surroundings? (c_{ice} = 2.02 J/(g·°C), L_{fusion} = 334 J/g)

Since ΔS depends on q, we need to think about how heat is added to this ice cube in order to make it melt. Well, in order to melt, the ice must first be warmed to 0.00 °C. The q for that is:

$$q = m \cdot c \cdot \Delta T = (50.0 \text{ g}) \cdot (2.02 \frac{J}{g°C}) \cdot (0.00 °C - -5.00 °C) = 505 \text{ J}$$

Now we can calculate ΔS, just taking the average temperature of the process, which is -2.50 C, or 270.65 K.

$$\Delta S_{rev} = \frac{505 \text{ J}}{270.65 \text{ K}} = 1.87 \frac{J}{K}$$

That's not the end of the story, however. Now that the ice is at 0.00 °C, it must be melted. The heat required for that is:

$$q = m \cdot L = (50.0 \text{ g}) \cdot (334 \, \frac{J}{g}) = 16,700 \text{ J}$$

The ΔS associated with that heat is:

$$\Delta S_{rev} = \frac{16,700 \, J}{273.15 \text{ K}} = 61.1 \, \frac{J}{K}$$

The total ΔS of the ice cube, then, is 63.0 J/K. Now, if this is to happen, the ΔS of the universe must be greater than or equal to 0. We have just calculated the ΔS of the system, so:

$$\Delta S_{system} + \Delta S_{surroudings} \geq 0$$

$$63.0 \, \frac{J}{K} + \Delta S_{surroundings} \geq 0$$

$$\Delta S_{surroundings} \geq -63.0 \, \frac{J}{K}$$

The entropy of the surroundings, then, can actually decrease, since the entropy of the system increases. This will, in fact, happen, since the system absorbs heat from the surroundings in order for the ice to melt. Thus, the q of the surroundings is negative, so the ΔS of the surroundings will be negative as well.

Now once again, I do not want you to concentrate on the mathematics so much that you lose the physical significance of what you are analyzing. First, let's look at the sign of the ΔS we calculated. It is positive. That means the entropy of the ice cube *increased*. This should make sense. First, we increased the ice cube's temperature. That makes the water molecules in the ice cube move faster. The faster the molecules move, the harder it is to "keep track" of them, so the more disordered the system is. Of course, if we had cooled the ice cube rather than warmed it, the value of q would be negative, and therefore the value of ΔS would be negative. When something absorbs heat, then, its entropy increases. When it releases heat, its entropy decreases. Second, we melted it. In a solid, the molecules are held in a tight, rigid structure and they are only allowed to vibrate. In a liquid, the molecules move around more freely. Thus, it is once again more difficult to "keep track" of them, so the entropy of a liquid is higher than that of a solid.

Notice also the numerical values we calculated. When the ice cube was warmed 5.00 degrees C, the ΔS was 1.87 J/K. Thus, entropy increased a bit. When the ice cube was melted, the ΔS was 61.1 J/K. In that step, then, the entropy increased *significantly more* than when the ice cube was heated. In general, the entropy changes associated with phase changes are much higher than those associated with simply warming or cooling a substance. This should make sense, as a phase change denotes a huge change in the behavior of the molecules, while warming or cooling produces only a change in the speed of the molecules.

Before we leave this section, I just want once again to emphasize that the ΔS of a system can be negative without violating the Second Law of Thermodynamics. As Equation (10.6) tells you, the second law says nothing about the ΔS of a system. It only says that when you *add* the ΔS of the system and the ΔS of the surroundings, you must come up with zero or a positive number. Thus, the ΔS of a system is free to be negative, as long as the ΔS of the surroundings is sufficiently positive so that the sum of both ΔS values is greater than or equal to 0.

The classic example of how this works is the freezing of water. When water freezes, it releases energy based on its mass and L_{fusion}. Since the water releases energy, its q is negative and thus its ΔS is negative. That does not violate the second law, however, because when it releases its energy, that energy heats up the surroundings, increasing the entropy of the surroundings. The increase in entropy of the surroundings is exactly equal to the decrease in entropy of the system, so the sum of the two ΔS's is 0. Thus, the freezing of water is consistent with the second law and can therefore occur.

ON YOUR OWN

10.8 A gas is compressed adiabatically so that its temperature changes from 273 K to 350 K. What is the ΔS of this process? ($C_p = 20.8$ J/K)

10.9 A gas expands isothermally at 314 K so that the work done is 2,450 J. What is the ΔS of the gas?

Heat Engines and the Carnot Cycle

One of the more interesting consequences of the Second Law of Thermodynamics is that we can never make a heat engine that is 100% efficient. To understand this statement, however, you need to first understand what a heat engine is. A common example of the heat engine is an automobile engine, so let me start there. The typical, 4-stroke automobile engine runs according to the **Otto cycle**, named after Nicholas Otto, a German scientist who described the cycle and built the first such engine in 1861.

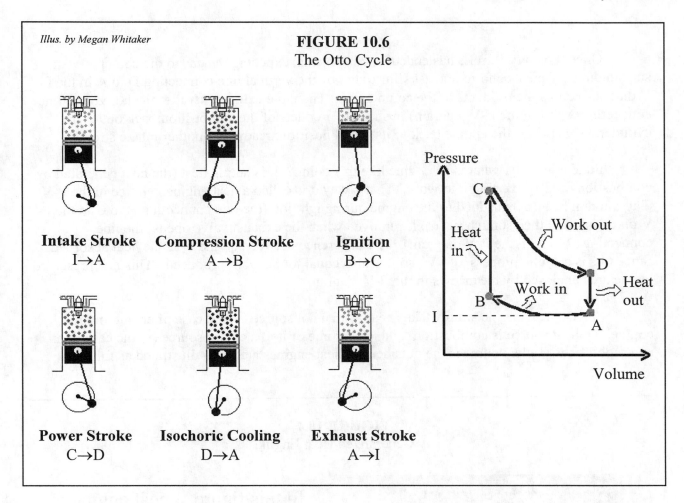

Illus. by Megan Whitaker

FIGURE 10.6
The Otto Cycle

Intake Stroke
I→A

Compression Stroke
A→B

Ignition
B→C

Power Stroke
C→D

Isochoric Cooling
D→A

Exhaust Stroke
A→I

In this figure, the steps of the Otto cycle are shown as is a P-V diagram of the situation. The Otto cycle starts with an **intake stroke**. In this stroke, a mixture of gasoline and air is pulled into the cylinder. This is essentially an isobaric process, since the cylinder and the air/gas mixture are both at atmospheric pressure. Thus, the intake stroke is illustrated as a horizontal line connecting I to A on the P-V diagram. Once the air/gas mixture is taken in, a **compression stroke** compresses the gas adiabatically. The gas therefore heats up. This step takes work, of course, but that's okay, because more work will be produced in an upcoming step. On the P-V diagram, the adiabatic compression is illustrated by the curve that connects A to B.

At the end of the compression stroke, the spark plug ignites the air/gas mixture, causing a rapid increase in pressure. Not surprisingly, this is called **ignition**, and it is represented as a vertical line connecting B to C in the P-V diagram. This is essentially an isochoric process, because combustion of the air/gas mixture happens much more quickly than the piston/cylinder can respond. Thus, the combustion essentially completes before the piston can move. After ignition, the increased pressure causes the piston to move down. This is the **power stroke**, and is illustrated by the curve connecting C to D in the P-V diagram. In the power stroke, the gas expands adiabatically. This produces an enormous amount of work, which is what powers both the automobile as well as the other steps in the cycle.

Once the power stroke has ended, a valve opens, exposing the gas to the cooler surroundings. This isochoric process (illustrated by the vertical line connecting D to A in the P-V diagram) cools the products of the combustion. Then, the **exhaust stroke** (the horizontal line connecting A to I in the P-V diagram) pushes the products of the combustion back out of the cylinder. This brings the engine back to its initial position, ready for another intake stroke.

Fundamentally, what is an engine like this doing? It is taking heat (the heat generated by combustion) and converting it to work. That's why it is called a heat engine. Notice in the P-V diagram that heat (q_h) is added to the engine during ignition (the line connecting B to C in the P-V diagram), and then some heat (q_c) is removed when the exhaust valve opens (the line connecting D to A in the P-V diagram). The difference between q_h and q_c is the heat absorbed. Since this is a cyclic process, q = W, so it is also equal to the work produced. This is represented by the area enclosed by the arrows in the P-V diagram.

Since a heat engine simply takes heat from a hot source (in the case of an automobile engine, the heat source is combustion) and loses some of it to a cooler source (in the case of an automobile, the cooler source is the outside air), heat engines are often illustrated as follows:

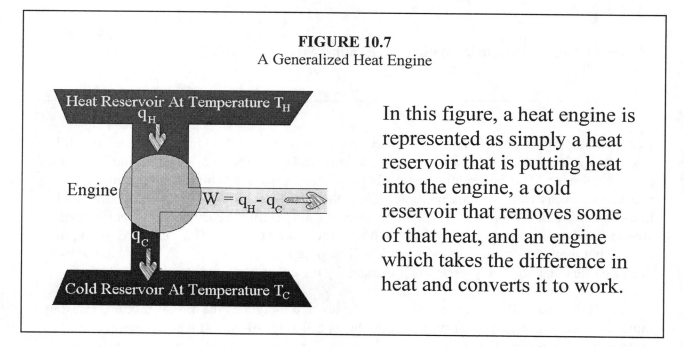

FIGURE 10.7
A Generalized Heat Engine

In this figure, a heat engine is represented as simply a heat reservoir that is putting heat into the engine, a cold reservoir that removes some of that heat, and an engine which takes the difference in heat and converts it to work.

If you remember my discussion of a refrigerator from a previous section, you might recognize that a refrigerator is just the opposite of a heat engine. In a heat engine, a hot reservoir puts heat into the engine, a cold reservoir removes some of the heat, and the difference is converted to work. In a refrigerator, work (as done by the compressor) is converted into heat, producing a hot reservoir (the pipes on the outside of the refrigerator) and a cold reservoir (the pipes on the inside of the refrigerator).

Not surprisingly, there has been a lot of work done on trying to make heat engines more efficient. The more we can reduce friction and spurious work loss in an automobile engine, the more efficiently it will convert fuel into motion, and the less fuel it will have to burn. Surprisingly, however, there is a fundamental limit to the efficiency we can achieve in a heat engine. If all friction and other sources of work loss were removed, we would still not have a 100% efficient engine. Why? The Second Law of Thermodynamics forbids it. As I stated in an earlier section of this module, the second law has many implications. This is another:

No cyclic heat engine can be 100% efficient. In other words, it is impossible to completely convert heat into useful work.

Remember, the Second Law of Thermodynamics states that the entropy of the universe must always increase or stay the same. If you could completely convert heat into useful work, you would be decreasing the entropy of the universe, because heat is a more disordered form of energy than useful work. Thus, when heat is converted to work, the entropy of the system decreases. This is okay, as long as the surroundings increase in entropy enough to offset the loss in entropy of the system. This is accomplished when a portion of the heat is "used" to disorder the surroundings. This means that you can never take heat and convert it completely into useful work. Some of that heat must be "used" to disorder the surroundings so as to satisfy the Second Law of Thermodynamics!

We can actually calculate the efficiency of a heat engine. It takes in a certain amount of energy (q_h) and then loses some of that energy (q_c). The work it creates is given by $W = q_h - q_c$. The efficiency (e), then, is:

$$e = \frac{\text{Work Done}}{\text{Total Energy Input}} = \frac{q_h - q_c}{q_h} = 1 - \frac{q_c}{q_h} \qquad (10.8)$$

Since the Second Law of Thermodynamics says that q_c cannot be zero (some of the heat must be lost to the surroundings), then the Second Law of Thermodynamics tells us that the efficiency of a heat engine can never be equal to 1.

Well, if the second law puts limits on the efficiency of a heat engine, it would be nice to determine what the most efficient heat engine design is. Equation (10.8) tells us the maximum efficiency for a generic heat engine, but some heat engines must be more efficient than others. What is the most efficient heat engine possible? Well, Sadi Carnot (kar' noh) answered that question in the early 1800's. He demonstrated that according to the Second Law of Thermodynamics, the most efficient heat engine possible would work according to the following cycle, which we now call the **Carnot cycle**.

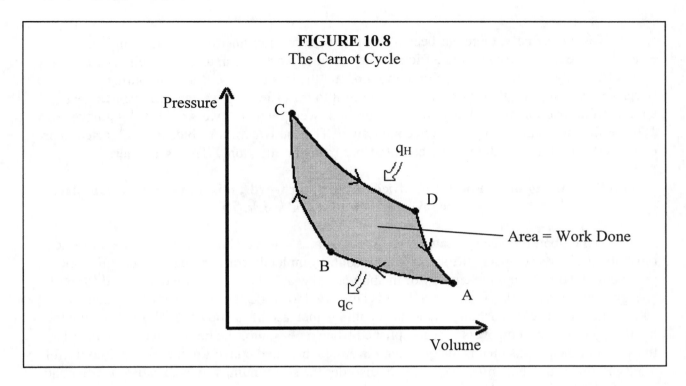

FIGURE 10.8
The Carnot Cycle

Notice that the Carnot cycle looks a lot like the Otto cycle, so the principles are the same. However, because of the differences in the steps, the Carnot cycle is more efficient.

The Carnot cycle is composed of four basic steps. First, a gas undergoes an **isothermal compression**. This is the step in which energy is lost. Since $\Delta U = 0$, that means $q = W$. Thus, the work it takes to compress the gas is lost. Physically, this happens because as energy is lost to the cold reservoir, the gas cools down. However, since this is isothermal, the gas's temperature does not decrease. It stays the same as the cold reservoir, T_C. Thus, the volume decreases instead.

The second step of the Carnot cycle is an **adiabatic compression**. No heat is added or lost in adiabatic processes, so $q = 0$. As a result, $\Delta U = -W$. Thus, as work is done on the gas, the internal energy and thus the temperature of the gas increases. Now remember, during the previous step, the temperature of the gas stayed steady at T_C. Now that work is being done on the gas, however, the temperature begins to increase. The temperature continues to increase until it reaches T_H, the temperature of the hot reservoir.

Once the gas has reached the high temperature, it is ready to start the third step, which is **isothermal expansion**. The gas is at the same temperature as the heat reservoir, so heat will not flow from the reservoir to the gas unless the gas begins to expand. Since it expands isothermally, $\Delta U = 0$ and thus $q = W$. Any energy absorbed from the heat reservoir, then, gets converted directly to work. This is the step in which the heat engine produces work. The problem is, the first step takes some of that work away, so the net work produced is the work produced in this step *minus* the work used in the first step (the isothermal compression).

Once the isothermal expansion is completed, an **adiabatic expansion** occurs in order to get the gas back to its original state so the process can start all over again. Since q = 0, the gas cools, because $\Delta U = -W$. Thus, the gas does work by expanding, and that work lowers the internal energy of the gas back to T_C.

As is the case with any cyclic process, the work done in the Carnot cycle is equal to the difference in the heat transferred from the heat reservoir and that taken away by the cold reservoir. This is also equal to the area enclosed in the P-V diagram.

Why is this such an efficient heat engine? Well, since the step that takes in heat (C to D) is isothermal, all heat taken in is converted to work. None is used to warm up the gas. In the same way, when heat is removed, that step (A to B) is isothermal as well. Thus, the gas loses no internal energy. Also, the two adiabatic steps which heat (B to C) and cool (D to A) the gas involve no heat transfer. They are adiabatic. Thus, the only time heat is transferred, that heat does work.

After Carnot proposed the Carnot cycle, Lord Kelvin (a devout Christian) demonstrated that the ratio of q_C to q_H is equal to the ratio of the two temperatures. Mathematically, we would say:

$$\text{For the Carnot cycle ONLY:} \quad \frac{q_c}{q_H} = \frac{T_C}{T_H}$$

This allows us to simplify Equation (10.8)

$$e_{Carnot} = 1 - \frac{T_c}{T_h} \tag{10.9}$$

Once again, in this equation, temperature must be in Kelvin! Equation (10.9) tells us two things. First, it tells us that even the most efficient heat engine designed is not 100% efficient. Its efficiency is reduced from one by the ratio of the temperature of the cold reservoir to the temperature of the hot reservoir. Second, it tells us that the hotter the hot reservoir and the cooler the cold reservoir, the more efficient the engine.

ON YOUR OWN

10.10 An inventor claims to have produced an engine that is 75% efficient. The engine's schematics show that it has a heat source with a temperature of 750 K and uses room temperature (25 °C) as its cold temperature. Do you believe the inventor?

The Third Law of Thermodynamics

Although the three laws of thermodynamics that we have already discussed are by far the most important, there is actually one more law of thermodynamics. It is, not surprisingly, the **Third Law of Thermodynamics**.

The Third Law of Thermodynamics - It is impossible to reach a temperature of 0 K in a finite number of cooling steps

This law should not surprise you if you took a good chemistry course. You should know that the purpose of the Kelvin temperature scale is to provide us with an absolute temperature which can never be less than or equal to zero. Thus, no matter how hard you try, you cannot cool something to absolute zero. You can get arbitrarily close to absolute zero, but you will never reach it.

Thermodynamics is considered one of the more difficult subjects in physics, but it is also one of the most interesting and fundamental. Because it is so difficult, however, it is often misunderstood by many people, including serious scientists. However, because it is so fundamental, a basic understanding of thermodynamics is essential to really understanding the world around you. I hope that this introduction to the laws of thermodynamics has helped you.

ANSWERS TO THE ON YOUR OWN PROBLEMS

10.1 <u>This can happen because the act of water freezing disorders the surroundings so that the entropy of the surroundings increases. That way, the total entropy of the universe increases or at least stays the same.</u> Remember, to freeze, a substance must release heat equal to its mass times its latent heat of fusion. That heat disorders the surroundings, offsetting the decrease in disorder experienced by the water.

10.2 We know ΔU and the two volumes. We need to find the pressure. Here's what we know:

$$\Delta U = q - W$$

$$-2570 \text{ J} = (2.50 \text{ moles}) \cdot (20.8 \frac{\text{J}}{\text{mole} \cdot \text{K}}) \cdot (T_{final} - T_{initial}) - P \cdot (0.0201 \text{ m}^3 - 0.0514 \text{ m}^3)$$

Note that ΔU is negative because the internal energy *drops*. This equation looks like we have three unknowns (T_{final}, $T_{initial}$, and P). However, we can get both temperatures in terms of P through the ideal gas law.

$$T_{final} = \frac{P_{final} \cdot V_{final}}{n \cdot R} = \frac{P \cdot (0.0201 \text{ m}^3)}{(2.50 \text{ moles}) \cdot (8.31 \frac{\text{J}}{\text{mole} \cdot \text{K}})} = \frac{P \cdot (0.0201 \text{ m}^3)}{(20.8 \frac{\text{J}}{\text{K}})}$$

$$T_{initial} = \frac{P_{initial} \cdot V_{initiall}}{n \cdot R} = \frac{P \cdot (0.0514 \text{ m}^3)}{(2.50 \text{ moles}) \cdot (8.31 \frac{\text{J}}{\text{mole} \cdot \text{K}})} = \frac{P \cdot (0.0514 \text{ m}^3)}{(20.8 \frac{\text{J}}{\text{K}})}$$

Since the pressure is constant, both P_{final} and $P_{initial}$ are just "P." Substituting into the equation above:

$$\Delta U = q - W$$

$$-2570 \text{ J} = (52.0 \frac{\text{J}}{\text{K}}) \cdot (\frac{P \cdot (0.0201 \text{ m}^3)}{20.8 \frac{\text{J}}{\text{K}}} - \frac{P \cdot (0.0514 \text{ m}^3)}{20.8 \frac{\text{J}}{\text{K}}}) - P \cdot (-0.0313 \text{ m}^3)$$

$$-2570 \text{ J} = P \cdot (-0.0783 \text{ m}^3) - P \cdot (-0.0313 \text{ m}^3)$$

$$P = 54{,}700 \frac{\text{J}}{\text{m}^3} = \underline{54{,}700 \text{ Pa}}$$

10.3 You might be tempted to say that no heat was added to the system, because the temperature did not change. However, remember, temperature is a measure of *internal energy*, not heat. Since the *temperature* did not change, that tells you the *internal energy* did not change, so $\Delta U = 0$. This means:

$$\Delta U = q - W$$

$$0 = q - W$$

$$q = W$$

Therefore, <u>2,020 J of heat were added to the gas</u>. Why didn't the gas's temperature increase when it absorbed heat? The heat powered the expansion only. Thus, there was no energy left over to increase the temperature of the gas.

10.4 The work done on the first gas is easy to calculate, because pressure is constant:

$$W = P \cdot \Delta V = (1.5 \times 10^5 \text{ Pa}) \cdot (0.20 \text{ m}^3 - 0.40 \text{ m}^3) = \underline{-3.0 \times 10^4 \text{ J}}$$

The work done on the second gas is more tricky. We must look at each step. In the first step, we must calculate the area under the line:

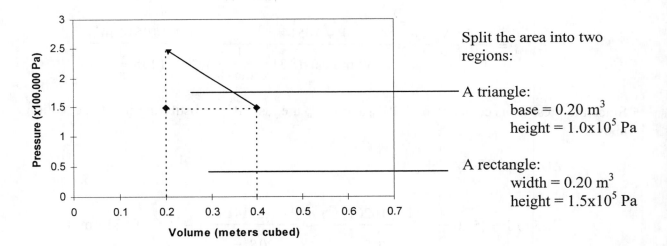

Split the area into two regions:

A triangle:
  base = 0.20 m³
  height = 1.0x10⁵ Pa

A rectangle:
  width = 0.20 m³
  height = 1.5x10⁵ Pa

Area of the triangle:

$$\text{Area} = \frac{1}{2} \cdot b \cdot h = \frac{1}{2} \cdot (0.20 \text{ m}^3) \cdot (1.0 \times 10^5 \text{ Pa}) = 1.0 \times 10^4 \text{ J}$$

Area of the rectangle:

$$\text{Area} = w \cdot h = (0.20 \text{ m}^3) \cdot (1.5 \times 10^5 \text{ Pa}) = 3.0 \times 10^4 \text{ J}$$

The total work for the first step, then, is -1.0x10^4 J + -3.0x10^4 J = -4.0x10^4 J. Note that the work is negative. We had to figure that out on our own, since the sign is not taken care of by any equation. We know that work is negative because something had to work *on* the gas to get it to compress. Work done by the gas is positive; work done *on* the gas is negative.

In the second step, the work is zero, because volume did not change. You can also see that work is zero because the line in the P-V diagram is vertical. There is no area under a vertical line, so no work is done. Thus, the work done in the case of the second gas is <u>-4.0x10^4 J</u>.

Notice that the work is *not the same*. Although both gases started and ended in the same state, the work done is different. That's because work can vary depending on the *path* through which the gas must go. The second gas was taken through a path that required more energy. You will find out later that the only quantity whose value is independent of path is U. Thus, the ΔU of both gases in this problem is the same, but both W and q are not.

10.5   a. In isothermal processes, ΔU = 0. Thus, <u>q = W</u>.

b. In an isochoric process, volume is constant. Thus, W = 0. That means <u>ΔU = q</u>.

c. In an adiabatic process, q = 0. This means <u>ΔU = - W</u>.

d. In an isobaric process, we can use Equation (10.4). Thus, W = P·ΔV. That means <u>ΔU = q - P·ΔV</u>.

10.6 In Example 10.2, you learned that the work done in a cyclic process is equal to the area enclosed by the cycle. Thus, all we have to do is calculate the area of the triangle. It has a base of 0.050 m^3 and a height of 2.0x10^4 Pa.

$$\text{Area} = \frac{1}{2} \cdot b \cdot h = \frac{1}{2} \cdot (0.050 \text{ m}^3) \cdot (2.0 \times 10^4 \text{ Pa}) = 5.0 \times 10^2 \text{ J}$$

Now remember, we have to determine the sign of the work. If we could use Equation (10.4), the equation would take care of the sign, but we cannot. Thus, we have to figure out the sign for ourselves.

In step 1, work is positive, since the gas expands. In step 2, the work is negative, since the gas contracts. In step 3, work is 0, since the volume is constant. The area under the step 1 line is greater than the area under the step 2 line, meaning there is more positive work than negative work, so the total work is positive. Thus, <u>the work is 5.0x10^2 J</u>.

In a cyclic process, ΔU = 0 for a complete cycle, which means q = W. Thus, <u>the heat is also 5.0x10^2 J</u>.

10.7 If the arrows were reversed, then the work in step 1 would be negative, because the gas would be contracting. The work in step 2 would therefore be positive, and the work in step 3 would still be zero. Since the area under step 1 is greater, <u>the work would be negative, which means the heat would be negative as well</u>.

10.8 <u>$\Delta S = 0$ for this process</u>. This might surprise you, but remember, ΔS depends on q. This is an adiabatic process, so q = 0. Thus, $\Delta S = 0$. How can $\Delta S = 0$ if the temperature increases? Doesn't that mean the molecules are moving around faster and thus are harder to keep track of? Well, the molecules *are* moving faster, but the volume has also reduced. The faster motion of the molecules increases entropy, but the smaller volume *decreases* entropy, because the gas molecules are easier to keep track of in a smaller volume. These two competing effects cancel out, and $\Delta S = 0$.

10.9 In an isothermal process, $\Delta U = 0$, so q = W. Thus, q = 2,450 J. Now we can calculate ΔS:

$$\Delta S_{rev} = \frac{2,450 \text{ J}}{314 \text{ K}} = \underline{7.80 \ \frac{J}{K}}$$

10.10 Even if this was the most efficient kind of engine (a Carnot engine), the efficiency would be:

$$e_{Carnot} = 1 - \frac{298 \text{ K}}{750 \text{ K}} = 0.60$$

Thus, even the most efficient engine running without friction, etc., would have an efficiency of 60%. Therefore, <u>you should not believe the inventor</u>!

REVIEW QUESTIONS FOR MODULE #10

1. State the laws of thermodynamics that you learned in this module.

2. State which of the three laws listed above forbids each of the following situations:

    a. The total amount of energy (including mass) is greater after a nuclear reaction than it was before the nuclear reaction.
    b. A person walks outside without a coat on a cool day and gets warmer.
    c. A cool ball sitting at rest on hot pavement suddenly rolls up a hill.

3. A gas is stored in an insulated container so that it cannot exchange heat with its surroundings. If the gas is compressed, what will happen to its temperature?

4. A physics student calculates the work for a given process by determining the area under the curve on a P-V diagram. The student determines that W = 1000 J. If the process is reversed, what is W?

5. A gas expands adiabatically. What happens to its temperature?

6. A gas is isothermally compressed. It takes 500 J of work to compress the gas. What is q for this process? What happens to the temperature of the surroundings?

7. Is it possible for a gas to expand both isothermally and adiabatically? Why or why not?

8. Is it possible for a gas to expand both isobarically and adiabatically? Why or why not?

9. A gas experiences a decrease in entropy and an increase in temperature. Is W positive or negative for this process? What happened to the entropy of the surroundings?

10. What is special about a Carnot engine? State the four steps by which such an engine operates.

PRACTICE PROBLEMS FOR MODULE #10

1. A balloon is inflated to a volume of 0.0050 m³ at a pressure of 1.01×10^5 Pa and a temperature of 25 °C. It is then placed in a freezer which is at the same pressure but has a temperature of -5 °C. What is the change in internal energy of the gas? ($C_p = 20.8$ J/[mole·K])

2. A gas expands both adiabatically and isobarically. It starts out at $P = 1.0 \times 10^5$ Pa, V = 0.020 m³. If the gas loses 1,560 J of internal energy, what is the volume after expansion?

Problems 3-8 refer to the situation discussed below:

Two 1.5-mole samples of gas begin at the same pressure (1.5×10^5 Pa) and volume (0.020 m³). They go through two different means of expansion, but they both end up at the same pressure (1.5×10^5 Pa) and volume (0.040 m³). The first gas expands according to the path given by the solid arrows in the P-V diagram to the right, while the second expands according to the dashed arrow in the P-V diagram to the right. ($C_p = 20.8$ J/[mole·K])

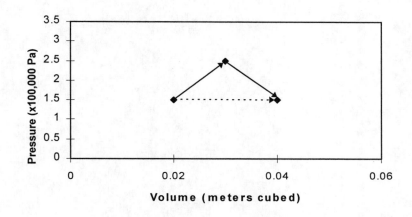

3. Calculate the work done in each case.

4. What is ΔU for the second gas?

5. You cannot use the same method you used in #4 to determine ΔU for the first gas. Why?

6. Although you cannot use the same method that you used in #4, you still can determine the ΔU of the first gas. What is it?

7. What is q for the first gas?

8. Suppose the figure above represented a cyclic process in which a single sample of gas started at $P = 1.5 \times 10^5$ Pa, V = 0.020 m³, expanded to $P = 1.5 \times 10^5$ Pa, V = 0.040 m³, was compressed to $P = 2.5 \times 10^5$ Pa, V = 0.030 m³, and then was compressed again to at $P = 1.5 \times 10^5$ Pa, V = 0.020 m³.
   a. What are q and W for this cyclic process?
   b. Does this cycle best represent a heat engine or a refrigerator?

9. A gas contracts isothermally at a temperature of 315 K. When the contraction is over, ΔS of the gas is -1.5 J/K.

       a. What is the work associated with this process?
       b. What is the minimum change in entropy of the surroundings?

10. Suppose you want to create a Carnot engine whose maximum efficiency is 0.800. If the heat source you use has a temperature of 565 °C, what must the cold temperature of the engine be?

Module #11: Electrostatics

Introduction

Over the previous ten modules, I have spent a significant amount of time on mechanics, thermal physics, and thermodynamics. However, I have only mentioned electricity and magnetism in passing. Of course, in your first-year physics course, you should have learned a lot about electricity and magnetism. Now it is time to revisit these fascinating aspects of physics and learn them in more detail.

Before we get into the details of electricity and magnetism, I want to remind you of something you ought to already know: electricity and magnetism are just *different aspects of the same thing*. Although this might sound odd to you, it is true. The same force that causes electrons to move through electrical circuits is also responsible for keeping the magnets sticking to your refrigerator. Of course, scientists always suspected that was true. As you learned in your first-year physics course, electricity can be used to make a magnet (called an electromagnet), and a magnet can be used to make electricity (as is the case in electrical power plants). It took the genius of James Clerk Maxwell (the founder of modern physics), however, to demonstrate this fact in a mathematically rigorous way. He developed a set of mathematical equations (Maxwell's equations) which not only showed that the electrostatic force and the magnetic force were really the same force, now called the electromagnetic force, but also showed that the speed of light was a fundamental constant in nature. As I have already mentioned, this led Einstein to develop his Special Theory of Relativity.

Maxwell's equations actually led to one other important finding in physics - that photons mediate the electromagnetic force. What do I mean by that? Well, in order for one object to exert a force on another object, there must be some method in which the two objects can "contact" one another. When you push on a table, for example, you touch the table with your hands, and the force you are exerting is transmitted through your hands to the table. In this case, then, your hands mediate the force between you and the table. Of course, charged particles and magnets do not have to touch one another in order to exert their mutual force. If I just bring two magnets close to one another, they will attract or repel each other, depending on the orientation of the poles.

How do magnets (and charged particles) exert a force between one another if they do not touch? Force is not magical. It must be transmitted in some way. How is it transmitted? It is transmitted through the exchange of photons. Each object interacts with the other by sending and receiving photons. This allows the two objects to "communicate" with one another, allowing them to exert forces on one another. Thus, as long as photons can travel between two charged particles (or two magnets), they will exert a force on one another. All forces must have some kind of mediator like this. The force that holds protons and neutrons together in the nucleus (the strong nuclear force) is mediated by the protons and neutrons exchanging tiny particles called pions. If there is a gravitational force (remember, Einstein says it is not really a force), then massive objects must exchange some kind of particle as well. Physicists have searched for such a particle (usually called a **graviton**) for some time, but they have never found one.

Since I am discussing James Clerk Maxwell's work, it is interesting to discuss the person as well. As I have stated previously, he was a devout Christian, as was the case with most of the great scientists of the past. He started every experiment with a prayer, because he really believed that through science, he was learning more about God. One such prayer was, "Teach us to study the works of Thy hands that we may subdue the earth to our use and strengthen our reason for Thy service." (*Scientists of Faith*, Dan Graves, Kregel resources, p. 153). At his request, the following Psalm was carved on the great door of Cambridge's famous Cavendish Laboratory: "Great are the works of the Lord; They are studied by all who delight in them" (Psalm 111:2 NASB). Maxwell was not only a brilliant scientist, but he was a scientist who had the right perspective. Science is an incredible pursuit, as long as it is done in reference to the Creator. Without that reference, science can lose its way, as we have seen in such pursuits as evolution, human cloning, abortion, etc.

In this module, we will start our discussion of electromagnetism with a discussion of electrostatics, which is the study of charged particles at rest. The best place to start is with a review of what you should have learned already.

Coulomb's Law

In your first-year physics course, you should have learned the mathematical expression for the electrostatic force between two charged particles. It is called Coulomb's Law, as it was elucidated by Charles Augustin de Coulomb.

$$F = \frac{k \cdot q_1 \cdot q_2}{r^2} \tag{11.1}$$

In this equation, "q_1" and "q_2" represent the charges of each object, while "r" represents the distance between the centers of the objects. Notice that this equation looks a lot like the equation for gravitational force. Thus, like gravitational force, the electrostatic force depends on the properties of the two objects (mass in the case of gravity and charge in the case of the electrostatic force), and the distance between the objects squared.

The Coulomb constant (k) has a value of $8.99 \times 10^9 \ \frac{N \cdot m^2}{C^2}$ and is often expressed in terms of the permittivity of free space (ε_o), which is a constant that shows up in other equations, such as Maxwell's equations. Since ε_o has a value of $8.85 \times 10^{-12} \ \frac{C^2}{N \cdot m^2}$, k and ε_o are related as follows:

$$k = \frac{1}{4 \cdot \pi \ \varepsilon_o} \tag{11.2}$$

Although I will always use "k" in the equation for Coulomb's Law, you need to be aware that some physics books use $\dfrac{1}{4\cdot\pi\ \varepsilon_{\text{o}}}$ instead. Both expressions are correct, of course, since they are equal to one another.

In your first-year course, you should have gotten lots of experience working with Coulomb's Law, so I just want to run through an example that illustrates one of the more difficult applications of the law. If you have trouble following this example, you should go back to your first-year course and review the material which covers Coulomb's Law.

EXAMPLE 11.1

Three charged particles are arranged as shown in the figure below. What is the instantaneous electrostatic force that exists on the 5.0 mC particle?

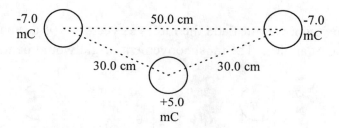

Now remember, we are interested only in the 5.0 mC charge. Thus, we only have to worry about the interactions between the 5.0 mC charge and the other two charges. The two -7.0 mC charges also interact with one another, but their interaction does not affect the 5.0 mC charge in any way. Also, note that we are determining the instantaneous electrostatic force that exists on the 5.0 mC charge. That's all we can determine because, unless all three of these particles are fixed, they will immediately move according to the various forces at play. That, then, will change the value of "r" in Equation (11.1), and thus the electrostatic force will change.

So, we just need to determine the forces that act on the 5.0 mC charge. That's pretty easy. We use Coulomb's Law. Now remember from your first-year course that although there is no vector notation in Coulomb's Law, force is definitely a vector, so we must figure out the direction of the force after we figure out the magnitude. Since each of the charges interacting with the 5.0 mC particle is the same, and since they are equidistant from the 5.0 mC charge, they exert the same magnitude of force:

$$F = \frac{k\cdot q_1 \cdot q_2}{r^2} = \frac{(8.99\times10^9\ \frac{\text{N}\cdot\cancel{\text{m}}^2}{\cancel{\text{C}}^2})\cdot(0.0050\ \cancel{\text{C}})\cdot(0.0070\ \cancel{\text{C}})}{(0.300\ \cancel{\text{m}})^2} = 3.5\times10^6\ \text{N}$$

Notice that I did not put the sign of the charge into the equation. That's because sign simply tells us direction, and we are going to figure that out ourselves. Thus, there is no reason to use the signs. Also, notice that I had to convert mC to C and cm to m in order to make the units consistent with the value of k.

Since the 5.0 mC charge has the opposite sign of the other two charges, we know that the 5.0 mC charge is attracted to each of the other charges. We just figured out the magnitude of that attractive force, so we can now draw the following picture:

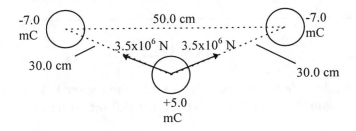

To find the total force, then, we must add the forces as vectors. To do that, we need to determine an origin and a couple of angles. The most convenient origin would be the center of the +5.0 mC charge.

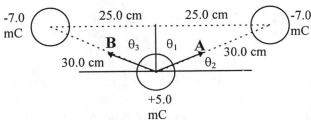

Since the triangle is isosceles, the solid line that intersects the 50.0 cm dashed line cuts it in half and is perpendicular to it. Thus, we now have two right triangles. Since θ_1 is opposite a 25.0 cm leg of its right triangle, we can calculate it:

$$\sin\theta_1 = \frac{25.0 \text{ cm}}{30.0 \text{ cm}}$$

$$\theta_1 = 56.4°$$

Of course, that's not the best angle to use. To make everything come out right in vector addition, we need to define our angles from the positive x-axis. Thus, θ_2 is the best angle to use for vector analysis, and that has a value of 33.6°, as it is the complement of θ_1. Using the same reasoning, we can get θ_3 from its right triangle and add 90.0° to it to get a properly-defined angle of 146.4°.

Now we have two magnitudes (each 3.5 x 10⁶ N) and two angles (33.6° and 146.4°). With that information, we can add the vectors A and B to get the final force, C:

$$A_x = (3.5 \times 10^6 \text{ N}) \cdot \cos(33.6°) = 2.9 \times 10^6 \text{ N}$$
$$A_y = (3.5 \times 10^6 \text{ N}) \cdot \sin(33.6°) = 1.9 \times 10^6 \text{ N}$$

$$B_x = (3.5 \times 10^6 \text{ N}) \cdot \cos(146.4°) = -2.9 \times 10^6 \text{ N}$$
$$B_y = (3.5 \times 10^6 \text{ N}) \cdot \sin(146.4°) = 1.9 \times 10^6 \text{ N}$$

$$C_x = A_x + B_x = 2.9 \times 10^6 \text{ N} - 2.9 \times 10^6 \text{ N} = 0$$
$$C_y = A_y + B_y = 1.9 \times 10^6 \text{ N} + 1.9 \times 10^6 \text{ N} = 3.8 \times 10^6 \text{ N}$$

The final vector, then, has a magnitude of 3.8 x 10⁶ N and is pointing straight up, since it has no x-component. This should make sense. The two charges attracting the 5.0 mC charge are equal in magnitude and equidistant in either horizontal direction. Thus, the horizontal components of the forces cancel, leaving only a force of 3.8 x 10⁶ N pointing straight up.

Now that might have seemed like a long problem, but there was nothing new in it. By now, you should be a veritable expert in vector analysis, and you should have learned Coulomb's Law last year. The example problem just blended those two concepts. To get you back into the swing of things, I want you to do the following "on your own" problems. Once again, there is nothing new here. These problems use only concepts that you should have learned in your first-year physics course.

ON YOUR OWN

11.1 Four charges are arranged at the vertices of a square, as shown to the right. The two gray spheres are charged to -1.0 mC. The two white spheres are equally charged. The net force on both gray spheres is zero.

a. What is the charge on each of the white spheres?
b. If a particle with a charge of +2.5 mC were placed at the center of the square, what would be the magnitude and direction of the force acting on it?

11.2 A ping pong ball (m = 2.2 g) is charged at +0.50 μC and placed at the bottom of a tube. Another ping pong ball is charged to +0.25 μC and dropped into the tube. What is the distance between the centers of the balls when the system comes to rest?

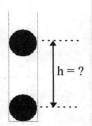

Now that you have cleared the cobwebs out of your mind when it comes to Coulomb's Law, I want you to perform the following experiment.

EXPERIMENT 11.1
A Repulsive Application of Coulomb's Law

<u>Supplies</u>:

- Aluminum foil (You really should use Reynolds Wrap® because you need the thickness, and the numbers I give you are for that brand. Other brands *should* be similar, however.)
- Thread
- Scissors
- Tape
- A blown-up balloon
- A plastic or wooden ruler (It cannot have conductive material in it.)
- An open door inside the house

<u>Introduction</u> - In this experiment, you get to pit gravity and the electrostatic force against one another. This will allow you to calculate the charge that you are able to give two little balls of foil.

<u>Procedure</u>:
1. Cut two lengths of thread so that they are both about 80 cm long.
2. Pull foil out of the box so that you have about 30 cm of foil and then tear it off. You now have a rectangle of foil. Measure the length and width of the rectangle.
3. Cut the rectangle precisely in half and wad each half into a tiny ball. As you wad the foil up, put one end of each thread into each ball so that the foil balls each become attached to one end of each thread.
4. Use tape to attach the strings to the same point at the top of the open door's frame. Adjust the length from the point of attachment to the balls so that the balls hang right next to one another. That way, the setup looks something like this:

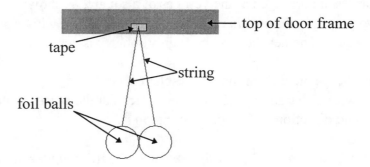

5. Take the balloon and rub it vigorously in your hair. Please note that for this experiment to work well, your hair must be clean and dry. Rubbing the balloon up against a cat would be ideal, because cat hair is meticulously clean. However, I doubt that you will get the cat to

consent! This will induce a negative charge on the balloon as it picks up stray electrons from your hair.

6. In one hand, hold the thread right above the foil balls. Then, touch the balls with the balloon. You are trying to transfer charge from the balloon to the balls. Make sure you don't touch the balls with your hands, or the charge will be conducted through you and away from the balls.

7. Pull the balloon away and gently let the thread go. Because both balls should now be negatively charged, and they should repel one another. Thus, they should move away from one another. If they do not, you did not charge the balls. Try again. It may take a little practice for you to get the balls charged up.

8. At first, the balls will probably move around a lot. You can stop the motion by holding the threads and then gently releasing them again. As long as you don't touch the balls themselves, you should not lose much charge.

9. Eventually, the balls will reach an equilibrium position where they hang in air because their mutual electrostatic repulsion equals the gravitational force pulling them together. Use the ruler to measure the distance between the centers of the balls as they hang there.

10. Measure the distance from the point of attachment on the door frame to the center of each ball. The two distances should be the same.

11. Regular Reynolds wrap is 1.65×10^{-5} meters thick, while heavy-duty Reynolds wrap is 2.39×10^{-5} meters thick, and the density of aluminum is 2700 kg/m^3. Use this information and the length and width of the foil rectangle you measured in step #2 to calculate the mass of aluminum used. Cut that mass in half so that you have the mass of each ball.

12. The information you got in steps 9,10, and 11 should be all you need to calculate the charge that you were able to give to the balls, assuming that they ended up equally charged. Try to do the calculation yourself, by balancing the gravitational force, the tension in the strings, and the electrostatic repulsion. If you cannot get it, look at the end of the answers to the "on your own" problems. The solution is there.

13. Clean everything up. Please note: you will use the foil balls again, so don't throw them away. Keep them on their strings as well.

Before I move on to electric fields, I just want to remind you that there are two ways in which to charge an object. You can charge by conduction (which you did in this experiment) or induction. You need to know these terms, but I will not go over them. Thus, if you have forgotten them, review your first-year physics course. These terms are also in the glossary of this course.

Electric Fields

Remember, force is not magical. As I said before, in order for two objects to interact in any way, something must mediate that interaction. It took the genius of James Clerk Maxwell to demonstrate that the exchange of photons between charged particles mediates the electrostatic force. Before Maxwell, however, scientists realized that there must be something which explains how charged particles interact. Thus, they used the **electric field** to visualize whatever it was that caused charged particles to interact. Although we now know that it is the exchange of photons which causes this, the electric field is still a useful visualization.

As you learned in your previous physics course, we use arrows to visualize the electric field. The arrows point in the direction of the force experienced by a positive charge that is put in the field, and the density of the lines illustrates the strength of the field. This is shown in Figure 11.1.

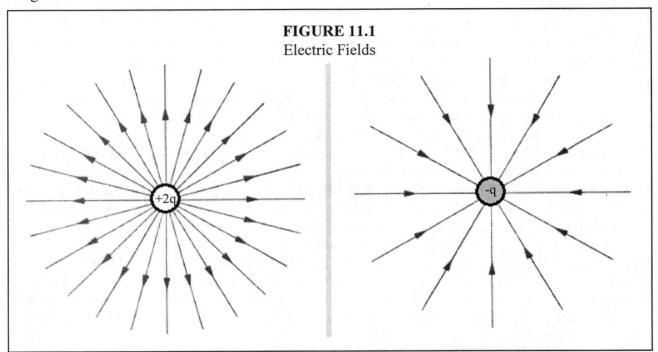

FIGURE 11.1
Electric Fields

Notice how, on the left-hand side of the figure, the arrows point away from the positive charge. That's because a positive charge placed in the field will move away from the positive charge generating the field. In the same way, the lines in the electric field on the right-hand side of the figure are pointed towards the negative charge, because a positive charge placed in the field will move towards the negative charge that is generating the field. Notice also that there are twice as many lines in the left-hand side of the figure as compared to the right-hand side of the figure. That's because the positive charge is twice as strong as the negative charge. As a result, the electric field it generates is twice as strong as the one generated by the negative charge, so the electric field is represented by twice as many lines. Finally, notice that as you move away from the charges, the lines get less dense (farther apart from each other). This illustrates the fact that the electrostatic force decreases with increasing distance.

If two charges are placed near one another, they each generate their own electric field. The *total* electric field, however, is the *vector sum* of each electric field line at every point in space. Of course, doing such a vector sum at several points in space is a relatively tedious job. However, if you learn some basic principles, you can qualitatively sketch the electric field produced by several charges placed next to each other. For example, examine Figure 11.2.

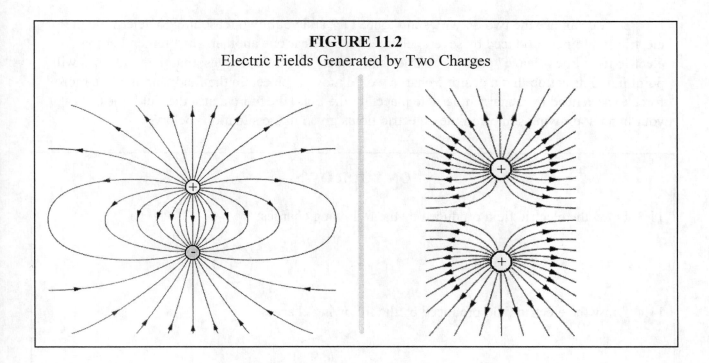

FIGURE 11.2
Electric Fields Generated by Two Charges

On the left-hand side of the figure, we have the electric field generated by two equal but opposite charges. This is often called an electric dipole.

<u>Electric dipole</u> - Two opposite electric charges separated by a certain distance in space

Notice the electric field produced by this electric dipole. Since electric field lines point in the direction that a positive charge would move if placed in the field, the lines point from the positive charge to the negative charge. In other words, the lines "leave" the positive charge and "enter" the negative charge. Since the charges are equal in magnitude, the number of lines for each is the same. Thus, every line that "leaves" the positive charge "enters" the negative charge. The lines are curved because of the results of the vector addition of the two fields.

On the right-hand side of the figure, the electric field produced by two equal positive charges is drawn. Note that there are the same number of lines "leaving" each charge, but they do not travel from one charge to another, because a positive charged placed in the vicinity of these two charges would not travel from one positive charge to the other. Instead, it would be repelled by *both* charges.

Please note that there are no electric field lines midway between the two charges. That's because, if I placed a positive charge midway between the two charges in the figure, it would not move. It would be repelled by each charge, and the two repulsive forces would cancel out, resulting in no net force on the charge. If there is no net force on the charge, there is no electric field.

You can use the two drawings in Figure 11.2 and your own reasoning to determine the electric field lines produced by several charges placed near one another. Just remember that electric field lines "leave" positive charges and "enter" negative charges; that the field lines will point in the direction that a positive charge would move if placed in the field; and that the more force experienced by a charged particle placed in the field, the more dense the field lines. Try your hand at drawing some complex electric fields given in the situations below.

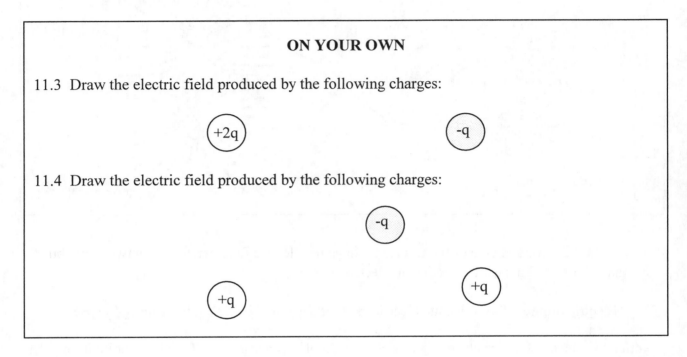

ON YOUR OWN

11.3 Draw the electric field produced by the following charges:

+2q   -q

11.4 Draw the electric field produced by the following charges:

-q

+q   +q

A Quantitative Description of the Electric Field

Although the density of the electric field lines gives you a qualitative notion of the strength of an electric field, we can actually calculate a value for it, using Equation (11.3):

$$E = \frac{k \cdot Q}{r^2}$$

(11.3)

In this equation, "k" is the Coulomb constant, "Q" is the charge of the particle generating the electric field, and "r" is the distance from the center of that charge. If you look at the units that result from this equation, you will find that the electric field strength is expressed in Newtons per Coulomb (N/C). Note that you do not use the sign of the charge (Q) in this equation, you use only its magnitude.

Notice that this equation looks a lot like Equation (11.1). That's not surprising, since the electric field is just a means of visualizing the electrostatic force. If you compare the two equations closely, you will find that if you want to calculate the force that a charged particle experiences when it is placed in an electric field, you would simply multiply the electric field strength by the charge of that particle:

$$\mathbf{F} = q \cdot \mathbf{E} \qquad (11.4)$$

Notice that force and electric field are both vectors in this equation. That should make sense, since force is a vector and charge is not. If force is a vector and charge is not, the electric field must also be a vector. It is a vector, of course, because we use arrows to represent it. Thus, it contains direction information. Why is "E" not expressed as a vector in Equation (11.3)? Because Equation (11.3) calculates only the strength of the electric field. Like the electrostatic force, you have to reason out the direction yourself. However, once you have E, you can use the sign of the charge in Equation (11.4) to determine direction. Thus, unlike Equation (11.3), you do use the sign of the charge in Equation (11.4). Study the following example problems to see what I mean.

EXAMPLE 11.2

A +5.00 mC charge is placed 25.0 cm away from a +15.0 mC charge, as shown in the diagram to the right. At what point is the electric field equal to zero ?

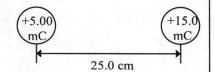

The electric field will equal zero when the vector addition of the two particles' electric fields equals zero. We know instinctively that the electric field must be zero somewhere in between the two particles. If the particles had equal charge, it would be directly in between them. Since one particle has more charge than the other, it won't be directly in between them; however, it will be on a line connecting the two charges. That's nice, because it turns this into a one-dimensional problem. If we use the black dot below to represent the point of zero electric field, we see that it will be a distance of "x" from the +5.00 mC charge and a distance of 25.0 cm - x from the +15.0 mC charge:

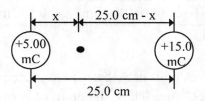

We can now use Equation (11.3) to determine the electric field from each particle and then add them together as vectors.

Since this is now a one-dimensional problem, we just use signs to designate the direction. However, since Equation (11.3) does not use signs, we have to figure that out on our own. The electric field points in the direction that a positive charge would accelerate if placed in the field.

Thus, the electric field from the +5.00 mC charge points to the right, and the electric field of the +15.0 mC charge points to the left. If we define motion to the right as positive, then we get:

$$\mathbf{E}_{tot} = \mathbf{E}_{5.00\,mC} + \mathbf{E}_{15.0\,mC}$$

$$\mathbf{E}_{tot} = \frac{k \cdot (0.00500\ C)}{x^2} - \frac{k \cdot (0.0150\ C)}{(0.250\ m - x)^2}$$

Notice what I did. I used Equation (11.3) to calculate the strength of each field, and then I used my definition of motion to the right as positive motion to see that the electric field from the +15.0 mC charge is negative. Since we are looking for the point at which the electric field is zero:

$$0 = \frac{\cancel{k} \cdot (0.00500\ C)}{x^2} - \frac{\cancel{k} \cdot (0.0150\ C)}{(0.250\ m - x)^2}$$

$$\frac{(0.00500\ \cancel{C})}{x^2} = \frac{(0.0150\ \cancel{C})}{(0.250\ m - x)^2}$$

$$\frac{(0.250\ m - x)^2}{x^2} = \frac{0.0150}{0.00500}$$

$$0.0625\,m^2 - (0.500\,m) \cdot x + x^2 = 3.00x^2$$

$$-2.00x^2 - (0.500\,m) \cdot x + 0.0625\,m^2 = 0$$

$$x = \frac{0.500\,m \pm \sqrt{(0.500\,m)^2 - 4 \cdot (-2.00) \cdot (0.0625\,m^2)}}{2 \cdot (-2.00)} = \frac{0.500\,m \pm \sqrt{0.750\ m^2}}{-4.00} = -0.342\ m, 0.0915\ m$$

Since the negative solution makes no sense (that would place it left of the +5.00 mC charge), the other solution must be the correct one. Thus, the point of zero electric field is 9.15 cm to the right of the 5.00 mC charge.

Three charges are arranged at the vertices of a right triangle, as shown in the figure to the right. What is the value of the electric field at the center of the hypotenuse? What force would a -5.00 μC charge experience if placed there?

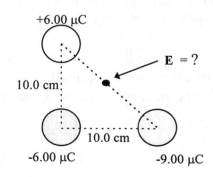

In order to calculate the electric field at the point shown in the figure, we will have to add all of the individual electric fields together as vectors. Thus, we need to figure out some geometry.

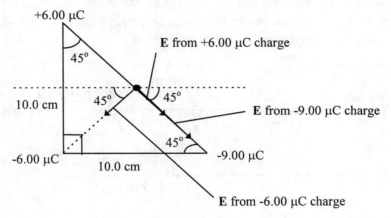

Before we discuss the angles, let's get the lengths out of the way. The hypotenuse of the triangle (via the Pythagorean theorem) is 14.1 cm. That means the point is 7.05 cm from both the +6.00 μC charge and the -9.00 μC charge. The dashed line drawn from the -6.00 μC charge to the point is one leg of a right triangle whose hypotenuse is 10.0 cm and whose other leg is 7.05 cm. Thus, the point (via the Pythagorean theorem) is 7.09 cm away from that charge.

Now we can deal with the angles. At the point in which we are interested, the +6.00 μC charge will push a positive charge directly away from it, so the vector for that electric field is oriented along the hypotenuse, towards the -9.00 μC charge. The -9.00 μC charge will pull a positive charge towards it, so its electric field is oriented in the same direction as that of the +6.00 μC charge, but it is stronger (same distance, greater charge), so I have drawn that vector a bit longer. Finally, the -6.00 μC charge pulls a positive charge towards it, so its electric field is pointed towards the right angle of the triangle.

Since the two legs of the big right triangle are equal in length (10.0 cm), this is a 45-45-90 triangle. Thus, the other two angles in the big triangle are 45°. When two parallel lines are cut by a transversal, alternating interior angles are congruent. Thus, the angle between the horizontal and the vectors from the +6.00 μC and -9.00 μC charges is 45° as well. Of course, to do vector math properly, we really need to define our angle counterclockwise from the horizontal, so the angle for both of those vectors will be 315°.

A line drawn from the center of the -6.00 μC charge to the point in which we are interested bisects the right angle of the triangle, since it goes from the vertex to the center of the hypotenuse. That means the angle between that line and each leg of the triangle is 45°. Once again, when two parallel lines are cut by a transversal, alternating interior angles are congruent. Thus, the angle between the horizontal and the vector from the -6.00 μC charge is 45°. Defined properly for vector math, however, that is 225°. Now we know all of the angles involved. Please note that since all of the angles came from strict geometry rules, they are infinitely precise. Thus, they will not enter into the significant figure calculations.

Well, now that we have worked out the geometry, all we have to do is chug through the vector math. I will call the electric field from the +6.00 μC charge vector A, the electric field from the -9.00 μC charge vector B, and the electric field from the -6.00 μC charge vector C. First, we get the components:

$$A_x = \frac{k \cdot Q}{r^2} \cdot \cos\theta = \frac{(8.99 \times 10^9 \; \frac{N \cdot m^2}{C^2}) \cdot (6.00 \times 10^{-6} C)}{(0.0705 \; m)^2} \cdot \cos(315) = 7.67 \times 10^6 \; \frac{N}{C}$$

$$A_y = \frac{k \cdot Q}{r^2} \cdot \sin\theta = \frac{(8.99 \times 10^9 \; \frac{N \cdot m^2}{C^2}) \cdot (6.00 \times 10^{-6} C)}{(0.0705 \; m)^2} \cdot \sin(315) = -7.67 \times 10^6 \; \frac{N}{C}$$

$$B_x = \frac{k \cdot Q}{r^2} \cdot \cos\theta = \frac{(8.99 \times 10^9 \; \frac{N \cdot m^2}{C^2}) \cdot (9.00 \times 10^{-6} C)}{(0.0705 \; m)^2} \cdot \cos(315) = 1.15 \times 10^7 \; \frac{N}{C}$$

$$B_y = \frac{k \cdot Q}{r^2} \cdot \sin\theta = \frac{(8.99 \times 10^9 \; \frac{N \cdot m^2}{C^2}) \cdot (9.00 \times 10^{-6} C)}{(0.0705 \; m)^2} \cdot \sin(315) = -1.15 \times 10^7 \; \frac{N}{C}$$

$$C_x = \frac{k \cdot Q}{r^2} \cdot \cos\theta = \frac{(8.99 \times 10^9 \; \frac{N \cdot m^2}{C^2}) \cdot (6.00 \times 10^{-6} C)}{(0.0709 \; m)^2} \cdot \cos(225) = -7.59 \times 10^6 \; \frac{N}{C}$$

$$C_y = \frac{k \cdot Q}{r^2} \cdot \sin\theta = \frac{(8.99 \times 10^9 \; \frac{N \cdot m^2}{C^2}) \cdot (6.00 \times 10^{-6} C)}{(0.0709 \; m)^2} \cdot \sin(225) = -7.59 \times 10^6 \; \frac{N}{C}$$

Now that we have the components, we just need to add them together to get the total electric field:

$$E_x = 7.67 \times 10^6 \; \frac{N}{C} + 1.15 \times 10^7 \; \frac{N}{C} - 7.59 \times 10^6 \; \frac{N}{C} = 1.16 \times 10^7 \; \frac{N}{C}$$

$$E_y = -7.67 \times 10^6 \; \frac{N}{C} - 1.15 \times 10^7 \; \frac{N}{C} - 7.59 \times 10^6 \; \frac{N}{C} = -2.68 \times 10^7 \; \frac{N}{C}$$

$$E = \sqrt{(1.16 \times 10^7 \ \frac{N}{C})^2 + (-2.68 \times 10^7 \ \frac{N}{C})^2} = 2.92 \times 10^7 \ \frac{N}{C}$$

$$\theta = \tan^{-1}\left(\frac{-2.68 \times 10^7 \ \frac{\cancel{N}}{\cancel{C}}}{1.16 \times 10^7 \ \frac{\cancel{N}}{\cancel{C}}} \right) = -66.6°$$

Since this vector has a positive x-component and a negative y-component, it is in the fourth quadrant of the Cartesian coordinate plane. This means to define the angle properly, we must add 360.0° to it. Thus, the electric field is <u>2.92 x 10^7 N/C directed at an angle of 293.4°</u>.

We are not quite done, however, as the problem also wants us to calculate the force experienced by a -5.00 µC charge placed at that point. That's a quick application of Equation (11.4). Now remember, in this equation, we must use the sign of the charge, as that helps determine direction:

$$\mathbf{F} = q \cdot \mathbf{E} = (-5.00 \times 10^{-6} \ \cancel{C}) \cdot (2.92 \times 10^7 \ \frac{N}{\cancel{C}}) = -146 \ N$$

Since the result is negative, it means the force is directed *opposite* the electric field. Thus, we could say that the force is <u>146 N opposite of the electric field</u>, or we could determine what opposite means. If the electric field is oriented at 239.4°, a vector pointed in the opposite direction would point at 59.4°. Thus, we could say the force is 146 N at an angle of 59.4°.

Now please don't get lost in the math here and miss what you are actually doing. In the previous section, you drew the electric field produced by one or more charged particles in a qualitative way. In this section, you actually learned to quantitatively calculate the electric field. Thus, suppose you programmed a computer to do the kind of calculations we just did above. You could give the computer the positions and charges of one or more particles, and it could do the calculation over and over again for many, many points in the vicinity of the charges. Then, it could plot the vectors produced at each point. What would that give you? That would give you an exact representation of the total electric field in the vicinity of the particles! Thus, the kinds of calculations you learned in this section of the module allow you to turn the *qualitative* pictures you drew in the previous section into *quantitative* pictures! Make sure you can do the math, then, by trying the following "on your own" problems.

ON YOUR OWN

11.5 Consider the midpoint of a dipole. The two charges which make up the dipole are +5.00 mC and -5.00 mC, and they are fixed in space 50.0 cm from each other. What is the strength of the electric field at the midpoint? What is the force experienced by a +14.0 mC charge placed there?

11.6 Three charges (-12.1 mC, -13.5 mC, and 11.0 mC) are placed at the vertices of an equilateral triangle whose sides are 35.0 cm long, as illustrated to the right. What is the strength of the electric field at the center of the triangle ?

+11.0 mC

35.0 cm   35.0 cm

35.0 cm

-12.1 mC   -13.5 mC

Insulators, Conductors, Semiconductors, and Superconductors

As you already know, we can categorize matter in terms of the way it conducts electricity. There are materials (like aluminum and copper) through which electricity flows freely. We call them **conductors**. There are also materials (such as plastic and wood) through which charge does not flow freely. We call them **insulators**. These are terms you should be familiar with from your first-year course. There is actually another term used for insulators which you probably did not learn in your first-year course. Insulators are also called **dielectrics**.

Dielectric - An insulating material

Although you learned the terms conductor and insulator in your first-year course, you probably did not learn *why* some materials are conductors and others are insulators.

In order for a substance to be a conductor, it must have charges that are free to move about. After all, the flow of electricity is the flow of charged particles. Thus, for electricity to flow, charged particles must be able to move freely. Think, for example, about a glass of pure water. As you know, water is a molecule made up of two hydrogen atoms and one oxygen atom. If you have taken chemistry, you know that these molecules are *polar*, which means there is a small negative charge on the oxygen atom and small positive charges on the hydrogen atoms. This makes water reactive to electric fields. For example, a thin stream of water flowing from a tap is attracted to a charged object. However, even though water molecules react to electric fields, pure water *cannot conduct electricity*. That's because the charges are not free to move. The small negative charge on the oxygen atom must stay on the oxygen atom, and the small positive charges on the hydrogen atoms must stay on the hydrogen atoms. Since all three of these atoms are held together by chemical bonds, the charges cannot move relative to one another, so pure water does not conduct electricity.

Even though *pure* water cannot conduct electricity, many *solutions made with water* can. For example, if I try to conduct electricity through a sample of pure water, nothing happens. However, electricity readily flows through a solution of saltwater! Why does saltwater conduct electricity? When salt dissolves in water, it actually splits up into positive and negative ions. The positive (sodium) ions are free to travel anywhere they "want" to travel in the water, and the negative (chloride) ions are free to travel anywhere they "want" to travel in the water. As a result, a solution of saltwater has electric charges (positive sodium ions and negative chloride ions) which are free to move, so saltwater is a conductor while pure water is an insulator. If you took chemistry, you probably did an experiment which demonstrated this fact.

So, saltwater conducts electricity because it contains charges which are free to move. How does a metal like copper conduct electricity? It also has charges which are free to move. A typical metal, like copper, has one or more electrons which are not tightly bound to the nucleus of the atom. As a result, at least one electron per atom is free to move around. Since a sample of copper has billions and billions of atoms of copper, there are literally billions and billions of electrons which are free to move around in a sample of copper. This "sea" of electrons can then rush towards a positive charge and away from a negative charge. Thus, when both sides of a battery are connected to a sample of copper, the electrons move towards the positive side of the battery and away from the negative side. That's the flow of electricity.

Now that you know why conductors can conduct electricity, it should be obvious why insulators do not. Insulators do not have charges which are free to move about. A substance such as plastic, for example, has no loosely-bound electrons. The electrons in plastic are all tightly-bound to the molecules which make up the plastic. As a result, they are not free to move. In fact, even if I add extra electrons to the insulator, those electrons will not be able to move freely. They will become bound to a molecule and will tend to stay with that molecule. Perform the following experiment to see what I mean.

EXPERIMENT 11.2
Conductors and Insulators

Supplies:

- The aluminum foil balls from the previous experiment. One still needs to be on its thread.
- Tape
- A balloon
- An open door inside the house

Introduction - In this experiment, you will see how electrical charge moves in a conductor and not in an insulator. Like the last experiment, this experiment will not work unless your hair is clean and dry.

Procedure:

1. Hang one of the foil balls from the door frame.
2. Blow up the balloon and tie it off.
3. Hold the balloon near the bottom where you tied it off and rub the balloon vigorously in your hair to allow it to develop a negative charge. Be sure to rub only one side of the balloon.
4. Without changing your grip on the balloon, point the side of the balloon that you were rubbing in your hair *away from* the suspended ball. Slowly bring the balloon close to the ball.

5. Note whether or not the foil ball seems attracted to the balloon. If it is attracted, note how close the ball had to get to the balloon in order for you to notice that it was attracted.
6. Pull the balloon away from the foil ball and this time (without changing your grip on the balloon) turn the side that you rubbed in your hair *towards* the foil ball.
7. Once again, bring the balloon near the foil ball.
8. This time, long before the balloon reaches the ball, you should see the ball rising to meet the balloon. However, when the ball actually touches the balloon, it should immediately swing away from the balloon.
9. Grab the foil ball (discharging it), and steady it so that it hangs straight down again.
10. Once again, rub the balloon vigorously in your hair.
11. Once again, point the side of the balloon that you rubbed in your hair towards the foil ball. However, before you start to move the balloon towards the foil ball, hold the *other* foil ball in your hand and put it about two inches *behind* the foil ball that is hanging.
12. Now bring the balloon near the hanging foil ball again. This time, the hanging foil ball should rise up to meet the balloon, bounce back off the balloon, hit the foil ball you are holding in your hand, and bounce back to the balloon again. This might actually happen several times.
13. If the hanging foil ball sticks to the balloon, just move the balloon a bit, and the ball should eventually swing away from the balloon again.
14. Clean everything up.

What happened in the experiment? Well, the first part of the experiment is designed to show you that even when you add extra charge to an insulator, that charge is not free to move. However, charge is free to move even in a neutral conductor. In the experiment, you rubbed one part of the balloon in your hair. This part of the balloon picked up some stray electrons in your hair and became negatively charged. However, since the charge was not free to move, *only that part of the balloon* was negatively charged. The rest of the balloon was still neutral. In steps 6-8, you pointed *that* part of the balloon at the foil ball and brought it close to the ball. When that happened, the electrons which were in the foil were repelled by the negative charge. Since they are free to move, they moved to the other side of the foil. This created a net *positive* charge on the foil near the balloon, so the foil ball was attracted to the balloon. This is illustrated in Figure 11.3.

FIGURE 11.3
The Charges in Your Experiment

The foil ball is neutral, and the balloon has a negatively-charged portion.

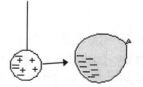

The negative charges in the foil ball move away from the balloon, giving the part of the ball nearest to the balloon a positive charge, which makes that side of the ball attracted to the balloon.

Okay, then. If the foil ball was attracted to the balloon, why didn't it stick to the balloon when it reached the balloon? Instead, once the foil ball touched the balloon, it immediately bounced away. Think about it. Those electrons on the balloon didn't want to stay confined to one part of the balloon. They *repel* each other. Thus, when the foil ball touched the balloon, the electrons rushed to the foil ball. If they could have moved farther away from each other on the balloon (the insulator), they would have. However, they couldn't. When the foil ball (the conductor) touched the charges however, they could freely flow *into* the foil ball, so they did. At that point, however, the foil ball developed a net *negative* charge, since it received extra electrons. That caused it to be repelled from the balloon (which still has some extra negative charges on it), so it bounced away from the balloon.

FIGURE 11.4
What Happened Once the Ball Touched the Balloon

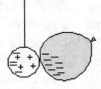

Once the foil ball touched the balloon, negative charges could travel into the foil ball.

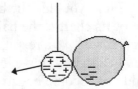

When the negative charges traveled into the foil ball, the ball became negatively-charged overall, repelling it from the balloon, which still had some negative charge left.

Why did I have you do steps 3-5 in the experiment? I wanted you to see that the charges really cannot move around on the balloon. Only the side that you rubbed in your hair had the negative charge. Thus, when you brought the *other* side of the balloon near the foil ball it did not attract the foil ball very strongly, because that side of the balloon was not negatively charged. This shows that the charges could not move while they were on the insulator.

What happened in the last part of the experiment (steps 10-13)? Well, once the foil ball touched the balloon and became negatively charged, it sped away from the balloon. This time, however, it ran into the other foil ball. The extra electrons were able to move into the other foil ball and, since you are also a conductor, through you to the ground. As a result, when the hanging foil ball hit the foil ball you were holding, it lost all of its extra charge. Thus, it once again became neutral. Through the process explained in Figure11.3, that made it attracted to the balloon again, so it moved to the balloon. However, once it touched the balloon, some of the negative charge still on the balloon went into the foil ball, making it negatively-charged again and repulsed by the balloon. Thus, it bounced away again, heading back to the foil ball in your hand. This repeated until you drained most of the negative charge from the balloon.

FIGURE 11.5
What Happened When the Hanging Ball Hit the Other Ball

This represents
your arm and
hand.

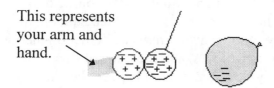

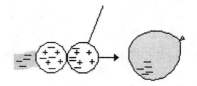

When the hanging ball hit the ball you
were holding, it was able to transfer
electrons to that ball. Those electrons
then traveled through you to the ground.

Once the electrons left the ball, it was
(overall) neutral again, but since the balloon
was nearby, the electrons bunched up on one
side of the ball so that the ball was once
again attracted back to the balloon.

In step 13, I told you that the ball might get stuck to the balloon. Why? Well, when the
balloon lost most of its charge, the ball might hit the balloon *near some of the excess charge, but
not on the excess charge.* As a result, the ball would just stick to the balloon, being attracted to
the nearby negative charges. However, since the negative charges could not move to get to the
ball, the ball could not become negatively-charged. Moving the balloon around would have
brought the nearby charges into contact with the foil ball so that the bouncing could continue.

From this experiment, then, you really can see that charges are not able to move in an
insulator, but they can move freely in a conductor. The charges on the balloon, which was an
insulator, were fixed. They could not move unless they touched the foil ball, which was a
conductor. However, they were free to travel into the conductor, and even when that conductor
hit another conductor (the foil ball in your hand), they were free to travel into that other
conductor and through another conductor (you) into the ground.

That's enough about conductors and insulators, don't you think? There are actually two
other classes of materials about which you have probably not learned. One class is called
semiconductors.

Semiconductor - A substance whose conductivity changes remarkably based on certain
                conditions

As the name implies, a semiconductor is a material that is "in between" a conductor and an
insulator. Under certain conditions, a semiconductor will not conduct electricity. If you change
the conditions properly, however, it will conduct electricity.

What do I mean by "changing the conditions?" Well, that depends on the application.
Silicon, for example, is a semiconductor. Pure silicon does not conduct electricity very well.
However, if you add just a little bit of the right kind of impurity, it will then conduct electricity
very well. The reason this happens is a bit beyond the scope of this module. However, this
property is what makes silicon so useful when it comes to making electronic devices.

There is also a class of exotic substances called **superconductors**.

Superconductor - A substance that conducts electricity with virtually no energy loss

If you think about it, this is an amazing kind of material. Remember, electricity can be conducted because charges move within a substance. What can you almost always assume exists whenever there is motion? *Friction!* No matter what, it is virtually impossible to get rid of friction. Well, when electrons move through a conductor, there is also friction. This friction reduces the kinetic energy of the electrons, and the kinetic energy that is lost is mostly turned into heat. That's why a wire gets hot when electricity runs through it - the friction associated with the motion of the electrons heats the wire. In superconductors, however, there is no significant energy lost. The electrons travel through the superconductor without experiencing any friction!

The phenomenon of superconductivity is actually relatively new in physics. It was discovered in 1911 by the Dutch physicist H. Kamerlingh-Onnes. He noticed that at temperatures of 4.2 K (-269.0 °C), mercury conducts electricity with no energy loss. It took until 1957 for physicists to develop a reasonable theory (called BCS theory) to explain superconductivity. Like semiconductors, a detailed discussion of superconductors is simply beyond the scope of this module. However, I do want to note that even though BCS theory is still the prevalent theory used to explain superconductivity, we know that it is wrong. One of the predictions of BCS theory is that the maximum temperature possible for superconductivity is about 30 K. However, we know of materials which are superconductors at temperatures higher than 100 K. Thus, even though BCS theory is the "accepted" explanation for superconductivity, we know that it is not completely correct.

ON YOUR OWN

11.7 Suppose I hook both sides of a battery up to a conductor. The free electrons immediately rush towards the positive side of the battery. Does this mean that part or all of the conductor is now positively charged, since its electrons moved into the battery? Why or why not?

11.8 Consider the following graph of electron energy versus time. There are four curves, each of which plots the behavior of electrons in different materials. Identify each curve as representing the behavior of electrons in a conductor, an insulator, a semiconductor, or a superconductor.

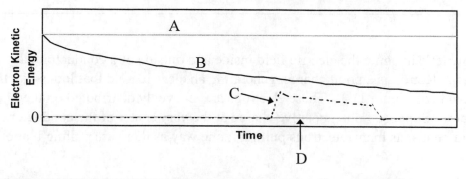

The Electric Field of a Conductor

The last thing I want to deal with in this module is the electric field produced by a charged conductor. Consider, for example, a slab of copper (a great conductor). If I were to add some extra electrons to the copper slab, what would happen to them? Think about it. The electrons repel each other, right? Thus, they want to get as far away from each other as possible. Well, they are free to move, so they move away from each other until they hit the surface of the copper slab. At that point, they cannot go any farther, because there is no more conductor. Thus, the electrons will stay evenly distributed on the *surface* of the copper, since that allows them to be as far apart from one another as possible. This is a very important point.

Excess charge in a conductor always resides entirely on the outer surface.

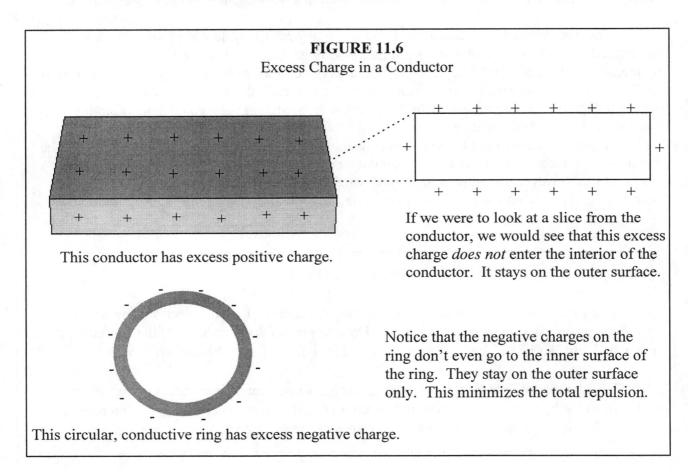

FIGURE 11.6
Excess Charge in a Conductor

This conductor has excess positive charge.

If we were to look at a slice from the conductor, we would see that this excess charge *does not* enter the interior of the conductor. It stays on the outer surface.

Notice that the negative charges on the ring don't even go to the inner surface of the ring. They stay on the outer surface only. This minimizes the total repulsion.

This circular, conductive ring has excess negative charge.

Now let's imagine the electric field inside and outside of a conductor, starting with the inside. Each electron is a point charge, generating an electric field that looks like the one on the right-hand side of Figure 11.1. These electrons are all evenly distributed on the *outer* surface of the conductor. Suppose I put a positive charge at the very center of the conductor. At that point, there would be just as many electrons pulling it one way as there are pulling it another. Since it is at the center, it would be equidistant from the charges, so all of the pulling would cancel out, leaving no net force on the positive charge. If there is no net electrostatic force on the charge, then there is no net electric field. Thus, at the very center, the electric field is zero.

Now suppose I put the positive charge a bit off-center to the right, but still inside the conductor. What would be the net force on the charge? Well, it is closer to the charges on the right side of the conductor, so they will pull it harder. However, there is *less total charge* pulling it that way, because there is less conductor to the right of the particle than there is to the left. Thus, there will be more total charge pulling it to the left, since there is more conductor there. It turns out that these effects cancel one another out. Thus, no matter *where* the positive charge is inside the conductor, there is no electric field. This is another very important point.

There is no electric field inside a conductor.

Does this discussion sound familiar? Remember in Module 8 (pp. 293-295) when we discussed gravity and extended bodies? We found that if you are inside a sphere of mass, the only gravitational force you feel is from the mass *below* you. Any mass *above* you can be ignored, because the gravitational forces from that mass cancel out. Thus, if you have a spherical shell of mass and you are inside that shell, you feel no gravitational force from the shell. In a conductor, the excess electrical charge stays as a "shell" around the outer edge of the conductor. Thus, just as there is no gravitational force inside a spherical shell of mass, there is no electrostatic force inside a conductor and thus no electric field. Perform the following experiment to see that this is the case.

EXPERIMENT 11.3
There Is No Electric Field Inside a Conductor

Supplies:

- A small radio
- A plate that is larger than the radio (The plate cannot be metal.)
- A bowl that will cover the radio (The bowl cannot be metal.)
- Aluminum foil

Introduction - This experiment will demonstrate in a very clear way that there is no electric field inside a conductor, regardless of the shape of the conductor.

Procedure:

1. Place the radio on the plate.
2. Tune the radio to a strong station so that you get nice audio with no background noise.
3. Cover the radio with the bowl.

4. Now the radio is completely surrounding by the plate and the bowl. Do you still hear the radio? It is probably muffled, but you should still hear it.
5. Pull out enough aluminum foil to completely wrap the radio with it.
6. Wrap the radio with aluminum foil, including the antenna, if there is one.
7. Do you hear the radio station now?
8. Clean everything up.

What happened in the experiment? Well, remember that radio waves are, in fact, electromagnetic (light) waves (Figure 7.9). In order for a radio to get a signal, then, it must receive electromagnetic waves. Thus, a radio uses an electromagnetic field. Since the bowl and plate were insulators, and since there are no restrictions about the electric field inside an insulator, the radio was able to receive the radio station while surrounded by the bowl and plate. However, when you wrapped it in aluminum foil, the radio was *inside a conductor*. Since there can be no electric field inside a conductor, the radio could no longer receive the radio station!

Now please understand that the aluminum foil was not "blocking" the radio signal. After all, the aluminum foil was very thin compared to the bowl and plate. If it were just a matter of "blocking" the signal, the bowl and plate would have done a *much better* job. However, since the bowl and plate were insulators, an electric field could exist inside them and the radio continued to receive the radio station. However, an incredibly thin conductor caused the radio to stop receiving, because electric fields cannot exist inside a conductor.

Okay, then. Let's think about what happens outside of the conductor. Since there is no electric field inside the conductor, any electric field line that enters the conductor simply does not exist. In addition, any electric field line that is pointed even a little bit towards another electron will be canceled out. After all, if electron "A" has an electric field line that is pointed even a bit towards electron "B," then electron "B" will have an electric field line going towards "A." These two electric field lines will cancel. What's left then? Well, each electron produces an electric field line that is directed perpendicular to the surface of the conductor. Those electric field lines are not pointed towards any of the other electrons - they are all just pointed directly away from the conductor and thus directly away from the other electrons. *Those are the only electric field lines that exist*. This is another important point.

The electric field outside a conductor is oriented perpendicular to the surface.

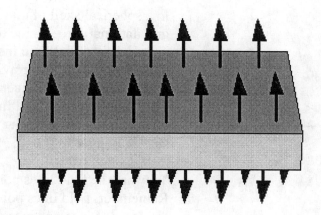

FIGURE 11.7
The Electric Field Outside of a Conductor With Excess Positive Charge

Illus. by Megan Whitaker

Now instead of considering a slab of conductor, consider a spherical conductor. If the electric field lines are all perpendicular to the sphere, what does the electric field look like? It looks like Figure 11.1! Thus, in a spherical conductor, there is no electric field *inside* the conductor, but the electric field outside the conductor acts as if the entire charge on the conductor exists at the very center of the conductor.

Outside of the conductor, a spherical conductor emits an electric field that acts as if all of its excess charge is concentrated at the center of the sphere.

This is like gravity, isn't it? In terms of the gravitational force, you can take any extended body and treat it as if it is a point particle with all of its mass concentrated at the center of mass as long as you are not inside the body. With spherical conductors, you can take all of the excess charge and act as if it is concentrated at the center of the sphere, as long as you are outside of the sphere.

I want to discuss the similarity between the gravitational force and the electrostatic force in a bit more detail. You can see how similar they are by just examining the force equations, Equation (8.3) and Equation (11.1). They both depend on the charge (or mass) of both bodies involved, and they both depend on the square of the distance between the bodies. Thus, it is not surprising that the gravitational force inside and outside of an extended body behaves similar to the electrostatic force inside and outside of a conductor.

Since there is so much similarity between the two forces, some physicists like to discuss **"gravitational fields"** like they discuss "electric fields." Thus, just as a conductor has no electric field inside and a perpendicular field outside, we can visualize that a spherical shell of mass has no gravitational field inside and a perpendicular gravitational field outside.

FIGURE 11.8
The Gravitational Field of a Ring of Mass

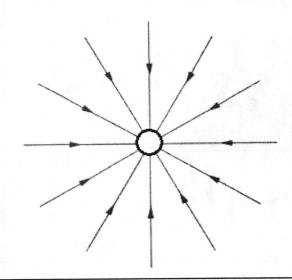

In a spherical shell of mass, there is no gravitational force inside the shell. Thus, there is no gravitational field inside the shell. Outside the shell, the gravitational force acts as if all of the mass is concentrated at its center. Thus, gravitational field lines point into the mass. Notice how similar this is to the right side of Figure 11.1.

Why are the field lines pointing *into* the mass? Remember, field lines point in the direction of the force. Since one mass always attracts another, the field lines point into the mass.

Of course, since the electrostatic and gravitational forces are so similar, you might expect that they are produced similarly. We know from Maxwell's equations that the electrostatic force is mediated by the exchange of photons. Thus, there are some who think that the gravitational force (since it is so similar in so many ways to the electrostatic force) is also governed by the exchange of particles called gravitons. However, as I mentioned before, no one has detected these particles, and this seems to contradict general relativity, which says that gravity is not really a force at all - it is just a consequence of how mass bends spacetime. This leads to a bit of a mystery in physics. If general relativity is correct (and there is a lot of evidence backing it up), then *why* are the gravitational force and electrostatic force so similar? Is it really just coincidence, or is there some deeper connection that we are missing? That's one of the many unanswered questions in physics.

ON YOUR OWN

11.9 Draw the electric field inside and outside of the conductor on the right, which has been given a positive charge. Use a total of 8 lines in your drawing.

11.10 Suppose the conductor in problem 11.9 was 20.0 cm from the bottom to the top. If it were charged to -154 mC, what would be magnitude and direction of the electric field at a point due north from the conductor and 15.0 cm away from its *surface*? Treat this conductor as if it were a sphere.

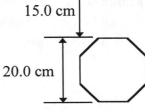

15.0 cm

20.0 cm

ANSWERS TO THE ON YOUR OWN QUESTIONS

11.1 a. Let's concentrate on the forces affecting one of the gray spheres. The other gray sphere will repel it, and the two white spheres will attract it. As the problem says, it must be zero:

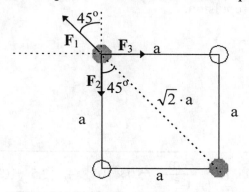

In order to make the sum of these three vectors equal to zero, the vector pulling straight down (F_2) must counteract the *vertical component* of the repulsive force from the gray sphere (F_1).

The geometry is not that bad. The distance between the gray sphere and the white ones is a. Since the length of the diagonal is $\sqrt{2} \cdot a$, the distance from the gray sphere to the other gray sphere is $\sqrt{2} \cdot a$. The diagonal forms a 45-45-90 triangle, so the angle between F_1 and the vertical is $45°$. Defined properly for vector addition, however, it is $135°$. Once again, since F_2 must counteract the vertical component of F_1:

$$F_{1y} + F_2 = 0$$

$$\frac{k \cdot (1.0 \text{ mC}) \cdot (1.0 \text{ mC})}{(\sqrt{2} \cdot a)^2} \cdot \sin(135) - \frac{k \cdot (1.0 \text{ mC}) \cdot (q_{white})}{(a)^2} = 0$$

$$q_{white} = \frac{k \cdot (1.0 \text{ mC}) \cdot (1.0 \text{ mC}) \cdot a^2}{k \cdot (1.0 \text{ mC}) \cdot 2 \cdot a^2} \cdot \sin(135) = 0.35 \text{ mC}$$

The charge on the bottom white sphere, then, is 0.35 mC. Notice what I did here. Remember, Equation (11.1) does not deal with direction. Thus, we leave the charge out and determine the direction ourselves. Using the common convention that up is positive, F_{1y} would be positive and F_2 would be negative. That's where the negative sign comes from in the equation.

You can do the same thing for the other white sphere, noting that it must cancel out the horizontal component of F_1. However, since everything is symmetric, the result will be the same. Thus, the white spheres each have a 0.35 mC charge.

b. This one is easy. At the very center of the square, the two positive charges would repel it equally, and the two negative charges would attract it equally. Thus, the net force would be zero.

11.2 In this situation, the top ping pong ball will come to rest when the force due to gravity (m·g) is balanced by the electrical repulsion:

$$F_{Coulomb} + F_{gravity} = 0$$

$$\frac{k \cdot q_1 \cdot q_2}{r^2} = m \cdot g$$

$$r = \sqrt{\frac{k \cdot q_1 \cdot q_2}{m \cdot g}} = \sqrt{\frac{(8.99 \times 10^9 \ \frac{N \cdot m^2}{C^2}) \cdot (5.0 \times 10^{-7} \ C) \cdot (2.5 \times 10^{-7} \ C)}{(0.0022 \ kg) \cdot (9.81 \ \frac{m}{sec^2})}} = 0.23 \ m$$

Since "r" is defined as the distance between the centers of the charges, then r = h. Thus, the height is 23 cm.

11.3 Since the positive particle has twice as much charge, it must have twice as many field lines going out of it as the negative charge has going into it. Thus, you get a drawing that looks like the one on the right.

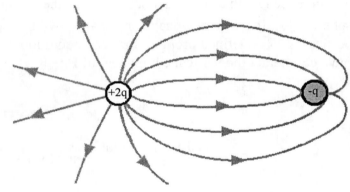

11.4 Since the charges are all the same, the negative charge must have the same number of lines entering it as the positive charges have leaving them. Since there are two positive charges, however, that means only half of the lines leaving each positive charge can end up entering the negative charge.

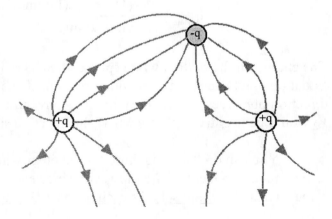

11.5 This problem is not so hard, since the setup makes it one-dimensional:

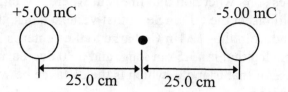

At the midpoint between the charges, the positive charge creates an electric field pointed to the right (repelling another positive charge), and the negative charge produces an electric field also pointed to the right (attracting a positive charge). Thus, the two electric fields just add together:

$$\mathbf{E}_{tot} = \mathbf{E}_{5.00\,mC} + \mathbf{E}_{-5.00\,mC}$$

$$E_{tot} = \frac{(8.99 \times 10^9 \frac{N \cdot m^2}{C^2}) \cdot (0.00500\ C)}{(0.25\ m)^2} + \frac{(8.99 \times 10^9 \frac{N \cdot m^2}{C^2}) \cdot (0.00500\ C)}{(0.25\ m)^2} = 1.44 \times 10^9\ \frac{N}{C}$$

The electric field, then, is <u>1.44 x 10⁹ N/C pointed to the right</u>.

The problem also wants to know the force felt by a 14.0 mC charge placed there. That's an easy application of Equation (11.2):

$$\mathbf{F} = q \cdot \mathbf{E} = (0.0140\ C) \cdot (1.44 \times 10^9\ \frac{N}{C}) = 2.02 \times 10^7\ N$$

Remember, in this equation, direction is taken into account by sign. Thus, the force felt is <u>2.02 x 10⁷ N to the right</u>.

11.6 This is more difficult than the previous problem only because we must now add the electric fields in two dimensions. Therefore, we first have to do some geometry:

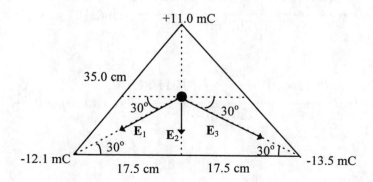

Let's work on distances first. Because the triangle is equilateral, the height of the triangle (the vertical dashed line) bisects the base. Thus, the vertical dashed splits the base into two 17.5 cm segments. The center lies somewhere on that line, but where? Well, if I draw a line from any vertex to the center, it should bisect the 60° angle of that vertex. Thus, the angle from the base of the triangle to the dashed line from the -12.1 mC charge to the center is 30°. Notice that we now have a right triangle with one leg that is 17.5 cm long, and a 30 degree angle adjacent to it. We can figure out the hypotenuse of that triangle, which is the distance between the center of the triangle and the -12.1 mC charge:

$$\cos\theta = \frac{adj}{hyp}$$

$$hyp = \frac{adj}{\cos\theta} = \frac{17.5 \text{ cm}}{\cos(30)} = 20.2 \text{ cm}$$

Since this is an equilateral triangle, all charges must be equidistant from the center. Thus, all distances are 20.2 cm.

What about angles? E_2 is the easiest to figure out. It is pointed straight down, which is an angle of 270°. For E_1 and E_3, you have to remember that the interior angles of an equilateral triangle are all 60°. A line drawn from the center of the triangle to the vertex (the diagonal dashed lines) bisect this angle, so the diagonal dashed lines form 30° angles with the base. When two parallel lines are cut by a transversal, alternating interior angles are congruent. Thus, E_1 and E_3 each make a 30° angle below the horizontal. Converting to the proper definition of angles for vector addition, E_1 has an angle of 210° while E_3 has an angle of 330°. Please note that *all of these angles are exact*, as they all come from geometry definitions. There is no measurement involved. Thus, they do not contribute to the significant figures determination.

Now we are finally ready to do the vector addition.

$$E_{1x} = \frac{k \cdot Q}{r^2} \cdot \cos\theta = \frac{(8.99 \times 10^9 \ \frac{N \cdot m^2}{C^2}) \cdot (0.0121 \ C)}{(0.202 \text{ m})^2} \cdot \cos(210) = -2.31 \times 10^9 \ \frac{N}{C}$$

$$E_{1y} = \frac{k \cdot Q}{r^2} \cdot \sin\theta = \frac{(8.99 \times 10^9 \ \frac{N \cdot m^2}{C^2}) \cdot (0.0121 \ C)}{(0.202 \text{ m})^2} \cdot \sin(210) = -1.33 \times 10^9 \ \frac{N}{C}$$

$$E_{2x} = \frac{k \cdot Q}{r^2} \cdot \cos\theta = \frac{(8.99 \times 10^9 \ \frac{N \cdot m^2}{C^2}) \cdot (0.0110 \ C)}{(0.202 \text{ m})^2} \cdot \cos(270) = 0 \ \frac{N}{C}$$

$$E_{2y} = \frac{k \cdot Q}{r^2} \cdot \sin\theta = \frac{(8.99 \times 10^9 \ \frac{N \cdot m^2}{C^2}) \cdot (0.0110 \ C)}{(0.202 \ m)^2} \cdot \sin(270) = -2.42 \times 10^9 \ \frac{N}{C}$$

$$E_{3x} = \frac{k \cdot Q}{r^2} \cdot \cos\theta = \frac{(8.99 \times 10^9 \ \frac{N \cdot m^2}{C^2}) \cdot (0.0135 \ C)}{(0.202 \ m)^2} \cdot \cos(330) = 2.58 \times 10^9 \ \frac{N}{C}$$

$$E_{3y} = \frac{k \cdot Q}{r^2} \cdot \sin\theta = \frac{(8.99 \times 10^9 \ \frac{N \cdot m^2}{C^2}) \cdot (0.0135 \ C)}{(0.202 \ m)^2} \cdot \sin(330) = -1.49 \times 10^9 \ \frac{N}{C}$$

Now we just add the components together:

$$E_x = -2.31 \times 10^9 \ \frac{N}{C} + 2.58 \times 10^9 \ \frac{N}{C} = 2.7 \times 10^8 \ \frac{N}{C}$$

$$E_y = -1.33 \times 10^9 \ \frac{N}{C} - 2.42 \times 10^9 \ \frac{N}{C} - 1.49 \times 10^9 \ \frac{N}{C} = -5.24 \times 10^9 \ \frac{N}{C}$$

$$E = \sqrt{(2.7 \times 10^8 \ \frac{N}{C})^2 + (-5.24 \times 10^9 \ \frac{N}{C})^2} = 5.25 \times 10^9 \ \frac{N}{C}$$

$$\theta = \tan^{-1}\left(\frac{-5.24 \times 10^9 \ \frac{N}{C}}{2.7 \times 10^8 \ \frac{N}{C}} \right) = -87°$$

Since the vector has a positive x component and a negative y component, it is in the fourth Cartesian quadrant. That means we must add 360.0° to the answer. So the electric field is 5.25 x 10^9 N/C directed at 273°.

11.7 No. The conductor is still neutral. Even though electrons left the conductor to travel into the positive side of the battery, electrons also travel *into* the conductor from the positive side of the battery. That's why both sides of a battery have to be connected in order for electricity to flow. Thus, electrons are leaving and entering the conductor at the same rate, keeping the conductor neutral overall.

11.8 In graph A, the electrons lose no kinetic energy as they travel. That means there is no friction, which means A represents a superconductor. In graph B, the electrons continually lose energy. Thus, B represents a conductor, as electrons lose energy while traveling through a conductor. In graph D, the electrons have *zero* kinetic energy the entire time. That means they are not moving. Thus, D represents an insulator. Finally, in graph C, the electrons have zero energy for a while and then suddenly have kinetic energy and slowly start losing it. Then, they have zero again. This means the electrons *weren't moving, then started moving*. Thus, C represents a semiconductor.

11.9 Remember, the electric field lines must be perpendicular to the surface.

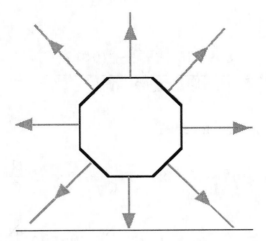

11.10 In the vicinity of the point, the electric field lines point straight down. Remember, electric field lines point into negative charges. The direction, then, is down. The magnitude is determined by Equation (11.3), but remember that the distance is the distance between the *centers*, which is 15.0 cm + 10.0 cm = 25.0 cm.

$$E = \frac{(8.99 \times 10^9 \ \frac{N \cdot m^2}{C^2}) \cdot (0.154 \ C)}{(0.25 \ m)^2} = 2.22 \times 10^{10} \ \frac{N}{C}$$

The electric field, then, is 2.22 x 10^{10} N/C pointing straight down.

Solution to Experiment 11.1

When the ping pong balls repel one another, they end up rising like this:

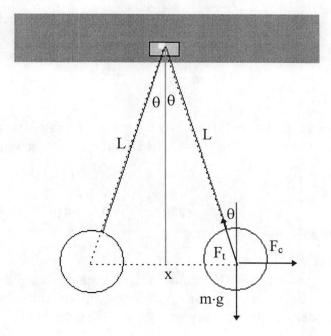

In the figure, "x" represents the distance between the centers of the ping pong balls (measured in step #6), and "L" represents the distance from the center of the ping pong ball to the point of attachment (measured in step #7). The two legs labeled "L" and the leg labeled "x" form an isosceles triangle, so the height (drawn as a gray line) bisects the base of the triangle and forms a right angle with it.

Since the triangle formed by ½·x, L, and the height of the isosceles triangle is a right triangle, we know that

$$\sin\theta = \frac{\frac{1}{2}\cdot x}{L}$$

Since we measured both x and L, we can use the above equation to calculate θ.

Now we can look at the forces at play on a ball. Gravity (m·g) pulls down on the ball, the Coulomb repulsion (F_c) pushes the ball away from the other ball, and the tension in the string (F_t) pulls at an angle. We need to get all of the forces in the same dimensions, so we can break F_t into its vertical and horizontal components. The vertical component (F_t·cosθ) fights against gravity, and the horizontal component (F_t·sinθ) fights the Coulomb repulsion. Note that in this case the vertical component uses the cosine of the angle and the horizontal component uses the sine. This is because of where θ is. Since the vertical component of F_t is adjacent to the angle, we use the cosine to calculate it.

Since the ball is not moving, the vertical and horizontal forces must cancel. Let's start with the vertical forces:

$$F_t \cdot \cos\theta - m \cdot g = 0$$

$$F_t = \frac{m \cdot g}{\cos\theta}$$

We know θ and g, we can calculate m. Thus, we can get F_t. To calculate m, we must use the length (l) and width (w) we measured in step #2. Remember, units are important here. Convert your units to *meters*!

$$\text{mass of one ball} = \frac{\rho \cdot V}{2} = \frac{(2700\, \frac{kg}{m^3}) \cdot (1.65 \times 10^{-5}\, m) \cdot (l) \cdot (w)}{2}$$

Note that this calculation is for regular Reynolds Wrap®, because I used that thickness. If you used heavy-duty foil, use the larger thickness given in the experiment. Since you measured l and w, you can determine mass. Then, you can plug that into the equation for F_t and thus calculate F_t.

Now let's move to the horizontal dimension:

$$F_c - F_t \cdot \sin\theta = 0$$

$$F_c = F_t \cdot \sin\theta$$

We know F_t and θ, so we can calculate F_c. With that, we can use Equation (11.1) to determine q, assuming that each ball had equal charge:

$$F_c = \frac{k \cdot q \cdot q}{r^2}$$

$$q = \sqrt{\frac{F_c \cdot x^2}{k}}$$

Notice two things. First, I put "x" in for "r." That's because "r" is the distance between the centers, which we call "x" in the diagram above. Second, if you work out the units on the right-hand side of the equation, you will be left with C, which is the right unit for charge. Your answer will probably be on the order of billionths of a Coulomb.

REVIEW QUESTIONS FOR MODULE #11

1. The electrostatic force between two charged objects is measured. If the distance between the charges is then quadrupled and the charge on each object is doubled, what is the new electrostatic force compared to the old one?

2. A negatively-charged particle is fixed so that it cannot move. A positively-charged particle is placed in the vicinity and then released. Describe how both the velocity and the acceleration of the positively-charged particle changes with time.

3. A negatively-charged particle is fixed so that it cannot move. Another negatively-charged particle is placed in the vicinity and then released. Describe how both the velocity and the acceleration of the freely-moving charged particle changes with time.

4. A particle charged to -q is placed in an electric field. As a result, it is acted on by a force, **F**. If that particle is removed and a different particle, charged to +3q, is put in its place, give the force that will act on that particle, in terms of **F**.

5. Draw the electric field that results in the following situation:

6. In problem #5, is it possible for the electric field to be zero anywhere in the vicinity of the charges? If so, where is it in relation to the two particles? You do not have to give a number, just a general idea.

Questions 7 - 9 refer to the following electric field diagram:

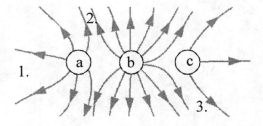

7. What is the sign of the charge for each particle?

8. If the magnitude of the charge on particle "a" is Q, what is the magnitude of the charge on each of the other two particles?

9. Order the regions 1, 2, and 3 in terms of *increasing* electric field.

10. Two masses, each 1.0 kg, are placed 1.0 m apart, and the magnitude of their mutual gravitational force is then measured as F_g. Two charged particles, each with a charge of +1 C, are also placed 1.0 m apart. Their mutual electrostatic force is measured as F_c. Is F_g smaller than, larger than, or equal to F_c?

PRACTICE PROBLEMS FOR MODULE #11

1. A negatively-charged particle of mass 34.5 grams is placed above a large, conductive sheet that has been negatively charged. The electric field at the point over which the particle has been placed is 3.40×10^5 N/C. If the particle hangs at that point without rising or falling, what is the charge on the particle?

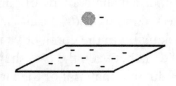

2. Draw the electric field lines that result from the charged conductive sheet.

3. Three charges are shown below. The charge labeled "-q" is a distance "x" away from the charge "-2q," which is a distance "y" from the charge "-3q." The charges all lie on a straight line. If the charge labeled "-2q" experiences no force acting on it, what is the value of x/y?

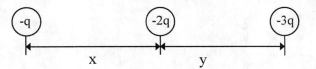

NOTE: x and y are not drawn to scale.

4. In the diagram given above, suppose q = 3.0 μC and x = y = 50.0 cm. What is the magnitude and direction of the force experienced by the charge labeled "-q?"

5. Referring once again to problem #3, suppose the charge labeled "-2q" was removed and nothing was put in its place. Also, suppose q = 3.0 μC again. If the distance between the charged labeled "-q" and "-3q" is 100.0 cm, what is the electric field at the midpoint between the charges?

6. Three charges, each -4.50 μC, are placed on the vertices of a right triangle whose legs are each 15.0 cm long. What is the magnitude and direction of the electric field at a point that is 4.00 cm from each leg?

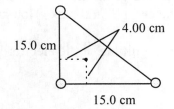

7. If a -1.50 μC charge were placed at the point shown in problem #6, what electrostatic force would it experience?

Questions 8-10 refer to the following situation:

Two spherical shells made of conductive material are concentric. The first shell is charged to +q and the second to +2q. Point "a" is inside the first shell, a distance of "x" from the center. Point "b" is actually in the conductive material of the first shell, a distance of "2x" from the center. Point "c" is between the two shells, a distance of "3x" from the center. Point "d" is actually in the conductive material of the larger shell, a distance of "4x" from the center. Finally, point "e" is outside both shells, a distance "5x" from the center.

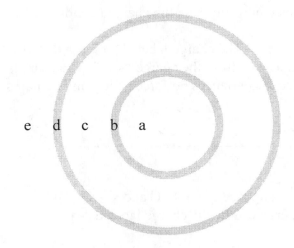

8. a. What is the charge on the interior surface of the smaller shell?
   b. What is the charge on the exterior surface of the smaller shell?

9. a. What is the charge on the interior surface of the larger shell?
   b. What is the charge on the exterior surface of the larger shell?

10. What is the magnitude of the electric field (in terms of k, q, and x) at each point (a-e)?

Module #12: Electrical Potential Energy and Electric Potential

Introduction

Think about a rock sitting on top of a cliff. We know that the rock has potential energy, because if it were to fall off the cliff, it would begin accelerating downward, gaining kinetic energy. That kinetic energy comes from the work that the gravitational force does as the rock falls. The gravitational force is pulling the rock down, and the rock gets displaced in that direction. The gravitational force times the distance that the rock falls down is equal to the work done, and that work adds directly to the kinetic energy, making the rock fall faster. The gravitational potential energy that the rock has before it fell, then, is a result of the fact that gravity will work on the rock (increasing its kinetic energy) if it were to fall off of the cliff.

Now imagine a charged particle that is being held in place in an electric field. As soon as that particle is released, it will begin to accelerate. If it is positively charged, it will accelerate in the direction of the electric field. If it is negatively charged, it will accelerate in the opposite direction of the electric field. Either way, it *will* accelerate. That means it will gain kinetic energy. Why? Because the electric field *will work* on the particle. That work adds directly to the kinetic energy. Well, if the electric field can work on the particle, the charged particle must have *potential energy* while it is in the electric field. In this module, we will discuss that potential energy as well as the concept of **electrical potential**. As you should have learned in your first-year physics course, electrical potential is *not* the same as the potential energy of a charged particle in an electric field!

Electrical Potential Energy

In your first-year course, you probably learned about electrical potential energy, but you probably learned it in terms of the potential energy associated with a point charge. That is a valuable subject to learn, and I will review it in the next section of this module, but first, I want to discuss the electrical potential energy associated with *a uniform* electric field, not just the electric field generated by a point charge. Suppose, for example, I put a charged particle in a uniform electric field as illustrated below.

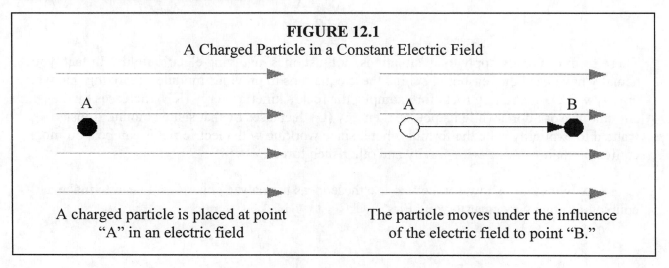

FIGURE 12.1
A Charged Particle in a Constant Electric Field

A charged particle is placed at point "A" in an electric field

The particle moves under the influence of the electric field to point "B."

Now why did the particle move? It moved because the electric field *worked* on it. The electric field exerted a force, which Equation (11.4) says is equal to q·**E**. That force pushed the particle through the field. Note that based on the drawing and Equation (11.4), you know that the particle in the picture is a positive particle. The particle moved in the same direction as the electric field. Since the electrostatic force generated by the field is the only force working on the particle, that means the force is pushing in the same direction as the electric field. Thus, the charge must be positive so that Equation (11.4) gives us a force that is directed the same as the electric field.

That force obviously was exerted over a distance, so work was done. Equation (1.8) tells us that work is the dot product of the force vector (q·**E**) and the displacement vector (**x**). Thus, in this case:

$$W = (q·\mathbf{E})\bullet\mathbf{x} \tag{12.1}$$

where **x** is the displacement vector from point "A" to point "B." Well, we know that the dot product between two vectors is the same as the magnitude of the vectors times the cosine of the angle between them (see Module #1). That means:

$$W = q·E·x·\cos\theta \tag{12.2}$$

where θ is the angle between the electric field and the displacement of the charged particle. In Figure 12.1, the displacement is parallel to the electric field, so $\theta = 0$. Thus, in this case, if I multiply the charge of the particle times the strength of the electric field times the distance from point "A" to point "B," I get the work done on the charged particle by the electric field. Please note that in order for this equation to work properly, you must include the sign of the charge. If the particle is negatively-charged, the negative sign must be included.

Now what does work do to the particle? It changes the kinetic and potential energies of the particle, doesn't it? In Figure 12.1, the work *increases* the kinetic energy of the particle, making it move faster and faster. Well, if kinetic energy *increases*, what happens to potential energy? It *decreases*. Thus, any work done alters the kinetic and potential energies according to the following formulas:

$$\Delta U = -W \tag{12.3}$$
$$\Delta KE = W \tag{12.4}$$

These formulas really apply to all situations, not just ones involving electric fields. In fact, you actually have used the reasoning behind these equations in previous modules, realizing that when gravity works on a falling rock, for example, the rock's kinetic energy (KE) increases by the amount of work done while its potential energy (U) decreases by that same amount. I just wanted to explicitly state the formulas here, since working with electric fields can be a bit more confusing than working with gravity and other such forces.

Now before I show you how to use these ideas to analyze situations, I need to make a couple of things very clear to you. First:

Equations (12.1) and (12.2) are valid *only* for constant electric fields.

If the electric field varies as the charge moves, we cannot use these equations. That will not happen in this section of the module, but it will happen in the next section. However, note that Equations (12.3) and (12.4) are valid regardless of the type of electric field involved. In fact, they are valid for all situations, not just ones related to electric fields.

The other thing of which I want to make you aware is that the electrostatic force is a **conservative force**.

Conservative force - A force in which the total work done is independent of the path taken

Nonconservative force - A force in which the work done is dependent of the path taken

When you deal with conservative forces, the total amount of work done is not dependent on the path taken. It only depends on where you started and where you finished. You can do all of the zigzagging you want in between, but as long as you start at point "A" and end at point "B," the work done is exactly the same as if you moved directly from point "A" to point "B" in a straight line. Nonconservative forces (often called **dissipative forces**) are not like that. The amount of work done depends on path. If you take one path from point "A" to point "B," the work done by a nonconservative force will be different than if you take another path from point "A" to point "B."

As I just said, the electrostatic force is a conservative force. So is the gravitational force. If you drop a rock from a certain height and let it fall to the ground, gravity does a certain amount of work on the rock. If you take another rock of the same mass and throw it *up* from that same height, by the time it reaches the ground, gravity will have done the same amount of work as it did on the first rock. How in the world is that possible? Doesn't gravity exert its force on the second rock much longer than on the first rock? Yes, of course. Then how can work be the same in both cases? Well, when the rock is thrown upwards, the force of gravity is *opposite* the displacement. Since $W = \mathbf{F} \bullet \mathbf{x}$, that means work will be *negative*. The work of gravity will continue to be negative as long as the rock travels upwards. Once the rock stops moving upwards and starts to fall, the force of gravity and the displacement will be parallel, so work will be *positive*. Once the rock gets back to the height from which you threw it, gravity will have done just as much positive work as it did negative work, so the net amount of work for that entire trip will be zero. Thus, the *total* work that gravity will end up doing will be the same as if you had simply dropped the rock from that height. Thus, gravity is a conservative force. The electrostatic force is conservative as well.

Can you think of a nonconservative force? The first one that comes to my mind is friction. If I slide a box across a floor in a straight line, friction will not work as much as when I "zigzag" across the floor. Thus, while the gravitational force and the electrostatic force are conservative forces, the frictional force is nonconservative. That's why nonconservative forces are often called "dissipative" forces. Typically, a nonconservative force is something like friction, which takes (dissipates) energy out of the system.

What good does it do us to know that the electrostatic force is conservative? Well, consider the example problem below.

EXAMPLE 12.1

A charged particle (q = -15.0 mC, m = 1.0 kg) enters a constant electric field pointed due west with a magnitude of 25.0 N/C. The particle enters the field with a speed of 2.5 m/sec. After a few seconds, it is 5.0 meters at an angle of 145 degrees from its initial position. What is its speed?

This sounds like a really hard problem, but all we have to do is think about the energy involved. Here is the situation:

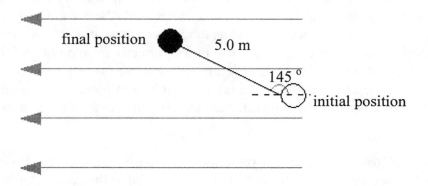

To figure out the new speed, I need to find out the new kinetic energy. I can do that by calculating the work done. Here is where the fact that the electrostatic force is a conservative force comes in *real* handy.

Since the electrostatic force is conservative, I can choose a *different path* than the one that the particle actually took. All the particle has to do is end up at the right place. The path doesn't matter. Thus, I will choose the path given in the dashed line below:

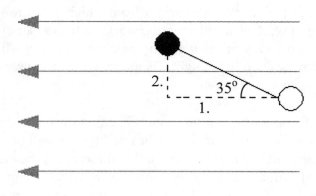

What's nice about this path is that in the second part of the path (labeled "2" in the drawing), *no work is done*. That's because the displacement during that part of the journey is perpendicular to the electric field. Thus, the dot product (q·**E**)•**x** is zero! Thus, work is only done during the first part of the journey (labeled "1" in the drawing). I can calculate that work rather easily. The path I chose forms a right triangle with the displacement, and the angle adjacent to the leg labeled "1" is 35°, since its supplement was given as 145°. Thus, the length of that leg is:

$$\text{adj} = (\text{hyp})\cdot\cos\theta = (5.0 \text{ m})\cdot\cos(35) = 4.1 \text{ m}$$

The angle between *that leg* of the journey and the electric field is zero, as they are parallel and pointing in the same direction. Thus, the work is:

$$W = q \cdot E \cdot x \cdot \cos\theta = (-0.0150 \; \cancel{C})\cdot(25.0 \; \frac{N}{\cancel{C}})\cdot(4.1 \text{ m})\cdot\cos(0) = -1.5 \text{ J}$$

Notice that since Coulombs cancels, we are left with the unit N·m, which is a Joule. That's good, since Joule is a unit for work. Notice also that the work is negative. That should make sense. The particle is negative, so the force it experiences is *opposite* the direction of the electric field. Thus, the electric field is slowing this particle down. That means it is removing kinetic energy. We now know, then, that $\Delta KE = -1.5$ J. Well, ΔKE can be expressed as:

$$\Delta KE = \frac{1}{2}\cdot m \cdot v_f{}^2 - \frac{1}{2}\cdot m \cdot v_i{}^2$$

We were given the initial speed (v_i) and the mass. We also know ΔKE.

$$-1.5 \text{ J} = \frac{1}{2}\cdot(1.0 \text{ kg})\cdot v_f{}^2 - \frac{1}{2}\cdot(1.0 \text{ kg})\cdot(2.5 \; \frac{m}{\sec})^2$$

$$v_f = 1.8 \; \frac{m}{\sec}$$

The final speed, then, is 1.8 m/sec, which is slower than the initial speed. This makes sense, since the electric field will push the particle in a direction that is opposed to its initial velocity.

Before I leave this problem, I want to make one point. We could have solved this problem without redefining the path. As long as we had recognized that the proper angle between the electric field and the displacement is 35° (because the electric field is pointing to the left), we could have calculated the work straight from Equation (12.2), using $\theta = 35°$. However, I solved it this way to demonstrate to you that we can choose whatever path we want to choose when it comes to solving these problems. I wanted to redefine the path so that you would be comfortable doing so. You will see why in the "on your own" problems that follow.

ON YOUR OWN

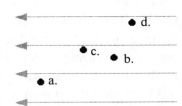

12.1 Four particles, each of which have the same amount of negative charge, are in an electric field, as shown to the right. Which has the highest electrical potential energy?

12.2 A physicist takes a particle (q = 120.0 mC) and moves it in an electric field (magnitude = 15.0 N/C) as shown in the diagram below. How much work did the physicist do in the process?

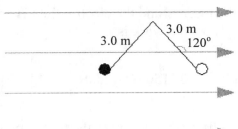

Electric Potential

In the previous section, we dealt with electrical potential energy. In determining the electrical potential energy, we needed to know the electric field, the position in the electric field, and the charge of the particle that is in the electric field. That's nice, but it is not ideal. We would actually like to have something that tells us about the properties of *just the field itself*. We do this by defining the **electric potential**. We say that the *potential energy* of a charged particle in an electric field is equal to that particle's charge times the electric potential.

$$U = q \cdot V \qquad\qquad (12.5)$$

Notice what this accomplishes. The charge of the individual particle is separated out, and the electric potential, V, deals only with the properties of the field. It is independent of the charge of whatever particle might be placed in the field.

Before we go on, let's think about the units involved here. Potential energy has energy units. The standard energy unit is the Joule. Charge has a standard unit of Coulombs. Thus, in order for Equation (12.5) to work out to units of Joules, the electric potential, V, must have units of Joules/Coulomb. This unit is renamed the **Volt**. Hopefully, this gives you an idea of what electric potential is. When I get a battery, it is rated in terms of Volts. That is a measure of how much the electric field created by the battery can change the potential energy of a charge. The higher the voltage, the more the battery can change a charged particle's potential energy. However, the voltage does not depend on the charged particle. It depends only on the battery. That's the purpose of the electric potential. It gives you an idea of how much "push" or "pull" the electric field can provide a charged particle.

Now it turns out that the electric potential of the field generated by a single charged particle is easy to determine. You probably learned it in your first-year course:

$$V = \frac{k \cdot Q}{r} \qquad (12.6)$$

Notice how the units work out in this equation. When you take the units for k, $\frac{N \cdot m^2}{C^2}$, and divide by meters and multiply by Coulombs, you get $\frac{N \cdot m}{C}$. Since a N·m is a Joule, that's J/C, which is a Volt. Please note that you need to put the sign of "Q" in this equation.

Although electric potential is a useful quantity to know, the **potential difference** is even more useful. Consider a particle in an electric field. As it sits at a given point, it experiences an electric potential. If it moves, the potential will most likely change. Thus, at the end of the motion, the particle experiences a different potential. The difference between the final and initial potentials that the particle experiences, ΔV, is directly related to the change in potential energy it experiences, according to the following equation:

$$\Delta U = q \cdot \Delta V \qquad (12.7)$$

Thus, if I know the change in the electric potential, I can calculate the change in the particle's potential energy.

Let's go back to discussing batteries for a moment. When you pick up a battery, the voltage rating actually tells you a *potential difference*. For example, consider a 1.5 Volt battery. The "1.5 Volts" means that if a charged particle travels from one terminal of the battery to the other, its potential changes by 1.5 V. Thus, the potential difference between one side of the battery and the other is 1.5V. Now please understand that this is independent of *how* the ends of the battery are hooked up. You might connect one end of the battery to the other with a short wire, or you might put the battery in an enormous electrical circuit that contains miles and miles of wire. Regardless, once a charged particle makes the trip from one end of the battery to the other, it will experience a change in potential of 1.5 Volts.

EXAMPLE 12.2

A +6.5 C charged particle (m = 42.3 kg) is placed 1.4 m from a +3.4 C stationary charge. If it starts from rest, how fast will the particle be traveling when it is 2.5 m away from the stationary charge?

To solve a problem like this, we just have to think about the energy involved. As the particle moves, it experiences a change in the electric potential. The potential is originally:

$$V = \frac{k \cdot Q}{r}$$

$$V_{initial} = \frac{(8.99 \times 10^9 \, \frac{N \cdot m^2}{C^2}) \cdot (3.4 \, C)}{1.4 \, m} = 2.2 \times 10^{10} \text{ Volts}$$

At the end of the problem, the particle experiences the following potential:

$$V = \frac{k \cdot Q}{r}$$

$$V_{final} = \frac{(8.99 \times 10^9 \, \frac{N \cdot m^2}{C^2}) \cdot (3.4 \, C)}{2.5 \, m} = 1.2 \times 10^{10} \text{ Volts}$$

Thus, the particle experiences a potential difference of:

$$\Delta V = 1.2 \times 10^{10} \text{ Volts} - 2.2 \times 10^{10} \text{ Volts} = -1.0 \times 10^{10} \text{ Volts}$$

That corresponds to a change in potential energy of:

$$\Delta U = q \cdot \Delta V$$

$$\Delta U = (6.5 \, C) \cdot (-1.0 \times 10^{10} \, \frac{J}{C}) = -6.5 \times 10^{10} \text{ J}$$

So what does that tell us? It tells us that the particle's potential energy *lowered* by 6.5 x 10^{10} J. Well, if the particle lost that potential energy, where did it go? It went into kinetic energy. Thus, the kinetic energy of the particle increased by 6.5 x 10^{10} J. Well, it had *no* kinetic energy to begin with (it was at rest), so the *final* kinetic energy is just 6.5 x 10^{10} J. Now we can determine the particle's speed.

$$KE = \frac{1}{2} \cdot m \cdot v^2$$

$$6.5 \times 10^{10} \text{ J} = \frac{1}{2} \cdot (42.3 \, kg) \cdot v^2$$

$$v = 5.5 \times 10^4 \, \frac{m}{sec}$$

When the particle has traveled to 2.5 m away from the stationary charge, then, its speed is 5.5 x 10^4 m/sec.

Hopefully, from the example, you can see how powerful a concept the potential difference is. I want to make it clear to you that virtually *any* kind of energy analysis that you want to do in a situation involving electrical charge can be aided by calculating the potential difference. Before I end this section, I want you to understand that electric potentials are additive. Thus, if I have more than one charged particle creating an electric field, the potential at any point is simply the sum of the potentials for each individual charge. You can see that in the following example.

EXAMPLE 12.3

Two stationary charges (q₁ = -1.5 mC, q₂ = -5.6 mC) are placed 50.0 cm apart. How much work would it take to bring a third charged particle (q = -3.4 mC) midway between q₁ and q₂?

-3.4 mC

-1.5 mC   -5.6 mC

50.0 cm

Obviously, it is going to take work to do this, since the negatively-charged particle is being repelled by the other two negatively-charged particles. The question asks us to calculate how much work it will take. To do that, all we have to do is consider the electric potentials involved. When the -3.4 mC particle is far, far away, it experiences no electric potential from the two charges. Thus, V = 0. When it is brought midway between the charges, it is 25.0 cm from each of them, and the total electric potential it feels is just the sum of the two individual electric potentials:

$$V_{tot} = V_1 + V_2 = \frac{k \cdot Q_1}{r_1} + \frac{k \cdot Q_2}{r_2}$$

$$V_{tot} = \frac{(8.99 \times 10^9 \frac{N \cdot m^2}{C^2}) \cdot (-0.0015 C)}{0.250 \text{ m}} + \frac{(8.99 \times 10^9 \frac{N \cdot m^2}{C^2}) \cdot (-0.0056 C)}{0.250 \text{ m}} = -2.5 \times 10^8 \text{ Volts}$$

So, the potential difference is just:

$$\Delta V = -2.5 \times 10^8 \text{ Volts} - 0 \text{ Volts} = -2.5 \times 10^8 \text{ Volts}$$

Now that we know how the electric potential changed, we can figure out how the potential energy changed:

$$\Delta U = q \cdot \Delta V$$

$$\Delta U = (-0.0034 C) \cdot (-2.5 \times 10^8 \frac{J}{C}) = 8.5 \times 10^5 \text{ J}$$

According to Equation (12.3), the change in potential energy is equal to the negative of the work. Thus, the work done is -8.5 x 10^5 J. What does the negative mean? It means that work was done *against* the electrostatic force. This makes sense, of course, since the electrostatic force would push the -3.4 mC charge away from the two stationary charges.

Make sure you understand the concept of the electric potential and potential difference by solving the following "on your own" problems.

ON YOUR OWN

12.3 An electron has a charge of -1.6 x 10^{-19} C and a mass of 9.1 x 10^{-31} kg. Ignoring friction, if an electron starts from rest and travels from the negative side of a 9.0 Volt battery to the positive side, how fast will it be going when it hits the positive side of the battery?

12.4 A charged particle (m = 1.50 kg, q = 12.2 mC) is fired towards a stationary 15.0 mC charge. If the initial speed of the particle is 2,000.0 m/sec, how fast will the particle be going when it is 1.00 meters from the stationary charge? Assume that the particle was fired very far from the stationary charge.

12.5 Two stationary charges, $q_1 = q_2 = 120.0$ mC are placed 80.0 cm apart. A third charged particle that is free to move (m = 1.34 kg, q = 88.0 mC) is placed 25.0 cm above the midpoint of the two charges and released. At what speed will the particle be moving when it is 100.0 cm above the midpoint?

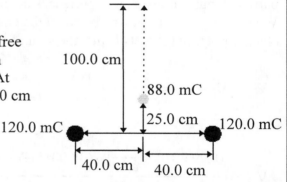

Capacitors and Uniform Electric Fields

In the first section of this module, we worked with uniform electric fields. I thought you might be interested in how we form these electric fields. After all, the electric field generated by a single charge is clearly not uniform. Its strength decreases the farther one gets from the particle. We could add a few more single charges so that their electric fields add together, but creating a uniform electric field that way would be quite difficult. How, then, do we produce uniform electric fields? Well, one way to do it is with a **capacitor**. To give you a good idea of what a capacitor is and how it is made, I want you to perform the following experiment.

EXPERIMENT 12.1
Making a Leyden Jar

<u>Supplies</u>

- A plastic or paper cup
- Aluminum foil
- A plastic comb
- Paper clips
- A balloon

<u>Introduction</u> - In 1745, Dutch scientist Pieter van Musschenbroek found that he could store charge in a jar that was lined with metal foil on both the inside and the outside. He demonstrated it at the University of Leyden, and it is therefore called the Leyden jar. The Leyden jar was the forerunner of the modern-day capacitor. In this experiment, you will make a Leyden jar.

<u>Procedure</u>

1. Take the cup and line the lower half of the inside with aluminum foil. Try to make the foil lie as flat as possible against the inside of the cup.
2. Cover the lower half of the outside of the cup with foil as well. In the end, then, you have foil covering the lower half of the cup on both the outside and the inside.

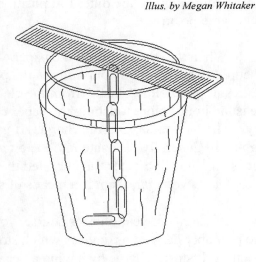

Illus. by Megan Whitaker

3. Hang a paper clip in the middle of the comb, and then attach more paper clips to it so that a line of paper clips dangle from the comb.
4. Place the comb across the top of the cup. If the paper clip line is not long enough to reach the bottom of the cup where the foil is, add more paper clips. The paper clips must touch each other, and the last one must touch the foil.
5. In the end, your setup should look like the drawing on the right.
6. Blow up the balloon and tie it off.
7. Grab the foil on the outside of the cup with your hand, but be sure you do not touch any of the foil on the inside of the cup.
8. Rub the balloon in your hair to build up charge.
9. Bring the balloon in contact with the tip of the paper clip that is attached to the comb. Make sure the balloon doesn't touch the foil on the outside of the cup at all. It should only touch the paper clip. You should hear a discharge as charge travels from the balloon to the paper clip. That charge will then run down the line of paper clips and into the foil on the inside of the cup.
10. Repeat steps (8) and (9) nine more times.
11. Set the balloon down far from the cup.

12. Slowly bring the index finger of the hand not holding the foil to the paper clip. What happens?
13. If you felt nothing when your finger got near or touched the paper clip, most likely the paper clips are not touching each other well enough to make electrical contact. You need solid electrical contact between each paper clip and the foil.
14. Repeat steps (7) - (11).
15. Now walk away from the setup. You need to tell everyone in the house not to touch the setup.
16. Wait at least an hour, and then grab the outside of the foil with one hand and, once again, bring the index finger of the other hand into contact with the paper clip. What happens?
17. Clean everything up.

What happened in the experiment? You *stored charge*. As you kept touching the charged balloon to the paper clips, negative charges traveled off of the balloon and into the foil. This built up a negative charge on the inner foil of the cup. That negative charge could not travel to the outside foil, because the cup is an insulator. Thus, the charge just built up on the inner foil. That charge, however, repelled electrons that were in the outer foil. Since your hand was touching the outer foil, those electrons streamed out of the foil, into your hand, and to ground. This, of course, made the outer foil positive. Thus, as the inner foil became negative, the outer foil became positive.

When you then touched the paper clip with your finger, the excess electrons in the inner foil could travel through your body to the positive outer foil, which you still had in your hand. As a result, you felt a "shock" from the electrons. When you repeated the experiment but waited at least an hour before touching the paper clip with your finger, you still got the same shock. Why? The jar was *storing* the charge. If you charge a conductor with an excess charge, that charge will generally dissipate into the air after some time. However, this charge did not. Why? Because the positive outer foil attracted the negative charges in the inner foil, keeping them there. The Leyden jar, then, is a means of storing charge.

In your first-year physics course, you probably learned something about capacitors. They were probably defined as devices which store charge. Well, the Leyden jar was the first capacitor. It stores charge by having a negatively-charged conductor separated from a positively-charged conductor by an insulator. Today's capacitors do the same thing, but typically with a different geometry. Figure 12.2 illustrates a common type of capacitor, the **parallel plate capacitor**.

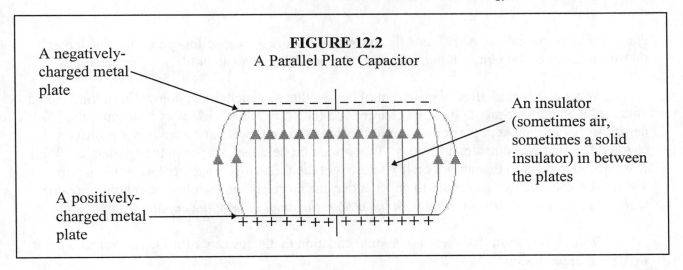

FIGURE 12.2
A Parallel Plate Capacitor

A negatively-charged metal plate

An insulator (sometimes air, sometimes a solid insulator) in between the plates

A positively-charged metal plate

A parallel plate capacitor consists of two parallel plates (imagine that) which are oppositely charged. The charges cannot travel to one another, however, since there is an insulator in between the plates. Sometimes, this insulator is simply air. Sometimes, it is a solid, such as plastic. When working with capacitors, we usually use the term "dielectric" rather than insulator, although the two terms are equivalent.

Note the electric field lines drawn in the figure. Ignoring the electric field lines on the ends of the capacitor, what do we have? We have a *uniform* electric field. Thus, this is one way that we can generate a uniform electric field. Except at the very edges of the plates, two parallel plates which are oppositely charged and separated by an insulator will have a uniform electric field in between them.

Okay, so now we know one way to generate a constant electric field. How do we determine the strength of that field? Well, not surprisingly, that depends on the amount of charge stored on the plates. The more charge stored on the plates, the stronger the electric field between them. Thus, to determine the electric field in a capacitor, we first have to determine the amount of charge the capacitor can hold.

Let's think about this for a moment. What physical characteristics of a parallel plate capacitor would affect how much charge it can hold? Well, the first one that comes to my mind is the *size* of the capacitor. The bigger the capacitor, the more charge it should be able to hold. After all, when one side of the capacitor is charged negatively, there are a lot of electrons stored on the negative plate. Those electrons repel each other. As more and more electrons are forced on the plate, they will be forced to get closer to one another. This, of course, will increase their repulsion. Thus, the smaller the capacitor, the harder it will be to continually push excess charge onto one of the plates.

So…the size of the capacitor affects how much charge it can store. We can actually be more specific than that, however. Remember, that in a conductor, the charge exists *on the outer surface*. It does not go inside the conductor. Thus, the *volume* of the conductor is not important when it comes to how much charge can be forced onto it. Only the *surface area* of the conductor matters, because the charges will stay on the surface. Therefore, *the surface area of the capacitor* (we will call it "A") affects the amount of charge the capacitor can hold. The larger the surface area of the plates in the capacitor, the more charge it can hold.

What else would affect the amount of charge that a capacitor can hold? Well, think about your Leyden jar experiment. It stored charge for a long time, didn't it? Why? Because the negative charges you kept putting on the foil inside of the cup were attracted to the positively-charged foil that was outside of the cup. That attraction held the charges in the Leyden jar. Well, what would happen to that attraction if you brought the foils closer together? It would go up. Thus, the closer the two plates are to one another, the more charge the plates can hold. In other words, the *smaller the distance between the plates, the more charge the capacitor can hold.*

Well, it turns out that there is a simple equation that takes care of these two effects. First, we define **capacitance**:

Capacitance - A measure of capacity for holding charge

The larger the capacitance, the more charge that can be stored. With that definition of capacitance, we come up with this formula for a parallel plate capacitor:

$$C = \frac{\varepsilon_o \cdot A}{d} \qquad (12.8)$$

where "C" is the capacitance, "A" is the surface area of one plate, and "d" is the distance between the plates. What is ε_o? It is the **permittivity of free space,** which you learned about in Module #11. It has a constant value of $8.85 \times 10^{-12} \frac{C^2}{N \cdot m^2}$.

Let's look at the units for capacitance. When I take the units for ε_o, multiply by meters^2 and divide by meters, I get $\frac{C^2}{N \cdot m}$, or $\frac{C^2}{J}$. Now remember that a Volt is a $\frac{J}{C}$, so $\frac{C^2}{J}$ is the same as $\frac{C}{V}$. That unit is renamed the **farad (F)**, in honor of Michael Faraday, a British chemist and physicist who was also a devout Christian. The unit farad turns out to be a huge unit. Typical capacitors have a capacitance on the order of microfarads (10^{-6} F), nanofarads (10^{-9} F), or picofarads (10^{-12} F). So that you have an idea of how big the farad unit is, consider the following example.

EXAMPLE 12.4

A physicist would like to make a parallel plate capacitor with a capacitance of 1.0 F. If he can place the plates 1.0 mm apart, how big do the plates have to be?

We know the equation for capacitance, and the only unknown in the equation is A, so we can solve for it:

$$C = \frac{\varepsilon_o \cdot A}{d}$$

$$1.0 \text{ F} = \frac{8.85 \times 10^{-12} \frac{C^2}{N \cdot m^2} \cdot A}{0.0010 \text{ m}}$$

$$A = \frac{(1.0 \frac{C}{V}) \cdot 0.0010 \text{ m}}{8.85 \times 10^{-12} \frac{C^2}{N \cdot m^2}} = 1.1 \times 10^8 \frac{N \cdot m^3}{C \cdot V} = 1.1 \times 10^8 \frac{\cancel{J} \cdot m^2}{\cancel{C} \cdot \frac{\cancel{J}}{\cancel{C}}} = \underline{1.1 \times 10^8 \text{ m}^2}$$

Notice how the units work out. When you substitute J/C in for Volt and J for N·m, everything cancels except for m², which is an area unit. If the plates were square, each plate would have to be about 10,000 meters on a side! That's what it would take to make a 1.0 F capacitor out of two plates spaced a millimeter apart. That should give you an idea of how big a farad really is!

Now that I have discussed capacitance, I can finally tell you how to calculate the charge that can be stored in a capacitor. Obviously, the charge will depend on the capacitance. The more capacitance, the more charge that can be stored. However, if you think about it, there is another factor as well. After all, to charge a conductor, I must push electrical charges into it. Once those electrical charges are there, however, it is harder for me to put more of the same electrical charges onto the conductor, because the ones that I already put there repel any others that I try to put there. However, I can take care of this by pushing harder. If I push the electrical charges harder than they are being repelled, they will have no choice but to go onto the conductor.

How do we measure the amount with which charges are "pushed?" That's the *electric potential*. The higher the electric potential, the more "push" the electric field is providing. Thus, the higher the potential difference between the plates in a parallel plate capacitor, the more charge we can put on the plates. In other words:

$$\Delta V = \frac{Q}{C} \tag{12.9}$$

So now we can calculate the charge stored on a capacitor. Notice that the equation tells us what we already have reasoned out. For a constant capacitance, a higher potential difference will result in a higher value for Q. For a constant potential difference, a higher capacitance will result in a higher Q.

Now remember what started this discussion. I really wanted to tell you how to calculate the strength of an electric field inside a parallel plate capacitor. So far, we only know how to calculate the charge. I want you to stop here for a moment, however, to make sure you understand what you need to understand when it comes to parallel plate capacitors. Solve the "on your own" problems below, and once you have mastered them, you can move on to determining the electric field inside a parallel plate capacitor.

ON YOUR OWN

12.6 A parallel plate capacitor is made up of two square plates, each of which are 2.21 millimeters on a side. The distance between the plates is 0.100 millimeters. How much charge will be stored on the capacitor when it is connected to a 9.00 Volt battery?

12.7 A parallel plate capacitor has a capacitance of 1.20 microfarads. The plates are 1.00 millimeter apart. The capacitor is charged up so that each plate holds 1.50 mC of charge. Suppose an electron ($q = -1.6 \times 10^{-19}$ C, $m = 9.1 \times 10^{-31}$ kg) is placed right next to the negative plate and then released. When it reaches the positive plate, how fast will it be traveling?

Now before I leave this discussion of capacitor electric fields and potential energy, I want to make one very important point. If you look at Equation (12.9), you might think that the charge we can put on a capacitor is unlimited. After all, if I want to put more charge on a capacitor, all I have to do is expose it to a high potential. If I hook a capacitor up to a 1.5 Volt battery, it will charge up to a certain charge, given by Equation (12.9). If I then hook it up to a 9.0 Volt battery, it will store *more* charge on its plate, because the potential difference between the plates increased from 1.5 Volts to 9.0 Volts. Thus, according to Equation (12.9), the amount of charge it will hold increases. That reasoning is correct, but there is a limit to how much you can increase the potential difference.

After all, remember what the potential difference tells us. It tells us how hard charge is being pushed around. Well, even though air is an insulator, it is not a *perfect* insulator (nothing is). If the potential difference between two surfaces is very high, the air can actually be forced to conduct electricity. This is what happens in a lightning strike. The potential difference between the ground and a cloud becomes so large that air is forced to conduct electricity, and you see a big spark as a result. Thus, as you continually increase the potential difference between two plates in a capacitor, you will eventually reach the point at which the air between the plates is no longer a good insulator. This is called **dielectric breakdown**. For dry air, dielectric breakdown occurs at an electric field strength of about 24 million Newtons per Coulomb. Thus, once you have charged a capacitor to the point that its uniform electric field reaches a strength near 24 million Newtons per Coulomb, you cannot put any more charge on it, or the air will break down, conducting charge across the gap.

The Electric Field and Energy of a Capacitor

Now that you are comfortable with the capacitance and charge of a capacitor, we can finally discuss how to calculate its electric field. To begin this discussion, I want you to imagine a situation similar to "on your own" problem 12.7. Imagine that you have a positively charged particle sitting right next to the positive plate of a parallel plate capacitor. When released, that particle will clearly begin accelerating towards the negative plate.

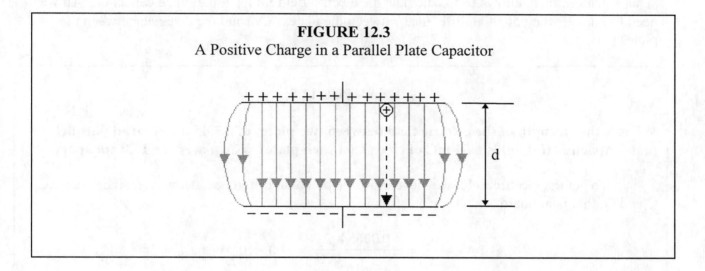

FIGURE 12.3
A Positive Charge in a Parallel Plate Capacitor

As you (hopefully) figured out in the "on your own" problem, you can determine the change in the charge's potential energy by using Equation (12.7):

$$\Delta U = q \cdot \Delta V \tag{12.7}$$

However, there is *another* way you can figure out the change in potential energy. As Equation (12.3) tells us, the change in potential energy is equal to the negative of the work done by the electric field.

$$\Delta U = -W \tag{12.3}$$

We can calculate the work done by the electric field using Equation (12.2). Now remember, this equation is only valid for *uniform* electric fields, but that's okay, because the electric field inside a capacitor is uniform!

$$W = q \cdot E \cdot d \cdot \cos\theta \tag{12.2}$$

Combining Equations (12.3) and (12.2) gives us the following:

$$\Delta U = -q \cdot E \cdot d \cdot \cos\theta \tag{12.10}$$

Now look what we have. Equation (12.7) is one expression for ΔU, and Equation (12.10) is another. Thus, we can combine them:

$$q \cdot \Delta V = -q \cdot E \cdot d \cdot \cos\theta \qquad (12.11)$$

Look what happens. The charges cancel. Also, for this particular situation, $\theta = 180$, because the particle will move parallel to the electric field lines. Thus, the equation reduces to:

$$\Delta V = E \cdot d \qquad (12.12)$$

This equation, then, allows us to calculate the electric field for a parallel plate capacitor. All we need to know is the potential difference between the plates (ΔV) and the distance between the plates (d).

EXAMPLE 12.5

What is the strength of the electric field between two plates of a 3.45 microfarad parallel plate capacitor if it holds 6.54 mC of charge on each plate? The plates are 15.0 cm apart.

To get the electric field, we must know the potential difference. However, since we have C and Q, that is not hard.

$$\Delta V = \frac{Q}{C} = \frac{0.00654\ C}{3.45 \times 10^{-6}\ \frac{C}{V}} = 1.90 \times 10^3\ V$$

The electric field can now be calculated:

$$\Delta V = E \cdot d$$

$$E = \frac{\Delta V}{d} = \frac{1.90 \times 10^3\ V}{0.150\ m} = 1.27 \times 10^4\ \frac{V}{m} = 1.27 \times 10^4\ \frac{\frac{J}{C}}{m} = 1.27 \times 10^4\ \frac{\frac{N \cdot m}{C}}{m} = \underline{1.27 \times 10^4\ \frac{N}{C}}$$

Notice that the unit we get in the equation (V/m) can be rearranged to yield the standard unit for electric field (N/C). This is why you will see electric field reported in V/m from time to time.

Before I leave this section, I want to spend a little time discussing the energy associated with a capacitor. Although a capacitor primarily stores charge, it also stores energy. After all, it takes work to charge up the plates on a capacitor. Imagine having two parallel plates, each of which is uncharged. If, one at a time, you took electrons off of the bottom plate and put them onto the top plate, you would slowly charge the top plate with a negative charge and the bottom plate with a positive charge. Think, however, about the work involved. As you pulled an electron off of the bottom plate, you would have to fight the attractive force trying to keep it on the bottom plate. In addition, once you started doing this, there would be a repulsive force pushing it away from the top plate. You would have to fight that force, too. Thus, you would be applying a force and moving the particle a distance (the distance between the plates). What, then, would you be doing? You would be doing *work*.

When you do work in this way, you will be storing up that energy in the capacitor. Think, for example, about a spring. When you compress the spring, you must work to compress it. However, the energy that you expended in the work gets stored in the spring, according to Equation (4.8). Thus, the work becomes *potential energy*. It is the same with a capacitor. The work that you exert in charging the capacitor becomes the potential energy stored in the capacitor. The equation that tells you how much energy is stored in the capacitor is:

$$U_{cap} = \frac{1}{2} \cdot \frac{Q^2}{C} \qquad (12.13)$$

Now, since C can be related to Q and ΔV according to Equation (12.9), there are a couple of other ways you can express this equation:

$$U_{cap} = \frac{1}{2} \cdot C \cdot (\Delta V)^2 \qquad (12.14)$$

or

$$U_{cap} = \frac{1}{2} \cdot Q \cdot \Delta V \qquad (12.15)$$

All three equations are valid, as they are all equivalent to one another.

EXAMPLE 12.6

A parallel plate capacitor is made from two square plates which are 2.50 cm on each side. The distance between the plates is 1.5 mm. If it takes 4.0 x 10^{-10} J of work to charge the plates up, what is the potential difference between the two plates?

The work necessary to charge the capacitor is equal to the energy stored in the capacitor. We are also given enough information to calculate the capacitance:

$$C = \frac{\varepsilon_o \cdot A}{d}$$

$$C = \frac{8.85 \times 10^{-12} \frac{C^2}{N \cdot m^2} \cdot (0.0250\,m) \cdot (0.0250\,m)}{0.0015\ m} = 3.7 \times 10^{-12} \frac{C^2}{N \cdot m} = 3.7 \times 10^{-12} \frac{C \cdot C}{J} = 3.7 \times 10^{-12} \frac{C}{V}$$

Now we know the energy and the capacitance, so to calculate the potential difference, Equation (12.14) is the most reasonable equation to use:

$$U_{cap} = \frac{1}{2} \cdot C \cdot (\Delta V)^2$$

$$\Delta V = \sqrt{\frac{2 \cdot U_{cap}}{C}} = \sqrt{\frac{2 \cdot 4.0 \times 10^{-10}\ J}{3.7 \times 10^{-12} \frac{C}{V}}} = 15 \sqrt{\frac{J}{\frac{C}{V}}} = 15 \sqrt{\frac{V}{\frac{1}{V}}} = 15 \sqrt{V^2} = \underline{15\ V}$$

ON YOUR OWN

12.8 A physicist wants to use a 500.0 microfarad parallel plate capacitor to generate a uniform electric field of 75.0 N/C. If the plates are 15.0 cm apart, what voltage must he use to charge the plates?

12.9 How much energy is stored in that capacitor once the physicist gets it charged?

12.10 As mentioned in the previous section, dielectric breakdown of air occurs at about 24 million Newtons per Coulomb. What is the maximum charge that could be stored in the capacitor in problem 12.8?

Capacitors with Dielectrics

Before you leave this module, I want to briefly cover the concept of placing a solid dielectric between the two plates of a parallel plate capacitor. Remember, you must have an insulator between the plates, or charge will simply travel from one plate to another. The insulator is usually air, but sometimes, it is a solid like Teflon, quartz, plastic, etc. When a solid is used like this, we generally say that the capacitor has a dielectric. It is kind of silly to say that, because air is a dielectric as well. Nevertheless, standard physics terminology is that a capacitor must have something other than air between the plates to be considered a capacitor with a dielectric.

Now why would someone put a dielectric other than air between the plates of a parallel plate capacitor? Well, the answer is that it can actually *increase* the capacitance of the capacitor. How? Well, let's think about what happens when you put a dielectric in between the plates.

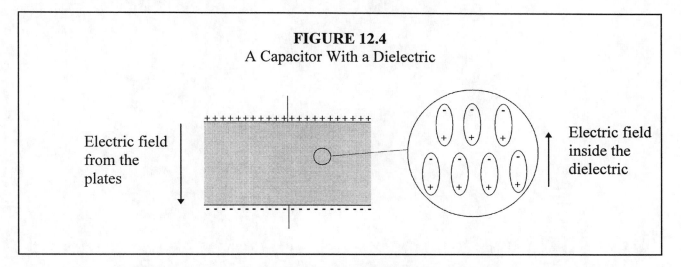

FIGURE 12.4
A Capacitor With a Dielectric

When a dielectric is placed in between the plates, it is subjected to the electric field. Now the electrons in the dielectric cannot move, but the molecules in the dielectric will tend to orient themselves so that their negative sides are closer to the positive plate and their positive sides are closer to the negative plate. But what does that do? That sets up an electric field inside the dielectric that is *opposed* to the electric field coming from the plates. Thus, *a dielectric tends to decrease the electric field in between the plates of a capacitor.*

How does that increase the capacitance? Well, think about Equation (12.12). It says that the potential difference is equal to the electric field times the distance between the plates. If the distance between the plates does not change, then, the potential difference between the plates will *lower* if the electric field lowers. Thus, a dielectric lowers the potential difference between the two plates. Well, since Equation (12.9) tells us that capacitance is equal to the charge divided by the potential difference, if the potential difference decreases, then the capacitance increases. Thus, putting a dielectric in between the plates of a capacitor will lower the electric field, lower the potential difference between the plates, and *raise* the capacitance. Some materials, of course, are better at raising the capacitance than others. Thus, dielectrics are often described by their **dielectric constant**. The larger the dielectric constant, the more it increases capacitance.

Since the size of electrical circuits are often limited, the smaller the capacitor, the better. However, as Equation (12.8) tells you, to increase the capacitance, you must increase the size (area) of the plates. For some circuits, that is just not practical. Thus, if you need to keep your capacitors small but need them to have a large capacitance, then you might try increasing the capacitance with a dielectric.

ANSWERS TO THE ON YOUR OWN PROBLEMS

12.1 The best way to think about this is to think about how the charges will all accelerate in the electric field. They are all negative, so they will travel opposite the electric field. Thus, they will travel to the right. The ones that can travel farthest will be worked on by the field more than those that do not travel as far. Since the electric field's work will reduce potential energy, the particles that will be worked on more must have more potential energy. Particle a, therefore, has the highest potential energy.

12.2 You can do this the hard way or the easy way. I will do it the easy way. If you connect a line from the particle to its ending location, you have an equilateral triangle. You know this because the two sides shown in the diagram are the same size, and since the angle shown in the diagram is 120 degrees, the interior angle on that leg is 60 degrees. Isosceles triangles have equal angles on the equal sides, so the other angle is 60 degrees as well. Since all interior angles add to 180, the last angle must also be 60, and thus we have an equilateral triangle.

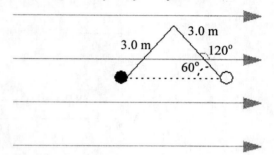

Therefore, the leg drawn from the particle to its ending location is also 3.0 m. Since the electrostatic force is conservative, the path does not matter, so I choose the path where the particle travels straight against the electric field ($\theta = 180°$).

$$W = q \cdot E \cdot x \cdot \cos\theta = (0.1200 \text{ C}) \cdot (15.0 \frac{N}{C}) \cdot (3.0 \text{ m}) \cdot \cos(180) = \underline{-5.4 \text{ J}}$$

What does the negative mean? It means that work was done against the field. That makes sense, since a positive particle is accelerated in the opposite direction by the electric field. Thus, the physicist worked against the field.

12.3 Since it travels from one side of the battery to the other, it experiences a potential difference of 9.0 Volts. Thus, it experiences the following change in potential energy:

$$\Delta U = q \cdot \Delta V$$

$$\Delta U = (-1.6 \times 10^{-19} \text{ C}) \cdot (9.0 \frac{J}{C}) = -1.4 \times 10^{-18} \text{ J}$$

Since the potential energy decreased, the kinetic energy increased. It had no kinetic energy to start with, so its final kinetic energy is 1.4 x 10^{-18} J. We can use that to get the speed:

$$KE = \frac{1}{2} \cdot m \cdot v^2$$

$$1.4 \times 10^{-18} \text{ J} = \frac{1}{2} \cdot (9.1 \times 10^{-31} \text{ kg}) \cdot v^2$$

$$v = 1.8 \times 10^6 \; \frac{m}{sec}$$

Notice that's almost 0.5% the speed of light!

12.4 If the particle starts far from the charge, then the initial potential is zero. When it is 1.00 m from the charge, the potential is:

$$V = \frac{k \cdot Q}{r}$$

$$V_{final} = \frac{(8.99 \times 10^9 \; \frac{N \cdot m^2}{C^2}) \cdot (0.0150\,C)}{1.00 \; m} = 1.35 \times 10^8 \text{ Volts}$$

The potential difference, then, is:

$$\Delta V = 1.35 \times 10^8 \text{ Volts} - 0 \text{ Volts} = 1.35 \times 10^8 \text{ Volts}$$

Now we can calculate the change in potential energy:

$$\Delta U = q \cdot \Delta V$$

$$\Delta U = (0.0122\,C) \cdot (1.35 \times 10^8 \; \frac{J}{C}) = 1.65 \times 10^6 \text{ J}$$

What does this tell us? It tells us that the potential energy increased. The only way that can happen is for the kinetic energy to decrease. Thus, the kinetic energy decreased by 1.65 x 10⁶ J. We will have to subtract that from the original kinetic energy:

$$KE_{final} = \frac{1}{2} \cdot m \cdot v^2 - 1.65 \times 10^6 \text{ J} = \frac{1}{2} \cdot (1.50\,kg) \cdot (2,000.0 \; \frac{m}{sec})^2 - 1.65 \times 10^6 \text{ J} = 1.35 \times 10^6 \text{ J}$$

Now we can determine the final speed:

$$KE = \frac{1}{2} \cdot m \cdot v^2$$

$$1.35 \times 10^6 \text{ J} = \frac{1}{2} \cdot (1.5\,kg) \cdot v^2$$

$$v = 1{,}340 \ \frac{m}{sec}$$

The particle slowed down, of course, because the stationary charge repels it. Eventually, the particle would stop and turn around, accelerating away from the stationary charge.

12.5 Although this is not part of the problem, you should recognize that the particle will, indeed, travel straight up. Both stationary charges repel it, and the horizontal components of that repulsion will cancel out because of the symmetry of the situation. Thus, the particle accelerates straight upward.

To determine the speed, all we need to do is figure out the potential difference that the particle experiences. To do that, we need the distance from the charges. That's not hard, however, since the charges form right triangles. Before the particle is released, the right triangles each have legs of 40.0 cm and 25.0 cm. Thus, by the Pythagorean theorem, the distance between the stationary charges and the moving charge is 47.2 cm. At the end, the two legs are 40.0 cm and 100.0 cm, making the charges 108 cm apart. Those are the distances we use in calculating the potential.

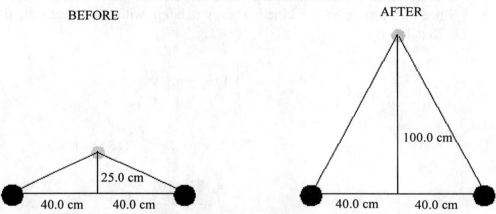

$$V_{initial} = V_1 + V_2 = \frac{k \cdot Q_1}{r_1} + \frac{k \cdot Q_2}{r_2}$$

$$V_{initial} = \frac{(8.99 \times 10^9 \ \frac{N \cdot m^2}{C^2}) \cdot (0.1200 \, C)}{0.472 \ m} + \frac{(8.99 \times 10^9 \ \frac{N \cdot m^2}{C^2}) \cdot (0.1200 \, C)}{0.472 \ m} = 4.57 \times 10^9 \ \text{Volts}$$

$$V_{final} = V_1 + V_2 = \frac{k \cdot Q_1}{r_1} + \frac{k \cdot Q_2}{r_2}$$

$$V_{final} = \frac{(8.99 \times 10^9 \ \frac{N \cdot m^2}{C^2}) \cdot (0.1200 \, C)}{1.08 \ m} + \frac{(8.99 \times 10^9 \ \frac{N \cdot m^2}{C^2}) \cdot (0.1200 \, C)}{1.08 \ m} = 2.00 \times 10^9 \ \text{Volts}$$

The particle, then, experiences a change in potential of:

$$\Delta V = 2.00 \times 10^9 \text{ Volts} - 4.57 \times 10^9 \text{ Volts} = -2.57 \times 10^9 \text{ Volts}$$

Now we can calculate the change in potential energy:

$$\Delta U = q \cdot \Delta V$$

$$\Delta U = (0.0880\,\mathrm{C}) \cdot (-2.57 \times 10^9 \, \frac{J}{\mathrm{C}}) = -2.26 \times 10^8 \text{ J}$$

That decrease in potential energy ends up increasing the kinetic energy by the same amount. Since the particle had no kinetic energy to begin with, that means the final kinetic energy is 2.26×10^8 J:

$$KE = \frac{1}{2} \cdot m \cdot v^2$$

$$2.26 \times 10^8 \text{ J} = \frac{1}{2} \cdot (1.34 \,\mathrm{kg}) \cdot v^2$$

$$\underline{v = 1.84 \times 10^4 \, \frac{m}{sec}}$$

12.6 The first part of the problem gives us enough to determine the capacitance:

$$C = \frac{\varepsilon_o \cdot A}{d}$$

$$C = \frac{8.85 \times 10^{-12} \, \frac{C^2}{N \cdot m^2} \cdot (0.00221 \,\mathrm{m}) \cdot (0.00221 \,\mathrm{m})}{0.000100 \text{ m}} = 4.32 \times 10^{-13} \, \frac{C^2}{N \cdot m} = 4.32 \times 10^{-13} \, \frac{C}{V}$$

If it is hooked up to a 9.00 Volt battery, it has a potential difference of 9.00 Volts. Therefore:

$$\Delta V = \frac{Q}{C}$$

$$Q = C \cdot V = 4.32 \times 10^{-13} \, \frac{C}{V} \cdot 9.00 \, \mathrm{V} = \underline{3.89 \times 10^{-12} \text{ C}}$$

That may not sound like a lot of charge, but it means approximately 2×10^7 extra electrons are on the negative plate!

12.7 This problem is a lot easier than it sounds. The distance between the plates was just put in to fool you. Since we know the capacitance and charge, we can calculate the potential difference between the plates:

$$\Delta V = \frac{Q}{C}$$

$$\Delta V = \frac{0.00150 \; \text{C}}{1.20 \times 10^{-6} \; \frac{\text{C}}{\text{V}}} = 1250 \; \text{V}$$

Now that we know the potential difference, the change in potential energy can be calculated:

$$\Delta U = q \cdot \Delta V$$

$$\Delta U = (-1.6 \times 10^{-19} \; \text{C}) \cdot (1250 \frac{\text{J}}{\text{C}}) = -2.0 \times 10^{-16} \; \text{J}$$

That decrease in potential energy ends up increasing the kinetic energy by the same amount. Since the electron had no kinetic energy to begin with, that means the final kinetic energy is 2.0×10^{-16} J:

$$KE = \frac{1}{2} \cdot m \cdot v^2$$

$$2..0 \times 10^{-16} \; \text{J} = \frac{1}{2} \cdot (9.1 \times 10^{-31} \; \text{kg}) \cdot v^2$$

$$\underline{v = 2.1 \times 10^7 \; \frac{\text{m}}{\text{sec}}}$$

That's almost 10% the speed of light! It turns out that when an object is moving at relativistic speeds, the above equation for kinetic energy is not quite right. Thus, this number is not quite accurate.

12.8 The capacitance is not important for this problem. To determine the potential difference, we need only know the electric field and the distance between the plates:

$$\Delta V = E \cdot d = (75.0 \; \frac{\text{N}}{\text{C}}) \cdot (0.150 \, \text{m}) = 11.3 \; \frac{\text{J}}{\text{C}}$$

Since a Volt is a J/C, the potential difference must be <u>11.3 Volts</u>.

12.9 We need to know the capacitance for *this* problem. Since we already know ΔV, and since the capacitance was given in the previous problem, the most reasonable equation to use is:

$$U_{cap} = \frac{1}{2} \cdot C \cdot (\Delta V)^2 = \frac{1}{2} \cdot (5.000 \times 10^{-4} \, \frac{C}{V}) \cdot (11.3 \, V)^2 = 0.00319 \, C \cdot V = 0.00319 \, \cancel{C} \cdot \frac{J}{\cancel{C}} = \underline{0.00319 \, J}$$

12.10 We can't store charge that creates an electric field larger than the dielectric breakdown of the electric field. Thus, the strongest electric field we can have is 24 million N/C. That would lead to the following potential difference:

$$\Delta V = E \cdot d = (2.4 \times 10^7 \, \frac{N}{C}) \cdot (0.150 \, m) = 3.6 \times 10^6 \, V$$

That potential difference would give the following charge:

$$\Delta V = \frac{Q}{C}$$

$$Q = \Delta V \cdot C = (3.6 \times 10^6 \, \cancel{V}) \cdot (5.000 \times 10^{-4} \, \frac{C}{\cancel{V}}) = \underline{1800 \, C}$$

REVIEW QUESTIONS FOR MODULE #12

1. The electric potential at a given point is zero. Is the electric field necessarily zero? Why or why not?

2. The electric field at a given point is zero. Is the electric potential necessarily zero? Why or why not?

3. A negative charge is placed in an electric field and released. If it is accelerated by the electric field only, will it move towards a higher or a lower electric potential?

4. Negative work is done on a positive particle as it moves in an electric field. Is the positive particle moving in the direction of the electric field or opposite the electric field?

5. In the electric field shown to the right, which two particles have the same amount of electric potential?

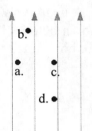

6. In the electric field shown to the right, which particle has the highest electric potential? Assume the particles are negatively-charged.

7. Is it possible for all of the particles in the electric field shown to the right to have equal amounts of potential energy?

8. A physicist makes a parallel plate capacitor, but it does not have a high enough capacitance. There are three things he could do to increase the capacitance. What are they?

9. A physicist hooks a capacitor up to a 1.5-Volt battery and measures the charge stored on the capacitor as q. The physicist then hooks the same capacitor up to a 9.0-Volt battery and measures the charge stored as Q. What is Q in terms of q?

10. Suppose that the physicist in question #9 also measured the energy stored in the capacitor. When it was hooked up to the 1.5-Volt battery, the energy was e. When it was hooked up to the 9.0-Volt battery, the energy was E. What is E in terms of e?

PRACTICE PROBLEMS FOR MODULE # 12

1. What is the work required to assemble the system shown to the right?

2. What is the electric potential at the center of the square pictured to the right?

3. What is the electric field at the center of the square pictured to the right ?

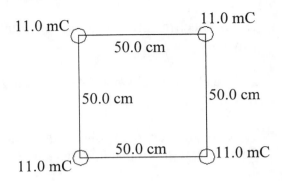

4. A negatively-charged particle (q = -34.5 mC) is being pushed in the 45.6 N/C electric field shown below. If the particle is forced to travel in a semicircle whose radius of curvature is 15.0 cm, how much work will have been done when it reaches the end of the semicircle?

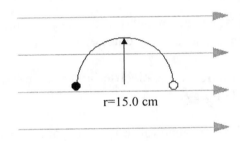

5. A +3.8 mC charged particle (m = 5.0 kg) is shot with an initial velocity of 245 m/sec towards a +1.5 mC stationary charge. If the particle starts out 1.2 meters from the stationary charge, how close will it come to the charge before turning around and moving away?

6. A proton (m = 1.7×10^{-27} kg, q = $+1.6 \times 10^{-19}$ C) is placed at edge of the positive plate of a 1.4×10^{-6} F capacitor. If the capacitor holds 2.2 mC of charge on its positive plate, how fast will the proton be moving when it reaches the negative plate of the capacitor?

7. An electron (m = 9.1×10^{-31} kg, q = -1.6×10^{-19} C) moves from the negative plate to the positive plate of a 5.1×10^{-6} F capacitor. If it starts from rest and reaches a speed of 3.2×10^{5} m/sec, how much charge is stored on the capacitor?

8. A parallel plate capacitor is made up of two square plates, each of which are 3.27 millimeters on a side. The distance between the plates is 0.200 millimeters. What potential difference must the capacitor have in order to hold 3.50 μC of charge?

9. Calculate the magnitude of the electric field in between the plates of the capacitor in problem #8.

10. How much energy is stored in the capacitor in problem #8?

Module #13: DC Electric Circuits

Introduction

Now that we have discussed electric fields, electric potential, and capacitors, we are now ready to discuss probably the most useful applications of the electrostatic force: electric circuits. You should have learned quite a bit about electric circuits in your first-year course, and I will review those concepts rather quickly so that we can move on to analyzing some really intricate electric circuits. However, before I review those concepts, I want to deal with something that was most likely glossed-over in your first-year course.

Resistance

In your first-year class, you probably learned a little about resistance. You probably learned that it is a measure of how much a conductor impedes the flow of electrical charges. I want to delve into this subject in a bit more detail. To begin with, imagine what happens when a battery is hooked up to a conductor. Remember, the atoms of a conductor hold one or more of their electrons loosely, and those electrons can move under the influence of the electric field established by the battery. Thus, the electrons move toward the positive side of the battery. In response, electrons flow out of the negative side of the battery, so that the conductor itself has no net electrical charge.

Now think about those electrons as they are moving through the conductor. Do you think that the electrons will have an easy time getting through the conductor? Not at all! Think about it. There are all sorts of atoms in the conductor, and they all have electrons, which *repel* the moving electrons. As the moving electrons come near an atom, they will be deflected away. Thus, the electrons must "bump around" a lot in order to get through the conductor. This is illustrated in Figure 13.1.

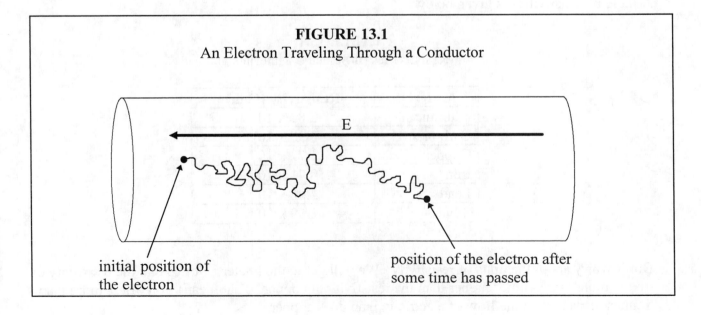

FIGURE 13.1
An Electron Traveling Through a Conductor

Notice that the electric field in the diagram is pointing to the left. That means the positive side of the battery is hooked to the right side of the conductor, and the negative side of the battery is hooked to the left side of the conductor. Now, if there were no atoms in the conductor, the electron in the diagram would just move straight to the right (negative charges move opposite the electric field). However, in the conductor, the electron keeps bumping into atoms as it moves. This causes the electron to take a crazy, zigzag path through the conductor. As you might imagine, this slows the electron down quite a bit. In fact, the speed at which an electron moves through a conductor is called the **drift speed** of the electron. Typically, the drift speed of an electron is on the order of a few millimeters per second. Thus, even though the electric field has the ability to accelerate the electrons to *very* high speeds, that ability is severely hampered by the collisions that the electron is constantly making with the atoms in the conductor. As a result, the electrons move relatively slowly through the conductor.

Consider, for example, an electron traveling between the plates of a parallel plate capacitor. Suppose the capacitor is charged so that there is a 9 Volt potential difference between the plates. Suppose further that the electron begins its journey from rest at the negative plate. It would be able to travel 10 cm in about 0.36 *microseconds*. If that same electron were traveling in copper wire that was hooked up to a 9 Volt battery, it would take the electron *several seconds* to travel 10 cm! That gives you an idea of how much "interference" exists for an electron traveling through a conductor.

Since the atomic structure of a conductor slows down the speed of an electron as it travels through an electric field, we say that a conductor has **resistance**. As you might imagine, this resistance is different for each conductor, because each conductor has its own atomic structure. Thus, physicists have developed a term called **resistivity**.

Resistivity - A measure of a conductor's inherent resistance to the flow of electricity

A table of resistivities is given below.

TABLE 13.1
Resistivities of Selected Materials

Material	Resistivity ($\Omega \cdot m$)
Aluminum	2.82×10^{-8}
Carbon	3.50×10^{-5}
Copper	1.72×10^{-8}
Iron	9.71×10^{-8}
Lead	2.06×10^{-7}
Silver	1.59×10^{-8}

Don't worry about the units of resistivity. We will get to them later. Notice that the resistivity of iron is more than 5 times higher than the resistivity of copper. That means iron offers more than 5 times resistance to the flow of electricity than does copper.

Now it turns out that resistivity is not the only thing that influences how a conductor resists the flow of electricity. The geometry of the conductor also plays a role. In the experiment which follows, you will discover those geometric effects for yourself.

EXPERIMENT 13.1
The Factors Which Influence Resistivity

Supplies

- Three #2 pencils (It turns out that *some* pencils will not work in this experiment, as they do not use enough graphite in their leads. Typically, the best pencils to use are pencils that are "natural" or "environmentally friendly," which is also called "green." A few examples of brands that do work are: Papermate® American Natural® pencils, Papermate® Earth Write® pencils, and Papermate® American® pencils.)
- One pencil with a significantly thicker lead than the others. (If you cannot find one of these, or if the one you find does not conduct electricity, go ahead and do the first part of this experiment.)
- Pencil sharpener
- A serrated knife
- Aluminum foil
- Tape
- Three "C" cell batteries
- The cardboard tube from a roll of toilet paper
- Scissors
- A flashlight

Introduction - In this experiment, you will see how geometric factors influence the resistance that carbon offers to the flow of electricity. As you can see from the table, carbon has a large resistivity (2,000 times that of copper), but it still does conduct electricity.

Procedure:

1. Take the top off of the flashlight so that you just have the assembly which houses the light bulb.
2. Tear a strip of aluminum foil which is at least 7 inches long and 1.5 inches wide.
3. Look for the point at which the batteries in the flashlight touch the assembly that you have. Typically, this point is directly under the light bulb on the back of the assembly. It is usually a circular metal area surrounded by plastic. This is the conductor which leads to the light bulb. Wad up one end of the aluminum foil strip so that it is the same size as this circular area of metal, and firmly tape it to the metal. Make sure the foil is pressing against the metal.
4. Tear another strip of aluminum foil which is at least 7 inches long and 1.5 inches wide.
5. Look for the return conductor on the assembly. This is typically a ring of metal that surrounds the assembly, and it is typically between the place you just taped the foil and the

top of the assembly. When you turn on the switch of the flashlight, the switch usually causes a piece of metal to touch this return conductor. This completes the circuit, giving one continuous loop of conductor from one end of the batteries to the other.

6. Fold one end of the second foil strip so that it is as wide as the return conductor, and firmly tape it to the return conductor. Once again, make sure that the foil is pressing against the metal. Also, make sure that the two foils are not touching, and make sure that they are each attached to their *own* conductor. You cannot have one piece of foil touching both conductors.

7. You now have two conductors which lead to the light bulb in the flashlight. Your assembly should look something like the drawing on the right. To see if everything is hooked up properly, take one of the batteries and put it in between the free ends of each strip of foil. With your fingers, press the end of one foil to one end of the battery and the end of the other foil to the other end of the battery. Don't worry, you won't feel any shock, as the vast majority of the current will run through the circuit, not you. Even if all of the current ran

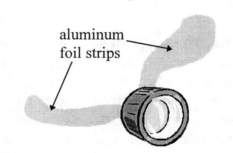

aluminum foil strips

through you, you still would not feel anything, as the current would be very low. **PLEASE NOTE THAT YOU SHOULD NEVER DO SOMETHING LIKE THIS UNLESS A KNOWLEDGEABLE PERSON TELLS YOU TO DO SO!** Electricity can be *very* dangerous, and touching a bare conductor could kill you if you don't know what you are doing!

8. If the light did not light when you touched the foil ends to opposite ends of the battery, there is something wrong with the electrical connections at the flashlight assembly. Go back and make sure the foils are firmly touching *only* their conductors and not touching each other.

9. Once you get the flashlight to light in this configuration, you are ready to continue.

10. Take the cardboard tube and use the scissors to cut along its length so that it opens up and can be laid flat.

11. Take one battery and lay it on top of the opened cardboard tube. Position the battery so that half of it is on top of the cardboard and the other half is sticking out over the edge of the cardboard. The flat end of the battery is the one that should be sticking over the edge of the cardboard.

12. Roll the battery up in the cardboard so that the cardboard is tightly-wound around the battery.

13. Tape the cardboard roll so that it does not come unrolled, and also tape the battery to the cardboard at the point where the battery is sticking out of the tube.

14. Drop the other two batteries in the tube. Make sure they are pointing in the same direction as the first battery, so that they all connect up properly. The third battery should be sticking out of the top. If it does not, cut the tube shorter so that it does.

15. You now should have a roll that contains three batteries stacked on top of one another. It should look something like the drawing on the right.

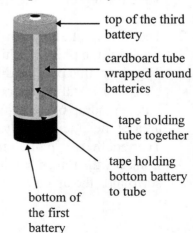

top of the third battery

cardboard tube wrapped around batteries

tape holding tube together

tape holding bottom battery to tube

bottom of the first battery

16. You are almost ready to begin the actual experiment. Take one of the #2 pencils and cut it with the serrated knife (use the knife like a saw) so that it is only about one-third of its original length and does not have an eraser on it.

17. Sharpen both ends of the pencil so that the pencil lead is exposed on both ends. However, do not make the ends very sharp. Also, don't expose too much of the lead, as it tends to break easily.

18. Although it is called a pencil "lead," it is actually made of carbon, which has a high resistivity but is still a conductor. You will place this conductor into an electrical circuit with the battery assembly and the flashlight assembly that you made.

19. First, take one more strip of aluminum foil which is at least 7 inches long and 1.5 inches wide. Tape one end to the top battery in the battery assembly.

20. Lay your flashlight assembly on the table, and set the battery assembly on top of the aluminum foil.

21. Finally, wad up the end of the foil coming from the top of the battery assembly as well as the free end of the foil coming from your flashlight assembly.

22. Hold the pencil in between these two wads of foil, pushing the pencil down so that the lead makes a good contact with the bottom foil and pushing the top foil down on the pencil so that good contact is made there. The final assembly should look like the drawing on the right.

23. If you get good contact between the foil and the pencil and the foil, the light should come on. If it does not, you either have a poor electrical connection somewhere, or your pencil does not have a lead that is mostly carbon.

24. Note how bright the light is.

25. Now take a second #2 pencil and use the knife to cut it to half of its original length. Once again, sharpen both ends and put that pencil in your electrical circuit. Once again, note how bright the light is.

26. Finally, take the third #2 pencil and cut just the eraser off. Once again, sharpen both ends and put that pencil in your electrical circuit. Once again, note how bright the light is.

27. Compare the three levels of brightness you observed. What was the pattern?

28. If you could find one, take the pencil with the thicker lead and cut it so that it is the length of one of the three pencils you have already used. Which one does not matter.

29. Sharpen that pencil on both ends and put it in your electrical circuit. Then, take that pencil out and put in the #2 pencil of the same length. What did you notice about the difference in brightness of the light?

30. Clean everything up, but don't throw anything away. You will use these items again.

What happened in the experiment? Well, when you put the #2 pencils into your electrical circuit, you should have noticed that the light was brightest for the *shorter* pencil, somewhat more dim for the medium-length pencil, and dimmest for the long pencil. Why? Well, think about the electrons flowing through the carbon. Carbon's resistivity is more than 1,200 times that of aluminum. Thus, the longer they have to spend traveling through the carbon, the harder it will be for them to get to the light bulb. As a result, fewer electrons will pass through the light bulb in a given amount of time, so the light bulb will not burn as brightly. That tells you that the resistance of a conductor is proportional to the length. The longer the conductor, the larger the resistance.

What happened when you compared the pencil with the thicker lead to the #2 pencil of the same length? You should have noticed that the light was brighter for the pencil with the thicker lead. Why? Well, in the thicker lead, the electrons have more room to spread out. They will still encounter the same number of carbon atoms, so the collisions between the atoms of the conductor and the electrons will be the same. However, the electrons will *collide with each other* less often the more they can spread out. Thus, the more "room" the electrons have, the lower the resistance. In the end, then, resistance is inversely proportional to the cross-sectional area of the conductor.

These two geometric considerations lead us to a rather simple formula for the resistance of a conductor:

$$R = \rho \cdot \frac{L}{A} \qquad (13.1)$$

In this equation, "R" is the resistance, "ρ" is the resistivity of the material, "L" is the length of the conductor, and "A" is the cross-sectional area of the conductor. As you should have learned in your first-year course, the unit for resistance is **Ohms (Ω)**. Since the standard unit for length is meters, and since the standard unit for area is meters^2, in order for resistance to come out in the unit of Ω, the units on resistivity must be $\Omega \cdot m$. That's where we get the unit listed in Table 13.1.

EXAMPLE 13.1

Assume that the pencil lead in your experiment was pure carbon. If the full-length pencil was 6.0 inches (15 cm) long, and the radius of the pencil lead was 0.79 mm, what was the resistance of the pencil?

To calculate resistance, we need resistivity (listed for carbon in Table 13.1), the length (given), and the cross-sectional area. The pencil lead is essentially a cylinder, and the cross-sectional area of a cylinder is $\pi \cdot r^2$.

$$A = \pi \cdot r^2 = (3.14) \cdot (0.00079 \text{ m})^2 = 2.0 \times 10^{-6} \text{ m}^2$$

Now we can use Equation (13.1).

$$R = \rho \cdot \frac{L}{A} = (3.50 \times 10^{-5} \ \Omega \cdot \text{m}) \cdot \frac{0.15 \ \text{m}}{2.0 \times 10^{-6} \ \text{m}^2} = \underline{2.6 \ \Omega}$$

I went through this example to give you an idea of the resistance that the pencil was giving in your experiment. Although 2.6 Ω is not a lot of resistance compared to many electrical circuits, it was enough to really decrease the brightness of the light. In fact, this resistance is the reason that you had to use three batteries in the experiment, rather than the two that you normally use for a flashlight. With even that small amount of resistance, two batteries (3 Volts) could not generate enough electrical current to light the light bulb. You had to have a third battery (for a total of 4.5 Volts) to generate sufficient electrical current.

Why did I have you make a complicated three-battery setup? If you needed more voltage, why didn't you just use a 9 Volt battery? Well, a 9 Volt battery would have produced too much electrical current, and it probably would have broken the filament in the light bulb as a result. Thus, you needed more voltage than one or two flashlight batteries could provide, but a 9 Volt battery would have just made too much current!

ON YOUR OWN

13.1 You want to make an electrical circuit that carries as much current as possible for the battery you have. If you had the choice of all of the materials listed in Table 13.1, which one would be the best conductor to use in the wires of your circuit?

13.2 A rectangular copper conductor is 1.0 m long and has a resistance of 8.6×10^{-5} Ω. Assuming that the width and length of the conductor are the same, give their value.

A Review of Circuits, Ohm's Law, and Other Equations

Now that we have delved into the concept of resistance, I want to take some time to quickly review what you have already learned from your first-year physics course. First, let's start with circuits. In the figure below, we see two circuits, each hooked up to a light bulb.

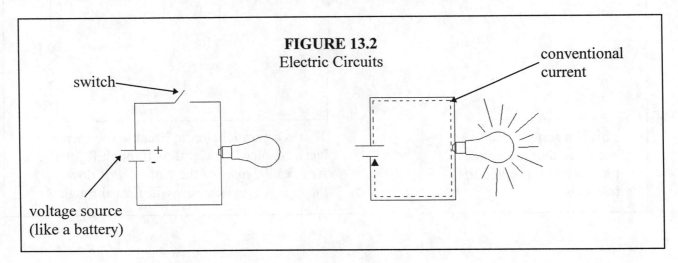

FIGURE 13.2
Electric Circuits

The first thing to note about these electric circuits is the way the voltage source is abbreviated. The long line represents the positive side of the voltage source, and the short line represents the negative side. The most common voltage source in the kind of electric circuits we are studying is a battery, so from now on, I will use that term to reference the voltage source.

The next thing to notice is that in the circuit on the left-hand side of the figure, electricity cannot flow. That's because there is not a complete path connecting the positive side of the battery to the negative side. Remember, electricity is the flow of charges through a conductor. If the charges are to flow, they must have a source out of which to flow and a place to go. In the case of electrons in a wire, the electrons will not move unless there is a source of excess electrons (the negative side of the battery) and a place for the electrons to go (the positive side of the battery). In the circuit on the left of the figure, the switch is open, and the two sides of the battery are not connected. Thus, no electricity will flow.

In the circuit on the right-hand side of the figure, the switch has been closed. Thus, both sides of the battery are connected, and current can flow. Notice, however, that in the diagram, the current (illustrated by the dashed line) is depicted as flowing from the positive side of the battery to the negative side. This is called **conventional current**. Even though we know that it is actually the flow of electrons that causes electricity in these circuits, we depict the flow as the flow of positive ions for historical reasons which you should have learned in your first-year course. Thus, when we deal with electric circuits, we always trace the current as the flow of positive charges.

Of course, it is really annoying to always draw a light bulb, refrigerator, or whatever is actually connected to your circuit. Thus, we use an abbreviation for these devices. Since most electrical appliances generate work by offering resistance to the flow of electrons, we can say that appliances are really just resistors. Thus, we can abbreviate them as such.

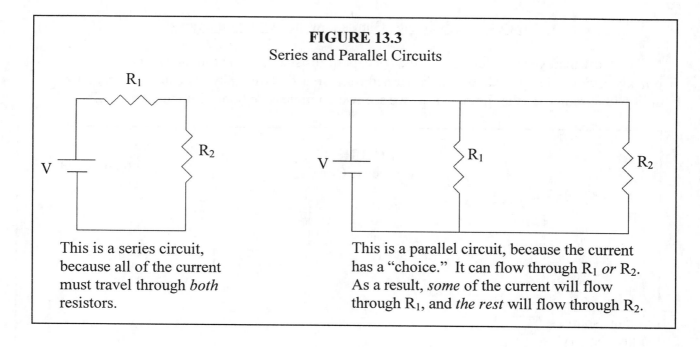

FIGURE 13.3
Series and Parallel Circuits

This is a series circuit, because all of the current must travel through *both* resistors.

This is a parallel circuit, because the current has a "choice." It can flow through R_1 *or* R_2. As a result, *some* of the current will flow through R_1, and *the rest* will flow through R_2.

Notice first the jagged lines in the circuit. Those represent resistors. They could be anything which resists the flow of electricity - a toaster, a refrigerator, a light bulb - anything. Now please understand that electric circuits are idealized representations. As you learned earlier, *all* conductors have some resistance. Thus, even the wires represented in the circuit offer some resistance to the flow of electricity. However, we generally use a low-resistivity metal such as copper for wires, so the resistance is very low - much lower than that of an appliance that uses the electricity to do work. Thus, *compared to the resistors* in the circuit, the wires have essentially zero resistance.

Notice also that the figure shows you two possible configurations for the two resistors. If the resistors are hooked in **series**, all of the electricity flowing through the circuit must pass through both resistors. If the resistors are hooked up in **parallel**, then each electron passing through the circuit has a "choice." It can flow through one resistor or the other. It cannot, however, flow through both. Since there are lots of electrons flowing through the circuit, some will make one "choice" and others will make the other "choice." As a result, some of the current will flow through one resistor, and the rest of the current will flow through the other. I will discuss in an upcoming section how to calculate the amount of current that flows through each.

One big difference between series and parallel circuits can be seen when a resistor becomes damaged and can no longer conduct electricity. Suppose someone crushed R_1 so that it no longer could conduct electricity. What would happen to the current in each circuit in Figure 13.2? Well, in the series circuit, electricity would simply stop flowing. If R_1 is damaged, there is no longer a complete path from the positive side of the battery to the negative side, so electricity simply will not flow. In the parallel circuit, however, things are different. When R_1 is damaged, electricity will no longer flow through R_1, but there is *still a complete path* from the positive side of the battery to the negative side. The current can flow just through R_2. Thus, in a series circuit, when one resistor stops conducting, the circuit is dead. In a parallel circuit, when one resistor stops conducting, *that* resistor is dead, but the other resistor continues to have current pass through it.

Now that I have reminded you about circuit diagrams, it is time to remind you of the equations we use to analyze circuits. The first is the definition of **current**.

$$I = \frac{\Delta Q}{\Delta t} \qquad (13.2)$$

Current is defined as the amount of charge that flows through a circuit per second. Thus, if I take the charge that flows and divide by the time it takes to flow, the result is the current. The standard unit works out to C/sec, which is called the **Ampere (A)**.

The amount of current that can flow through a circuit depends on the potential difference (given by the battery) and the resistance of the circuit. These three quantities are related through **Ohm's Law**:

$$V = I \cdot R \qquad (13.3)$$

In this equation, "V" is the potential difference, "I" is the current, and "R" is the *total* resistance. Notice that because V must have the unit Volt, we can deduce that the unit for resistance must be Volt/Ampere. This tells us that an Ω is a Volt/Ampere. Please note that any conductor which obeys Ohm's law (not all materials do) is called an **ohmic** conductor.

Since we generally make electrical circuits to do some sort of work (light a light bulb, run a toaster, spin a motor, etc.), it is good to learn about how much work a circuit can do. We can figure this out by calculating the power, which as you know is the amount of work per unit time:

$$P = I \cdot V \tag{13.4}$$

In this equation, "P" stands for power, which as you know has the unit of Watt, which is a Joule/sec. Now "I" has units of Amperes, which is also Coulombs per second, and "V" has units of Volts, which is also Joules per Coulomb. If you multiply Amperes by Volts, then, you get Joules/sec, which is a Watt. There is actually another way to calculate power as well. Since Ohm's Law, Equation (13.3), gives us an expression for V, we can plug that expression into Equation (13.4) and get:

$$P = I^2 \cdot R \tag{13.5}$$

Either equation for power can be used, as they are 100% equivalent.

Okay, I just threw a *lot* of equations at you, but they really should be review. However, just to make sure you have all of this, let's look at a simple circuit.

EXAMPLE 13.2

Given the circuit below, calculate the current that runs through the circuit and the power.

We can get the current from Ohm's Law.

$$V = I \cdot R$$

$$I = \frac{V}{R} = \frac{9.00 \text{ V}}{15.0 \text{ }\Omega} = \frac{9.00 \text{ V}}{15.0 \frac{\text{V}}{\text{A}}} = \underline{0.600 \text{ A}}$$

Now to get the power, we can use either Equation (13.4) or Equation (13.5). I will use the former:

$$P = I \cdot V = (0.600 \text{ A}) \cdot (9.00 \text{ V}) = (0.600 \, \frac{\text{C}}{\text{sec}}) \cdot (9.00 \, \frac{\text{J}}{\text{C}}) = 5.40 \, \frac{\text{J}}{\text{sec}} = \underline{5.40 \text{ Watts}}$$

That's how we analyze a really simple circuit. Don't worry, it gets a lot more difficult!

To make sure you understand how to use the equations, perform the "on your own" problem which follows. It is critically important that you dust the cobwebs out of your mind on these equations, because you will have to be incredibly comfortable with them to continue on.

ON YOUR OWN

13.3 A physicist wants to design a circuit that has a power output of 14.5 Watts. She decides to use a 25.0 Ω resistor. What must the voltage be on the battery she wants to use?

Combinations of Resistors

We still have one subject to review before we delve more deeply into electric circuits. As I mentioned in the previous section, resistors can be hooked up in different ways in an electric circuit. You can put resistors in series or in parallel, and you can have combinations of the two as well. As you might imagine, the current in an electric circuit is greatly affected by the way in which the resistors are arranged. Perform the following experiment to see what I mean.

EXPERIMENT 13.2
Resistors in Series and Parallel

Supplies

- The circuit apparatus you used in the last experiment, including the light, the foil strips, the battery assembly, and the #2 pencils
- More aluminum foil
- Tape
- Serrated knife

Introduction - This experiment will show you the dramatic difference between wiring resistors in series or in parallel.

Procedure:

1. You should have three #2 pencils from the last experiment, sharpened on both ends. You should have a short one, a medium-length one, and a long one. Take the long one and cut it down and sharpen it so that it is the same length as the medium-length pencil.
2. Take a strip of foil and wad it up into a ball.
3. Take the two equal-length pencils (sharpened on both sides) and stick them in opposite ends of the ball so that their leads are fully imbedded in the foil.
4. Stick that assembly in your circuit, as shown on the right.
5. Note the brightness of the light. It is possible that the light will not come on. If so, remove one of the pencils and touch the foil coming from the battery to the foil ball. If the light shines then, you probably had a good connection, but not enough current. That's fine. If the light does not come on, there is probably a bad connection, and you should try to find it and fix it.
6. Take the pencils out of the foil ball and get rid of the foil ball.
7. Put the pencils next to each other and tape them together. Now you have two parallel pencils.
8. Stick the two pencils in the electrical circuit, as shown on the right. Make sure you press the foil against *both* pencil leads.
9. Note the brightness of the light.
10. Clean everything up. You can now throw away the things you do not want to keep.

Foil ball with pencils stuck into it.

What happened in the experiment? You should have seen that the light was much, much dimmer in the first part of the experiment than in the second part. Why? In the first part of the experiment, the resistors (the pencils) were in series. All of the current had to travel through both resistors. In the second part of the experiment, the resistors were in parallel. Each electron could travel *either* through one pencil or the other. If you think about it, the second configuration results in *less* resistance than the first. After all, since some electrons go through one resistor and the rest go down the other, the electrons are more spread out. As a result, they interfere with one another less. Thus, wiring resistors in parallel is somewhat like using a resistor with a larger cross-sectional area. Since the electrons can spread out, they do not interfere with each other as much, and resistance goes down.

This can be quantified in terms of equations that you should have learned in your first-year course:

For resistors in series: $R_{eff} = R_1 + R_2 + R_3 + ...$ (13.6)

For resistors in parallel: $\dfrac{1}{R_{eff}} = \dfrac{1}{R_1} + \dfrac{1}{R_2} + \dfrac{1}{R_3} + ...$ (13.7)

When resistors are hooked up in series, the effective resistance is the sum of each individual resistance. If two 5 Ω resistors are hooked up in series, for example, the total resistance is simply 10 Ω. However, if those same two 5 Ω resistors are hooked up in parallel, the effective resistance is *less* than either individual resistor: 2.5 Ω! Wiring resistors in parallel, then, *lowers* the total resistance, while wiring them in series *raises* the total resistance.

Since resistors affect a circuit differently depending on whether they are wired in series or parallel, circuits can sometimes be a bit hard to analyze. See what I mean by studying the following example.

EXAMPLE 13.3

What is the total current running through the following circuit?

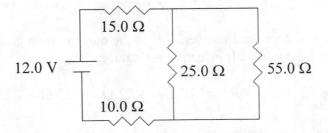

As you learned in your first-year course, one way to analyze a circuit is to reduce it to a very simple circuit. If we could get this circuit down to a battery and a single effective resistor, calculating the total current would be a simple application of Ohm's Law. The trick is, of course, reducing the 4 resistors in the circuit to one effective resistor. To do that, we have to know which resistors are hooked in series and which are hooked in parallel.

How do we do that? We imagine the conventional current traveling from the positive end of the battery to the negative end. When the current runs into a "choice" as to which way to go, we have a parallel part of the circuit. When the current has no "choice," we have a series part of the circuit. The *first thing to do* is to reduce the parallel resistors to one effective resistor, and *then* we can deal with the series resistors.

Okay, start at the positive side of the battery and begin traveling through the wire. Does the current have a choice as to whether or not to go through the 15.0 Ω resistor? No! All current must go through that resistor. Thus, it is a series resistor, and we can save it for later. Once the current gets through *that* resistor, it *does* have a choice. It can "turn right" and go through the 25.0 Ω resistor, or it can "go straight" and go around the end and travel through the 55.0 Ω resistor. Thus, the 25.0 Ω resistor and 55.0 Ω resistor are hooked in parallel. We can therefore calculate their effective resistance:

$$\frac{1}{R_{eff}} = \frac{1}{R_1} + \frac{1}{R_2} = \frac{1}{25.0\ \Omega} + \frac{1}{55.0\ \Omega} = 0.0582\ \frac{1}{\Omega}$$

$$R_{eff} = \frac{1}{0.0582\ \dfrac{1}{\Omega}} = 17.2\ \Omega$$

Now we can redraw the circuit, replacing the parallel resistors with one effective 17.2 Ω resistor:

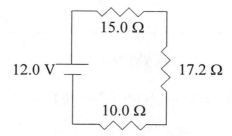

At this point, all of these resistors are in series. All of the current must go through all three of them. Thus, we can now calculate their effective resistance:

$$R_{eff} = R_1 + R_2 + R_3 = 15.0\ \Omega + 17.2\ \Omega + 10.0\ \Omega = 42.2\ \Omega$$

All three of these resistors, then, can be replaced by one effective 42.2 Ω resistor. This entire circuit (from a resistance point of view) is therefore equivalent to the following simple circuit:

Calculating the total current is now a snap!

$$V = I \cdot R$$

$$I = \frac{V}{R} = \frac{12.0\ V}{42.2\ \Omega} = \frac{12.0\ \cancel{V}}{42.2\ \dfrac{\cancel{V}}{A}} = \underline{0.284\ A}$$

At this point, I ought to have covered what you did in your first-year course. Thus, once you have completely cleared the cobwebs out of your brain concerning this kind of analysis, we can go on to discuss more detailed analyses of circuits. Perform the following "on your own" problems to make sure you are "back in the groove," and then it will start to get *really* interesting!

ON YOUR OWN

13.4 How much power is drawn by the following circuit?

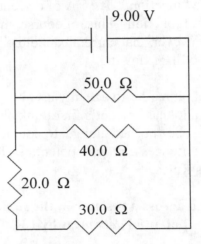

13.5 The following circuit draws 0.500 A. What is the value of the resistor labeled with a question mark?

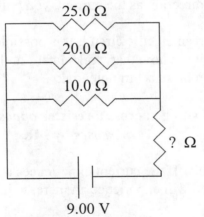

Kirchhoff's Rules

Although it is nice to be able to calculate the *total* current drawn in a circuit, it would also be nice to know how much current runs through *each resistor*. For example, consider the circuit from on your own problem 13.5. How much current runs through the 25.0 Ω resistor? We can calculate that using **Kirchhoff's Rules**.

<u>Kirchhoff's First Rule (The Loop Rule)</u> - The change in potential around a closed loop is always equal to zero.

<u>Kirchhoff's Second Rule (The Junction Rule)</u> - The sum of the currents entering a junction must equal the sum of currents leaving a junction.

Kirchhoff's Second Rule is the easiest to understand. When the current encounters a "choice" as to where it will go, that is called a "junction." If 15 A of current enter a junction, when the junction ends, 15 A must leave that junction. This, of course, makes sense. When the current has a "choice," it can split up. However, that current cannot be lost. When the "choice" ends, the same amount of current must still be flowing.

Kirchhoff's First Rule is a bit harder to actually use, but if you remember some guidelines, it will make your life a lot easier. Let's first think about resistors. If current travels through a resistor, the current must be "pushed along," to counter the resistance. This takes work. As a result, the current experiences a *drop* in potential. This brings us to our first guideline when using Kirchhoff's Rules:

When tracing a loop, if you go across a resistor in the *same direction* as the current, the potential *decreases* by I·R.

This is just using Ohm's Law in the case of a single resistor. Before passing through a resistor, the current has a higher potential than it does on the other side of the resistor. Thus, if you are following a loop in the same direction as the current, you will record a drop in potential.

When tracing a loop in an electric circuit, it is possible that you will find yourself moving opposite the current. You will see how that works later on. If that happens and you encounter a resistor, you must treat it as an *increase* in potential:

When tracing a loop, if you go across a resistor *opposing* the current, the potential *increases* by I·R.

This should make sense as well. If the current experiences a drop in potential, and if you are going opposite the current, you will experience an increase in potential.

Eventually, we will start dealing with circuits that have more than one battery. That makes the circuit more difficult to analyze, but it is not impossible. You just have to follow two guidelines when the loop you are tracing contains a battery:

When tracing a loop, if you encounter the *negative* side of the battery first, the potential *increases* by the battery's voltage.

This should make sense. A battery is a source of potential. If your loop includes a battery and you cross the battery in the direction of the current flow, you get the "push" of the battery, and the potential increases. However, if you go against the current, the opposite happens.

When tracing a loop, if you encounter the *positive* side of the battery first, the potential *decreases* by the battery's voltage.

These four guidelines might seem strange right now, but once you have done some circuit analysis with them, they make sense. Let's start, then, with a "simple" circuit. Let's start with the circuit in "on your own" problem 13.5.

EXAMPLE 13.4

In the circuit diagram below, how much current is running through the 20.0 Ω resistor?

25.0 Ω

20.0 Ω

10.0 Ω

12.7 Ω

9.00 V

Getting the total current is easy. We just turn all of the resistors into one effective resistor as you learned in the previous section, then we use Ohm's Law. However, the question doesn't ask for the total current. It wants the current going through the 20.0 Ω resistor. How do we get that? We use Kirchhoff's Rules. First, we choose a loop - any loop. Let's choose the bottom one, as illustrated on the right. We start the loop at the positive side of the battery, and trace the path of conventional current. When we leave the battery, all current is traveling in the loop, because it has not encountered a choice yet. Thus, the current is I_{tot}. However, when the current reaches the top of the loop, it has a choice. It can go through the 10.0 Ω resistor or the 20.0 Ω resistor or the 25.0 Ω resistor. Thus, only a portion of the current (which we will call I_1) goes through the 10.0 Ω resistor. However, once the current reaches the right side of the loop, all of the other branches merge together. Thus, all of the current must come together again. As a result, I_{tot} runs through the 12.7 Ω resistor.

10.0 Ω

I_1

I_{tot} I_{tot} 12.7 Ω

9.00 V

Now we can use Kirchhoff's First Rule. The sum of the potentials in this loop must be zero. We are going with the current throughout the loop, so the potential drops across every resistor. By the time we actually *encounter* the battery on our trip, we encounter the negative end first. We started at the positive side of the battery, but we were already past it. We did not actually encounter the battery until the end of the loop, and when we did, we encountered the negative end first. Thus, the potential of the battery is added. This gives us an equation:

$$9.00 \text{ V} - I_1 \cdot (10.0 \text{ }\Omega) - I_{tot} \cdot (12.7 \text{ }\Omega) = 0$$

That's Kirchhoff's First Rule - the change in potential around the loop equals zero. This equation is useful, but we cannot solve it, because it has two variables. Thus, we need another equation. For that, we go to another loop.

Let's choose the next logical loop, as illustrated on the right. In this loop, we once again start out in front of the battery. At that point, we are tracing all of the current. Then, we will skip the first branch and head to the second branch. Only a portion of the total current will travel through that branch, so we will call it I_2. Finally, when the branches converge, all of the current flows through the 12.7 Ω resistor, so that is I_{tot} once again. Following the same logic as before, we come up with the following equation for this loop:

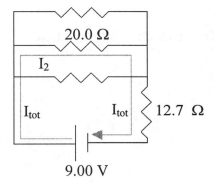

$$9.00 \text{ V} - I_2 \cdot (20.0 \text{ }\Omega) - I_{tot} \cdot (12.7 \text{ }\Omega) = 0$$

You might not think this helps, because we now have *yet another variable*. Well, that's true, but if we keep going, we will eventually get what we need. Let's look at the last loop. Once again, we start in front of the battery and then skip the first two branches but go through the last one. Since only a portion of the current runs through that branch, we will call it I_3. Once again, however, by the time we encounter the 12.7 Ω resistor, all of the branches have merged, so we are dealing with I_{tot} again. This leads to yet another equation:

$$9.00 \text{ V} - I_3 \cdot (25.0 \text{ }\Omega) - I_{tot} \cdot (12.7 \text{ }\Omega) = 0$$

At this point, we have three equations and four unknowns. However, there is one more equation we can develop. We can use Kirchhoff's Second Rule to say that the sum of I_1, I_2, and I_3 must be equal to I_{tot}, because we cannot lose current.

$$I_{tot} = I_1 + I_2 + I_3$$

Now we have four equations and four unknowns, so we can solve for the four unknowns. Aren't you thrilled?

The easiest thing to do is get everything in terms of I_{tot}. We can do this using the first three equations. Let's start with the equation from loop 1:

$$9.00 \text{ V} - I_1 \cdot (10.0 \ \Omega) - I_{tot} \cdot (12.7 \ \Omega) = 0$$

$$I_1 = \frac{9.00 \text{ V} - I_{tot} \cdot (12.7 \ \Omega)}{10.0 \ \Omega}$$

Then we can go to the equation from loop 2:

$$9.00 \text{ V} - I_2 \cdot (20.0 \ \Omega) - I_{tot} \cdot (12.7 \ \Omega) = 0$$

$$I_2 = \frac{9.00 \text{ V} - I_{tot} \cdot (12.7 \ \Omega)}{20.0 \ \Omega}$$

Then we can go to the equation from loop 3:

$$9.00 \text{ V} - I_2 \cdot (25.0 \ \Omega) - I_{tot} \cdot (12.7 \ \Omega) = 0$$

$$I_3 = \frac{9.00 \text{ V} - I_{tot} \cdot (12.7 \ \Omega)}{25.0 \ \Omega}$$

Now we can put these three expressions into the last equation and solve for I_{tot}.

$$I_{tot} = I_1 + I_2 + I_3$$

$$I_{tot} = \frac{9.00 \text{ V} - I_{tot} \cdot (12.7 \ \Omega)}{10.0 \ \Omega} + \frac{9.00 \text{ V} - I_{tot} \cdot (12.7 \ \Omega)}{20.0 \ \Omega} + \frac{9.00 \text{ V} - I_{tot} \cdot (12.7 \ \Omega)}{25.0 \ \Omega}$$

$$(25.0 \ \Omega) \cdot I_{tot} = 22.5 \text{ V} - (2.50) \cdot I_{tot} \cdot (12.7 \ \Omega) + 11.3 \text{ V} - (1.25) \cdot I_{tot} \cdot (12.7 \ \Omega) + 9.00 \text{ V} - I_{tot} \cdot (12.7 \ \Omega)$$

$$I_{tot} = \frac{42.8}{85.3 \ \Omega} = 0.502$$

Now that we know I_{tot}, we can easily solve for I_2, which is what the question asked for!

$$I_2 = \frac{9.00 \text{ V} - I_{tot} \cdot (12.7 \ \Omega)}{20.0 \ \Omega} = \frac{9.00 \text{ V} - (0.502 \text{ A}) \cdot (12.7 \ \Omega)}{20.0 \ \Omega} = \underline{0.131 \text{ A}}$$

That was a long problem, wasn't it? You might even be a little annoyed to hear that there is actually an easier way to solve the problem. However, I don't want to teach that to you. I want you to learn Kirchhoff's Rules and how to use them, because they are so important. Now if all of that seemed a bit foreign to you, don't worry. I will go through another example in a moment. For right now, just step back and see what we did. We kept choosing loops and developing an equation for each loop until we got to the point where we had as many equations as we had unknowns. Then we solved the equations simultaneously. Although a nuisance, Kirchhoff's Rules are incredibly useful. Let's see how they work in more complicated circuits.

EXAMPLE 13.5

In the circuit below, determine the current that flows through the 15.0 Ω resistor. Also, determine the potential difference between points A and B.

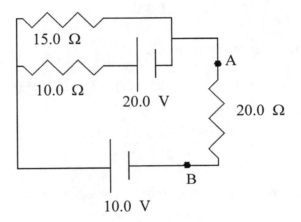

This is a more complicated circuit because it has two batteries. However, with Kirchhoff's Rules, it is pretty easy to analyze. Let's start with a loop that goes through the 10.0 Ω resistor. Current leaves the 10.0 V battery. Is it the total current? We don't know, because there is another battery to consider. Thus, we will call it I_1. When it reaches the top of the loop, it can go into the 10.0 Ω resistor or the 15.0 Ω resistor, so this is a branch. Thus, only a part of I_1 will go through the 10.0 Ω resistor, so we will call that I_2. Once the

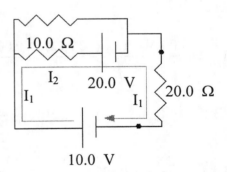

branch merges back, we cannot lose any current, so I_1 will go through the 20.0 Ω resistor. Now let's look at the potentials. When we go through the 10.0 Ω resistor, the potential will drop. The potential will also drop again when we pass through the 20.0 V battery, because we encounter the positive side first. When we go through the 20.0 Ω resistor, the potential will drop, and the potential will increase when we hit the 10.0 V battery. Thus, the equation is:

$$10.0 \text{ V} - I_2 \cdot (10.0 \text{ Ω}) - 20.0 \text{ V} - I_1 \cdot (20.0 \text{ Ω}) = 0$$

Now, let's choose the other possible loop. In this loop, we are following the other branch. Only a portion of I_1 goes through that branch, so we will call it I_3. It will pass through the 15.0 Ω resistor, and the potential will drop. Then, the branches merge, so all of I_1 will go through the 20.0 Ω resistor, where the potential will once again drop. We then encounter the battery, which raises the potential because we hit the negative side first. In this loop, then:

$$10.0 \text{ V} - I_3 \cdot (15.0 \ \Omega) - I_1 \cdot (20.0 \ \Omega) = 0$$

We now have two equations and three unknowns. However, we can use Kirchhoff's Second Rule to get a third equation. Since we cannot lose current:

$$I_1 = I_2 + I_3$$

To solve these equations, let's use the first two to get I_2 and I_3 in terms of I_1:

$$10.0 \text{ V} - I_2 \cdot (10.0 \ \Omega) - 20.0 \text{ V} - I_1 \cdot (20.0 \ \Omega) = 0$$

$$I_2 = \frac{-10.0 \text{ V} - I_1 \cdot (20.0 \ \Omega)}{10.0 \ \Omega}$$

$$10.0 \text{ V} - I_3 \cdot (15.0 \ \Omega) - I_1 \cdot (20.0 \ \Omega) = 0$$

$$I_3 = \frac{10.0 \text{ V} - I_1 \cdot (20.0 \ \Omega)}{15.0 \ \Omega}$$

We can now use these expressions in the third equation:

$$I_1 = I_2 + I_3$$

$$I_1 = \frac{-10.0 \text{ V} - I_1 \cdot (20.0 \ \Omega)}{10.0 \ \Omega} + \frac{10.0 \text{ V} - I_1 \cdot (20.0 \ \Omega)}{15.0 \ \Omega}$$

$$(15.0 \ \Omega) \cdot I_1 = -15.0 \text{ V} - (1.5) \cdot I_1 \cdot (20.0 \ \Omega) + 10.0 \text{ V} - I_1 \cdot (20.0 \ \Omega)$$

$$I_1 = \frac{-15.0 \text{ V} + 10.0 \text{ V}}{65.0 \ \Omega} = -0.0769 \text{ A}$$

What does the negative mean? It means we chose the *wrong direction* for current. We had I_1 traveling clockwise. It is really traveling counterclockwise. Does that matter, *not one bit!*

That's the great thing about Kirchhoff's Rules. You don't have to know how the current flows. Just pick a direction, and if you are wrong, you will find out in the equations!

Now that we have I_1, we can get the other two currents (although we only need one of them).

$$I_2 = \frac{-10.0 \text{ V} - I_1 \cdot (20.0 \text{ } \Omega)}{10.0 \text{ } \Omega} = \frac{-10.0 \text{ V} - (-0.0769) \cdot (20.0 \text{ } \Omega)}{10.0 \text{ } \Omega} = -0.846 \text{ A}$$

$$I_3 = \frac{10.0 \text{ V} - I_1 \cdot (20.0 \text{ } \Omega)}{15.0 \text{ } \Omega} = \frac{10.0 \text{ V} - (-0.0769) \cdot (20.0 \text{ } \Omega)}{15.0 \text{ } \Omega} = 0.769 \text{ A}$$

The question only wanted the current flowing through the 15.0 Ω resistor, which is I_3. Thus, the answer to the first part of the question is 0.7692 A. However, now that we know the directions of the current, I want to go ahead and draw how the current *really* flows. Since I_1 and I_2 are negative, we have their directions reversed in our original drawings. However, I_3 is fine as is. Thus, the real directions for current are:

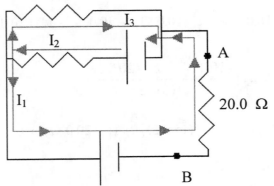

In reality, then, I_2 splits up into I_1 and I_3. However, we did not need to know that. Using Kirchhoff's Rules actually showed us that.

The last part of the question asks for the potential difference between A and B. Well, if we travel from point A to point B, we go *against* the current. This means the potential *raises*.

$$V = I_1 \cdot R = (0.0769 \text{ A}) \cdot (20.0 \text{ } \Omega) = 1.54 \text{ V}$$

This indicates that point A is 1.54 V *lower* in potential than point B, because this is the amount by which the voltage *raises* as we go from point A to point B.

I would like to make one quick point before I end this section. Kirchhoff's Rules lead to a couple of conclusions that may not be obvious at first glance. Therefore, I just want to explicitly state them for you:

Resistors in parallel are all exposed to an equal potential difference.

Resistors in series all carry an equal amount of current.

Since we will use Kirchhoff's Rules in analyzing circuits, we will not use these conclusions per se. However, they are nice to know.

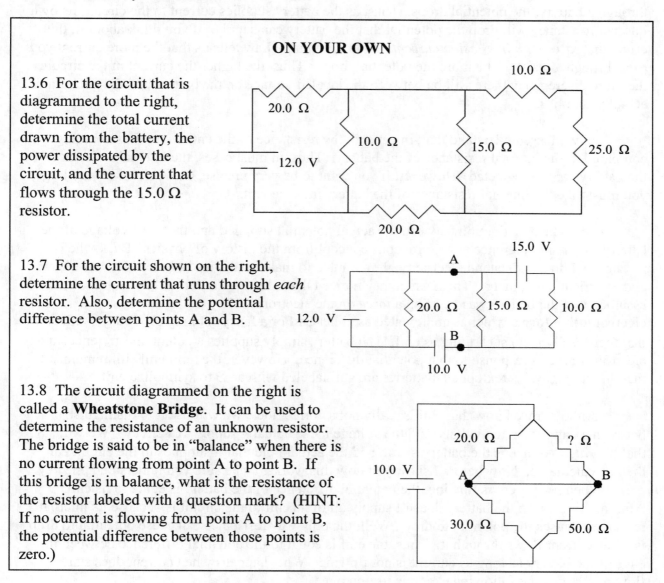

ON YOUR OWN

13.6 For the circuit that is diagrammed to the right, determine the total current drawn from the battery, the power dissipated by the circuit, and the current that flows through the 15.0 Ω resistor.

13.7 For the circuit shown on the right, determine the current that runs through *each* resistor. Also, determine the potential difference between points A and B.

13.8 The circuit diagrammed on the right is called a **Wheatstone Bridge**. It can be used to determine the resistance of an unknown resistor. The bridge is said to be in "balance" when there is no current flowing from point A to point B. If this bridge is in balance, what is the resistance of the resistor labeled with a question mark? (HINT: If no current is flowing from point A to point B, the potential difference between those points is zero.)

Batteries, Electromotive Force, and Internal Resistance

Now that you have learned to analyze rather complex electric circuits, I want to discuss something that we have been simplifying up to this point: the battery. In our circuit diagrams, we have been labeling the battery with a voltage rating, which tells us the potential that the battery is giving to the circuit. However, that voltage rating is *not* the same as the voltage that is printed on the battery. If I pick up a flashlight battery, for example, I see that it is labeled as a 1.5 Volt battery. However, if I put that battery in an electric circuit, it will provide *less than 1.5 Volts of potential* to the circuit. Why? Because batteries have **internal resistance**.

Remember, no conductor (except a superconductor) is perfect, and a battery must supply current through a conductor. Thus, the battery itself will have some resistance to current. What does resistance do to the potential? It *decreases* the potential. Remember, as current passes through a battery, the potential drops. Thus, as the battery supplies current to the circuit, its own internal resistance will drop the potential that the battery can supply. If you think about it, this effect *increases with increasing current*. After all, Ohm's Law tells us that the more current you pass through a resistor, the more the potential drops. Thus, the higher the current in the circuit, the more discrepancy there will be between the labeled voltage on the battery and the potential it actually supplies.

Now please understand that, in general, the resistance of the entire circuit is very large compared to the internal resistance of the battery. Thus, in most cases, the internal resistance of the battery can be neglected. However, if you want to be very precise, or if current is very large, you must take the internal resistance of the battery into account.

To make a distinction between the actual potential supplied and the rated voltage of the battery, we make reference to an erroneous concept from the history of physics. Back when physicists didn't understand electricity, they wanted to make analogies between Newton's Laws and electrical phenomena. Thus, when they noticed that a battery caused electrons to move, they assumed that the battery was exerting a *force* on the electrons. They called this the **electromotive force**, which is abbreviated as either **emf** or a fancy-looking $\mathcal{E}$. Today, we know that there really is no such thing as emf. The battery simply supplies a potential difference, and electrons move in response to that potential difference. However, the term emf still remains. In fact, in many physics textbooks, batteries are still labeled with an $\mathcal{E}$ to symbolize emf.

Although we know that emf is really not a correct idea, we will use it to distinguish between a battery's rated voltage and the voltage it can actually supply to a circuit. We will say that the *rated* voltage is the battery's emf, and the actual potential it supplies to the circuit can then be calculated. Now before I show you how this works, make sure you understand one key point: When no current is flowing, the potential difference of the battery is equal to its emf. After all, the reason the battery doesn't supply all of its emf to the circuit is because its internal resistance causes the potential to drop. Well, the only way resistance can cause potential to drop is when current flows through it. Thus, the emf is equal to the potential difference between the ends of the battery as long as current is not flowing. What happens when current does start flowing? Study the following example to find out.

EXAMPLE 13.6

In the circuit to the right, the battery has an emf of 12.0 volts and an internal resistance of 2.00 Ω. Calculate the actual potential that the battery supplies to the circuit if R = 55.0 Ω and if R = 5.00 Ω.

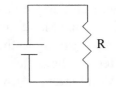

The first thing that I want to do is to change the circuit diagram a little. After all, we know that the battery has an internal resistance. Let's draw that explicitly.

The gray rectangle contains the entire battery. I have just separated out the resistor from the emf. Now we see that the internal resistance of the battery is really just a resistor which is in series with the 55.0 Ω resistor. Thus, we can treat this circuit as containing an ideal battery (supplying 12.0 V) and a circuit with a total resistance of 57.0 Ω. We can therefore use Ohm's Law to calculate the total current in this circuit:

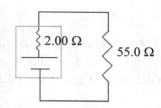

$$V = I \cdot R$$

$$I = \frac{V}{R} = \frac{12.0 \text{ V}}{57.0 \text{ } \Omega} = 0.211 \text{A}$$

This is not the answer, of course, but it can lead us quickly to the answer. Now that we know the total current, we can calculate the potential drop across the internal resistor of the battery:

$$V = I \cdot R = (0.211 \text{ A}) \cdot (2.00 \text{ } \Omega) = 0.422 \text{ V}$$

If the internal resistance causes the potential to drop 0.422 V, then the actual potential that the battery provides to the circuit is simply 12.0 V - 0.422 V, which equals <u>11.6 V</u>. In this circuit, then, the battery supplies 11.6 V of potential.

We can now redo the calculation when R = 5.00 Ω. When that is the case, the total resistance of the circuit (including the internal resistance of the battery) is 7.00 Ω.

$$V = I \cdot R$$

$$I = \frac{V}{R} = \frac{12.0 \text{ V}}{7.00 \text{ } \Omega} = 1.71 \text{A}$$

That current causes the following voltage drop over the internal resistor of the battery:

$$V = I \cdot R = (1.71 \text{ A}) \cdot (2.00 \text{ } \Omega) = 3.42 \text{ V}$$

If the internal resistance causes the potential to drop 3.42 V, then the actual potential that the battery provides to the circuit is simply 12.0 V - 3.42 V, which equals <u>8.6 V</u>. Notice how much lower the actual potential supplied to the circuit is. That's because the larger current in the circuit causes a greater potential drop across the battery's internal resistance.

In most circuits that you will analyze, we will assume that the battery's internal resistance is so small that it does not affect the potential significantly. However, if a problem specifically mentions the internal resistance of a battery, you must take it into account!

ON YOUR OWN

13.9 In the circuit drawn to the right, the battery is labeled as a 9.00 V battery. In the circuit, however, it provides only 8.59 V of potential. What is the battery's internal resistance?

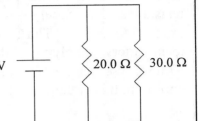

$\varepsilon = 9.00$ V   20.0 Ω   30.0 Ω

Resistance-Capacitance (RC) Circuits

In the previous module, you learned about how capacitors store charge. In the experiment you did with the Leyden jar, you charged your capacitor by rubbing a balloon in your hair and transferring the charge to the capacitor. Of course, this is not the typical way a capacitor is charged. Generally, capacitors are charged in a circuit. These circuits are called **RC**, or **resistance-capacitance** circuits. Consider, for example, the following simple RC circuit.

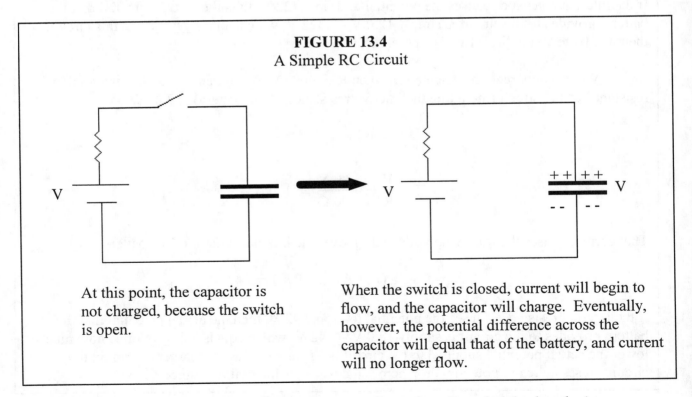

FIGURE 13.4
A Simple RC Circuit

At this point, the capacitor is not charged, because the switch is open.

When the switch is closed, current will begin to flow, and the capacitor will charge. Eventually, however, the potential difference across the capacitor will equal that of the battery, and current will no longer flow.

In this simple RC circuit, current will start to flow when the switch is closed. As conventional current flows to the top plate of the capacitor, the plate will become positively-charged. That positive charge will repel positive charges on the bottom plate, and those positive charges will leave the bottom plate and go to the negative side of the battery. As this happens, a potential will build across the plates of the capacitor. Eventually, the plates will have the same potential between them as the battery does between its positive and negative sides. At that point, the potential from the capacitor will offset the potential from the battery, and *current will no longer flow*. In an RC circuit like this one, then, current does not continually flow. It flows until the capacitor charges, and then it stops.

Why would you build a circuit like this if current only flows for a brief time? Well, there are several reasons, but I will only explain one of them. Consider, for example, the following circuit.

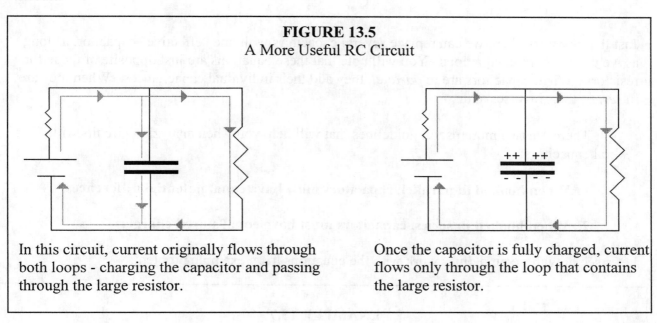

FIGURE 13.5
A More Useful RC Circuit

In this circuit, current originally flows through both loops - charging the capacitor and passing through the large resistor.

Once the capacitor is fully charged, current flows only through the loop that contains the large resistor.

Why is this a more useful RC circuit? Well, consider what happens if the battery's voltage drops a bit. When that happens, the current from the battery will decrease. However, since the capacitor has voltage equal to the original potential difference of the battery, it will begin to supply some current to the circuit. This will tend to "even out" temporary drops in the battery's output. In the same way, if the battery voltage surges for some reason, the current from the battery will increase. However, if the battery voltage surges, the capacitor will take in more charge. This will tend to decrease the current that the large resistor gets, because some of the battery's extra current will go to the capacitor. Thus, the capacitor will tend to "even out" temporary increases in the battery's output as well. In the end, then, a capacitor put into a circuit as shown above can "smooth out" the performance of a circuit.

Capacitors are used for many other applications as well, but they go beyond the scope of this course. A detailed electronics course will give you a good feel for the importance of capacitors in electric circuits. For right now, however, I do want to cover one more aspect of capacitors in circuits. Since they can be so useful, they tend to appear in many electric circuits. Often, they appear in combination with other capacitors, so it would be nice to know how capacitors work in concert with one another.

Remember from Experiment 13.2 that when resistors are put in a circuit, the way that they work together depends on whether they are hooked in parallel or series. Not surprisingly, the same can be said of capacitors. Interestingly enough, the equations for capacitors are very similar to those of resistors:

For capacitors in parallel: $C_{eff} = C_1 + C_2 + C_3 + ...$ (13.8)

For capacitors in series: $\dfrac{1}{C_{eff}} = \dfrac{1}{C_1} + \dfrac{1}{C_2} + \dfrac{1}{C_3} + ...$ (13.9)

Just like resistors, then, we can replace several capacitors with one "effective" capacitor, as long as we use the correct equations. You will note that these equations are just opposite of those for resistors. When capacitors are in *parallel*, they add their individual capacitances. When they are in *series*, their inverses add.

There are two more useful guidelines that will help you when analyzing circuits with several capacitors:

1. When hooked in parallel, capacitors must have equal potential differences.

2. When hooked in series, capacitors must have equal stored charge.

Let's see how these guidelines work with the equations in an example problem.

EXAMPLE 13.7

In the circuit on the right, the battery has a potential difference of 9.00 V. The capacitors have values as follows:

$C_1 = 10.0\ \mu F$, $C_2 = 20.0\ \mu F$, $C_3 = 30.0\ \mu F$

Determine the charge stored on each capacitor.

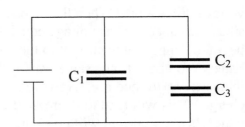

When faced with several capacitors in series and parallel, we reduce the circuit with effective capacitors. First, let's take C_2 and C_3, which are hooked in series, and replace them with an effective capacitor:

$$\frac{1}{C_{eff}} = \frac{1}{C_1} + \frac{1}{C_2} = \frac{1}{20.0\ \mu F} + \frac{1}{30.0\ \mu F}$$

$$C_{eff} = 12.0 \ \mu F$$

This reduces the circuit to the one shown on the right. Now we just have two capacitors which are hooked in parallel. Thus, we can use Equation (13.8) to determine their effective capacitance:

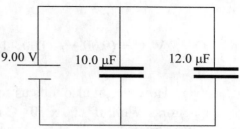

$$C_{eff} = C_1 + C_2 = 10.0 \ \mu F + 12.0 \ \mu F = 22.0 \ \mu F$$

Now we have a very simple circuit:

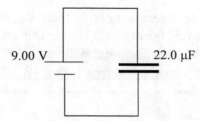

The charge stored on the effective capacitor is easy to calculate now, remembering Equation (12.9) from the previous module:

$$\Delta V = \frac{Q}{C}$$

$$Q = \Delta V \cdot C = (9.00 \ \cancel{V}) \cdot (2.20 \times 10^{-5} \ \frac{C}{\cancel{V}}) = 1.98 \times 10^{-4} \ C$$

That's the total charge, but it is not the answer, is it? We want to know the charge on *each capacitor*. Here is where we use the guidelines. We know that capacitors in parallel must have the same voltage. Thus, in the second diagram we had:

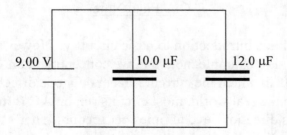

The 10.0 μF capacitor must have a potential of 9.00 V, as must the effective, 12.0 μF capacitor. Since we know V and C for the 10.0 μF capacitor, we can immediately get the charge on it:

$$\Delta V = \frac{Q}{C}$$

$$Q = \Delta V \cdot C = (9.00 \ \cancel{V}) \cdot (1.00 \times 10^{-5} \ \frac{C}{\cancel{V}}) = 9.00 \times 10^{-5} \ C$$

That's part of the answer. However, it also tells us something else. A total of 1.98×10^{-4} C are stored on *all three* capacitors. Well, if 9.00×10^{-5} C is stored on the 10.0 µF capacitor, the rest must be stored on the other two:

$$\text{charge on other two} = 1.98 \times 10^{-4} \ C - 9.00 \times 10^{-5} \ C = 1.08 \times 10^{-4} \ C$$

Since capacitors in series must have the same charge, then the other two capacitors each store 1.08×10^{-4} C. You can check that this is correct by using this charge to calculate the potential difference in each of the two capacitors. The total will add to 9.00 V, as is should. Thus, C₁ stores 9.00×10^{-5} C, while each of the others stores 1.08×10^{-4} C.

ON YOUR OWN

13.10 In the circuit to the right, determine the charge on each capacitor.

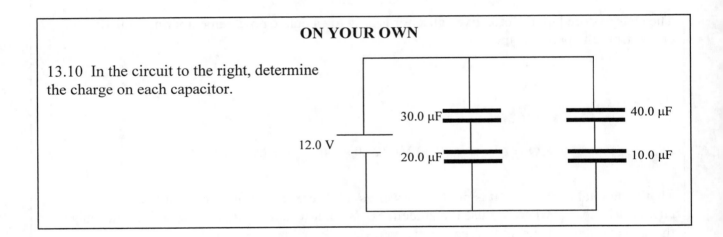

One Final Note

I hope you enjoyed this introduction to basic circuitry. However, please note that the introduction is very basic. For example, note that we concentrated on **DC (direct current) circuits**. These are circuits in which the current runs in only one direction. Batteries provide such current. However, in the real world, most circuits run on **AC (alternating current)**, in which the current switches direction several times per second. That's the kind of current which comes from an electrical outlet. We have not even touched on those kinds of circuits in this module, nor will we discuss them in this course. If you are really interested in this subject, I suggest that you look for a detailed electronics course.

ANSWERS TO THE ON YOUR OWN PROBLEMS

13.1 If you want the maximum current, you want the least resistance. Thus, you want to use the material with the lowest resistivity. Of the materials listed in the table, <u>silver</u> has the lowest resistivity. Of course, this is not practical in most applications, as silver is expensive. Thus, copper is more often used, because it has a very low resistivity but is not as expensive as silver.

13.2 We know that resistance depends on resistivity (which we have in the table), length (given), and cross-sectional area. We can calculate that:

$$R = \rho \cdot \frac{L}{A}$$

$$A = \rho \cdot \frac{L}{R} = (1.72 \times 10^{-8}\ \Omega \cdot m) \cdot \frac{1.0\ m}{8.6 \times 10^{-5}\ \Omega} = 0.00020\ m^2$$

Assuming the width and height are equal, the length of each is simply the square root of the area, or <u>0.014 m</u>.

13.3 To answer this question, we first need to know what the current is. We can get that from Equation (13.5):

$$P = I^2 \cdot R$$

$$I = \sqrt{\frac{P}{R}} = \sqrt{\frac{14.5\ \frac{J}{sec}}{25.0\ \frac{V}{A}}} = \sqrt{0.580\ \frac{J \cdot A}{V \cdot sec}} = \sqrt{0.580\ \frac{J \cdot A}{\frac{J}{C} \cdot sec}} = \sqrt{0.580\ \frac{C \cdot A}{sec}} = \sqrt{0.580\ A^2} = 0.762\ A$$

Notice how the units work out. Since a Volt is a J/C, Joules cancel and we are left with A^2 under the square root. Now that we have current, we can use Equation (13.4) to get voltage:

$$P = I \cdot V$$

$$V = \frac{P}{I} = \frac{14.5\ \frac{J}{sec}}{0.762\ \frac{C}{sec}} = 19.0\ \frac{J}{C} = \underline{19.0\ V}$$

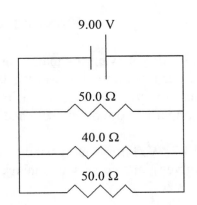

13.4 The first thing we need to do is to replace all of the resistors with an equivalent resistor. To do that, we need to determine which resistors are in parallel and which are in series. The 30.0 Ω and 20.0 Ω resistors are in series, because any current which goes through one must go through the other. Thus, we can add their resistances and come up with a simplified circuit, given to the right.

In this circuit, all resistors are in parallel. Thus, we can find an equivalent resistor for them:

$$\frac{1}{R_{eff}} = \frac{1}{R_1} + \frac{1}{R_2} + \frac{1}{R_3} = \frac{1}{50.0 \ \Omega} + \frac{1}{40.0 \ \Omega} + \frac{1}{50.0 \ \Omega} = 0.0650 \ \frac{1}{\Omega}$$

$$R_{eff} = \frac{1}{0.0650 \ \frac{1}{\Omega}} = 15.4 \ \Omega$$

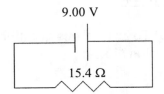

This takes us down to the battery and one 15.4 Ω resistor. To determine the power that this circuit draws, we must first determine the current:

$$V = I \cdot R$$

$$I = \frac{V}{R} = \frac{9.00 \ V}{15.4 \ \Omega} = \frac{9.00 \ \cancel{V}}{15.4 \ \frac{\cancel{V}}{A}} = 0.584 \ A$$

Now we can get power from either Equation (13.4) or (13.5):

$$P = I \cdot V = (0.584 \ A) \cdot (9.00 \ V) = (0.584 \ \frac{\mathcal{C}}{sec}) \cdot (9.00 \ \frac{J}{\mathcal{C}}) = \underline{5.26 \ Watts}$$

13.5 Note that the resistor with the question mark is not a part of the parallel circuit. The other resistors are in parallel, but *all* of the current must travel through the unknown resistor. First, then, we can reduce the three parallel resistors to one effective resistor:

$$\frac{1}{R_{eff}} = \frac{1}{R_1} + \frac{1}{R_2} + \frac{1}{R_3} = \frac{1}{25.0 \ \Omega} + \frac{1}{20.0 \ \Omega} + \frac{1}{10.0 \ \Omega} = 0.190 \ \frac{1}{\Omega}$$

$$R_{eff} = \frac{1}{0.190 \ \dfrac{1}{\Omega}} = 5.26 \ \Omega$$

The circuit, then, looks like the one drawn on the right. Since these resistors are in series, they add. Thus, if we could find some way to get the total resistance, getting the unknown resistance is easy. Well, we know the voltage and the current, so Ohm's Law will tell us the resistance:

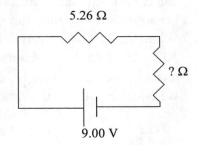

$$V = I \cdot R$$

$$R = \frac{V}{I} = \frac{9.00 \ V}{0.500 \ A} = 18.0 \ \Omega$$

That's the effective resistance. Thus, we can now calculate the unknown resistance:

$$R_{eff} = R_1 + \ ?$$

$$? = R_{eff} - R_1 = 18.0 \ \Omega - 5.26 \ \Omega = \underline{12.7 \ \Omega}$$

13.6 To solve a problem like this, we might as well do Kirchhoff's Rules. There is another way to solve the problem, but it is no easier, so we might as well stick with the process we need to know. Let's start with the first loop:

In this loop, we have I_1 going through the 20.0 Ω resistor, but then the current has a choice. Thus, only part of the current (I_2) will go through the 10.0 Ω resistor. Then, we encounter the battery, negative side first. Thus:

20.0 Ω 10.0 Ω

I_1

I_2 10.0 Ω 15.0 Ω

25.0 Ω

12.0 V   20.0 Ω

12.0 V - $I_1 \cdot (20.0 \ \Omega)$ - $I_2 \cdot (10.0 \ \Omega)$ = 0

That gives us our first equation, but we have two unknowns. Thus, we have to continue. The next most logical loop is given to the right. In this loop, we have I_1 going through the 20.0 Ω resistor, but then the current has a choice. Thus, only part of the current (I_3) will go through the 15.0 Ω resistor. Look at the other 20.0 Ω resistor on this loop, however. We cannot say that I_3 runs through it, because there is a junction behind it. Whatever is running through the

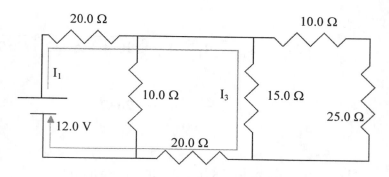

10.0 Ω and 25.0 Ω resistors on the far right of the circuit will also run through this 20.0 Ω resistor. Let's call that I_4. This means that *both* I_3 and I_4 run through the 20.0 Ω resistor. Then, we encounter the battery, negative side first. Thus:

$$12.0 \text{ V} - I_1 \cdot (20.0 \text{ Ω}) - I_3 \cdot (15.0 \text{ Ω}) - (I_3 + I_4) \cdot (20.0 \text{ Ω}) = 0$$

Now we have two equations, but four unknowns. Thus, we have go on to the next loop. In this loop, we have I_1 going through the 20.0 Ω resistor, but then the current has a choice. We already called the current that runs through the far right of the circuit I_4, and it will go through the 10.0 Ω and 25.0 Ω resistors. Then, we encounter the 20.0 Ω resistor. We already determined that both I_3 and I_4 will run through that one. Finally, we encounter the battery, negative side first. Thus:

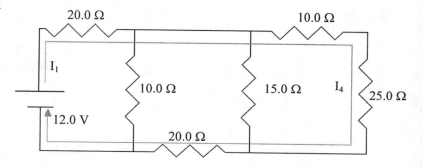

$$12.0 \text{ V} - I_1 \cdot (20.0 \text{ Ω}) - I_4 \cdot (10.0 \text{ Ω}) - I_4 \cdot (25.0 \text{ Ω}) - (I_3 + I_4) \cdot (20.0 \text{ Ω}) = 0$$

Finally, we know that all of the current must recombine once it comes back from the last junction. Thus:

$$I_1 = I_2 + I_3 + I_4$$

We now have a system of 4 equations and 4 unknowns. They are a little harder to solve than the examples, but we should be masters at this kind of algebra by now! Let's get I_2 in terms of I_1 using the first equation:

$$12.0 \text{ V} - I_1 \cdot (20 \text{ Ω}) - I_2 \cdot (10.0 \text{ Ω}) = 0$$

$$I_2 = \frac{12.0 \text{ V} - I_1 \cdot (20 \text{ Ω})}{10.0 \text{ Ω}}$$

That was the easy part. It gets a bit trickier from here. Let's use the second equation to get an expression for I_3.

$$12.0 \text{ V} - I_1 \cdot (20 \text{ }\Omega) - I_3 \cdot (15.0 \text{ }\Omega) - (I_3 + I_4) \cdot (20.0 \text{ }\Omega) = 0$$

Now we are presented with a problem. We have both I_3 and I_4 in this equation. How do we solve for I_3? Well, remember, we know that $I_1 = I_2 + I_3 + I_4$. This means

$$I_3 + I_4 = I_1 - I_2$$

We can stick *that* into the equation where $(I_3 + I_4)$ is.

$$12.0 \text{ V} - I_1 \cdot (20 \text{ }\Omega) - I_3 \cdot (15.0 \text{ }\Omega) - (I_1 - I_2) \cdot (20.0 \text{ }\Omega) = 0$$

$$I_3 = \frac{12.0 \text{ V} - I_1 \cdot (40.0 \text{ }\Omega) + I_2 \cdot (20.0 \text{ }\Omega)}{15.0 \text{ }\Omega}$$

How does this help? Well, we have an equation for I_2 in terms of I_1. We can stick that into this equation:

$$I_3 = \frac{12.0 \text{ V} - I_1 \cdot (40.0 \text{ }\Omega) + I_2 \cdot (20.0 \text{ }\Omega)}{15.0 \text{ }\Omega} = \frac{12.0 \text{ V} - I_1 \cdot (40.0 \text{ }\Omega) + [\frac{12.0 \text{ V} - I_1 \cdot (20.0 \text{ }\Omega)}{10.0 \text{ }\Omega}] \cdot (20.0 \text{ }\Omega)}{15.0 \text{ }\Omega}$$

$$I_3 = \frac{36.0 \text{ V} - I_1 \cdot (80.0 \text{ }\Omega)}{15.0 \text{ }\Omega}$$

We have to do the same thing again with the third equation:

$$12.0 \text{ V} - I_1 \cdot (20 \text{ }\Omega) - I_4 \cdot (10.0 \text{ }\Omega) - I_4 \cdot (25.0 \text{ }\Omega) - (I_3 + I_4) \cdot (20.0 \text{ }\Omega) = 0$$

$$12.0 \text{ V} - I_1 \cdot (20 \text{ }\Omega) - I_4 \cdot (10.0 \text{ }\Omega) - I_4 \cdot (25.0 \text{ }\Omega) - (I_1 - I_2) \cdot (20.0 \text{ }\Omega) = 0$$

$$I_4 = \frac{12.0 \text{ V} - I_1 \cdot (40.0 \text{ }\Omega) + I_2 \cdot (20.0 \text{ }\Omega)}{35.0 \text{ }\Omega} = \frac{12.0 \text{ V} - I_1 \cdot (40 \text{ }\Omega) + [\frac{12.0 \text{ V} - I_1 \cdot (20.0 \text{ }\Omega)}{10.0 \text{ }\Omega}] \cdot (20.0 \text{ }\Omega)}{35.0 \text{ }\Omega}$$

$$I_4 = \frac{36.0 \text{ V} - I_1 \cdot (80.0 \text{ }\Omega)}{35.0 \text{ }\Omega}$$

Whew! Now we can put all of these expressions for I_1, I_2, and I_3 into the fourth equation:

$$I_1 = I_2 + I_3 + I_4$$

$$I_1 = \frac{12.0\ V - I_1 \cdot (20.0\ \Omega)}{10.0\ \Omega} + \frac{36.0\ V - I_1 \cdot (80.0\ \Omega)}{15.0\ \Omega} + \frac{36.0\ V - I_1 \cdot (80.0\ \Omega)}{35.0\ \Omega}$$

$$(35.0\ \Omega) \cdot I_1 = 42.0\ V - I_1 \cdot (70.0\ \Omega) + 84.0\ V - I_1 \cdot (187\ \Omega) + 36.0\ V - I_1 \cdot (80.0\ \Omega)$$

$$I_1 = \frac{42.0\ V + 84.0\ V + 36.0\ V}{372\ \Omega} = 0.435\ A$$

Since that's the sum of all the individual currents, it is the total current. Thus, the total current is 0.435 A. The power drawn is easy:

$$P = I \cdot V = (0.435\ \frac{C}{sec}) \cdot (12.0\ \frac{J}{C}) = 5.22\ Watts$$

Finally, the problem asks for the current in the 15.0 Ω resistor. According to our definitions, that was I_3.

$$I_3 = \frac{36.0\ V - I_1 \cdot (80.0\ \Omega)}{15.0\ \Omega} = \frac{36.0\ V - (0.435\ A) \cdot (80.0\ \Omega)}{15.0\ \Omega} = 0.080\ A$$

Therefore, 0.080 A flow through the 15.0 Ω resistor.

13.7 Once again, we have to use Kirchhoff's Rules here, so we need to start by picking a loop. The first one is shown to the right. In this loop, I_1 leaves the battery, but it soon has to make a choice. Only part of the current (I_2) will go through the 20.0 Ω resistor. Then, we encounter the negative side of the 12.0 V battery. Thus, this loop tells us:

$$12.0\ V - I_2 \cdot (20.0\ \Omega) = 0$$

Surprisingly, we can actually solve this equation for I_2!

$$I_2 = \frac{12.0 \text{ V}}{20.0 \text{ } \Omega} = 0.600 \text{ A}$$

We can now go to the next loop, which is shown to the right. In this loop, I_1 leaves the battery, but it soon has to make a choice. Only part of the current (I_3) will go through the 15.0 Ω resistor. Then, we encounter the positive side of the 10.0 V battery. Once we pass through that battery, we encounter the negative side of the 12.0 V battery. Thus, this loop tells us:

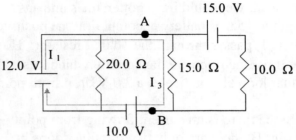

$$12.0 \text{ V} - 10.0 \text{ V} - I_3 \cdot (15.0 \text{ } \Omega) = 0$$

$$I_3 = \frac{2.0 \text{ V}}{15.0 \text{ } \Omega} = 0.13 \text{ A}$$

We can now go to the next loop, which is shown to the right. In this loop, I_1 leaves the battery, but it soon has to make a choice. Only part of the current (I_4) will go through the 10.0 Ω resistor. Before reaching the resistor, however, we encounter the positive side of the 15.0 V battery. Then, we encounter the resistor, then we encounter the positive side of the 10.0 V battery. Then we encounter the negative side of the 12.0 V battery. This loop, then, tells us:

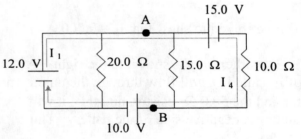

$$-15.0 \text{ V} - 10.0 \text{ V} + 12.0 \text{ V} - I_4 \cdot (10.0 \text{ } \Omega) = 0$$

$$I_4 = \frac{-13.0 \text{ V}}{10.0 \text{ } \Omega} = -1.30 \text{ A}$$

The negative sign tells us that the direction of the current is opposite of what we drew. This tells us, then, that <u>0.600 A run through the 20.0 Ω resistor; 0.13 A run through the 15.0 Ω resistor; and 1.30 A run through the 10.0 Ω resistor.</u>

We are not quite done, however. We also need to know the potential difference between points A and B. That's not too bad, however. Let's assume we are taking the second loop. At point A, I_3 and I_4 are running through the wire. If we follow the second loop, I_3 runs down the 15.0 Ω resistor. Then, it encounters point B. The difference in potential, then, is just the drop in voltage across that resistor.

$$V = I \cdot R = (0.13 \text{ A}) \cdot (15.0 \ \Omega) = 2.0 \text{ V}$$

Thus, <u>point B is 2.0 V lower in potential than point A</u>. Please note that had we chosen the third loop instead, we would have gotten the same answer. In the third loop, the current passes through the 15.0 V battery encountering the positive side first. That drops the potential by 15.0 V. Then, I_4 passes through the 10.0 Ω resistor. However, we have the direction backwards, so we are traveling opposite the current, which raises the potential by I·R, or 13.0 V. In the end, then, that loop also indicates a 2.0 V drop from point A to point B, as it should.

13.8 Since there is no current flowing from point A to point B, there are only two possible loops in which to travel. The first is drawn to the right. I_1 leaves the battery but reaches a choice. Part of the current (I_2) travels through the 20.0 Ω and 30.0 Ω resistors, and returns to the battery, encountering the 10.0 V battery negative side first. Thus:

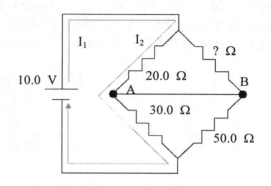

$$10.0 \text{ V} - I_2 \cdot (20.0 \ \Omega) - I_2 \cdot (30.0 \ \Omega) = 0$$

This can be solved to show that $I_2 = 0.200$ A.

The other loop is shown to the right. A part of I_1, called I_3, will flow through the unknown resistor and the 50.0 Ω resistor, and then it will encounter the negative side of the battery. Thus:

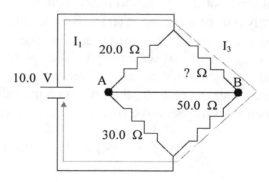

$$10.0 \text{ V} - I_3 \cdot (? \ \Omega) - I_3 \cdot (50.0 \ \Omega) = 0$$

This doesn't help, however, because there are two unknowns. We could say that $I_1 = I_2 + I_3$, but that doesn't help, either, since it just adds one more unknown.

What do we do, then? This is why I gave you the hint. Remember, there is no potential difference between point A and point B. That means whatever potential drop I_2 experiences as it travels through the 20.0 Ω resistor, I_3 must experience that exact same drop as it passes through the unknown resistor. After all, both currents are at the same potential before they encounter the resistors. To get to point A, I_2 must experience a drop as it passes through the 20.0 Ω resistor. To get to point B, I_3 must experience a drop as it passes through the unknown resistor. If those drops are not identical, there will be a potential difference between A and B. However, we know that there is not, so the drops must be the same. Thus:

$$I_2 \cdot (20.0 \ \Omega) = I_3 \cdot (? \ \Omega)$$

We already know I_2, so we can put it in:

$$(0.200 \text{ A}) \cdot (20.0 \text{ } \Omega) = I_3 \cdot (? \text{ } \Omega)$$

$$I_3 \cdot (? \text{ } \Omega) = 4.00 \text{ V}$$

Well, we can take the equation for loop 2 and just stick 4.00 V in for $I_3 \cdot (? \text{ } \Omega)$.

$$10.0 \text{ V} - 4.00 \text{ V} - I_3 \cdot (50.0 \text{ } \Omega) = 0$$

This tells us that $I_3 = 0.12$ A. With that, we can now get the resistance:

$$I_3 \cdot (? \text{ } \Omega) = 4.00 \text{ V}$$

$$(0.12 \text{ A}) \cdot (? \text{ } \Omega) = 4.00 \text{ V}$$

The unknown resistance, then, is <u>33 Ω</u>.

13.9 The two parallel resistors can be replaced by an effective resistor of 12.0 Ω. Now the total resistance must be *more* than 12.0 Ω, because of the internal resistance of the battery. How much more? Well, we know that after the internal resistor of the battery, the potential drops 0.41 V, because the battery has an emf of 9.00 V but delivers only 8.59 V. That means the internal resistor causes it to lose 0.41 V. Thus, we know that

$$0.41 \text{ V} = I \cdot r$$

where "r" is the internal resistor. The problem is, this has two unknowns. However, we do know something else. We know that the total current is simply the emf divided by the total resistance:

$$I = \frac{9.00 \text{ V}}{12.0 \text{ } \Omega + r}$$

We can put that expression into our first equation, giving us:

$$0.41 \text{ V} = \frac{9.00 \text{ V}}{12.0 \text{ } \Omega + r} \cdot r$$

$$4.9 \text{ V} \cdot \Omega + (0.41 \text{ V}) \cdot r = (9.00 \text{ V}) \cdot r$$

$$r = \frac{4.9 \text{ \textcancel{V}} \cdot \Omega}{8.59 \text{ \textcancel{V}}} = \underline{0.57 \text{ } \Omega}$$

13.10 We can first calculate an effective capacitance for the capacitors in series, using Equation (13.9):

$$\frac{1}{C_{eff}} = \frac{1}{C_1} + \frac{1}{C_2} = \frac{1}{30.0 \ \mu F} + \frac{1}{20.0 \ \mu F}$$

$$C_{eff} = 12.0 \ \mu F$$

$$\frac{1}{C_{eff}} = \frac{1}{C_1} + \frac{1}{C_2} = \frac{1}{40.0 \ \mu F} + \frac{1}{10.0 \ \mu F}$$

$$C_{eff} = 8.00 \ \mu F$$

This reduces the circuit to:

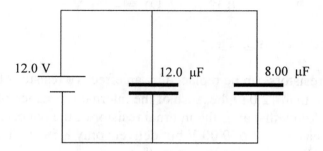

That's all I really need to know. Capacitors in parallel are subject to the same potential, so each effective capacitor has 12.0 V across its plates. That means the first branch stores:

$$\Delta V = \frac{Q}{C}$$

$$Q = \Delta V \cdot C = (12.0 \ \cancel{V}) \cdot (1.20 \times 10^{-5} \ \frac{C}{\cancel{V}}) = 1.44 \times 10^{-4} \ C$$

The second branch stores:

$$\Delta V = \frac{Q}{C}$$

$$Q = \Delta V \cdot C = (12.0 \ \cancel{V}) \cdot (8.00 \times 10^{-6} \ \frac{C}{\cancel{V}}) = 9.60 \times 10^{-5} \ C$$

Since capacitors in series store the same amount of charge, <u>the 20.0 µF and 30.0 µF capacitors store 1.44 x 10^{-4} C, and the other two capacitors store 9.60 x 10^{-5} C.</u>

REVIEW QUESTIONS

1. Two conductors identical in length and shape are connected to both sides of a battery. The first is made of lead, and the second is made of iron. What is the ratio of the current in the first conductor to the current in the second conductor? (See Table 13.1)

2. In the experiment described above, the lengths of the two conductors must stay the same. If you must use the two materials discussed above, what can you do to make the current equal in both cases? Be very specific.

3. When a light bulb burns out, it fails to conduct electricity. In the following circuit, all light bulbs start out lighting up. If light bulb #2 suddenly burns out, what other light bulb(s) will go out?

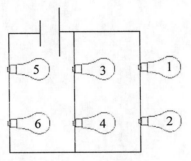

4. A "critical" bulb is a bulb that will cause the entire circuit to go dark if it burns out. List any critical bulbs in the circuit diagram above.

5. A circuit consists of a battery and a 15 Ω resistor. The power output of that circuit is measured and recorded as "P." The 15 Ω resistor is then replaced with a 45 Ω resistor. What is the new power output, in terms of "P?"

6. A battery is rated to produce 9.0 V of potential difference. When put in a circuit that has a total resistance of 10 Ω, however, it delivers only 8.5 V. If the same battery is put in a circuit whose total resistance is 100 Ω, will the potential it delivers increase, decrease, or stay the same?

7. In the circuit diagrammed to the right, switch S1 and switch S2 are initially open. S1 is then closed while S2 remains open. After a long time, S1 is opened and then S2 is closed. After a long time, what will be the potential across both capacitors?

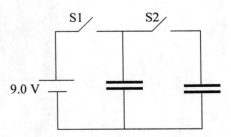

8. The current flowing through a circuit is measured as I. If the voltage of the battery in the circuit is suddenly tripled and nothing else is changed, what is the new current, in terms of I?

9. You have the simple circuit that is drawn to the right. You also have another 15 Ω resistor which you can place anywhere you would like in this circuit. Where would you place it to decrease the current flowing from the battery?

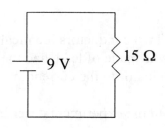

10. In the situation described in question #9, where would you place the resistor in order to *increase* the current flowing from the battery?

PRACTICE PROBLEMS

1. A 5.00 Watt electric motor runs on a 9.00 V battery. What is the resistance of the motor?

2. An Ohm-meter is a device that measures the resistance between two points. If an Ohm-meter was hooked up between points A and B in the diagram below, what resistance would it read?

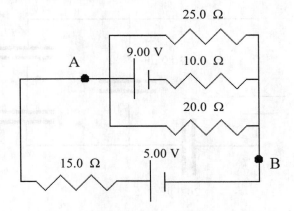

3. Suppose 5.00 A of current entered the circuit drawn above at point A. How much current would flow through the 35.0 Ω resistor? (HINT: You calculated the resistance from point A to point B. Think of the voltage drop that occurs between these two points as a result of the 5.00 A current running through that resistance.)

Questions 4 - 7   refer to the following circuit diagram:

4. Calculate the current that travels through the 25.0 Ω resistor.

5. Draw the current as it flows in this circuit, labeling the direction as well as the amount of current in each part of the circuit.

6. Calculate the potential difference between points A and B.

7. Calculate the amount of energy dissipated by the 20.0 Ω resistor in 1.00 minute.

8. In the circuit diagram below, what is the potential difference between points A and B?

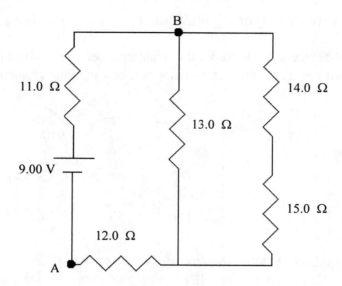

9. Work problem #8 again, assuming that the battery has an internal resistance of 3.0 Ω.

10. In the circuit below, how much charge is stored on each capacitor?

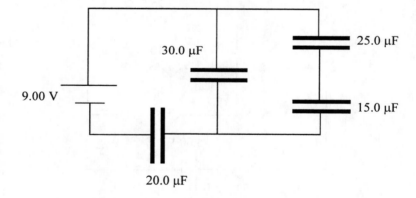

Module #14: Magnetism and Electromagnetic Induction

Introduction

We have been discussing the electrostatic force, electric potential, and electric circuits. It is now time to move on to a brief discussion of magnetism. Before we begin that discussion, however, I must remind you that Maxwell unified electricity and magnetism into a single phenomenon. The force with which two positive charges repel one another is really the same as the force with which two north magnetic poles repel one another. These forces, which Maxwell unified, are now simply called the **electromagnetic force**. It is not surprising, then, that electric charges in motion are the *source* of magnetic fields. This is actually something you should have learned in your first-year physics course. To bring you up to speed on this and other concepts, let's start with a brief review.

A Review of Magnetic Fields and Their Source

We know that a bar magnet can exert a force on another magnet or certain other metals. We say, therefore, that a bar magnet has a **magnetic field**. Just like an electric field, a magnetic field can be illustrated with fields lines, as shown in Figure 14.1

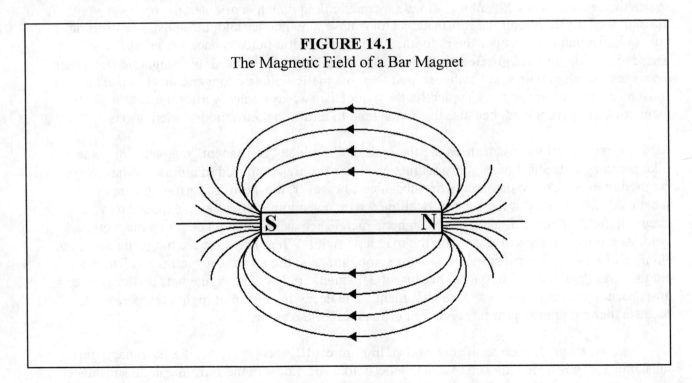

FIGURE 14.1
The Magnetic Field of a Bar Magnet

A magnet has two poles, which are called **north** and **south**. Just as like charges repel one another and opposite charges attract one another, like poles repel one another and opposite poles attract one another. The magnetic field is illustrated by drawing lines that begin at the north pole and head to the south pole. Just as is the case with electric fields, the density of lines indicates the strength of the field.

Although there are no obvious charges moving in a bar magnet, the magnetic field of a bar magnet is, nevertheless, made from moving charges. Those moving charges, of course, are in the *atoms* of the molecules that make up the bar magnet. Remember, all atoms are composed of electrons which orbit the nucleus. Those are moving charges and thus produce magnetic fields. As a result, it is possible for atoms to produce magnetic fields.

Do all atoms produce magnetic fields? No. The electron configuration of many atoms results in the magnetic fields of the individual electrons canceling out. This leaves the atom with no net magnetic field. A substance composed of such atoms is called a **diamagnetic substance**. When a diamagnetic substance is exposed to a magnetic field, a weak, *opposing* magnetic field is induced in the substance. As a result, diamagnetic substances are actually weakly repelled by magnetic fields.

Other atoms have permanent magnetic fields because the magnetic fields of their individual electrons don't cancel out. However, even if a substance is composed of atoms that have a magnetic field, the substance itself might not be a magnet. Why? Well, suppose the atoms are all randomly-oriented in the substance. Each atom has a magnetic field, but that magnetic field cancels with another atom's magnetic field which is oriented the opposite way. In the end, then, even though the substance's atoms have a magnetic field, the substance itself does not act like a magnet, because the individual atoms' magnetic fields cancel one another out. These are called **paramagnetic substances**, and when they are exposed to a magnetic field, their atoms tend to align with one another so that their magnetic fields no longer cancel out. Thus, the substance becomes magnetic. Typically, the magnetism decays quickly after the external magnetic field is removed, because the atoms tend to return to their random orientations.

Ferromagnetic substances are the ones out of which "permanent" magnets are made. Like paramagnetic substances, ferromagnetic substances are composed of atoms that have magnetic fields. Unlike paramagnetic substances, however, the atoms of ferromagnetic substances tend to stay at least partially aligned with one another after being exposed to a magnetic field. Thus, if I take a ferromagnetic metal such as iron and place it in a magnetic field, its atoms will tend to align with the magnetic field. When I remove the magnetic field, the atoms will stay at least partially aligned for some time, and the result is a "permanent" magnet. I put the term "permanent" in quotes because the magnetic fields of such magnets do decay over time, because the atoms tend to lose alignment. The decay is quicker at higher temperatures, because thermal energy promotes random orientation of the atoms.

A bar magnet, such as the one shown in Figure 14.1, then, is made of a ferromagnetic substance that has been exposed to a magnetic field. The atoms in the ferromagnetic substance aligned as a result of being placed in the magnetic field, and once removed from the magnetic field, they stayed at least partially aligned. As a result, the bar now produces a magnetic field of its own. In your first-year course, you learned how to draw magnetic field lines in the presence of several such magnets, much like you learned to draw electric field lines in the presence of several charges.

Throughout most of the rest of this module, I want to concentrate on the effects that magnetic fields produce on moving charges. However, rather than working with magnetic fields such as the one shown in Figure 14.1, I want to spend a lot of time working with uniform magnetic fields. How do we produce such fields? Not surprisingly, we produce a uniform magnetic field much like we produce a uniform electric field:

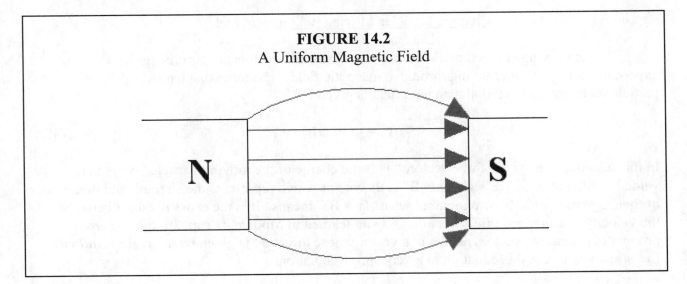

FIGURE 14.2
A Uniform Magnetic Field

Just as we can produce a uniform electric field between two oppositely-charged parallel plates, we can produce a uniform magnetic field between two parallel, opposite poles. As long as you are not near the edges of the poles, the magnetic field between the two poles will be uniform.

Before I leave this review, I want to remind you of one more thing. Although the majority of your experience with magnets is probably centered around bar magnets such as the one in Figure 14.1, the easiest way to produce magnetic fields is through the use of electricity. After all, moving charges are what produce magnetic fields, and electric current is a flow of charged particles. Thus, electric current produces magnetic fields. You probably did an experiment in your first-year course where you wrapped a current-carrying conductor around an iron substance and made a magnet out of it. When we use the flow of electricity to make a magnet, we usually call it an **electromagnet**.

Although you probably didn't really learn this in your first-year course, magnetic fields have strengths which can be measured. An electric field's strength is measured in Newtons per Coulomb, which as you know is also equivalent to Volts per meter. The strength of a magnetic field is measured in $\frac{\text{Newtons}}{\text{Ampere} \cdot \text{meter}}$, which is called the **Tesla (T)**, in honor of Nikola Tesla, a brilliant engineer and inventor. Since magnetic fields obviously have direction as well, the magnetic field is a vector quantity and is usually abbreviated as "**B**."

ON YOUR OWN

14.1 Suppose a substance was placed directly in between the north and south poles pictured in Figure 14.2. If the substance was diamagnetic, which way would the magnetic field inside the substance point? What if the substance was paramagnetic? What if the substance was ferromagnetic?

Charged Particles Moving in Magnetic Fields

Since moving charged particles create magnetic fields, it is not surprising that they experience a force when moving through a magnetic field. The force that a moving charged particle feels from an external magnetic field is given by:

$$\mathbf{F} = q \cdot (\mathbf{v} \times \mathbf{B}) \tag{14.1}$$

In this equation, "**F**" is the force vector, "q" is the charge of the moving particle, "**v**" is the velocity of the moving particle, and "**B**" is the vector which represents the strength and direction of the magnetic field. Now remember what "(**v** x **B**)" means. It is the **cross product** between the velocity and magnetic field vectors. As you learned in Module #1 (pp. 20-26), the cross product between two vectors results in a vector whose direction is given by the **right hand rule**. Let's see how to use this equation in a very simple situation.

EXAMPLE 14.1

A charged particle (q = -0.561 mC) is moving with a velocity of 3.40 x 10⁴ m/sec at an angle of 45.0° in a uniform magnetic field of 0.350 Teslas at 180.0°. What is the force experienced by the particle?

Let's first draw the situation:

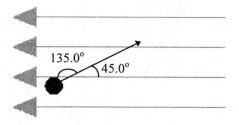

The magnetic field is pointed to the left (θ = 180.0°), and the particle is moving at an angle of 45.0°. According to Equation (14.1), the force it experiences will be determined by the cross product of **v** and **B**. Thus, we must first remember how to get the magnitude of the cross product. According to Equation (1.9):

$$|\mathbf{v} \times \mathbf{B}| = v \cdot B \cdot \sin\theta$$

In this equation, however, θ is the angle *between* the two vectors. Notice that since **B** is pointed to the left, the angle between the vectors is not 45.0°, but 135.0°. Thus, the magnitude of the force is:

$$F = q \cdot v \cdot B \cdot \sin\theta$$

$$F = (-0.000561 \text{ C}) \cdot (3.40 \times 10^4 \, \frac{\cancel{m}}{\sec}) \cdot (0.350 \, \frac{N}{A \cdot \cancel{m}}) \cdot \sin(135.0) = -4.72 \, \cancel{A} \cdot \frac{N}{\cancel{A}} = -4.72 \text{ N}$$

Notice that the units do work out to give us Newtons in the end.

Now what does that negative mean? Well, the force vector has a direction, which is given by the right hand rule. Since the magnitude came out negative, it means that the direction of the force vector is *opposite* that which is given by the right hand rule. So, let's do the right hand rule and determine the direction. In the right hand rule, we take the fingers of our right hand and point them in the direction of the first vector (**v**). Then, we curl our fingers to the second vector (**B**), along the arc of the angle between the two vectors. When we are finished, our thumb points in the direction of the cross product.

Well, when we do that here, our thumb points in the direction *above* the plane of the paper. Thus, the cross product is directed perpendicular to the paper, pointing *above* it. We typically say that the direction is "pointing out of" the plane of the paper. Remember, however, that the magnitude came out negative. Thus, the direction of the force is opposite that of the cross product. In other words, it is pointing *below* the paper. We typically say that this is "pointing into" the plane of the paper. The force, then, is 4.72 N directed perpendicular to and pointing into the plane of the paper.

Now that you know the mechanics of how to use the equation, I want you to sit and think about what this means for a moment. When you use the right hand rule, you will always come up with a direction that is perpendicular to both vectors. Thus, since the magnetic force depends on the cross product between the velocity and magnetic field vectors, the magnetic force experienced by a moving charged particle in a magnetic field will always be perpendicular to the particle's velocity vector. Think about what this means. What happens when an object experiences a force which is perpendicular to its velocity? It moves in a *circle*, because a force perpendicular to the velocity acts as a *centripetal* force.

I want to explore this a bit more, but before I do, I want to show you one way that we illustrate uniform magnetic fields. Since a lot of the "action" associated with uniform magnetic fields occurs perpendicular to those fields, I would like to illustrate them so that they are perpendicular to the paper that I am writing on. I will do this as illustrated in Figure 14.3.

FIGURE 14.3
Uniform Magnetic Fields Oriented Perpendicular to the Plane of the Paper

X X X X X X X   • • • • • • •

X X X X X X X   • • • • • • •

X X X X X X X   • • • • • • •

X X X X X X X   • • • • • • •

These X's represent magnetic field lines which are perpendicular to and pointed into the plane of the paper.   These dots represent magnetic field lines which are perpendicular to and pointed out of the plane of the paper.

When you see a series of X's, then, you will know that the magnetic field lines are pointing into the plane of the paper. If you were to point your fingers in the direction of the magnetic field, you would hold your hand above the paper and point directly down at the paper. On the other hand, a series of dots means that the magnetic field is perpendicular to and pointing out of the plane of the paper. If you were to point in the direction of the magnetic field, then, you would hold your hand above the paper and then point straight up.

With this in mind, let's think about the situation in which a positively-charged particle is traveling due north in a perpendicular magnetic field:

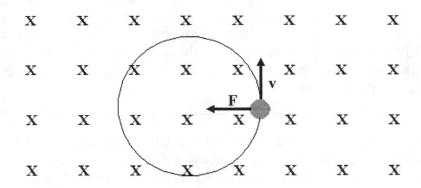

Notice that the way I have drawn this, the magnetic field is pointed into the plane of the paper. We can determine the direction of the magnetic force that the charged particle will experience using the right hand rule. If we point our right hand fingers in the direction of **v** and then curl them into the paper (the direction of **B**), our thumb points to the left. Thus, the force that the particle experiences is perpendicular to the velocity, pointed to the left. Since the particle experiences a force perpendicular to its velocity, it moves in a circle, as illustrated.

If the magnetic force is the only force experienced by the charged particle, it will continue to move in uniform circular motion. The force will never change the magnitude of the velocity, so the speed will remain constant. However, the *direction* of the velocity will continually change, as the particle continues to sweep out a circle. If the magnetic field is not perpendicular to the velocity, the motion will not be a perfect circle. Instead, it will be a spiral. In this course, we will concentrate on situations in which the velocity and magnetic fields are perpendicular.

Think, for a moment, about the centripetal force that the particle experiences. We know an equation for the centripetal force, Equation (6.14). We also know that the magnetic field is causing that centripetal force, so Equation (14.1) is an alternate expression for the centripetal force. Thus, we can put these two equations together:

$$q \cdot (\mathbf{v} \times \mathbf{B}) = \frac{m \cdot v^2}{r} \tag{14.2}$$

Since the right side of the equation is not a vector, we can just use the magnitude of $\mathbf{v} \times \mathbf{B}$:

$$q \cdot v \cdot B \cdot \sin\theta = \frac{m \cdot v^2}{r} \tag{14.3}$$

The velocity and magnetic field are perpendicular to one another, so $\theta = 90$. Thus:

$$q \cdot v \cdot B = \frac{m \cdot v^2}{r} \tag{14.4}$$

$$\boxed{r = \frac{m \cdot v}{q \cdot B}} \tag{14.5}$$

Equation 14.5, then, allows us to calculate the radius of the circle in which the charged particle will travel in a perpendicular magnetic field. We do not use the sign of the charge in this equation. This has led to an incredibly useful experimental device called a **mass spectrometer**, which can measure the mass of something as small as an *atom*!

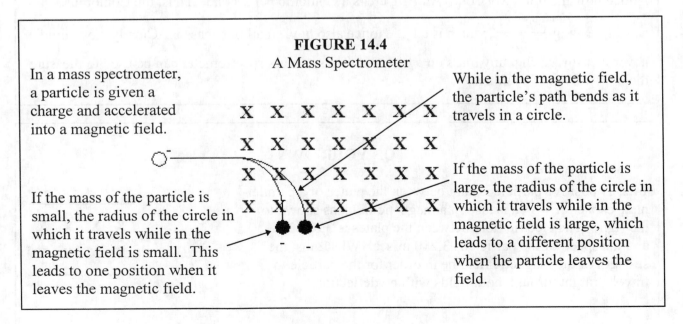

FIGURE 14.4
A Mass Spectrometer

In a mass spectrometer, a particle is given a charge and accelerated into a magnetic field.

While in the magnetic field, the particle's path bends as it travels in a circle.

If the mass of the particle is small, the radius of the circle in which it travels while in the magnetic field is small. This leads to one position when it leaves the magnetic field.

If the mass of the particle is large, the radius of the circle in which it travels while in the magnetic field is large, which leads to a different position when the particle leaves the field.

In a mass spectrometer, a particle of unknown mass is given a known electric charge. It is then accelerated to a known speed and sent into a perpendicular magnetic field. Because of what we discussed above, it begins to move in a circle. The larger the mass, the larger the circle. When the particle leaves the magnetic field, its position is measured by a detector, and the radius of the circle in which it traveled while in the magnetic field is measured. As a result, the mass is determined. Study the example below to understand how the mass is determined.

EXAMPLE 14.2

In a mass spectrometer, a particle of unknown mass is given an extra electron, so that its electric charge is -1.6 x 10^{-19} C. The particle is then accelerated to 1.3 x 10^4 m/sec and sent into a perpendicular magnetic field of strength 0.050 T. The particle's final position indicates that while it was in the magnetic field, it moved in a circle with a radius of 1.3 cm. What is the mass of the particle?

This is really a simple application of Equation (14.5). Remember, we do not use the sign of the charge in the equation.

$$r = \frac{m \cdot v}{q \cdot B}$$

$$m = \frac{q \cdot B \cdot r}{v} = \frac{(1.6 \times 10^{-19}\ C) \cdot (0.050\ \frac{N}{A \cdot m}) \cdot (0.013\ m)}{1.3 \times 10^4\ \frac{m}{sec}} = 8.0 \times 10^{-27}\ \frac{C \cdot sec \cdot N}{m \cdot A} = \underline{8.0 \times 10^{-27}\ kg}$$

Notice how the units work out. An Ampere is a Coulomb per second. Thus, the Coulombs cancel, leaving $\frac{sec^2 \cdot N}{m}$, which is a kg. Notice also how small this mass is. Clearly, you could never measure such a tiny mass on a balance! Thus, a mass spectrometer can be used to measure the mass of very tiny things!

ON YOUR OWN

14.2 A positive particle is shot between the plates of a parallel-plate capacitor which is also in a magnetic field, as shown to the right. The electric field between the plates is 3,014 N/C, and the speed of the particle is 3,210 m/sec. What must the strength of the magnetic field be in order for the particle to travel straight through both fields with no deflection?

14.3 If the electric field in the previous problem was shut off, but the magnetic field that you calculated in your answer was used, what would be the radius of the circle in which the particle would travel while in the magnetic field? The mass of the particle is 15.0 g, and the charge is 0.340 C.

Cyclotrons

Another very useful tool that comes from the interaction between charged particles in motion and magnetic fields is the **cyclotron**. This is a device that accelerates charged particles to high speeds. A cyclotron is made according to the diagram below:

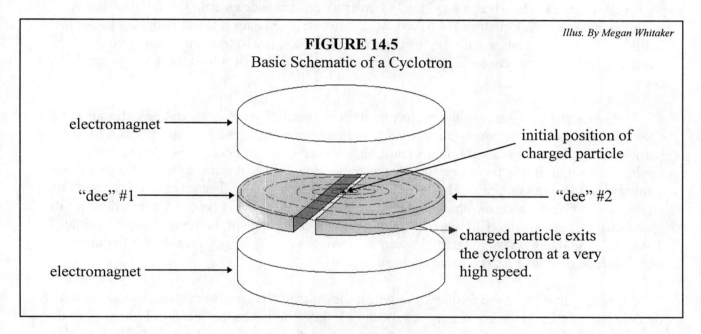

FIGURE 14.5
Basic Schematic of a Cyclotron

Illus. By Megan Whitaker

A cyclotron is composed of two electromagnets that create a uniform magnetic field perpendicular to the plane in which the charged particle moves. In between these electromagnets are two hollow, D-shaped conductors called **dee's**. The dee's are connected to an alternating voltage supply. A charged particle starts at the center of the cyclotron, and one dee is given the same charge as the particle while the other dee is given the opposite charge. In the figure above, for example, assume that the particle is negative. Dee #2 would be charged positive and dee #1 would be charged negative. What will happen as a result? The particle will start accelerating away from dee #1 and towards dee #2. Once it reaches dee #2, it will enter the hollow conductor.

What happens while it is in the conductor? As you learned previously, it *will not* feel the effects of the electric field from the dee's at all, because electric fields cannot exist inside a conductor. As a result, the particle does not accelerate. However, it is already traveling at a given speed, which means it will continue to travel at that speed. However, since it still feels the effect of the magnetic field, it will travel in a circle.

Eventually, its motion will result in the charged particle leaving dee #2. *Before that happens, however, the voltage source will switch potential.* That way, dee #1 will be positive and dee #2 will be negative. What will happen as a result? When the charged particle leaves dee #2, it will suddenly feel the effects of the electric field again, and it will accelerate towards dee #1. Once it enters dee #1, it no longer feels the effects of the electric field and begins to travel in a circle at constant speed again. However, once again, before it leaves dee #1, the voltage source switches potential again, so that when the particle leaves dee #1, it sees that dee #2 is positively charged and begins accelerating towards that.

Do you see how this accelerates the particle? Each time it leaves a dee, the voltage has been switched so that it is always nearest to the negatively-charged dee and farthest from the positively-charged dee. Thus, every time it leaves a dee, it is accelerated. Once in the dee, it travels in a circle. As Equation (14.5) tells you, however, the faster it is traveling, the larger the radius of the circle. Thus, each time the particle accelerates, it will travel in a larger circle. Eventually, the circle becomes as large as the cyclotron, and the particle exits at a high rate of speed.

Here's the neat part about a cyclotron: until the particle reaches speeds near the speed of light, *the frequency at which the voltage must switch is constant*! Think about it. Each time the particle leaves a dee, it is accelerated. Thus, once it enters the next dee, it travels in a larger circle. You might think, therefore, that it takes more time for the particle to leave the dee, since it must travel in a larger circle. However, it is also traveling *faster*. These two effects cancel one another out. The distance the charged particle travels increases every time it enters a dee, but its speed also increases, which allows it to travel that longer distance in the same amount of time. Thus, the time that the charged particle spends in a dee is *constant*. As a result, the frequency with which the voltage must change is constant as well!

Notice that I said the frequency at which the voltage changes is constant, as long as the particle has not reached a speed near the speed of light. What does the speed of light have to do with it? Well, once the particle reaches a speed near that of light, special relativity starts to play a role, and that throws off the timing. As a result, a cyclotron is a useful tool for accelerating particles, but it cannot accelerate particles to speeds near that of light, because of the effects of special relativity. This fact is actually another of the many experimental evidences in favor of special relativity.

ON YOUR OWN

14.4 A cyclotron uses a magnetic field of strength B to accelerate a particle of mass m and charge q. Develop an equation for the period with which the voltage must be switched. The only variables in the equation should be B, q, and m. (HINT: The particle travels in a circle for a distance of $2\pi r$. The period of its motion, therefore, is $\frac{2\pi r}{v}$.)

Magnetic Fields and Current-Carrying Wires

Since magnetic fields are produced by charged particles in motion, a current-carrying wire must produce a magnetic field. Of course, you should already know that. In your first-year course, you should have learned that the magnetic field produced by a current-carrying wire forms circles around the wire. Although you should have already learned to determine the direction of the magnetic field circles in a current-carrying wire, I want to go over it again, because there are two methods that are used. They each reach the same conclusion, but they can be confusing to students. One method uses the *left hand rule*. I personally like this method better, because it reflects physical reality. However, the other method (the *right hand rule*) has become more popular over the last decade, so more and more textbooks are going that way. To stay consistent with the more current textbooks, we will use the *right hand rule*, even though it does not refer to physical reality.

In the left hand rule, you take your left hand and point your thumb in the direction of the *electron flow* through a wire. When you do that, your fingers curl in the direction of the magnetic field produced by the current. That, of course, refers to physical reality, because electrons are what flow in an electric circuit. However, circuit diagrams use *conventional current*. Conventional current is the flow of positive ions. Even though positive ions do not flow in an electric circuit, we use conventional current for historical reasons. The *right hand rule* uses conventional current. In the right hand rule, you take your *right* hand and point your thumb in the direction of the conventional current. Then, your fingers curl in the direction of the magnetic field. Of course, the left hand rule and right hand rule produce the same results, as illustrated in Figure 14.6.

FIGURE 14.6

Left Hand and Right Hand Rules for Drawing the Magnetic Field of a Current-Carrying Wire

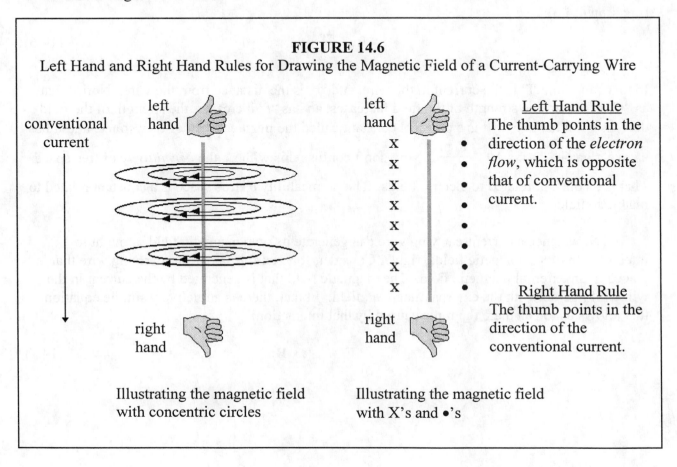

conventional current

left hand

left hand

Left Hand Rule
The thumb points in the direction of the *electron flow*, which is opposite that of conventional current.

right hand

right hand

Right Hand Rule
The thumb points in the direction of the conventional current.

Illustrating the magnetic field with concentric circles

Illustrating the magnetic field with X's and •'s

In the figure, the gray wire carries conventional current that is traveling downwards. If you want to determine the direction of the magnetic field using the left hand rule, you would take your left hand and point your thumb in the direction of the *electron flow*, which is opposite that of conventional current. If you did that, the curl of your fingers would indicate that the magnetic field forms concentric circles that come out of the plane of the paper on the right of the wire and go into the plane of the paper on the left of the wire. I have illustrated this two ways. On the left, you have the concentric circles drawn out. On the right, you have the X's and •'s that we have been using up to this point. Both indicate that the magnetic field comes out of the paper on the right of the wire and into the paper on the left of the wire.

If you use the right hand rule, you get the same result. You take your right hand and point your thumb in the direction of the conventional current. When you do that, your fingers curl in the direction of the magnetic field. The magnetic field comes out of the paper to the right of the wire and goes into the paper to the left of the wire. Thus, either method works. Although I prefer the left hand rule (as it is more physically real), I will solve all of the problems using the right hand rule, as it is the rule which the more recent textbooks use. Thus, all of the I's shown in the problems will refer to conventional current.

Although you learned how to determine the direction of the magnetic field generated by a current-carrying wire, you probably did not learn how to calculate its strength. As you might imagine, the strength of the magnetic field produced by a current-carrying wire depends on how far you are from the wire. After all, the closer you are to the wire, the more you should feel the effects of the magnetic field it generates. It should also be related to the current. The larger the current, the stronger the magnetic field. Indeed, both of these effects are accounted for in Equation (14.6):

$$B = \frac{\mu_0 \cdot I}{2\pi \cdot r} \tag{14.6}$$

In this equation, "I" is the current in the wire, and "r" is the distance from the wire. Notice that as "I" increases, the strength of the field increases, and as "r" increases, the strength of the field decreases. What is μ_0? It is a physical constant called the **permeability of free space**, and it has an exact value of $4\pi \times 10^{-7} \frac{T \cdot m}{A}$. Now don't confuse this with ε_0, the *permittivity* of free space. That is a constant related to electric fields. The permeability of free space is a constant related to magnetic fields.

Now, since a current-carrying wire can generate its own magnetic field, it ought to interact with other magnetic fields, right? Consider, for example, a current-carrying wire that is placed in an external magnetic field. The magnetic field that is generated by the current in the wire will interact with the external magnetic field. In fact, there is a relatively simple equation that allows us to calculate the force caused by that interaction:

$$\mathbf{F} = I \cdot (\ell \times \mathbf{B}) \tag{14.7}$$

In this equation, "I" is the current, and "**B**" is the external magnetic field vector. The "ℓ" in the equation is a vector whose magnitude is equal to the length of the wire that is in the magnetic field, and the direction is equal to the direction of the conventional current going through the wire. See how we use this equation in the following example.

EXAMPLE 14.3

A wire carrying 0.0450 A of current is placed in a 0.0512 Tesla magnetic field as illustrated to the right. The length of the wire in the magnetic field is 35.0 cm. What are the magnitude and direction of the magnetic force on the wire?

     This is a simple application of Equation (14.7), but it is important to go over it so that you know what you are doing. First, we can get the magnitude using the equation that gives us the magnitude of the cross product:

$$F = I \cdot (\ell \cdot B \cdot \sin\theta)$$

Since the external magnetic field is coming out of the plane of the paper, and since the current is in the plane of the paper, the angle between them is 90.0 degrees.

$$F = (0.0450 \text{ A}) \cdot [(0.350 \text{ m}) \cdot (0.0512 \, \frac{N}{A \cdot m}) \cdot \sin(90.0)] = 8.06 \times 10^{-4} \text{ N}$$

What about the direction? To determine that, we take our right hand and point our fingers in the direction of the current. Then we curl them out of the plane of the paper (in the direction of the magnetic field). That means the force is directed straight down. Thus, the force is <u>8.06 x 10^{-4} N directed straight down</u>.

     Although Equation (14.7) is relatively easy to use, its consequences can be profound. Consider the following example.

EXAMPLE 14.4

A "U"-shaped wire is suspended in a uniform 0.456 T magnetic field as shown to the right. What are the magnitude and direction of the net force exerted on the "U?" The current is 0.0654 A, and the length of each side of the "U" is 10.0 cm.

     We can treat this situation as if there were three individual wires carrying current. The "wire" on the left carries current down. The "wire" on the right carries current up, and the wire running across the bottom carries current to the right. If we think about the cross product that determines the force, we see something that simplifies the situation enormously. The "wire" on the left carries current down. If we take our right hand and point our fingers down, and then curl them into the page (the direction of the magnetic field), we see that the force on that "wire" is pointed to the right. The "wire" on the right carries current up. If we take our right hand, point our fingers up, and then curl them into the page, we see that the force is pointed to the left. Since both "wires" carry the same current and are exposed to the same magnetic field, the magnitude of the forces on each "wire" are the same, but the directions are opposite. Thus, *these forces cancel out, and the only force remaining is the force on the bottom "wire."*

The bottom wire is perpendicular to the magnetic field, so the angle between ℓ and **B** is 90.0 degrees. Thus:

$$F = I \cdot (\ell \cdot B \cdot \sin\theta) = (0.0654 \text{ A}) \cdot [(0.100 \text{ m}) \cdot (0.456 \frac{N}{A \cdot m}) \cdot \sin(90.0)] = 2.98 \times 10^{-3} \text{ N}$$

That's the magnitude. What's the direction? The current is carried to the right, and the magnetic field is pointing into the paper. If we take our right hand, point the fingers to the right and curl them into the paper, our thumb points up. Thus, the force is 2.98 x 10^{-3} N pointing straight up.

ON YOUR OWN

14.5 A physicist wants to use a current-carrying wire to generate a magnetic field. If she wants to produce a magnetic field of strength 4.32 x 10^{-5} T at a distance of 10.0 cm from the wire, what current will she need to pass through the wire? Based on the illustration to the right, 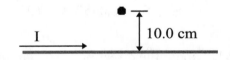 will the magnetic field be pointed into or out of the plane of the paper at the point which she is studying?

14.6 A square of wire that is free to rotate is placed in a magnetic field as shown to the right. The current in the wire is 0.500 A, and the magnetic field strength is 0.126 T. If each side of the wire is 15.0 cm long, what is the total torque experienced by the square? Ignore the tiny gap on the left. Treat this as a complete square.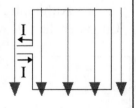

Motional EMF

As you already know, moving charges experience a magnetic force when they are in a magnetic field. With that in mind, can you tell me what will happen when a conductor moves through a magnetic field? Think about it. The conductor is full of electrons that are free to move about. These electrons all have negative charge, and are moving with the conductor. Thus, they are all charged particles moving in a magnetic field. As a result, they will experience a force. What will happen? Well, consider Figure 14.7.

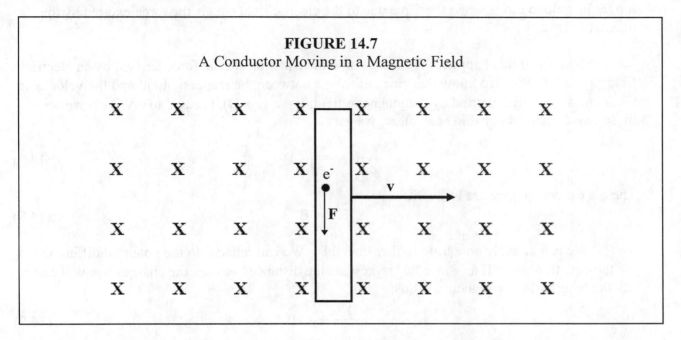

FIGURE 14.7
A Conductor Moving in a Magnetic Field

Each electron in the conductor has a net velocity equal to that of the conductor, **v**. Since they are all moving charges, they experience a force given by Equation (14.1). The direction of that force is given by the negative of the cross product **v** x **B**, since electrons are negatively charged. If we apply the right hand rule, we see that the direction of the cross product is up, which means the direction of the force is down. Thus, the electrons that are free to move in the conductor will move down in response to that force. As a result, electrons will concentrate near the bottom of the conductor. This will leave a net negative charge near the bottom of the conductor and a net positive charge near the top.

What do you have in such a situation? You have a *potential difference*. Anything near the positive charge will have a higher potential than anything near the negative charge. Thus, when a conductor moves through a magnetic field, a potential difference is established within the conductor. This is called **motional emf**.

Motional emf - A potential difference established by the motion of a conductor in a magnetic field

The value of this emf is actually rather easy to calculate.

Think about the situation. When the conductor begins moving in the magnetic field, the electrons experience the force and start moving down the conductor. This causes the bottom of the conductor to get negatively charged and the top to get positively charged. This sets up an electric field, E. That electric field will begin to exert a force on the electrons in the *opposite* direction as the force exerted by the magnetic field, because electrons want to move away from the negative charge and towards the positive charge. As electrons move towards the bottom of the conductor, then, a force resisting any further motion begins to build up. The electrons will no longer be able to move when the force due to the electric field equals the force exerted by the magnetic field.

When will this happen? Well, we know the equation for the force exerted by an electric field ($F = q \cdot E$). We also know that since the angle between the magnetic field and the velocity is 90 degrees, the force exerted by the magnetic field, $F = q \cdot (\mathbf{v} \times \mathbf{B})$, is equal to $q \cdot v \cdot B$. If we set those two equations equal to each other, we get:

$$q \cdot E = q \cdot v \cdot B \qquad (14.7)$$

The q's cancel, and we are left with:

$$E = v \cdot B \qquad (14.8)$$

We can actually go a little farther than this. We can relate E to the potential difference via the equation $\Delta V = E \cdot d$. Since "d" represents the distance between the charges, we will call it "ℓ," the length of the conductor. Thus:

$$\frac{\Delta V}{\ell} = v \cdot B \qquad (14.9)$$

$$\boxed{\Delta V = v \cdot B \cdot \ell} \qquad (14.10)$$

Equation (14.10) is an important one. It tells us the potential difference (in old terminology, the emf) in a conductor that is moving within a magnetic field.

EXAMPLE 14.5

A 50.0 cm conductor is placed on stationary, conductive bars which have a total resistance of 2.0 Ω. If the conductor moves with a speed of 2.0 m/sec in a 0.067 T magnetic field as illustrated in the drawing to the right, what is the current that moves in the conductive bars? What is the direction of the current?

When the conductor moves, it will generate a potential difference. Thus, it will act like a battery. Since it is in contact with conductive bars, the voltage will cause current to flow. If we figure out the voltage, we can use Ohm's Law to figure out the current.

$$\Delta V = v \cdot B \cdot \ell = (2.0\, \frac{m}{sec}) \cdot (0.067\, \frac{N}{A \cdot m}) \cdot (0.500\, m) = 0.067\, \frac{N \cdot m}{sec \cdot \frac{C}{sec}} = 0.067\, \frac{J}{C} = 0.067\, V$$

Notice how the units work out. Since an Ampere is a C/sec, a Joule is a N·m, and a Volt is a J/C, the potential difference comes out with the unit of Volt, which it should. Now that we have the potential difference, Ohm's Law can give us the current.

$$V = I \cdot R$$

$$I = \frac{V}{R} = \frac{0.067 \text{ V}}{2.0 \text{ }\Omega} = \underline{0.034 \text{ A}}$$

The problem also asked for the direction of the current. To determine that, we just need to determine which side of the "battery" (the moving conductor) is positive. If we apply the right hand rule to determine **v** x **B**, we get that the cross product is pointed down the conductor. However, electrons experience a force (**F**$_e$) opposite the cross product, because of their negative charge. Thus, the electrons move up the conductor. That means the top of the conductor is negative, and the bottom is positive.

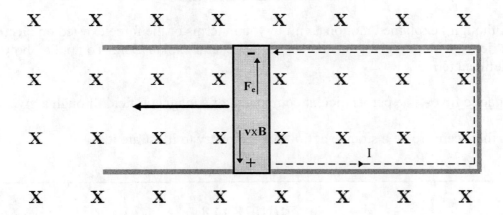

Thus, conventional current (which we just refer to as "current" in this course) flows <u>counterclockwise</u> around the bars.

Before I leave this section, I want to make one very important point. You might think that in a situation such as the one discussed above, we are producing electricity at no cost. However, that is obviously not true. *It takes energy to move the conductor.* That energy is being converted (via the magnetic field) into electrical energy. Ideally, the energy used to move the conductor would be equal to the electrical energy produced. You will actually demonstrate that in the "on your own" problem that follows. However, because of both friction and the Second Law of Thermodynamics, the amount of electrical energy produced will be less than the energy it takes to move the conductor.

ON YOUR OWN

14.7 For the situation given in the example above, demonstrate that the power required to move the conductor is equal to the power dissipated in the resistance of the bars. (HINT: The moving conductor acts like a current-carrying wire. Think about the force exerted by the magnetic field on the current-carrying wire.)

14.8 A 75.0 cm conductor moves on stationary, conductive bars in a 0.0557 T magnetic field as shown to the right. The bars have essentially zero resistance, but there is a 15.0 Ω resistor connecting them. If 0.0433 A of current run through the resistor, what is the speed at which the bar is moving? What is the direction of the current?

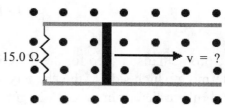

Electromagnetic Induction

Although I explained motional emf to you in terms of the force exerted on electrons by magnetic fields, I want to give you another, more general explanation. To do that, however, I need to define a term.

Magnetic flux - The perpendicular component of a magnetic field through a given area

Although that seems to be a strange definition, let me try to illustrate it.

FIGURE 14.8
Magnetic Flux

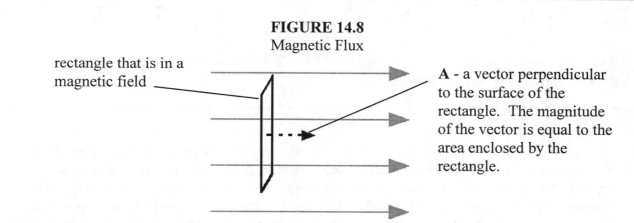

rectangle that is in a magnetic field

A - a vector perpendicular to the surface of the rectangle. The magnitude of the vector is equal to the area enclosed by the rectangle.

The magnetic flux is the perpendicular component of the magnetic field through the area of the rectangle. If we define a vector which is perpendicular to the face of the rectangle and has a magnitude equal to the area enclosed by the rectangle, then the magnetic flux (Φ) can be determined via a dot product between the magnetic field (**B**) and **A**.

Remember, the dot product takes one vector and multiplies it by the perpendicular component of the other vector. Thus, the **magnetic flux** (Φ) is defined as:

$$\Phi = \mathbf{B} \bullet \mathbf{A} \qquad (14.11)$$

What does the magnetic flux mean? It is really just a quantity which allows us to estimate how many magnetic field lines are enclosed in a given area. Although that may not mean much to you now, it will in a moment! Before we go on, however, I want you to look at the units associated with Φ. Magnetic field has the unit of Tesla, and area has the standard unit of m^2. Thus, magnetic flux has the unit $T \cdot m^2$, which is called the **Weber (Wb)** in honor of Wilhelm Eduard Weber, a German physicist whose work in electrostatics and electrodynamics was very important in the development of Maxwell's equations.

Given that definition of magnetic flux, let's return to the situation in which a moving conductor slides along stationary bars in a magnetic field:

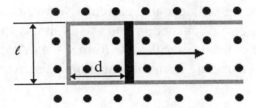

Notice that the moving conductor and the stationary bars form a rectangle. Since there is a magnetic field here, that means there is a magnetic flux through the rectangle. We can even calculate that flux. The height of the rectangle is "ℓ", the length of the conductor, and the width we will call "d." That means the magnitude of the vector **A** that we must define is $\ell \cdot$d. Since the vector's direction is perpendicular to the face of the rectangle, it is pointing out of the paper. That is the same as the magnetic field. Thus, **B** and **A** are parallel, so the angle between them is zero. That means:

$$\Phi = \mathbf{B} \bullet \mathbf{A} = B \cdot \ell \cdot d \cdot \cos(0) = B \cdot \ell \cdot d \qquad (14.12)$$

So the magnetic flux is equal to $B \cdot \ell \cdot d$. What does that tell us?

Think for a moment about what happens to the area of the rectangle as the conductor moves. It increases, right? How much does it increase? Well, "ℓ" doesn't change while the conductor moves, but "d" does. As "d" changes, the flux changes. Thus, we could say:

$$\Delta\Phi = B \cdot \ell \cdot \Delta d \qquad (14.13)$$

That's how the flux changes, but how does it change over time? Well, if we divide both sides of the equation by Δt, we would get the average rate at which the flux changes:

$$\frac{\Delta\Phi}{\Delta t} = B \cdot \ell \cdot \frac{\Delta d}{\Delta t} \tag{14.14}$$

Look at what we have here. The ratio of Δd to Δt is the *speed* at which the conductor is moving, which we called "v" in the previous section. If I put this in for $\Delta d/\Delta t$, look what I get:

$$\frac{\Delta\Phi}{\Delta t} = B \cdot \ell \cdot v \tag{14.14}$$

What is $B \cdot \ell \cdot v$? It is the potential difference developed in the conductor, as given by Equation (14.10). In other words:

$$\boxed{\frac{\Delta\Phi}{\Delta t} = \Delta V} \tag{14.15}$$

This is an incredibly important equation. It tells us that if magnetic flux changes in a conductor, an emf is produced. That, of course, will lead to a current. Now it is important to note that since Δt is a finite amount of time, the emf calculated in this way is simply the *average* emf produced over the time interval. Just as the speed you calculate from $v = \Delta x/\Delta t$ is the *average* speed over the time interval Δt, the emf you calculate from this equation is the average emf over the time period of Δt.

You probably learned this fact (without the equation) in your first-year course. You should have learned that when a conductive loop is exposed to a varying magnetic field, electric current is produced. This was called **Faraday's Law of Electromagnetic Induction**. I want to give you that law again, with the language we have developed here.

Faraday's Law of Electromagnetic Induction - The emf induced in a circuit is equal to the time rate of change of the magnetic flux through that circuit.

As you probably have already learned, this is how a generator generates electricity. A coil of wires is either rotated through a magnetic field, or a magnet is rotated within a coil of wires. Either way, the coil of wires is exposed to a magnetic flux that changes over time. This induces an emf according to Equation (14.15), which produces a current.

Although Equation (14.15) looks pretty simple, you really have to think if you want to use it. Thus, I want to give you two examples of how to calculate the emf produced by a varying magnetic flux. Before I do that, however, I want to tell you how you can determine the *direction* of the electric current produced by a varying magnetic flux.

Look for a moment at the final drawing in Example 14.5. In that drawing, the current runs counterclockwise in the rectangle. If you look at any straight section of that rectangle and apply the right hand rule to determine the direction of the magnetic field produced by that current, you would find that the magnetic field produced by the current goes *out* of the paper on the inside of the rectangle and into the paper on the outside of the rectangle. Thus, when a varying magnetic flux produces a current, the current in turn produces a magnetic field that *opposes* the change in flux. This is called **Lens's Law**.

> Lens's Law - The current produced by a change in magnetic flux will flow in the direction that will cause *its* magnetic field to oppose the change in flux.

This is a hard law to understand unless you are given some examples.

EXAMPLE 14.6

A rectangular loop of wire (20.0 cm x 50.0 cm) is placed in a perpendicular 0.176 T magnetic field as illustrated to the right. The strength of the magnetic field is then increased to 0.500 T over a period of 20.0 seconds. What is the average emf produced in this way? If the resistance of the loop is 1.50 Ω, what is the average current produced? What is the direction of the current in the loop?

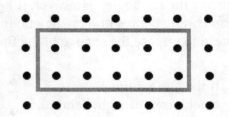

Do you think that I ask too many questions? Too bad. Let's start with the emf. The area of the rectangle is (0.200 m)·(0.500 m), or 0.100 m². If we define the vector **A** as coming straight out of the paper towards us, then **A** and **B** are parallel. Thus, the angle between them is zero. The initial magnetic flux, then, is:

$$\Phi_o = \mathbf{B} \bullet \mathbf{A} = B \cdot A \cdot \cos(0) = (0.176 \text{ T}) \cdot (0.100 \text{ m}^2) = 0.0176 \text{ T} \cdot \text{m}^2 = 0.0176 \text{ Wb}$$

Once the magnetic field is increased to 0.500 T, the magnetic flux is:

$$\Phi_f = \mathbf{B} \bullet \mathbf{A} = B \cdot A \cdot \cos(0) = (0.500 \text{ T}) \cdot (0.100 \text{ m}^2) = 0.0500 \text{ T} \cdot \text{m}^2 = 0.0500 \text{ Wb}$$

This change in flux happened in 20.0 seconds, so the average flux rate of change is equal to:

$$\frac{\Delta\Phi}{\Delta t} = \frac{0.0500 \text{ T} \cdot \text{m}^2 - 0.0176 \text{ T} \cdot \text{m}^2}{20.0 \text{ sec}} = 0.00162 \frac{\frac{\text{N}}{\text{A} \cdot \text{m}} \cdot \text{m}^2}{\text{sec}} = 0.00162 \frac{\frac{\text{J} \cdot \text{sec}}{\text{C}}}{\text{sec}} = \underline{0.00162 \text{ V}}$$

Notice that when I plug in the definitions of T and A, the units cancel to leave Volts. That's the answer to the first question! The second question just requires Ohm's Law:

$$V = I \cdot R$$

$$I = \frac{V}{R} = \frac{0.00162 \text{ V}}{1.50 \ \Omega} = \underline{0.00108 \text{ A}}$$

The third question requires the use of Lens's Law. The current will flow so that its magnetic field opposes the change in flux. Well, the magnetic field inside the rectangle is pointing out of the page, and it is increasing. Thus, the magnetic field is increasing out of the page. The current, then, will produce a magnetic field inside the rectangle that is increasing *into* the page. How will the current flow? If I look at the bottom of the rectangle and point my right hand's thumb to the right (so that the current flows counterclockwise), my fingers curl *out* of the page on the inside of the rectangle. No matter what part of the rectangle I try, if I point my right hand's thumb so that the current flows counterclockwise, the resulting magnetic field always comes out of the paper inside the rectangle. However, if I point my right hand's thumb so that the current travels *clockwise*, the resulting magnetic field goes *into* the paper inside the rectangle, which is what I need to oppose the change in the flux.

If the current travels clockwise, the right hand rule says that the resulting magnetic field goes into the paper inside the rectangle and out of the paper outside of the rectangle.

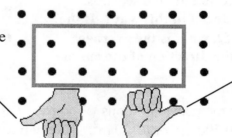

If the current travels counterclockwise, the right hand rule says that the resulting magnetic field goes out of the paper inside the rectangle and into the paper outside of the rectangle.

As a result, <u>the current runs clockwise</u> so that the resulting magnetic field opposes the change in flux.

I want to give you one more example, because there is another way that flux can change. If the magnetic field stays constant, the flux can vary if the loop of conductor moves so that the angle between the surface of the loop and the magnetic field changes. That will produce an emf as well.

EXAMPLE 14.7

A square is made out of 200 individual wire loops which are each 15.0 cm x 15.0 cm. This square is placed between two poles of a

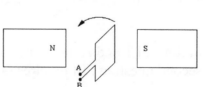

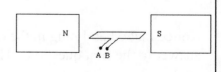

permanent magnet so that it experiences a uniform magnetic field of 0.0145 T. The loop is initially placed so that its surface is perpendicular to the magnetic field. In 0.500 seconds, the loop is twisted so that its surface is parallel to the magnetic field lines. Which point (A or B) has the higher potential, and how much potential difference exists between them?

Remember, magnetic field lines go from the north pole to the south pole. Thus, the situation looks like this:

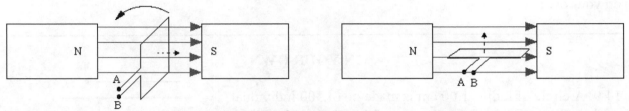

The dashed arrow is **A**, the vector that represents the surface area. At the beginning, **A** is parallel to **B**, so the angle between them is zero. Now remember, this square actually contains 200 individual squares. They *each* have their own flux. As a result, the *total* flux will be the sum of all of their individual fluxes. This means that the initial flux is:

$$\Phi_o = \mathbf{B} \bullet (200 \cdot \mathbf{A}) = \mathbf{B} \cdot 200 \cdot \mathbf{A} \cdot \cos(0) = (0.0145 \text{ T}) \cdot (200) \cdot (0.150 \text{ m}) \cdot (0.150 \text{ m}) = 0.0653 \text{ Wb}$$

At the end, the vector **A** is perpendicular to the magnetic field. Thus, the angle between **A** and **B** is 90:

$$\Phi_f = \mathbf{B} \bullet (200 \cdot \mathbf{A}) = \mathbf{B} \cdot 200 \cdot \mathbf{A} \cdot \cos(90) = 0$$

The change in flux over time, then, is:

$$\frac{\Delta\Phi}{\Delta t} = \frac{0 \text{ T} \cdot \text{m}^2 - 0.0653 \text{ T} \cdot \text{m}^2}{0.500 \text{ sec}} = -0.131 \frac{\frac{\text{N}}{\text{A} \cdot \text{m}} \cdot \text{m}^2}{\text{sec}} = -0.131 \frac{\frac{\text{J} \cdot \text{sec}}{\text{C}}}{\text{sec}} = -0.131 \text{ V}$$

What does the negative mean? It means that the flux *decreased* over time. Well, of course it did, because it started out at 0.0653 Wb and ended up at zero! However, that is important, because we need that to determine the direction of the current that would be produced.

    To determine the direction of the current (which will also tell us which point has the higher potential), let's look at the first drawing. The flux is to the right, because the magnetic field lines pass through the rectangle, pointed to the right. However, the flux to the right *decreases* over time. The current would produce a magnetic field that is opposed to that change. Thus, the current will produce a magnetic field that *increases* to the right as it passes through the loop. Using the right hand rule, then, the current travels from point B to point A, because that current will produce a magnetic field that points to the right inside the loop. Since current flows from point B to point A, that means B has the highest potential. Thus, <u>point B is at a potential that is 1.31 V higher than point A</u>.

    This is how you analyze situations that produce electricity through changes in magnetic flux. You can calculate the emf by using Equation (14.15), and you can determine the direction of the current by using Lens's Law. If the flux *increases* to the right, for example, the current will be produced so that the current's magnetic field will point to the left at all points inside the loop. If the flux *decreases* to the right, however, the current will be produced so that the current's magnetic field will point to the right at all points inside the loop. See if you can do this on your own.

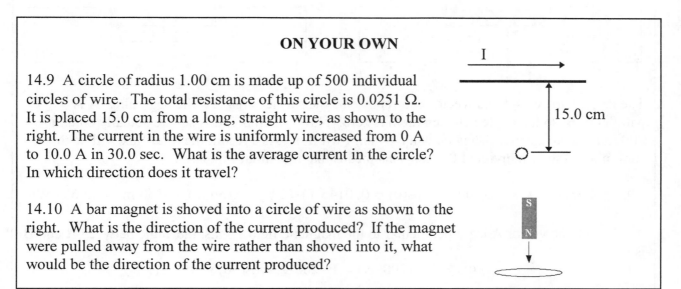

ON YOUR OWN

14.9 A circle of radius 1.00 cm is made up of 500 individual circles of wire. The total resistance of this circle is 0.0251 Ω. It is placed 15.0 cm from a long, straight wire, as shown to the right. The current in the wire is uniformly increased from 0 A to 10.0 A in 30.0 sec. What is the average current in the circle? In which direction does it travel?

14.10 A bar magnet is shoved into a circle of wire as shown to the right. What is the direction of the current produced? If the magnet were pulled away from the wire rather than shoved into it, what would be the direction of the current produced?

Alternating Current

Before I leave this module, I want to briefly discuss alternating current. When you plug an appliance into an outlet, the appliance does not get a constant electrical current like the resistors you were analyzing in Module #13. Instead, the current varies over time. In your first-year course, you should have learned that the current you get from an outlet in your home actually varies like a sine function. Now that you know Faraday's Law and Lens's Law, you can understand why. Consider, for example, a square of wire turning in a uniform magnetic field:

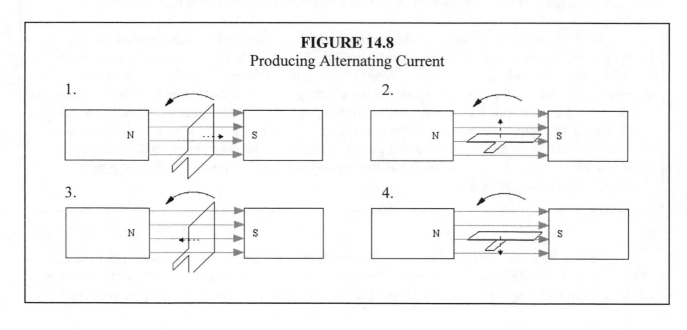

FIGURE 14.8
Producing Alternating Current

For the situation depicted in Figure 14.8, we know that current will be produced, because the magnetic flux through the square of wire is changing. However, let's think about *how* that magnetic flux is changing and in what direction current will flow. Let's start at position "1" in the figure. In this position, the flux through the square is at its maximum. As the loop turns from position "1" to position "2," the flux decreases. Since flux is to the right and is decreasing, Lens's Law states that the current must flow so that its magnetic field opposes this change. Thus, current must flow so that its magnetic field is pointed to the right while inside the rectangle. Thus, current flows counterclockwise through the square.

What happens from position "2" to position "3?" Well, the flux is *still decreasing* during this time, because the dot product between **A** and **B** starts becoming more and more negative. When the loop finally reaches position "3," the flux is at its largest negative value, which means it is at its lowest. Since flux is still decreasing from position "2" to position "3," then, the current still moves counterclockwise.

Once the wire starts turning from position "3" to position "4," however, things change. At this point, the flux starts getting *less negative*. Thus, the flux (which is pointed to the right) starts increasing. Lens's Law states that the current's magnetic field must oppose this change, so the current's magnetic field must point to the left. Thus, the current must *switch directions* and start flowing clockwise!

From position "4" back to the starting position, flux is still increasing. Thus, the magnetic field of the current still must point to the left, so the current still must flow clockwise. In the end, then, if we define counterclockwise current as positive, the current can be graphed as follows:

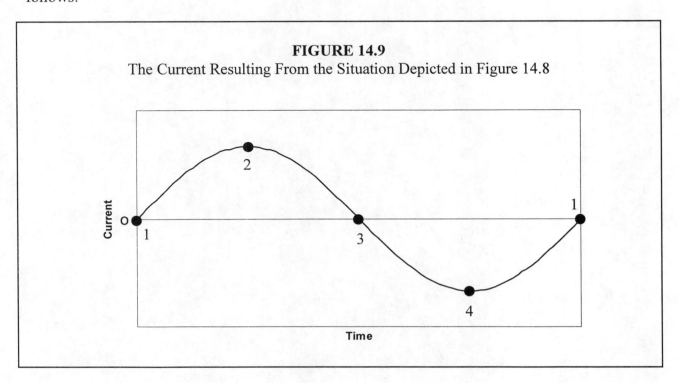

FIGURE 14.9
The Current Resulting From the Situation Depicted in Figure 14.8

As you can see from the graph, in position "1," the current is zero. It starts increasing in the counterclockwise direction (that's the direction we defined as positive) until it reaches position "2," where it is at its maximum. Then, the current *still runs counterclockwise*, but it begins to decrease until, at position "3," it is back to zero. At that point, the change in the flux reverses direction, so the current must reverse direction as well. Thus, it begins to move clockwise (that's why it is negative) until it reaches its maximum clockwise value at position "4." As the loop moves so as to return to its initial position, the current decreases again, but still flows clockwise. Once it reaches position "1" again, the whole process repeats itself.

Now you see why we have alternating current. In a generator, the flux through the wires increases for a while, but then it must decrease again (or vice-versa). Since the change in flux alternates, the current must alternate as well.

I hope that you have enjoyed your study of electricity and magnetism. Certainly, there is a *lot* more to cover in this area, but it goes beyond the scope of this course. In the next module, however, we will use some of what we have learned in this fascinating field so that we can better understand the makeup of atoms.

ANSWERS TO THE ON YOUR OWN PROBLEMS

14.1 In diamagnetic substances, the induced magnetic field is weak and opposes the applied magnetic field. Thus, <u>in the diamagnetic substance, the field would point to the left</u>. In paramagnetic substances and ferromagnetic substances, the magnetic atoms align with the field. Thus, <u>in the paramagnetic and ferromagnetic substances, it would point to the right</u>.

14.2 When the positive particle enters the plates, it will be pulled down by the electric field. Equation (11.4) gives us the force in terms of E and q:

$$\mathbf{F} = \mathbf{q \cdot E}$$

Based on the right hand rule, the magnetic field will pull up on the particle (point your right hand's fingers in the direction of the velocity and curl them into the paper (the direction of the magnetic field), and your thumb points up. We also know that force, from Equation (14.1). For no deflection, the forces must be equal, since they are opposite. If we therefore set the magnitudes of the forces equal to one another, we get:

$$q \cdot E = q \cdot v \cdot B \cdot \sin(90)$$

$$B = \frac{E}{v} = \frac{3{,}014 \ \frac{N}{C}}{3{,}210 \ \frac{m}{sec}} = 0.939 \ \frac{N \cdot sec}{C \cdot m} = 0.939 \ \frac{N}{A \cdot m} = \underline{0.939 \ T}$$

Notice that since an Ampere is a C/sec, the units work out to give us Teslas.

14.3 Without the electric field, the particle will travel in a circle, with a radius given by Equation (14.5):

$$r = \frac{(0.0150 \ kg) \cdot (3210 \ \frac{m}{sec})}{(0.340 \ C) \cdot (0.939 \ \frac{N}{A \cdot m})} = 151 \ \frac{kg \cdot m^2 \cdot A}{C \cdot sec \cdot N} = 151 \ \frac{kg \cdot m^2 \cdot \cancel{C}}{\cancel{C} \cdot sec^2 \cdot N} = 151 \ \frac{\cancel{N} \cdot m}{\cancel{N}} = \underline{151 \ m}$$

Notice that because an Ampere is a C/sec and a Newton is a $\frac{kg \cdot m}{sec^2}$, the units work out to give us meters.

14.4 In order for the cyclotron to work, it must reverse the voltage twice for each trip that the charged particle makes around the cyclotron. Thus, the period of the voltage switching must equal the period of the charged particle's orbit. Remember, period means how long it takes for a *complete cycle* to happen. A complete cycle would be switching the voltage, and then switching it back. The hint already told us the particle's period:

$$T_{\text{voltage switch}} = T_{\text{particle}}$$

$$T_{\text{voltage switch}} = \frac{2\pi r}{v}$$

Using Equation (14.5) for r:

$$T_{\text{voltage switch}} = \frac{2\pi \cdot \dfrac{m \cdot \cancel{v}}{q \cdot B}}{\cancel{v}} = 2\pi \cdot \frac{m}{q \cdot B}$$

14.5 Equation (14.6) will give us the strength:

$$B = \frac{\mu_0 \cdot I}{2\pi \cdot r}$$

$$I = \frac{B \cdot 2\pi \cdot r}{\mu_0} = \frac{(4.32 \times 10^{-5}\ \cancel{T}) \cdot (2\cancel{\pi}) \cdot (0.100\ \cancel{m})}{4\cancel{\pi} \times 10^{-7}\ \dfrac{\cancel{T} \cdot \cancel{m}}{A}} = \underline{21.6\ A}$$

That's a *lot* of current. Most household circuits run less than 20 A, so even a large amount of current produces a small magnetic field. Also, notice that since the value for μ_o is *exact* (as stated in the text), it does not enter into consideration for significant figures.

We are not quite done, however. The problem also asks for the direction of the magnetic field. Pointing your right thumb in the direction of the conventional current, your fingers curl out of the page above the wire and into the page below the wire. Thus, <u>the magnetic field points out of the page at the point the physicist is studying</u>.

14.6 The force that a current-carrying wire experiences in a magnetic field is given by Equation (14.7). We can treat the square of wire as four individual straight wires, so we really just apply Equation (14.7) four times. Two of those applications are easy, however.

As you can see in the figure, the current (shown by the black arrows) is *parallel* to the magnetic field on the left side of the square and directly opposite the magnetic field on the right. Since the force exerted by the magnetic field depends on the cross product between the direction of the current and the magnetic field, the force on both sides is *zero*. Thus, the only sides that experience a force are the top and bottom of the square.

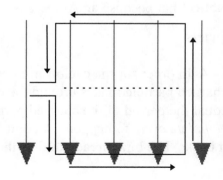

To determine the direction of the force experienced by the top and bottom of the square, we can use the right hand rule. The current in the top of the square is moving to the left. Pointing the fingers of your right hand to the left and curling them down (in the direction of the magnetic field), you find that the force is directed out of the plane of the paper. The current on the bottom is traveling to the right. Doing the same thing there, you find that the force is pointing into the plane of the paper. Thus, we have a force on top of the square pushing out of the plane of the paper and a force on the bottom pushing into the plane of the paper. What will this do? It will cause the square to *rotate* around the axis shown by the dashed line in the drawing.

The loop, then, experiences a torque, which is equal to $\mathbf{r} \times \mathbf{F}$, or $r \cdot F \cdot \sin\theta$. The "r" is the lever arm, which is the distance between the axis of rotation and the force. In this case, since each side of the square is 15.0 cm long, the distance from the force to the axis is 7.50 cm. The "θ" is the angle between the lever arm and the force, which is 90.0 degrees:

$$\tau = r \cdot F \cdot \sin\theta = r \cdot F$$

Since equation (14.7) allows us to calculate the magnitude of the force:

$$\tau = r \cdot I \cdot \ell \cdot B \cdot \sin\theta$$

This "θ" is the angle between the current and the magnetic field, which is also 90.0 degrees:

$$\tau = r \cdot I \cdot \ell \cdot B = (0.0750 \text{ m}) \cdot (0.500 \text{ A}) \cdot (0.150 \text{ m}) \cdot (0.126 \frac{N}{A \cdot m}) = 0.000709 \text{ N} \cdot \text{m}$$

That is the torque experienced by *one* of the two wires. Since both wires will have the same r, I, ℓ, and B, they will each have the same magnitude. Also, since they both promote rotation in the same direction, they are both pointing in the same direction. Thus, we can just take the number above and multiply by 2. The total torque, then, is 0.00142 N·m.

14.7 Since the moving conductor is like a current-carrying wire, we know that it experiences a force from the magnetic field, given by Equation (14.7):

$$\mathbf{F} = I \cdot (\boldsymbol{\ell} \times \mathbf{B})$$

The angle between the magnetic field and the current is 90 degrees, so the magnitude of the force is:

$$F = I \cdot \ell \cdot B \cdot \sin(90) = I \cdot \ell \cdot B$$

The direction is given by the right hand rule. Point your fingers in the direction of the conventional current in the conductor (down), and curl them into the page (the direction of the magnetic field), and you find that the force is *opposite* the motion. Thus, there must be an external force (F_{ext}) being exerted on the conductor in order to keep it moving.

Since the conductor moves at constant velocity, the sum of the forces must be zero. Thus:

$$F_{ext} = I \cdot \ell \cdot B$$

According to Equation (4.10), $P = F \cdot v$ when F and v are constant. Thus:

$$P = F \cdot v = I \cdot \ell \cdot B \cdot v$$

That's the power required to move the conductor. Well, according to Equation (13.4):

$$P = I \cdot V$$

Since motional emf is $B \cdot \ell \cdot v$, that means the power produced by the current is:

$$P = I \cdot B \cdot \ell \cdot v$$

The power required to pull the conductor, then, is the same as the power produced by the electrical current, in compliance with the First Law of Thermodynamics.

14.8 We know the resistance and the current, so if we go to Ohm's Law, we can get the voltage:

$$V = I \cdot R = (0.0433\,A) \cdot (15.0\,\Omega) = 0.650\,V$$

That's the potential difference supplied by the emf, which is equal to:

$$\Delta V = v \cdot B \cdot \ell$$

$$v = \frac{\Delta V}{B \cdot \ell} = \frac{0.650\,V}{0.0557\,\dfrac{N}{A \cdot m} \cdot 0.750\,m} = 15.6\,\frac{V \cdot A}{N} = 15.6\,\frac{\dfrac{J}{C} \cdot \dfrac{C}{sec}}{N} = 15.6\,\frac{N \cdot m}{N \cdot sec} = 15.6\,\frac{m}{sec}$$

Notice that since a Volt is a Joule per Coulomb, an Amp is a Coulomb per second, and a Joule is a Newton·meter, the units work out to give us m/sec.

The problem also asks for the direction of the current. The electrons are moving to the right, along with the conductor. When we take **v** x **B**, we point our fingers to the right (direction of the velocity) and curl them out of the page (the direction of the magnetic field). As a result, our thumb points down. Since electrons are negative, however, that means they move opposite, or up. Thus, the top of the conductor is negative, and the bottom is positive. Conventional current runs from the positive end of the "battery," around the circuit, and to the negative end. Thus, the current runs <u>clockwise</u>.

14.9 The current-carrying wire will produce a magnetic field, which will produce a flux through the circles of wire. Initially, there is no flux, because there is no magnetic field. At the end, the magnetic field in the center of the circle is:

$$B = \frac{\mu_0 \cdot I}{2\pi \cdot r} = \frac{4\pi \times 10^{-7} \, \frac{T \cdot m}{A} \cdot (10.0 \, A)}{2\pi \cdot (0.150 \, m)} = 1.33 \times 10^{-5} \, T$$

Please note that the "r" in this equation is *not* the radius of the circle, but the distance from the wire.

There are 500 individual circles, so they all experience a change in magnetic field from 0 to 1.33 x 10^{-5} T. They experience the following rate of change in flux:

$$\frac{\Delta\Phi}{\Delta t} = \frac{500 \cdot (1.33 \times 10^{-5} \, T) \cdot [\pi \cdot (0.0100m)^2]}{30.0 \, sec} = 6.96 \times 10^{-8} \, \frac{\frac{N}{A \cdot m} \cdot m^2}{sec} = 6.96 \times 10^{-8} \, \frac{\frac{J \cdot sec}{C}}{sec} = 6.96 \times 10^{-8} \, V$$

That's the emf produced by the changing magnetic flux. Using Ohm's Law, we can calculate the resulting current:

$$V = I \cdot R$$

$$I = \frac{V}{R} = \frac{6.96 \times 10^{-8} \, V}{0.0251 \, \Omega} = \underline{2.77 \times 10^{-6} \, A}$$

The current must be produced so that its magnetic field opposes the change in flux. According to the right hand rule (point your thumb in the direction of the conventional current and the fingers curl in the direction of the field), the magnetic field goes into the paper at the point where the circles of wire are. The flux increases over time, so the current in the circles must produce a magnetic field which comes up out of the paper. Using your right hand, then, your fingers must curl out of the paper inside the circle. Your thumb indicates that the current must therefore travel <u>counterclockwise</u>.

14.10 To solve this correctly, you first must think of the direction of the magnetic field lines. They come out of the magnet's north pole and end up in its south pole. Thus, as the magnet is pushed into the loop of wire, the magnetic field points *down* through the circle, and the flux is increasing. The current must produce a magnetic field which opposes this, so the current's magnetic field would have to point *up* out of the circle. Curling your right hand fingers up out of the circle makes your thumb point so that the current flows counterclockwise around the circle.

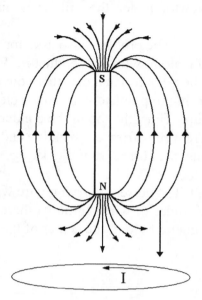

If the magnet were pulled away from the circle, the magnetic field lines would still be pointed down, but the flux would *decrease* in that direction. If the flux decreased in that direction, the current's magnetic field would oppose it by pointing in the same direction (so as to "fight" the decrease). The right hand rule tells us that to produce a magnetic field which travels down through the circle, the current would have to flow clockwise. Thus, if the magnet were pulled away, the current would flow clockwise.

REVIEW QUESTIONS

1. Is it possible for a charged particle to move through a magnetic field without experiencing a force? If so, how?

2. Is it possible for the kinetic energy of a charged particle to change as it moves through a magnetic field? If so, how?

3. A negatively-charged particle moves in a magnetic field. As shown to the right, the magnetic field lines point to the left and the charge experiences a magnetic force directed downwards. What is the direction of the particle's velocity?

4. Two wires are placed parallel and 15.0 cm apart from one another. They each carry 15.0 A of current in the same direction. What is the magnetic field at a point directly in between the two wires?

5. A conductor is moved through a magnetic field so that it develops a potential difference between the ends. However, it is not attached to any circuit, so current does not flow. When the conductor is stopped (assume the magnetic field is still present), what will happen to the potential difference?

6. A permanent magnet is pulled through a loop of wire as shown to the right. The current in the loop is measured during the entire process. Does the direction of the current change? If so, why?

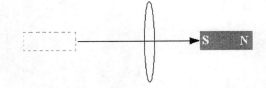

7. In the situation above, what would happen to the current if, once the magnet was inside the loop, it was held stationary?

8. Imagine two charged particles moving directly up this page. Suddenly, a magnetic field is turned on. One particle is deflected out of the page, while the other is deflected into the page. What can you say about these two charged particles?

9. What is wrong with the following statement:

"A cyclotron uses magnetic fields to accelerate charged particles."

10. A permanent magnet is repeatedly pushed in and out of a loop of wire.

   a. Will the current produced be alternating current or direct current?
   b. As the frequency with which the magnet is pushed in and out increases, what happens to the magnitude of the current produced?

PRACTICE PROBLEMS

$$(\mu_0 = 4\pi \times 10^{-7} \; \frac{T \cdot m}{A})$$

Problems 1-3 refer to the following situation:

A charged particle is traveling at a speed of 3,014 m/sec and enters a perpendicular magnetic field of 0.0456 T, as shown to the right. Its mass is 4.60 mg, and its charge is -2.50 C.

1. What are the magnitude and direction of the force that the particle will experience the instant it enters the magnetic field?

2. The charged particle exits the magnetic field on the same side which it entered, with a velocity pointed in exactly the opposite direction. How far is its point of exit from its point of entry? Is its point of exit above or below its point of entry?

3. How much time elapses from the moment it enters the field until the moment it leaves the field?

4. A portion of a current-carrying circuit is suspended (without support) in a magnetic field, as shown to the right. The circuit has a mass of 50.0 g, and it carries a current of 3.40 A. What must be the strength and direction of the magnetic field if the loop simply "floats" in that position?

5. Suppose, in the situation described above, you suspended the circuit with a string so that the circuit did not have to be held up by the magnetic field. Then, instead of pointing the field as you determined in problem #4, you pointed it directly to the right. What would happen to the circuit? What is the net torque that the circuit would experience?

6. A 25.0 cm conductor is moved at a constant velocity in a 0.861 T magnetic field as illustrated in the drawing to the right. The potential difference between the ends of the conductor is measured to be 1.86 V. What is the speed at which the conductor is moved, and which end (top or bottom) of the conductor is at the higher potential?

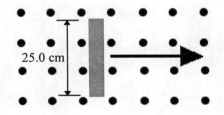

7. In the situation discussed above, suppose the conductor started at rest and *immediately* began moving at the speed which you determined. Qualitatively plot the current in the conductor as a function of time.

8. A loop of wire (R = 0.0340 Ω) is placed in between two current-carrying wires which each carry 1.00 A to the right, as illustrated in the drawing to the right. The radius of the loop of wire is 0.500 cm. Over a period of 0.500 sec, the current in the bottom wire is reduced to zero. What are the magnitude and direction of the current that will develop?

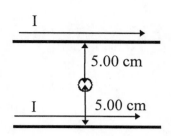

9. In the situation described above, what will be the magnitude and direction of the current in the loop once the current in the bottom wire is reduced and held at zero?

10. A square made of 500 individual squares of wire is turned in a magnetic field as illustrated below. The squares are all 50.0 cm x 50.0 cm, and the strength of the magnetic field is 0.987 T. If the square is turned as illustrated over a period of 0.300 sec, what is the average total current? In what direction does it flow? The total resistance of all of the loops combined is 1.20 Ω.

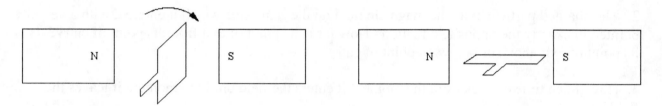

Module #15: Atomic Physics

Introduction

Most of the material that you have learned up to this point has been known since before the 1900's. Einstein proposed his Special Theory of Relativity in 1905 and followed with his General Theory of Relativity in 1915. Thus, even these two "modern" physics theories are nearly 100 years old. In this module and the next, I want to bring you a bit more "up to date" by discussing some of the more recent advances in physics, which center around our understanding of atomic and nuclear physics. Now please understand that even though these advances are more "recent," they are still relatively old, having mostly occurred prior to the 1950's. Nevertheless, the material that we will discuss in this course is commonly used as a student's first introduction to the world of modern physics. This brings me to a quick point of terminology. The term **classical physics** is generally used to refer to the physics that was developed prior to the 1900's. This includes almost all of what you have learned so far, with the exception of relativity. The term **modern physics** is generally used to refer to the physics which includes relativity as well as the topics you will learn in the next two modules.

The Photoelectric Effect: Light as a Particle

Near the end of the 19th century, physicists thought they had figured out virtually everything. Armed with Newton's Laws, Snell's Law, Faraday's Law, etc., physicists had explained a wealth of experimental data. However, there were a few "oddities" that they could not explain. Most thought that eventually, someone would figure those oddities out using the physics that was already known, but those physicists were in for a shock!

One of the little oddities that bothered physicists at the turn of the century was the **photoelectric effect**. In this process, light is shined on a metal surface and, as a result, electrons fly off the metal. These electrons are typically called **photoelectrons**, because they come as a result of light shining on metal. Now, the fact that shining light on metal will liberate electrons was no problem to explain in terms of classical physics. After all, light is a form of energy. Electrons in the metal could absorb that energy and, once they had enough energy to overcome the hold that the metal had on them, they could break free of the metal. Typically, physicists use the term **work function** to refer to the energy with which a metal holds onto its electrons. If an electron could absorb enough energy so that it had more energy than the work function of the metal, the electron could break free of the metal.

All of that makes complete sense in terms of classical physics. What didn't make sense were the following *details* of what happens in the photoelectric effect:

1. **Electrons were ejected within a few billions of a second after the light was turned on.**
2. **The intensity of the light had *no effect* on the energy of the electrons after they left the metal. The more intense the light, the greater *number* of electrons, but the energy of the electrons was independent of the light intensity.**

3. **Each metal had a unique "cutoff" frequency. If the light used was below this frequency, electrons would not be emitted.**
4. **The maximum kinetic energy of the emitted electrons was directly proportional to the *frequency* of the light used.**

None of the details discussed above were consistent with the ideas of classical physics. As you have already learned, light is considered a wave in classical physics. Thus, the energy that the light imparts should be proportional to its intensity, not its frequency. The larger the wave, the more energetic it is. After all, think of a sound wave. The sound from thunder is much more energetic than the sound from a stone hitting the ground because the thunder sound wave is much more intense (has a larger amplitude) than the sound wave from the stone hitting the ground. However, since each metal had a "cutoff" frequency under which light could not eject the electrons, and since the maximum kinetic energy of the electrons depended on the frequency of the light and not the intensity, the results of the photoelectric effect indicated that the frequency of light had something to do with its energy.

In addition, the fact that electrons were liberated from the metal so quickly made no sense in terms of thinking about light as a wave. After all, if the electrons needed to absorb energy from the wave, they would have to "soak up" that energy as they encountered the waves. That should take some time. The lower the intensity of the light, the longer time it should take. However, regardless of intensity, photoelectrons were emitted from the metal within just an instant after the light began to hit the metal.

Since these results were so contrary to the idea that light is a wave, you might think at first that physicists would stop thinking of light in that way. However, if you remember back to what you learned in Module #7, there are experiments (such as Experiment 7.2) that can only be understood if light is a wave. In the end, there was so much experimental evidence that light was a wave, physicists did not want to give up that notion.

Enter Albert Einstein. Einstein was willing to put aside the notion that light was a wave and simply said that he was willing to assume that a beam of light was something like a stream of particles, much like the water coming from a hose is made up of a stream of individual water molecules. He assumed that light came in little "electromagnetic bundles" called **photons**, and that the energy of each photon was proportional to the frequency of the light, according to the following equation:

$$E = h \cdot f \tag{15.1}$$

In this equation, "E" is the energy of the light; "f" is its frequency; and "h" is a fundamental constant in nature which is now known as **Planck's constant**. Named after Max Planck, a German physicist which many credit as the originator of quantum theory, the value of the constant is 6.63×10^{-34} J·sec.

This view explained all of the experimental data associated with the photoelectric effect. After all, if light was composed of individual photons, then it was *collisions* between the photons and the electrons in the metal which transferred energy. When those collisions resulted in more energy going to the electron than the work function of the metal, the electron would break free of the metal. Thus, the electrons should be liberated from the metal almost as soon as the light was turned on, because energy would be transferred almost immediately by the collisions (this explains observation #1). Also, the intensity of the light would not mean more energy, it would simply mean more photons. Thus, more electrons would be emitted, but their energy would not depend on the intensity of the light (this explains observation #2).

Since the energy of the photons depends on the frequency, there would be a frequency under which the photons would simply not be able to provide energy above the metal's work function. Thus, there would be a "cutoff" frequency under which the light could not liberate electrons from the metal. Since this would depend on the strength with which the metal holds onto its electrons, the "cutoff" frequency would be different for each type of metal (this explains observation #3). Finally, since the photon energy depends on the frequency, the maximum kinetic energy of the electrons should depend on the light frequency as well (this explains observation #4).

So by assuming that light was actually composed of a stream of photons, Einstein could explain the photoelectric effect. It was this discovery that put Einstein into the scientific limelight. His insights regarding relativity were not appreciated by the physics community in general until later. Now please realize that Einstein's explanations for the photoelectric effect were not just qualitative, as I discussed above. They could actually predict the data in a quantitative way. I want to give you an example of how Einstein's explanation gives actual numerical predictions for the photoelectric effect, but first, I would like to introduce a new energy unit which is very convenient to use when discussing atomic and nuclear physics.

Consider an electron that starts at rest and is accelerated through a potential difference of 1.000 V. The electron will have a certain amount of energy as a result of moving through the potential, right? We can actually calculate the value of that energy:

$$E = q \cdot \Delta V = (1.602 \times 10^{-19} \text{ C}) \cdot (1.000 \text{ V}) = 1.602 \times 10^{-19} \text{ J}$$

We will call that amount of energy one **electron volt (eV)**. In other words, an electron volt is the energy that an electron will receive when it is accelerated through a one Volt potential difference. Thus, we know that:

$$1 \text{ eV} = 1.602 \times 10^{-19} \text{ J} \qquad (15.2)$$

Now please realize that this is just another energy unit. There is no new physics here. If I have 3.204×10^{-19} J of energy, I can say that I have 2.000 eV of energy. Why do we use this energy unit? The energy of individual atoms is quite small, and generally stays in the range of a few eV to a few million eV. Thus, using the electron volt allows us to avoiding writing very tiny numbers in scientific notation when dealing with energy in atomic and nuclear physics. Of course, with this new unit, we can give another value to Planck's constant, 4.14×10^{-15} eV·sec.

Now that you know this useful energy unit, let's see how Einstein's explanation of the photoelectric effect works.

EXAMPLE 15.1

Sodium metal has a work function of 2.28 eV. If blue light (λ = 4.25 x 10^{-7} m) is shined on sodium, what is the maximum kinetic energy of the electrons that are emitted from the metal?

Remember, the work function tells us how much energy it takes for an electron to escape the metal's grasp on it. If an electron has 2.28 eV, it can break free of the metal, but it will use all of its energy doing so. Thus, it will have no kinetic energy once it escapes. Thus, the work function is the energy that the electron will lose as it escapes the metal. To determine how much energy the electrons get from the light, we must first figure out the light's frequency. According to Equation (6.13), the wavelength and frequency are related by:

$$f = \frac{v}{\lambda} = \frac{2.998 \times 10^8 \frac{m}{sec}}{4.25 \times 10^{-7} m} = 7.05 \times 10^{14} \frac{1}{sec}$$

Notice that since we are dealing with light, I used the speed of light for "v." Now that we know the frequency, we can get the energy of each photon:

$$E = h \cdot f = (4.14 \times 10^{-15} eV \cdot sec) \cdot (7.05 \times 10^{14} \frac{1}{sec}) = 2.92 \ eV$$

Since the work function was given in eV, I decided to get the photon's energy in eV. I could have gotten the energy in Joules, but I would have had to convert at some point. By using Planck's constant in eV·sec, I can avoid the conversion.

Okay, so the photons shining on the metal have 2.92 eV of energy. If a collision occurs and a photon gives *all* of its energy to an electron, the electron will suddenly have 2.92 eV of extra kinetic energy. It can use 2.28 eV to break free of the hold that the metal has on it, leaving the following amount of energy as kinetic energy:

$$KE = 2.92 \ eV - 2.28 \ eV = 0.64 \ eV$$

Now, of course, not every collision will result in all of a photon's energy being transferred to an electron. Thus, electrons can have *less* kinetic energy than that, but the maximum possible electron energy is 0.64 eV.

Using this kind of reasoning, Einstein could predict the maximum kinetic energy of the electrons coming off of a metal, and the prediction was always correct. He could also predict the minimum frequency for which electrons could be emitted from the metal. This provided strong evidence that Einstein's explanation of the photoelectric effect is correct.

Of course, Einstein's explanation leads to a major problem. If light is truly a stream of photons (as is assumed in the explanation of the photoelectric effect), why does it exhibit wavelike properties, such as the ability to produce interference patterns like the one you created in Experiment 7.2? Even today, we do not have a really good answer to that question. Thus, we "fudge" the explanation by giving this phenomenon a name. We say that this illustrates the **particle-wave duality** of light. In some situations, we can best describe light as a wave. In other situations, we can best describe it as a particle. That's just what the experimental evidence shows.

Almost a generation after Einstein's explanation of the photoelectric effect, French physicist Louis de Broglie wondered if the particle-wave duality of light was simply a special case of a general particle-wave duality. If light was a wave that sometimes behaved as a particle, what about particles like electrons? Could they sometimes behave as waves? The answer is yes! In fact, all particles have wavelike properties. However, for macroscopic systems (things you can see with your naked eye), the wavelengths are far too tiny to be noticeable. Tiny particles, however, have noticeable wavelike properties. For example, a beam of electrons accelerated through a series of tiny slits will produce an interference pattern, just as light produced an interference pattern in Experiment 7.2.

De Broglie said that in order to generalize particle-wave duality to all systems, all you would need is to calculate the wavelength of a particle. He proposed the following equation, which now has all sorts of experimental evidence in its favor:

$$\lambda = \frac{h}{p} \tag{15.3}$$

In this equation, "λ" is the wavelength of the particle, which is usually called the **de Broglie wavelength**. In addition, "h" is Planck's constant, and "p" is the particle's momentum.

EXAMPLE 15.2

Calculate the de Broglie wavelength of a tennis ball (m = 56.69 g) moving at a speed of 25 m/sec.

This is a simple application of Equation (15.3), as long as we remember how to calculate momentum from Equation (4.11).

$$\lambda = \frac{h}{p} = \frac{6.63 \times 10^{-34} \ J \cdot sec}{(0.05669 \ kg) \cdot (25 \ \frac{m}{sec})} = 4.7 \times 10^{-34} \ \frac{J \cdot sec^2}{kg \cdot m} = 4.7 \times 10^{-34} \ \frac{\frac{kg \cdot m^2}{sec^2} \cdot \cancel{sec}^2}{kg \cdot m} = \underline{4.7 \times 10^{-34} \ m}$$

Notice how the units work out to meters. This, of course, is simply too small to notice. However, if you do the calculation for an electron moving at relatively high speeds (as you will in an "on your own" problem below), you will see that for small particles at high speeds, the wavelength is quite noticeable.

The explanation of the photoelectric effect, then, led to the general idea that all moving objects (light, tennis balls, electrons, etc.) behave sometimes as waves and sometimes as particles. This had escaped physicists until the early 1900's, because physicists had been dealing mostly in the macroscopic world, where the wave properties were simply not noticeable. Once physicists began studying atoms and electrons, however, these wavelike properties became noticeable and had to be taken into account to explain experimental data.

ON YOUR OWN

15.1 Silver emits electrons when illuminated with light. However, if the light wavelength is below 264 nanometers, no electrons are emitted. What is the work function of silver?
(1 nm = 10^{-9} m)

15.2 Calculate the de Broglie wavelength of an electron moving at 1,510 m/sec. How does this compare to the wavelength of visible light (roughly 400 - 700 nm)? ($m_e = 9.11$ x 10^{-31} kg)

The Bohr Model of the Atom

As you should have learned in chemistry, the view of the atom radically changed in the early 1900's. Physicists already knew that atoms were comprised of electrons and protons, but the discovery of the neutron would take more time. However, prior to 1911, scientists thought that the atom was made of a positively-charged "gel" or "pudding" with negatively-charged electrons sprinkled throughout the pudding. This view of the atom was commonly called the **"plum pudding model** of the atom." In 1909-1911, however Ernest Rutherford performed his famous experiment (which you should have learned about in chemistry) which showed that the atom is composed of a dense, positively-charged center, called the **nucleus**, with electrons orbiting the nucleus much like the planets in our solar system orbit the sun. Rutherford's view of the atom was called the **"planetary model** of the atom," because of its similarity to that of our solar system.

Although Rutherford's model was a major step forward in our understanding of the atom, there was still a great deal of mystery related to how atoms behaved. For example, since about 1860, scientists knew that gaseous atoms, when excited by electricity, emitted light. This was not a problem for classical physics, because physicists rightly concluded that the electricity provided energy to the atoms, and the atoms later released that energy in the form of light. Once again, however, the *details* of the data were beyond the explanation of classical physics.

The atoms, it turns out, would not emit just *any* light when excited by electricity. Each atom seemed to emit *specific wavelengths* of light, and those specific wavelengths varied from atom to atom. The wavelengths would be both visible and non-visible, but the amazing thing was that atoms emitted only specific wavelengths of light, and that those specific wavelengths were unique for each element. These patterns of specific wavelengths emitted by excited atoms are called **atomic emission spectra**, and they are completely unexplainable by classical physics.

Enter Niels Bohr. In 1915 he suggested that the atom was, indeed, structured as Rutherford postulated, but that the electrons had only *specific orbits* in which they could orbit the nucleus, as illustrated in Figure 15.1.

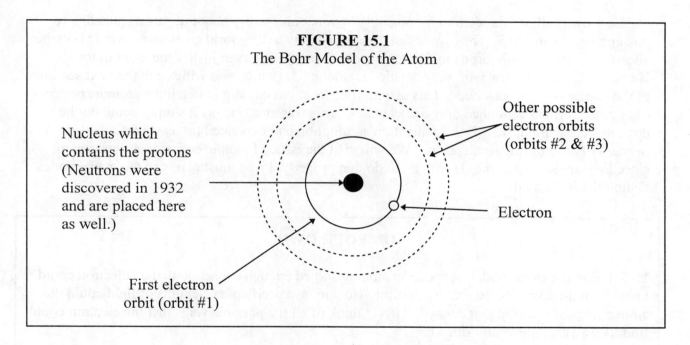

FIGURE 15.1
The Bohr Model of the Atom

Nucleus which contains the protons (Neutrons were discovered in 1932 and are placed here as well.)

Other possible electron orbits (orbits #2 & #3)

Electron

First electron orbit (orbit #1)

Bohr gave no rationality for his assumption that the electrons could only orbit the nucleus in specific orbits. He simply noted that Einstein solved the photoelectric effect by assuming that light comes in discrete packets (photons) and that de Broglie had solved another major problem in physics (the description of blackbody radiation, which we will not discuss) by assuming that energy comes in discrete packets. Thus, he said that perhaps electron orbits are discrete as well. The assumption that things like light, energy, and electron orbits come in discrete packages is called the **quantum assumption**, and it is what revolutionized atomic physics. You will see how a quantum assumption is made mathematically in a moment.

How does the Bohr model explain atomic emission spectra? Well, according to Bohr, an electron can orbit in the first orbit, in the second orbit, the third orbit, etc., but it *cannot orbit anywhere in between*. Thus, if an atom is excited, an electron can jump from orbit #1 to orbit #2, but in order to do so, it would need a *specific amount of energy*. If it received more than that energy, nothing would happen. If it received less than that energy, nothing would happen.

However, if it received exactly the right amount of energy, it could make the jump from orbit #1 to orbit #2.

When the atom then wanted to get rid of that energy, it could emit light, but it would have to emit a photon with the *specific energy* to allow the electron to jump from orbit #2 to orbit #1. If the atom were given enough energy so that the electron could jump from orbit #1 to orbit #3, it could do that, assuming that it was given *just the right amount* of energy. Then, it could release that energy by making the electron take the leap from orbit #3 down to orbit #1, or it could have the electron jump from orbit #3 to orbit #2 and then later on jump from orbit #2 to orbit #1. In either case, however, each jump would correspond to a photon of specific energy, which would result in light of a specific frequency, given by Equation (15.1), and thus a specific wavelength.

Now if all of this seems a bit puzzling to you, don't worry about it. It was puzzling to most physicists in 1915. They could not understand why in the world an electron would only be allowed to orbit specific orbits in the nucleus. Bohr could not even justify the assumption. However, Bohr did show with very detailed mathematics (which you will see in the next section of the course) that if you *believed* his assumption, he could explain in detail the atomic spectrum of any atom which contained only one electron. This was amazing, as it simply could not be done by classical physics. Bohr's quantum assumption had explained (at least partially) the mystery of atomic emission spectra. We will visit the issue of atomic emission spectra again, since they are so important. However, to do that properly, I first must give you the mathematics behind the Bohr model.

ON YOUR OWN

15.3 Using the Bohr model, suppose an atom absorbed enough energy so that an electron could jump from the first orbit to the fourth orbit. How many specific wavelengths of light could the atom emit as it released that energy? HINT: think of all the possible ways that the electron could find its way back down to orbit #1.

A Detailed Look at the Bohr Model

I now want to go into the mathematics of the Bohr model. However, before I do that, I need to remind you of something you should have learned in physical science and chemistry. The nature of an atom depends fundamentally on the number of protons its nucleus contains. In addition, atoms have the same number of electrons as protons and are therefore neutral. However, *ions* have either an excess of protons or electrons and thus have electrical charge. To help keep all of this straight, chemists and physicists use the Periodic Table of the Elements, which I have given to you on the last page of this module, before the answers to the "on your own" problems. In the periodic table, the **atomic number** of an atom is given above the atom's symbol. This number indicates the number of protons in the atom. Thus, a helium atom (He) has 2 protons, as there is a "2" above its symbol. A helium *atom* has 2 electrons as well.

However, a He$^+$ *ion* would have one proton more than its number of electrons. Since helium must have only 2 protons, that means a H$^+$ ion has 2 protons but only 1 electron. A He^{2+} ion would have *no electrons* and two protons, while a He^{2-} atom would have 4 electrons and 2 protons.

Now let's look at the Bohr model. To make the mathematics as simple as possible, let's concentrate on the *simplest* atom in Creation, the hydrogen atom. Hydrogen has only one proton, and only one electron orbits that proton. What keeps the electron in orbit? Why doesn't the electron just go off on its own? Well, electrons are negatively charged and protons are positively charged. The mutual attraction between these opposite charges keeps the electron orbiting the proton. Of course, since the electron is moving in a circle, the electrostatic force, which we know from Equation (11.1), must be providing the centripetal force, which we know from Equation (6.14). That means:

$$\frac{m \cdot v^2}{r} = \frac{k \cdot q_1 \cdot q_2}{r^2}$$ (15.4)

To make the equation specific to our situation, we need to fill in the particulars of what we are studying. For example, we are studying an electron moving in a circle, so we will replace the "m" in the equation with "m_e", to explicitly denote that this is an electron. Also, since we are dealing with the attraction between an electron and a proton, we can actually put in the charge of the electron and a proton. Let's keep the equation a bit general, though, by introducing some notation. Remember that the electrical charge on an electron is equal and opposite that of a proton. It is also the smallest amount of electrical charge in Creation, so we call the electrical charge of a proton and electron the "fundamental unit of charge." Its value is 1.602 x 10^{-19} C, but it is usually abbreviated as "e." That's what we'll put in for the electrical charge of the electron.

Now I want this analysis to be as general as possible, so I actually want to make it true for anything that has only *one electron*. A hydrogen atom, for example, has one electron, but a helium atom has two electrons. However, if I removed one of the electrons from the helium atom, I would have a He$^+$ ion, which has only one electron. Thus, in this derivation, we will assume that there is only one electron present, but we will allow for more than one proton. In atomic chemistry and physics, the number of protons in an atom is called "Z." Since each proton has a charge of "e," the charge of the nucleus is "Z·e." Making all of the substitutions, then, we get:

$$\frac{m_e \cdot v^2}{r} = \frac{k \cdot e \cdot Z \cdot e}{r^2}$$ (15.5)

which simplifies to:

$$\frac{m_e \cdot v^2}{r} = \frac{k \cdot Z \cdot e^2}{r^2}$$ (15.6)

Now once again, think about what this equation means. The term on the right is the force of the attraction between the electron and the nucleus. The term on the left is the centripetal force. Thus, the equation simply says that the attractive force between the electron and the nucleus must be strong enough to keep the electron orbiting in a circle.

That's all well and good, but so what? How does this help us understand the nature of the atom? So far, it doesn't. This kind of physics was well-known long before Bohr developed his theory of the atom, but Bohr added something. He added the quantum assumption. You see, according to Equation (15.6), an electron can orbit the nucleus at *any* distance. As long as the electrical force was equal to the centripetal force necessary, then the value of "r" could be anything. Bohr looked at this situation and decided to add his quantum assumption. To do this, he proposed the following equation:

$$m_e \cdot v \cdot r = n \cdot \hbar \tag{15.7}$$

where "m_e" is the mass of the electron, "v" is the electron's speed, "r" is the radius of the electron's orbit, and "n" is any integer (1, 2, 3, 4...). The "$\hbar$" in the equation is a modified version of **Planck's constant**, given by the following equation:

$$\hbar = \frac{h}{2 \cdot \pi} \tag{15.8}$$

It turns out that because of the circular nature of the electron's orbit, dividing Planck's constant by $2 \cdot \pi$ just makes the math less messy in the end. That's the only reason it is modified.

How in the world does Equation (15.7) restrict the electron to be in only certain orbits? Well, you should recognize the left-hand side of the equation. The formula $m \cdot v \cdot r$ is the *angular momentum* of a particle traveling in a circle. Since "n" can only have integer values (1, 2, 3, 4...), the equation is only valid for certain values of "r." Thus, Equation (15.7) is simply a mathematical way of stating Bohr's quantum assumption: that the electron can be only in certain orbits, and thus its angular momentum can have only certain, discrete values. Now we simply have to solve Equation (15.7) for "r":

$$r = \frac{n \cdot \hbar}{m_e \cdot v} \tag{15.9}$$

Then we can plug that value of "r" into Equation (15.6) and simplify:

$$\frac{m_e \cdot v^2}{\dfrac{n \cdot \hbar}{m_e \cdot v}} = \frac{k \cdot Z \cdot e^2}{\left(\dfrac{n \cdot \hbar}{m_e \cdot v}\right)^2}$$

$$m_e \cdot v^2 = \frac{k \cdot Z \cdot e^2}{\left(\dfrac{n \cdot \hbar}{m_e \cdot v}\right)}$$

$$m_e \cdot v^2 = \frac{k \cdot Z \cdot e^2 \cdot m_e \cdot v}{n \cdot \hbar}$$

$$v = \frac{k \cdot Z \cdot e^2}{n \cdot \hbar} \qquad (15.10)$$

Notice that aside from "n," there are no real variables on the right side of the equation. The letters "k," and "$\hbar$," and "e" stand for physical constants, while "Z" is determined by the atom that we are investigating. Equation (15.10), then, tells us the speed of the electron in any orbit (n) of the Bohr atom. Now it turns out that even though speed is a very important physical quantity to measure, chemists usually like to talk about the energy of an electron instead. Thus, we can use the definition of kinetic energy to get Equation (15.10) in terms of energy:

$$E = \frac{1}{2} \cdot m \cdot v^2 = \frac{1}{2} \cdot m_e \cdot \left(\frac{k \cdot Z \cdot e^2}{n \cdot \hbar} \right)^2$$

$$E = \frac{m_e \cdot k^2 \cdot Z^2 \cdot e^4}{2 \cdot \hbar^2} \cdot \left(\frac{1}{n} \right)^2 \qquad (15.11)$$

Notice that I segregated the "1/n" term out. I did that to emphasize the fact that the "n" is the only real variable. All of the other terms in the equation are either physical constants or, in the case of "Z," determined by the atom of interest.

So now we know the energy of an electron in any orbit of the Bohr atom, right? Well, not quite. I now need to do something that drives students nuts. I want to introduce a negative sign. The electron is not moving freely in the Bohr orbit. It is bound to move in a circle by the proton. Remember, when an object is bound, we generally refer to its energy as negative. Thus, we will put a negative sign into Equation (15.11).

$$E = -\frac{m_e \cdot k^2 \cdot Z^2 \cdot e^4}{2 \cdot \hbar^2} \cdot \left(\frac{1}{n} \right)^2 \qquad (15.12)$$

Equation (15.12), then, gives us the energy of an electron in any Bohr orbit. In order to simplify this equation, we will actually put in the numbers for all of the physical constants in the equation. The mass of the electron (m_e) is 9.11×10^{-31} kg, the Coulomb constant (k) is 8.99×10^9 $N \cdot m^2 \cdot C^{-2}$, the fundamental charge unit is 1.60×10^{-19} C, and $\hbar$ is 1.05×10^{-34} J·s. When we do the math, then, we find that all of the physical constants work out to 2.18×10^{-18} J, or 13.6 eV. This number actually has a name. It is called the "**Rydberg constant**" in honor of Swedish scientist J. R. Rydberg, who came up with the number *before* Bohr came up with his theory. You will learn how that happened in the next section. In the end, then, the energy of an electron in any Bohr orbit can be calculated using the following equation:

$$E = -R_h \cdot Z^2 \cdot \left(\frac{1}{n}\right)^2 \qquad (15.13)$$

Where "R_h" is the Rydberg constant, 2.18×10^{-18} J or 13.6 eV, Z is the atomic number of the nucleus, and "n" is the number corresponding to the Bohr orbit which the electron occupies.

Equation (15.13) has a box around it because it is important. You will therefore have to memorize it. In addition to knowing the equation, you will also need to know *when you can* use it and *when you can not*. As I derived this formula, I made a really big assumption. You might not see it, but it is there. In Equation (15.5), I assumed that there was only one electron in the atom. How did I make that assumption? Well, Equation (15.5) attempts to balance all of the forces in the problem. I assumed there were two: the attractive force between the electron and the nucleus and the centripetal force. Had there been another electron in the atom, there would have been a third force: the electrical repulsion between the two electrons. That would have completely changed Equation (15.5), and it would have ultimately made the equation too hard to solve. In the end, then, although Equation (15.13) is important, its use is limited. It can be used only in situations where there is one electron.

Does this mean that Equation (15.13) can only be used for hydrogen atoms? Well, not exactly. It can be used for He^+ ions as well. After all, He^+ is the ion that results when helium loses an electron. Since helium has 2 electrons, He^+ has 1 electron. In the same way, Equation (15.13) works on Li^{2+} ions as well, since Li^{2+} ions also have only one electron. Even so, the use of Equation (15.13) is rather limited. Nevertheless, without it, we would not know nearly as much about atoms as we know today. Thus, the use of Equation (15.13) is important. In order to help you use this equation with some other concepts that will be discussed later in this module, a periodic chart is given at the end of this module. You should have learned how to read it in your chemistry course, so I will not teach you how to do that. If you have forgotten how to read the periodic chart, please review your chemistry course.

EXAMPLE 15.3

What is the energy of an electron in the third Bohr orbit of a He^+ ion?

Since helium has two electrons, an He^+ ion has only one electron, so Equation (15.13) works. The atomic number of helium is 2, so Z = 2. Since the electron is in the third Bohr orbit, n = 3.

$$E = -R_h \cdot Z^2 \cdot \left(\frac{1}{n}\right)^2$$

$$E = -(13.6 \text{ eV}) \cdot 2^2 \cdot \left(\frac{1}{3}\right)^2 = -6.04 \text{ eV}$$

So the electron has an energy of <u>-6.04 eV</u>. Notice that the answer has three significant figures. This is because the Rydberg constant has three significant figures, while "Z" and "n" are perfect integers. As a result, they have infinite precision. Thus, the number of significant figures is determined only by the Rydberg constant. Now don't worry that this number means nothing to you. You will see in the next section how this equation can be used to calculate something quite meaningful.

ON YOUR OWN

15.4 For which of the following atoms or ions can we use Equation (15.13)?

$$H, Li^+, Be, Li^{2+}, H^+, Be^{3+}, He$$

15.5 An electron in a hydrogen atom has an energy of -5.45×10^{-19} J. Which Bohr orbit does it occupy?

The Bohr Model and Atomic Spectra

Now we are finally to the point where we can see how Bohr's model was able to explain atomic emission spectra. Electrons in the Bohr model have a certain amount of energy when they sit in a given Bohr orbit. Based on Equation (15.13), we can say that when "n" is small, the energy is large and negative. On the other hand, when "n" is large, the energy is small and negative. Well, the smaller the negative number the larger the value, so in the end, orbits with large values of "n" are considered **high energy orbits** while orbits with low values of "n" are considered **low energy orbits**. Well, suppose an electron is sitting in a low energy orbit. If it can absorb exactly the right amount of energy, it will jump up to a high energy orbit. This energy can be absorbed from the heat of the surroundings, or it can be absorbed by capturing light. In nature, however, everything wishes to end up in its lowest energy state, which is called the **ground state**. Thus, the electron will not stay in the high energy orbit to which it jumped. Instead, it will want to go back to the lowest energy orbit that it can find. The only way it can do this is to release energy. How does an electron release energy? Usually, it does so by emitting light.

So, in order to jump up to a higher energy orbit, electrons need to absorb energy. Sometimes they absorb the energy from heat, sometimes from light, sometimes from other sources such as electricity. In order to jump back down into a lower energy orbit, the electron must release energy, usually in the form of light. How much energy does an electron need to absorb or release? Well, that depends on what orbit it is in and what orbit it is going to. For example, suppose an electron is in the third Bohr orbit and wants to jump back down to the first Bohr orbit. Well, according to Equation (15.13), the electron has a certain amount of energy in the third Bohr orbit, and it needs to have a certain amount of energy to be in the first Bohr orbit. The *difference* between these two energies is what the electron must release. Mathematically, we would say:

$$\Delta E = E_{initial} - E_{final} = -(R_h) \cdot Z^2 \cdot \left(\frac{1}{n_{initial}}\right)^2 - \left[-(R_h) \cdot Z^2 \cdot \left(\frac{1}{n_{final}}\right)^2\right] \qquad (15.14)$$

This simplifies to:

$$\Delta E = (R_h) \cdot Z^2 \cdot \left[\left(\frac{1}{n_{final}}\right)^2 - \left(\frac{1}{n_{initial}}\right)^2\right] \qquad (15.15)$$

In the end, then, Equation (15.13) leads us to another equation, Equation (15.15), which allows us to calculate the energy that an electron must either absorb or release in order to change orbits in the Bohr model of the atom.

So what? Well, think about it. If an electron must absorb or emit light when it moves from one orbit to another, then Equation (15.15) allows us to calculate the energy of that light. That energy can be used to calculate the frequency of the light, using Equation (15.1), and the frequency can be used to determine the wavelength, via Equation (6.13). The wavelength of light tells you its *color*! So, by using some relatively "simple" mathematics, we have derived a formula that lets you determine the color of light emitted (if it is visible light) or absorbed by an electron as it moves from one orbit to another in an atom! In order to help you do this yourself, here is a figure that tells you what wavelengths of light correspond to what color:

FIGURE 15.2
The Visible Spectrum (Wavelengths are in nanometers)

Red	Orange	Yellow	Green	Blue	Indigo	Violet
λ=700-655	λ=655-615	λ=615-570	λ=570-505	λ=505-460	λ=460-420	λ=420-390

Now remember, it is possible for light to have virtually *any* wavelength, so a great deal of the light in Creation is not in the visible spectrum. Nevertheless, if the energy of light corresponds to a wavelength between 390 nm and 700 nm, then the light is visible and its color is given by the figure above. Now I'll pull all of this together with an example.

EXAMPLE 15.4

What color of light is emitted when the electron of a hydrogen atom moves from the fourth Bohr orbit to the second Bohr orbit?

In this example, Z = 1 because we are dealing with hydrogen. The electron starts out in the fourth Bohr orbit, so $n_{initial} = 4$. It ends up in the second Bohr orbit, so $n_{final} = 2$.

$$\Delta E = (13.6\,eV) \cdot Z^2 \cdot \left[\left(\frac{1}{n_{final}} \right)^2 - \left(\frac{1}{n_{initial}} \right)^2 \right]$$

$$\Delta E = (13.6\,eV) \cdot 1^2 \cdot \left[\left(\frac{1}{2} \right)^2 - \left(\frac{1}{4} \right)^2 \right] = 2.55\ eV$$

This tells us, then, that the electron must lose 2.55 eV to make the transition, so that is the energy of the light that it emits. To get the wavelength, we first determine the frequency:

$$E = h \cdot f$$

$$2.55\ eV = (4.14 \times 10^{-15}\ eV \cdot s) \cdot f$$

$$f = 6.16 \times 10^{14}\ \frac{1}{s}$$

Then, we use the speed of light to go from frequency to wavelength, via Equation (6.13)

$$f = \frac{v}{\lambda}$$

$$6.16 \times 10^{14}\ \frac{1}{s} = \frac{3.00 \times 10^8\ \frac{m}{s}}{\lambda}$$

$$\lambda = 4.87 \times 10^{-7}\ m = 487\ nm$$

The electron must emit light with a wavelength of 487 nm, which is <u>blue light</u>, according to Figure 15.2.

Now that you have seen how to use Equation (15.15) to calculate something really useful, it is important to realize a few things. First, when an electron has energy to absorb, it can jump up to any orbit, provided there is enough energy at its disposal. When the electron goes down to a lower energy orbit, it need not jump directly down to the lowest orbit available. Instead, it can make several jumps on its way down. Suppose, for example, that an electron jumps to the n = 5 orbit. In order to jump back down to the n = 1 orbit, it can do so in one jump, or it can go from n = 5 to n = 3 and then from n = 3 to n = 1. In that case, it would release light twice. First, it would release light that has the same energy as the difference between the energy in the fifth Bohr orbit and the third Bohr orbit, and then it would emit light that has energy equal to the difference in energy between the third Bohr orbit and the first Bohr orbit. Alternatively, it could jump down one orbit at a time, releasing light of four different energies. Because there are so many paths that an electron can take when jumping from a high energy orbit back to its ground state, there are many different energies of light that electrons will emit once they have absorbed energy. As a result, when atoms are exposed to a large amount of energy, they emit many different wavelengths of light. The sum total of all of those different wavelengths is the emission spectrum of the atom.

The next thing that you need to realize is that most of the light electrons emit is not visible. Remember, there are many different kinds of light, and only a small portion of it is visible. Thus, the visible spectrum is only a tiny fraction of an atom's emission spectrum.

Think, for example, about neon lights. Neon lights are made of tubes full of neon gas. Electricity is used to excite the neon atoms in the tube and, as a result, the electrons in the neon atoms move up into higher energy orbits. When they move back to lower energy orbits, they emit light. One of those electron transitions results in the emission of yellow-orange light that we call "neon" light. Originally, that was the only color in neon lights. However, as we learned more about chemistry, other gases which emit other colors when excited by electricity were put in the tubes, and even though those gases are not neon, we still refer to signs that use such tubes of gas as "neon" lights. Fluorescent lights operate in the same way, but they contain a mixture of gases that emit so many different colors when excited that, in the end, we see the light that is emitted as white light.

ON YOUR OWN

15.6 An electron in a He^+ ion starts out in the first Bohr orbit and jumps to the fourth Bohr orbit. How much energy must it absorb?

15.7 An electron jumps from the n = 3 orbit of a hydrogen atom to the n = 2 orbit. What is the wavelength of the light emitted? Is it visible? If it is visible, what color is it?

15.8 An electron jumps from the fifth Bohr orbit to a lower orbit in a Li^{2+} ion. If the light emitted has a frequency of 6.67×10^{14} Hz, what orbit did the electron end up in?

Before we leave this section, I want to point out a couple of things. First of all, long before Bohr came along, lots of scientists went to great pains to try and explain the mystery of atomic emission spectra. Indeed, Swedish scientist J. R. Rydberg actually spent so much time puzzling over the data that he was able to "cook up" an equation to fit the data. Long before Bohr came along, he developed the following equation for the energy of visible light emitted from an excited hydrogen atom:

$$E = (2.18 \times 10^{-18} \text{ J}) \cdot \left[\left(\frac{1}{2} \right)^2 - \left(\frac{1}{n} \right)^2 \right] \text{ where n = 3,4,5,6 and 7}$$

Look at what that is. It is Bohr's equation, with n_{final} = 2 and $n_{initial}$ = 3, 4, 5, 6, and 7. Now Rydberg did not derive this formula. He had no idea what it meant. He just looked at the data so long and so hard that he finally dreamed up an equation that would fit it!

What Bohr's model did was explain the data by making the assumption that only certain orbits were possible. That way, there would be only certain energies involved, and that would explain the existence of only certain wavelengths of emitted light. Once he worked out the math, he showed that Rydberg's equation was just a special case of his general equation. It was the case in which the electron was starting in the third through seventh orbit and was jumping down to the second orbit. Thus, even though Rydberg's equation was not all that useful, we still honor him by naming the constant after him. After all, he was actually able to stumble onto part of Bohr's equation before Bohr did! Thanks to Bohr's quantum assumption, however, Bohr was able to derive the full equation.

Now you must realize that *to this day* we do not understand *why* there are only certain possible orbits in an atom. As a matter of fact, that very assumption goes against common sense. After all, why shouldn't an electron be wherever it "wants" to be, provided it has the correct energy? We have no idea. We do know this, however. By making this wild assumption, Bohr was able to explain a wealth of scientific data that could not have been explained before. Thus, *despite the fact that the quantum assumption which Bohr made goes against common sense, we believe in it because it explains the data.* Even though we know that there are some mistakes in the Bohr model, our current model of the atom (the quantum mechanical model) makes a quantum assumption very similar to what Bohr's model makes. Thus, science today holds strongly to the quantum assumption, despite the fact that it makes no sense. Science holds to the quantum assumption *only* because it explains the data.

Now I hope that you can make the obvious connection between faith in Christ and faith in the quantum assumption. The only reason to believe in the quantum assumption is that it explains the data. Scientists did not believe in the Bohr model because it made sense. Scientists do not currently believe in the quantum mechanical model because it makes sense. In fact, both models *go against* sense. They believe in it because it explains the data. It is the same with faith in Christ. It doesn't matter whether Christ as Lord and Savior makes any sense to you. There are certainly things in the Christian faith (like the Trinity) that are really *hard* to understand and probably do not make sense to you. Just like our current models of the atom, however, that's irrelevant. The only question (from a scientific point of view) is, "Does it explain the data?" After studying Creation, the scientist must admit that an all-powerful Designer does "explain the data." After studying the scientific evidence for the validity of the Bible (see Josh McDowell's

Evidence That Demands a Verdict or Jay Wile's *Reasonable Faith: The Scientific Case for Christianity*), you will also find that the Christian faith "explains the data." Thus, the next time someone tells you that faith in Christ is "not scientific," you can tell them that it is just as scientific as current atomic science!

The other thing I wanted to point out to you is rather simple. Because the atomic number (Z) is in Equation (15.15), the light emitted and absorbed by any element will be unique because each element has its own atomic number. Each molecule also has its own electronic structure and, as a result, the light that it can absorb or emit is unique to that molecule. As a result, if we excite an element or compound (typically by heat or electricity) and look at the pattern of wavelengths (visible and not visible) of light that it emits, we can unambiguously determine that element or compound. This technique is called **emission spectroscopy**, and it is used to examine the elemental makeup of stars and to analyze chemicals. Alternatively, we could shine light through a compound or element and see what wavelengths of light are absorbed. This is called **absorption spectroscopy** and is typically used more frequently, because it does not risk destroying the compound or element being studied.

The Size of an Atom

Although you are aware that atoms are small, it is time to get a good handle on exactly how small they are. You see, the Bohr model not only allows us to calculate the energy of an electron in any given orbit, but it also allows us to calculate the radius of the orbits that the electrons occupy. As I have said before, we now know that the Bohr model is not completely accurate, but for all one-electron atoms, it does a pretty good job, so it is still rather instructive, especially because the mathematics associated with it is so "simple."

Now remember, Equation (15.9) gives us a formula for the radius of the electron's orbit:

$$r = \frac{n \cdot \hbar}{m_e \cdot v} \tag{15.9}$$

Well, in our derivation of Equation (15.13), we came up with an expression for the velocity of an electron in the nth Bohr orbit:

$$v = \frac{k \cdot Z \cdot e^2}{n \cdot \hbar} \tag{15.10}$$

If we put that expression for "v" into Equation (15.9), look what happens:

$$r = \frac{n \cdot \hbar}{m_e \cdot \left(\dfrac{k \cdot Z \cdot e^2}{n \cdot \hbar}\right)} = \left(\frac{\hbar^2}{m_e \cdot k \cdot e^2}\right) \cdot \frac{n^2}{Z} \tag{15.16}$$

If we take that equation and replace the physical constants in parentheses with numbers, we get:

$$r = (5.29 \times 10^{-11} \text{ m}) \cdot \frac{n^2}{Z} \qquad (15.17)$$

Since atoms are so small, we usually replace the meters unit with the Angstrom unit, which is equal to 10^{-10} meters. Thus, the usual way you see the equation is:

$$r = (0.529 \text{ Å}) \cdot \frac{n^2}{Z} \qquad (15.18)$$

where "Å" is the symbol for the Angstrom unit.

Thus, the radius of the first Bohr orbit in the hydrogen atom (n = 1, Z = 1), according to Equation (15.18), is 0.529 Å, or 5.29 x 10^{-11} meters. Since there is only one electron in a hydrogen atom, in its ground state, the first Bohr orbit is the only orbit that is occupied. Thus, this tells us that the hydrogen atom itself has a radius of 0.529 Å in its ground state. Now think about that number for a moment. Take out a metric ruler and look at the markings that indicate millimeters. They are pretty close together, aren't they? Well, based on the size we just calculated, approximately 19,000,000 hydrogen atoms in their ground state could fit in between two of those millimeter dashes! Hopefully, you now have some idea how small atoms really are!

ON YOUR OWN

15.9 An electron in a hydrogen atom has an energy of -2.42 x 10^{-19} J. How far from the nucleus is it orbiting?

15.10 What it the radius of a Li^{2+} ion in its ground state?

Moving From the Bohr Model to the Quantum Mechanical Model

Although the Bohr model of the atom was a triumph in its day, we now know that it is a bit flawed. As a result, scientists do not accept it as the standard view of the atom. Today, atomic scientists are committed to the **quantum mechanical model** of the atom. In fact, there are many similarities between the quantum mechanical model and the Bohr model. As its name implies, the quantum mechanical model of the atom still makes use of the quantum assumption. Instead of talking about orbits, however, the quantum assumption in the quantum mechanical model says that there are only specific energies that an electron in an atom can have. An electron is not free to take on any energy. Instead, it is constrained to have only certain, distinct energies.

Instead of circular orbits like those of the Bohr model, the quantum mechanical model of the atom says that electrons, depending on their energy, can orbit the nucleus in "clouds" that sometimes have quite interesting shapes. The shapes of these clouds (called **orbitals**), as well as their size, are governed by certain numbers called **quantum numbers**. In your chemistry course, you probably learned the shapes of some of these orbitals when you learned about electron configurations. In this course, I just want to give you an idea of where those shapes come from.

The quantum mechanical model of the atom is governed by a very complicated equation called the **Schrodinger equation**. This equation takes two years of post calculus mathematics to understand and an additional year of math beyond that to really learn how it is solved. Obviously, then, I am not going to try and make you learn it! However, I will tell you that when you apply the Schrodinger equation to the situation of an electron orbiting a nucleus, you get some reasonably "simple" results. The solution of the Schrodinger equation tells us that electrons orbiting a nucleus can have only certain, distinct energies and positions within the atom. Those energies and positions are determined by a series of four numbers called quantum numbers. Once you determine those four quantum numbers for an electron, you know how much energy it has and roughly where it is in the atom.

The first quantum number, called the **principal quantum number**, is abbreviated as "n." This is no accident. The principal quantum number turns out to be the same integer that Bohr used in his model to describe the orbit that the electron is in. Much like the Bohr model, this principal quantum number indicates how far the electron is from the nucleus. Just as is the case with the Bohr model, the larger the value for "n," the farther away the electron is (on average) from the nucleus. In addition, the value for "n" affects energy greatly. When two electrons in the same shape orbital have two different values for "n," the electron with the larger value for "n" has *substantially more energy* than the other electron. Once again, as is the case for the Bohr atom, the principal quantum number can have any whole number value other than zero.

Principal Quantum Number: n = 1, 2, 3, 4...

The second quantum number that results from solving the Schrodinger equation is called the **azimuthal** (az uh myoo' thuhl) **quantum number** and it is usually abbreviated as "ℓ." This quantum number tells you what shape orbital the electron is using to orbit the nucleus. It also affects the energy, but not nearly as significantly as does the principal quantum number. Now the azimuthal quantum number can have any integer value, including zero, but the range of integer values is restricted by the value of n. For example, when "n" equals one, the only possible value of "ℓ" is zero. When "n" equals 2, "ℓ" can be either zero or one. In general, then, "ℓ" can have any integer value from zero to one less than the principal quantum number.

Azimuthal Quantum Number: ℓ = 0, 1, ... (n-1)

Now at this point that may make no sense to you, but don't worry. I'll explain why this is the case in a minute. For right now, I need to tell you a little more about "ℓ."

As I said before, the azimuthal quantum number tells you what shape orbital the electron occupies. For some strange reason, chemists associate letters with these orbital shapes. Figure 15.3 illustrates the basic shapes of electron orbitals for the first 6 values of the azimuthal quantum number, along with the letter associated with that shape:

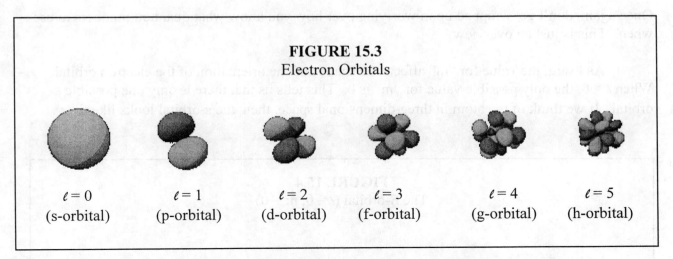

FIGURE 15.3
Electron Orbitals

| $\ell = 0$ | $\ell = 1$ | $\ell = 2$ | $\ell = 3$ | $\ell = 4$ | $\ell = 5$ |
| (s-orbital) | (p-orbital) | (d-orbital) | (f-orbital) | (g-orbital) | (h-orbital) |

You probably learned the shape and letters associated with the first few orbitals (s, p, and d) when you studied chemistry. In this course, you see that these orbitals are determined by the azimuthal quantum number, which comes from solving the Schrodinger equation in the quantum mechanical model of the atom.

Now why does the value of "ℓ" depend on the value of "n?" Well, think about what the value of "n" tells us. It tells us the average distance that the electron is from the nucleus. As the value for "n" gets larger, the larger that distance becomes. Well, when n = 1, the electron is rather close to the nucleus; thus, there is not much room. As a result, only one orbital can "fit" within that space. Thus, only the s-orbital ($\ell = 0$) is present when n = 1. When n = 2, however, the electron is farther away from the nucleus. As a result, there is more room, so more orbitals can "fit" within that space. As we will learn in a moment, there are actually three p-orbitals, so when n = 2, there is room for an s-orbital and three p-orbitals, so "ℓ" can equal either 0 or 1. Likewise, when n = 3, the electron is even farther out, so now there is room for an s-orbital, three p-orbitals, and five d-orbitals. As a result, when n = 3, "ℓ" can equal 0, 1, or 2.

So the reason the value of "ℓ" depends on the value of "n" all relates to space. There are spatial limitations that slowly go away as "n" increases. Thus, for low values of "n," there are only a few possible orbitals. For large values of "n," however, many more orbitals are available.

The next quantum number is called the **magnetic quantum number**, and it is usually abbreviated as "m." This number affects certain details of an orbital's shape, as well as its orientation in space. Just as the value of "ℓ" depends on the value of "n," the value of "m" depends on the value of "ℓ." The magnetic quantum number can have all integer values from -ℓ to + ℓ. Thus, when $\ell = 0$, the only possible value for "m" is zero. When $\ell = 1$, however, "m" can take on any of three values: -1, 0, or 1. Likewise, when $\ell = 2$, the value of "m" can be -2, -1, 0, 1, or 2.

Magnetic Quantum Number: m ranges from -ℓ to +ℓ in integer steps

Once again, don't get wrapped up in worrying over how you know what quantum numbers to use when. This is just an overview.

As I said, the value for "m" affects the shape and the orientation of the electron orbital. When $\ell = 0$, the only possible value for "m" is 0. This tells us that there is only one possible s-orbital. If we think of the atom in three-dimensional space, then, the s-orbital looks like this:

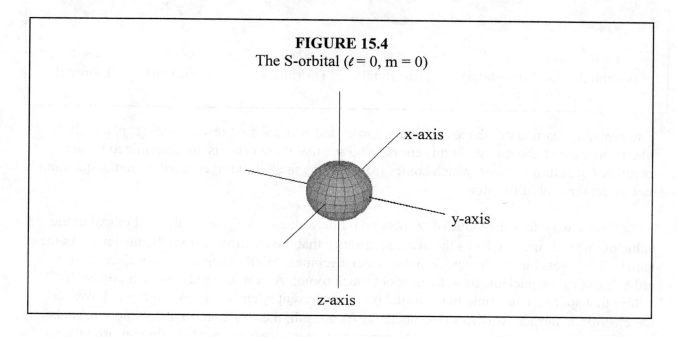

FIGURE 15.4
The S-orbital ($\ell = 0$, m = 0)

When $\ell = 1$, three values for "m" are possible, -1, 0, or 1. Since $\ell = 1$ means we are dealing with p-orbitals, then this tells us that there are 3 different kinds of p-orbitals. There is a p-orbital for which m = 1, a p-orbital for which m = 0, and a p-orbital for which m = -1. Those three orbitals are shown in Figure 15.5:

FIGURE 15.5
The Three P-orbitals ($\ell = 1$, m = -1, 0, 1)

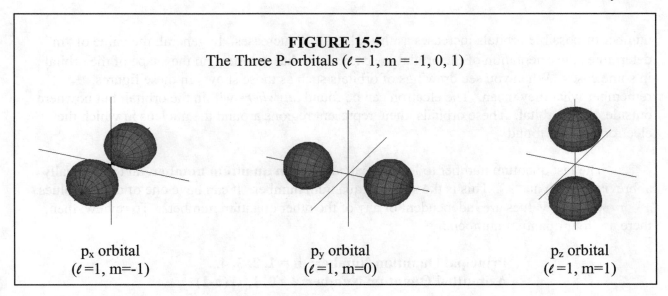

p$_x$ orbital
(ℓ =1, m=-1)

p$_y$ orbital
(ℓ =1, m=0)

p$_z$ orbital
(ℓ =1, m=1)

Notice that the basic shape of these three orbitals are the same. That's because, for the most part, orbital shape is determined by "ℓ." What's different between the three is the orientation. If we imagine the nucleus of the atom at the origin of our three-dimensional axis, you can see that all three of these orbitals can exist simultaneously around the atom. Now realize that the electron can be *anywhere* within the orbital, but it cannot be anywhere outside of the orbital. Thus, you can see that the electron cannot be anywhere right near the nucleus, but it can be anywhere within the two lobes of the orbital.

To carry the illustration just one step further, when $\ell = 2$, there are five possible values of "m": -2, -1, 0, 1, and 2. This means there are five different types of d-orbitals, as shown below:

FIGURE 15.6
The Five D-orbitals ($\ell = 2$, m = -2, -1, 0, 1, 2)

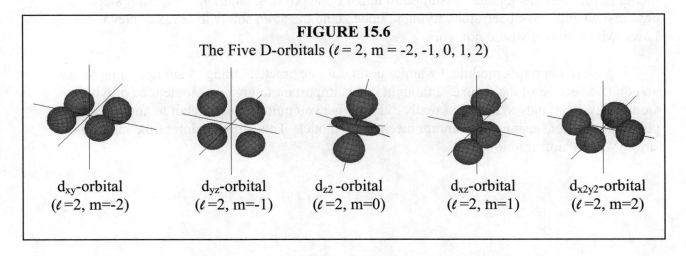

d$_{xy}$-orbital
(ℓ =2, m=-2)

d$_{yz}$-orbital
(ℓ =2, m=-1)

d$_{z2}$ -orbital
(ℓ =2, m=0)

d$_{xz}$-orbital
(ℓ =2, m=1)

d$_{x2y2}$-orbital
(ℓ =2, m=2)

Notice that the value of "m" mostly affects the orientation of the orbital, except in the case where m = 0. There, the value of m does affect the shape. If you are good at three-dimensional visualization, you can see that all of these orbitals can exist simultaneously with the nucleus at the origin of the three-dimensional axis. I could go on with $\ell = 4$, 5, and 6, but we will stop there. The point should be clear. Because of the relationship between "ℓ" and "m," the number of possible orbitals increases as the value of "ℓ" increases. In general, the value of "m" determines the orientation of the orbital in space, and it has an effect on the shape of the orbital in some cases. When you see drawings of orbitals such as those shown in these figures, remember what they mean. The electron can be found *anywhere* within the orbital, but nowhere outside of the orbital. These orbitals, then, represent regions around the nucleus in which the electrons can be found.

The last quantum number to learn is called the **spin quantum number**, and it is usually abbreviated with an "s." This is the simplest quantum number. It can have one of only 2 values, $+\frac{1}{2}$ or $-\frac{1}{2}$. These values are independent of any of the other quantum numbers. To review, then, there are four quantum numbers:

Principal Quantum Number: n = 1, 2, 3, 4...
Azimuthal Quantum Number: ℓ = 0, 1, ... (n-1)
Magnetic Quantum Number: m ranges from - ℓ to + ℓ in integer steps
Spin Quantum Number: $+\frac{1}{2}$ or $-\frac{1}{2}$

When you put together a list of four quantum numbers that meet these criteria, you have uniquely determined the average distance from the nucleus, general orbital shape, orbital orientation, and energy of an electron in an atom.

If you study chemistry to any great depth, you will use these quantum numbers. In this course, I just wanted to give you an idea of where atomic physics has moved now that the Bohr model is known to be flawed. It is important to note, however, that without the Bohr model of the atom, we would have never developed the quantum mechanical model, because the Bohr model introduced the quantum assumption into atomic physics. Without that major step, physicists would have been stuck trying to understand the atom solely in terms of Newton's Laws, which simply would not work.

Before I end this module, I want to point out one practical thing. I am not going to test you on this section of the course. I thought it was important to give you some idea of where atomic physics stands today, but I really did not give you quite enough detail to analyze any physical situations using the quantum mechanical model. Thus, this section of the module is simply "extra" information.

The Periodic Table of Elements

1A	2A	3B	4B	5B	6B	7B	8B	8B	8B	1B	2B	3A	4A	5A	6A	7A	8A
1 **H** 1.01																	2 **He** 4.0
3 **Li** 6.94	4 **Be** 9.01											5 **B** 10.8	6 **C** 12.0	7 **N** 14.0	8 **O** 16.0	9 **F** 19.0	10 **Ne** 20.2
11 **Na** 23.0	12 **Mg** 24.3											13 **Al** 27.0	14 **Si** 28.1	15 **P** 31.0	16 **S** 32.1	17 **Cl** 35.5	18 **Ar** 39.9
19 **K** 39.1	20 **Ca** 40.1	21 **Sc** 45.0	22 **Ti** 47.9	23 **V** 50.9	24 **Cr** 52.0	25 **Mn** 54.9	26 **Fe** 55.8	27 **Co** 58.9	28 **Ni** 58.7	29 **Cu** 63.5	30 **Zn** 65.4	31 **Ga** 69.7	32 **Ge** 72.6	33 **As** 74.9	34 **Se** 79.0	35 **Br** 79.9	36 **Kr** 83.8
37 **Rb** 85.5	38 **Sr** 87.6	39 **Y** 88.9	40 **Zr** 91.2	41 **Nb** 92.9	42 **Mo** 95.9	43 **Tc** (98)	44 **Ru** 101.1	45 **Rh** 102.9	46 **Pd** 106.4	47 **Ag** 107.9	48 **Cd** 112.4	49 **In** 114.8	50 **Sn** 118.7	51 **Sb** 121.8	52 **Te** 127.6	53 **I** 126.9	54 **Xe** 131.3
55 **Cs** 132.9	56 **Ba** 137.3	57 **La** 138.9	72 **Hf** 178.5	73 **Ta** 180.9	74 **W** 183.9	75 **Re** 186.2	76 **Os** 190.2	77 **Ir** 192.2	78 **Pt** 195.1	79 **Au** 197.0	80 **Hg** 200.6	81 **Tl** 204.4	82 **Pb** 207.2	83 **Bi** 209.0	84 **Po** (209)	85 **At** (210)	86 **Rn** (222)
87 **Fr** (223)	88 **Ra** 226.0	89 **Ac** 227.0	104 **Unq** (261)	105 **Unp** (262)	106 **Unh** (263)	107 **Uns** (262)	108 **Uno** (265)	109 **Une** (266)									

58 **Ce** 140.1	59 **Pr** 140.9	60 **Nd** 144.2	61 **Pm** (145)	62 **Sm** 150.4	63 **Eu** 152.0	64 **Gd** 157.3	65 **Tb** 158.9	66 **Dy** 162.5	67 **Ho** 164.9	68 **Er** 167.3	69 **Tm** 168.9	70 **Yb** 173.0	71 **Lu** 175.0
90 **Th** 232.0	91 **Pa** 231.0	92 **U** 238.0	93 **Np** 237.0	94 **Pu** (244)	95 **Am** (243)	96 **Cm** (247)	97 **Bk** (247)	98 **Cf** (251)	99 **Es** (252)	100 **Fm** (257)	101 **Md** (258)	102 **No** (259)	103 **Lr** (260)

ANSWERS TO THE ON YOUR OWN PROBLEMS

15.1 If electrons cannot be emitted once the wavelength of light falls below 264 nm, we know that the energy of the light below 264 nm is less than the work function. Thus, the energy of light at 264 nm is equal to the work function. To get the energy, we start with the frequency:

$$f = \frac{v}{\lambda} = \frac{2.998 \times 10^8 \ \frac{\cancel{m}}{sec}}{2.64 \times 10^{-7} \ \cancel{m}} = 1.14 \times 10^{15} \ \frac{1}{sec}$$

Now we can get the energy:

$$E = h \cdot f = (4.14 \times 10^{-15} \ eV \cdot \cancel{sec}) \cdot (1.14 \times 10^{15} \ \frac{1}{\cancel{sec}}) = 4.72 \ eV$$

The work function, then, is 4.72 eV. If you did it in Joules, the answer is 7.56×10^{-19} J.

15.2 The de Broglie wavelength comes from the momentum:

$$\lambda = \frac{h}{p} = \frac{6.63 \times 10^{-34} \ J \cdot sec}{(9.11 \times 10^{-31} \ kg) \cdot (1510 \ \frac{m}{sec})} = 4.82 \times 10^{-7} \ \frac{\frac{\cancel{kg} \cdot m^2}{\cancel{sec^2}} \cdot \cancel{sec^2}}{\cancel{kg} \cdot m} = 4.82 \times 10^{-7} \ m$$

The wavelength of the electron, then, is 482 nm, which is right in the range of visible light. Thus, the wave characteristics of this electron cannot be ignored, since the wavelength is not small compared to other waves with which we are familiar.

15.3 Once the electron got up to the fourth orbit, there are *many* ways it could get down. First, it could jump straight from the fourth orbit back to the first. That would result in one wavelength of light. It could also jump from the fourth to the third (another wavelength of light for a total of 2 so far), from the third to the second (another wavelength for a total of 3), and then from the second to the first (yet another wavelength for a total of 4). However, it could jump from the fourth to the third (we already considered that wavelength), and *then* jump straight from the third to the first (that's a new wavelength, so the total is now 5). Also, it could jump from the fourth to the second (another new one for a total of 6) and then from the second to the first (we already considered that one, however). Thus, there are a total of 6 possible wavelengths of light that can be emitted when the electron decays from the fourth orbit back to the first one.

15.4 The Bohr model can only be used on atoms or ions with just one electron. Thus, the following atoms or ions will work: H, Li^{2+}, Be^{3+}.

15.5 In this problem, we know that Z = 1 because we are dealing with a hydrogen atom. We also know the energy. Equation (15.13), therefore, can be used to solve for n. Since the energy was given in Joules, we will have to use R_h in Joules as well.

$$E = -R_h \cdot Z^2 \cdot \left(\frac{1}{n}\right)^2$$

$$-5.45 \times 10^{-19} \text{ J} = -(2.18 \times 10^{-18} \text{ J}) \cdot 1^2 \cdot \left(\frac{1}{n}\right)^2$$

$$\left(\frac{1}{n}\right)^2 = \frac{-5.45 \times 10^{-19} \text{ J}}{-2.18 \times 10^{-18} \text{ J}} = 0.25$$

$$\frac{1}{n} = 0.5$$

$$n = 2$$

The electron is in the second Bohr orbit.

15.6 To jump from low energy orbits to high energy orbits, electrons must gain energy. The amount of energy is determined by the difference in energy between the two orbits, which is calculated using Equation (15.15). Since we are dealing with a helium ion here, Z = 2.

$$\Delta E = (13.6 \text{ eV}) \cdot Z^2 \cdot \left[\left(\frac{1}{n_{final}}\right)^2 - \left(\frac{1}{n_{initial}}\right)^2\right]$$

$$\Delta E = (13.6 \text{ eV}) \cdot 2^2 \cdot \left[\left(\frac{1}{4}\right)^2 - \left(\frac{1}{1}\right)^2\right] = -51.0 \text{ eV}$$

The negative sign simply means that the electron absorbs energy rather than emits it. Thus, the electron must absorb 51.0 eV of energy.

15.7 In this problem, Z = 1 because we are dealing with hydrogen. The electron starts out in the third Bohr orbit, so $n_{initial} = 3$. It ends up in the second Bohr orbit, so $n_{final} = 2$.

$$\Delta E = (13.6 \text{ eV}) \cdot Z^2 \cdot \left[\left(\frac{1}{n_{final}} \right)^2 - \left(\frac{1}{n_{initial}} \right)^2 \right]$$

$$\Delta E = (13.6 \text{ eV}) \cdot 1^2 \cdot \left[\left(\frac{1}{2} \right)^2 - \left(\frac{1}{3} \right)^2 \right] = 1.89 \text{ eV}$$

This tells us, then, that the electron must emit light with energy of 1.89eV to make the transition. From the energy, we can get the frequency:

$$E = h \cdot f$$

$$1.89 \text{ eV} = (4.14 \times 10^{-15} \text{ eV} \cdot \text{s}) \cdot f$$

$$f = 4.57 \times 10^{14} \frac{1}{\text{s}}$$

Then, we use the speed of light to go from frequency to wavelength.

$$f = \frac{v}{\lambda}$$

$$4.57 \times 10^{14} \frac{1}{\text{s}} = \frac{3.00 \times 10^8 \frac{\text{m}}{\text{s}}}{\lambda}$$

$$\lambda = 6.56 \times 10^{-7} \text{ m} = 656 \text{ nm}$$

The electron must emit light with a wavelength of 656 nm, which is red light, according to Figure 15.2.

15.8 In this problem, $Z = 3$ because we are dealing with Li^{2+}. The first thing to realize is that we have the frequency of the light emitted. In order to find the final orbit (n_{final}), we are going to need energy. Thus, we first need to calculate the energy:

$$E = h \cdot f$$

$$E = (4.14 \times 10^{-15} \text{ eV} \cdot \text{s}) \cdot (6.67 \times 10^{14} \text{ Hz}) = 2.76 \text{ eV}$$

Now that we know the energy of the light emitted, we can use Equation (15.15) to determine n_{final}:

$$\Delta E = (13.6 \text{ eV}) \cdot Z^2 \cdot \left[\left(\frac{1}{n_{final}} \right)^2 - \left(\frac{1}{n_{initial}} \right)^2 \right]$$

$$2.76 \text{ eV} = (13.6 \text{ eV}) \cdot 3^2 \cdot \left[\left(\frac{1}{n_{final}} \right)^2 - \left(\frac{1}{5} \right)^2 \right]$$

$$\frac{2.76 \text{ eV}}{(13.6 \text{ eV}) \cdot 3^2} = \left(\frac{1}{n_{final}} \right)^2 - \frac{1}{25}$$

$$0.0225 + \frac{1}{25} = \left(\frac{1}{n_{final}} \right)^2$$

$$\frac{1}{n_{final}} = 0.250$$

$$n_{final} = 4$$

The electron lands in the <u>fourth Bohr orbit</u>.

15.9 We are dealing with hydrogen again here, so $Z = 1$. In order to get the radius, we need to know "n." We don't have that, however. We only have the electron's energy. Well, Equation (15.13) relates energy to "n":

$$E = -R_h \cdot Z^2 \cdot \left(\frac{1}{n} \right)^2$$

$$-2.42 \times 10^{-19} \text{ J} = -(2.18 \times 10^{-18} \text{ J}) \cdot 1^2 \cdot \left(\frac{1}{n} \right)^2$$

$$\left(\frac{1}{n} \right)^2 = \frac{-2.42 \times 10^{-19} \text{ J}}{-2.18 \times 10^{-18} \text{ J}} = 0.111$$

$$\frac{1}{n} = 0.333$$

$$n = 3$$

Now that we know "n," calculating the radius is a snap:

$$r = (0.529 \text{ Å}) \cdot \frac{n^2}{Z} = (0.529 \text{ Å}) \cdot \frac{3^2}{1} = \underline{4.76 \text{ Å}}$$

Notice how much bigger the hydrogen atom is when the electron jumps to a higher energy orbit. When the electron moves from n = 1 to n = 3, the size of the hydrogen atom increases by a factor of 9!

15.10 This is a direct application of Equation (15.18). Since we are dealing with Li^{2+}, Z = 3, and since we are talking about the ground state (lowest possible energy), n = 1.

$$r = (0.529 \text{ Å}) \cdot \frac{n^2}{Z}$$

$$r = (0.529 \text{ Å}) \cdot \frac{1^2}{3}$$

$$r = \underline{0.176 \text{ Å}}$$

So we see that a Li^{2+} ion is actually *smaller* than a hydrogen atom. Now don't confuse Li^{2+} with Li. A lithium atom has three electrons, so the second Bohr orbit is occupied. Since the radius depends on n^2, the radius of the second Bohr orbit is 4 times larger than the radius of the first Bohr orbit, so a lithium *atom* is bigger than a hydrogen atom. A lithium 2+ *ion*, however, is smaller than a hydrogen atom.

REVIEW QUESTIONS FOR MODULE #15

1. Which of the following is the more correct statement:

   a. Physicists currently think that light has both wavelike and particle-like properties.
   b. Physicists currently think that light as well as matter has both wavelike and particle-like properties.

2. State whether or not classical physics could account for each of the following descriptions involving the photoelectric effect.

   a. When light is shined on a metal, electrons are emitted from the metal.
   b. The maximum kinetic energy of the electrons is independent of the light's intensity.
   c. There is a frequency of light under which electrons will not be emitted by the metal.
   d. The maximum kinetic energy of the electrons is proportional to the light's frequency.
   e. The electrons are emitted almost immediately once the light is turned on.

3. What was Einstein's major assumption in his explanation of the photoelectric effect?

4. If de Broglie is right, why doesn't a baseball thrown during a baseball game exhibit wavelike properties?

5. What assumption did Bohr make that led to the success of his theory?

6. What justification did Bohr use to support his assumption?

7. In the Bohr model, an electron can be in orbit #1 or orbit #2, but it cannot be anywhere in between. If that's the case, how does the electron jump from orbit #1 to orbit #2?

8. Suppose you excite an atom and you see no light coming from it. Does that mean electrons are not moving up and down in orbitals?

9. Suppose an electron in the Bohr atom absorbs energy and jumps to the n = 3 orbit. How many wavelengths of light can the electron possibly emit in getting back to the n = 1 orbit?

10. What is the difference between atomic emission spectroscopy and atomic absorption spectroscopy?

PRACTICE PROBLEMS FOR MODULE #15

$h = 6.63 \times 10^{-34}$ J·s $= 4.14 \times 10^{-15}$ eV·s $c = 2.998 \times 10^{8}$ m/sec
$R_h = -2.17 \times 10^{-18}$ J $= 13.6$ eV   1 nm $= 10^{-9}$ m
1 eV $= 1.602 \times 10^{-19}$ J

1. What is the maximum kinetic energy of electrons that are emitted by platinum when it is illuminated with light whose wavelength is 154 nm? (Platinum's work function is 6.35 eV.)

2. Aluminum is illuminated with light of unknown wavelength. The work function of aluminum is 4.08 eV, and the maximum kinetic energy of the electrons being emitted is 1.02 eV. What is the wavelength of the light being emitted?

3. A physicist wants to investigate the wavelike properties of protons and electrons. He accelerates a beam of electrons to a speed of "v_e." If he then wants to accelerate the protons so that they have the same wavelength as the electrons, what must the proton's speed be in terms of "v_e?" (mass of a proton $= 1.67 \times 10^{-27}$ kg, mass of an electron $= 9.11 \times 10^{-31}$ kg)

4. What is the energy of an electron in the n = 2 Bohr orbit of a He^{+} ion?

5. An electron in a hydrogen atom starts out in the first Bohr orbit and jumps to the fourth Bohr orbit. How much energy must it absorb?

6. An electron jumps from the n = 3 orbit of a Li^{2+} ion to the n = 1 orbit. What is the wavelength of the light emitted?

7. An electron jumps from the fifth Bohr orbit to a lower orbit in a hydrogen atom. If the light emitted has a frequency of 3.16×10^{15} Hz, what orbit did the electron end up in?

8. What is the radius of a He^{+} ion in its ground state?

9. An electron in a hydrogen atom has an energy of -0.379 eV. How far from the nucleus is it orbiting?

10. An electron in a He^{+} ion is orbiting the nucleus at a distance of 0.265 Å. What is the electron's energy?

Module #16: Nuclear Physics

Introduction

It is time now to discuss what I consider the most fascinating field of physics: nuclear physics, which is the study of the atom's nucleus. How do nuclear physicists study the nucleus of an atom? After all, an atom is small enough, but a nucleus is even smaller. For example, the average radius of the hydrogen atom is 0.529 angstroms (5.29×10^{-11} m). The radius of the nucleus of that atom (the proton), however, is a mere 1.3×10^{-15} m. That's pretty small. Think about it this way: if a hydrogen atom were expanded until its average radius were as big as the walls of a major league baseball stadium, the nucleus of the atom could be represented by a tiny marble located at the very center of the stadium!

There are three basic ways that nuclear physicists study the properties of the nucleus. First, they study how the mass number of an atom affects its properties. Since the mass number of an atom depends only on its nucleus, the way that the mass number affects the properties of an atom should tell you something about the properties of the nucleus itself. Second, nuclear physicists study radioactivity. This is a process governed almost exclusively by the nucleus, so by studying radioactivity in detail, nuclear physicists can come to a better understanding of the inner workings of the nucleus. Finally, physicists study what happens when two nuclei collide. If atoms are forced together with enough energy, sometimes the atoms' nuclei will collide and the results can tell us a lot about how the nucleus behaves when it is stressed. In this module, I will discuss each of these means by which nuclear physicists learn about the nucleus.

In the preceding discussion, I used a term that you might have forgotten from your physical science or chemistry course: **mass number**. The mass number of a nucleus is the sum total of the number of protons and number of neutrons in the nucleus. This mass number is usually written as a superscript in front of the symbol for an atom. For example, ^{12}C represents a carbon atom whose mass number is 12. Since all carbon atoms have 6 protons (we know that from the Periodic Table of the Elements), a ^{12}C atom must have 6 protons and 6 neutrons, because its mass number is 12. In the same way, a ^{13}C atom must have 6 protons and 7 neutrons, while a ^{14}C atom must have 6 protons and 8 neutrons. You will be expected to remember all of this and use the periodic table to help you determine the number of neutrons in an atom given its mass number. Thus, if this sounds unfamiliar to you, please review your chemistry or physical science course. Also, please understand that you are free to use the Periodic Table of the Elements as much as you want. It was given to you in the previous module.

Binding Energy

When we disregard the electrons in an atom, only the nucleus is left. Since the nucleus contains both protons and neutrons, these particles are generically called **nucleons**.

Nucleon - A term used to refer to both protons and neutrons

Now remember, the nucleus is rather small. Nevertheless, all of the nucleons in an atom are packed tightly together in this small space. Now that should bother you. After all, protons are positively charged and neutrons have no charge. Thus, the nucleus is composed of several positively charged particles and several neutral particles crammed together in a tight space. What should those positive charges do to one another? They should repel each other. In fact, the nucleus is so small that the repulsive forces between these positive charges should be enormous. Since there are no negative charges in the nucleus to counteract this repulsive force, you should expect that a nucleus would simply be blown apart because of the repulsion between its protons.

Why doesn't the nucleus explode due to the repulsion between protons? This was one of the great mysteries of science in the early twentieth century. Since nuclei obviously do not explode, nuclear scientists postulated that there was something called the "nuclear force" that was strong enough to hold the nucleus together despite the repulsion between protons. Of course, they had no idea *what* the nuclear force was and *how* it worked. They simply assumed that it must exist, otherwise atoms would not exist.

Scientists began to get a clue as to what holds the nucleus together when nuclear chemists and physicists discovered that the mass of a nucleus is actually *less* than the sum total of the masses of the protons and neutrons which make it up. For example, a ^{4}He atom is composed of 2 protons and 2 neutrons. The mass of an individual neutron is 1.0087 amu, and the mass of an individual proton is 1.0073 amu. Thus, the sum total of the masses of all 4 nucleons that make up a helium-4 nucleus is 4.0320 amu (2x1.0087 + 2x1.0073). Nevertheless, a ^{4}He nucleus (composed of those exact particles) has a mass of only 4.0024 amu. There seems, then, to be a **mass deficit** in this nucleus. The nucleus is 0.0296 amu lighter than the sum of the masses of its individual nucleons. What causes this mass deficit?

The answer to that question can be found in the famous equation which you have already studied:

$$E = m \cdot c^2 \tag{8.7}$$

As you should recall from Module #8, this equation basically states that matter and energy are interchangeable. Thus, mass can be converted to energy, and energy can be converted to mass. As you learned in Module #8, both of those processes have been seen in the laboratory.

How does all of this relate to the nucleus? Well, if the mass of a nucleus is less than the sum total of the mass of its individual nucleons, then the nucleons must "lose" some of their mass when they form a nucleus. This mass is converted to energy via Equation (8.7), which nuclear scientists call the **binding energy** of the nucleus.

Binding energy - The energy formed from the mass deficit of a nucleus

As long as you know the exact mass of a nucleus, calculating its binding energy is rather easy.

EXAMPLE 16.1

The mass of a ^{7}Li nucleus is 7.0160 amu. What is the binding energy of the nucleus? (The mass of a proton is 1.0073 amu, and the mass of a neutron is 1.0087 amu. The speed of light is 3.00 x 10^8 m/sec and 1 amu = 1.6605 x 10^{-27} kg.)

Since lithium's atomic number is 3, all lithium atoms have 3 protons. The mass number, which is the sum of the protons and neutrons in a nucleus, therefore indicates that a ^{7}Li nucleus has 4 neutrons. The sum of the masses of 3 protons and 4 neutrons is:

$$3 \times (1.0073 \text{ amu}) + 4 \times (1.0087 \text{ amu}) = 7.0567 \text{ amu}$$

Since the mass of a ^{7}Li nucleus is only 7.0160 amu, there is a mass deficit of 7.0567 amu - 7.0160 amu = 0.0407 amu. This mass deficit is converted to energy according to Equation (8.7). To use this equation, however, we must have consistent units. Since we have the speed of light in m/sec, then the energy will come out in Joules as long as the mass is in kilograms (remember, a Joule is a $(kg \cdot m^2)/sec^2$). Thus, we must first convert the mass deficit to kg:

$$\frac{0.0407 \text{ amu}}{1} \times \frac{1.6605 \times 10^{-27} \text{ kg}}{1 \text{ amu}} = 6.76 \times 10^{-29} \text{ kg}$$

Now we can use Equation (8.7):

$$E = m \cdot c^2 = (6.76 \times 10^{-29} \text{ kg}) \cdot (2.998 \times 10^8 \frac{m}{sec})^2 = 6.08 \times 10^{-12} \frac{kg \cdot m^2}{sec^2} = \underline{6.08 \times 10^{-12} \text{ J}}$$

Although this doesn't sound like a lot of energy, remember that this is for a *single* atom. In a single gram of ^{7}Li atoms, the total binding energy is 5.21 x 10^{11} J, which is quite a bit of energy!

As its name implies, binding energy tells us how tightly bound the nucleons are in the nucleus. The larger the binding energy, the stronger the nucleus holds its nucleons together. If you take the binding energy of a nucleus and divide it by the total number of nucleons in the nucleus, you get the **binding energy per nucleon** for that nucleus. This quantity gives you an idea of how strongly each nucleon is bound within the nucleus. If you think about it, the binding energy per nucleon tells you how stable a nucleus is. After all, if the binding energy per nucleon is high in a nucleus, the nucleus holds tightly to each of its nucleons. If the binding energy per nucleon is low, the nucleus' hold on its nucleons is weak.

If you calculate the binding energy per nucleon for several nuclei, you will find that this important quantity changes from nucleus to nucleus. In other words, some nuclei are more stable than others. Figure 16.1 illustrates a plot of binding energy per nucleon as a function of the mass number of a nucleus.

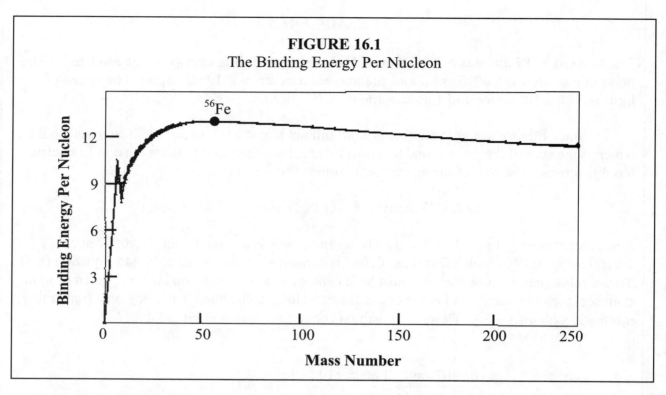

FIGURE 16.1
The Binding Energy Per Nucleon

As you can see from the figure, the binding energy per nucleon rises with increasing mass number until the mass number reaches 56, where the maximum binding energy per nucleon exists. For mass numbers higher than 56, the binding energy per nucleon decreases. This tells us that the most stable nuclei are those with mass numbers around 56. In fact, the most stable nucleus in Creation is ^{56}Fe, because it has the maximum binding energy per nucleon.

ON YOUR OWN

16.1 Calculate the binding energy per nucleon for ^{56}Fe. (Use the data given in the example as well as the fact that an ^{56}Fe nucleus has a mass of 55.9349 amu).

16.2 The binding energy of ^{7}Be is 5.739 x 10^{-12} J. What is the mass of ^{7}Be in amu?

The Strong Nuclear Force

So now we know what holds the nucleus together, right? The binding energy of a nucleus binds the nucleons together in the nucleus. That's all well and good, but there is still one important question we must answer: *how does the binding energy do it*? That question was a matter of speculation for quite some time. Some scientists thought that the binding energy formed some sort of "force field" around the nucleus, keeping the nucleons inside. Others thought that the energy somehow acted like glue, "sticking" the nucleons together.

In 1937, a nuclear physicist by the name of Heidiki Yukawa postulated that nucleons stayed together because, at short distances, they exchanged tiny particles called **pions** (pie' ons). Yukawa thought that the binding energy was used to give these pions kinetic energy, allowing them to travel from one nucleon to another. In other words, Yukawa believed that nucleons actually gave up a portion of their mass to form a small particle called a pion. Some of the mass that the nucleons gave up would go towards making the pion, and the rest would be converted to kinetic energy, allowing the pion to travel. Based on the properties of nuclei that were already known, Yukawa actually predicited what the mass of a pion should be.

Yukawa further believed that these pions can only exist for a very short time. As a result, he classified them as **short-lived particles**. Thus, Yukawa believed that a nucleon would form a pion, and the pion would begin to travel away from the nucleon. The pion, however, would not be able to live for very long. Thus, it would quickly encounter another nucleon and be absorbed by that nucleon. Since Yukawa believed that it is beneficial for nucleons to make, exchange, and absorb pions, he believed that nucleons crammed together into the nucleus in order to be able to do those things. Of course, all of this was just an hypothesis until 1947, when nuclear physicists discovered pions and found that they had almost exactly the mass that Yukawa predicted.

As a result of Yukawa's theorizing and the discovery of the pion, nuclear scientists now view the nucleus as a place full of busy activity. Nucleons in the nucleus are continually making, exchanging, absorbing, and re-making pions. The desire for nucleons to do this is so overwhelming that it overcomes the electromagnetic repulsion between protons, allowing protons to stay very close to one another. Because pions are short lived, nucleons can only exchange these particles when the nucleons are quite close. Thus, pion exchange exists only in the nucleus.

The binding energy of a nucleus, then, is mostly used to facilitate the exchange of pions. The attraction that nucleons feel as a result of this exchange is called the **strong nuclear force**. The strong nuclear force exists only between nucleons (because only they can exchange pions). It is also a very short-range force, because the pions that are exchanged can only exist for a brief period of time. Thus, a pion must travel from one nucleon to another before its lifetime is up. Finally, for very short distances, the nuclear force is incredibly strong, because the desire for nucleons to exchange pions is strong. As a result, for distances on the order of 10^{-15} m, the strong nuclear force is significantly stronger than the electromagnetic force.

The Stability of a Nucleus

Despite the fact that the strong nuclear force is able to hold nucleons together, it is not able to hold just any combination of nucleons together. As a result, a nucleus cannot be made from just any combination of neutrons and protons. Instead, there are certain combinations of neutrons and protons that are stable, and certain combinations that are not.

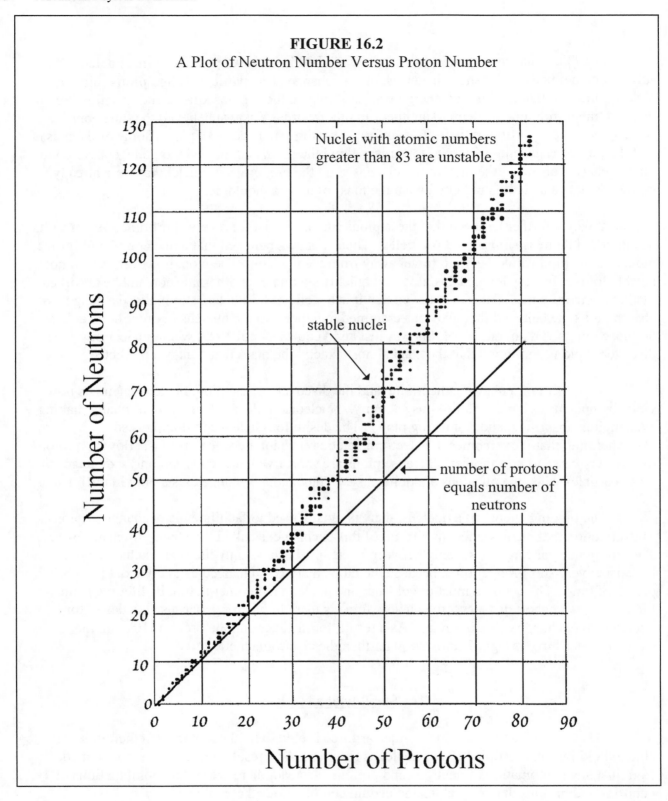

FIGURE 16.2
A Plot of Neutron Number Versus Proton Number

As noted in the figure, the dots represent the known, stable nuclei. Thus, if the number of protons and neutrons in a nucleus places it at one of the dots in the graph, then the nucleus is stable. If not, the nucleus is not stable. The reason that some nuclei are stable and some are not is beyond the scope of this course. In part, this is because nuclear scientists really don't fully understand the intricacies of what makes a nucleus stable and what makes it unstable.

If you look at the figure, you will see that for small nuclei (those that have only a few nucleons), the dots lie right along a line that corresponds to the number of protons equal to the number of neutrons. This means that for small nuclei, an equal number of neutrons and protons leads to a stable nucleus. Indeed, nuclei like ^{4}He, ^{16}O, and ^{40}Ca are all stable. Notice, however, that as the number of nucleons in the nucleus increases, the dots begin to rise farther and farther above the line that indicates an equal number of protons and neutrons. This tells us that as a nucleus gets larger, it can only be stable if it has more neutrons than protons.

Does this mean that the only nuclei in Creation are the ones represented by the dots? No, of course not. It means that the only *stable* nuclei in Creation are the ones represented by the dots. There are plenty of *unstable* nuclei in Creation as well. This might surprise you a bit. After all, if a nucleus is unstable, how can it exist? The answer is quite simple: it can exist, but only for a certain amount of time. When a nucleus is unstable, we call it **radioactive**. A radioactive nucleus, also called a **radioactive isotope**, will eventually change into another nucleus. As you will soon see, however, that can often take a *significant* amount of time.

ON YOUR OWN

16.3 Using Figure 16.2, determine whether or not each of the following nuclei is stable.

a. ^{237}U   b. ^{57}Fe   c. ^{100}La   d. ^{12}C

Radioactivity

The thick curve formed by the dots in Figure 16.2 is often called the **valley of stable nuclei**. If a nucleus is not in the valley of stable nuclei, then in order to become stable, it must get there. How can it do that? A nucleus can move to the valley of stable nuclei by changing its number of protons and/or neutrons. It accomplishes this through a process called **radioactive decay**.

Consider, for example, the nucleus ^{241}Am. According to its symbol, this nucleus has 95 protons and 146 neutrons. As stated in Figure 16.2, all elements with atomic number greater than 83 are unstable. To try and reach stability, then, the ^{241}Am nucleus emits a ^{4}He nucleus. Remember, a ^{4}He nucleus has 2 protons and 2 neutrons. Thus, the ^{241}Am nucleus actually loses 2 protons and 2 neutrons, which it ends up "spitting out" in the form of a ^{4}He nucleus. So, ^{241}Am has 95 protons and 146 neutrons. If it loses 2 protons and 2 neutrons, the result is a nucleus with 93 protons and 144 neutrons. This nucleus, ^{237}Np, is still unstable, so *it* will emit an alpha particle, continuing the decay. This will happen over and over again until the resulting nucleus is stable.

This process can be represented in the form of a reaction. Please understand that this is not a *chemical* reaction, it is a *nuclear* reaction:

$$^{241}_{95}\text{Am} \rightarrow \; ^{237}_{93}\text{Np} \; + \; ^{4}_{2}\text{He} \tag{16.1}$$

Radioactive   Daughter   Alpha
  isotope   product   particle

There are three important things I need to tell you about this equation. First notice that there are subscripts before the atomic symbols as well as superscripts. As always, those superscripts represent the mass number of the nucleus. The subscripts, on the other hand, represent the atomic number of the nucleus. Thus, the "95" subscript tells you that the atomic number of Am is 95. Now, of course, those subscripts are NOT necessary. After all, the symbol of the nucleus tells you the atomic number. All Am nuclei have 95 protons, so they all have an atomic number of 95. Even though the subscripts are not necessary, they will make things convenient a little later on, so I will keep using them throughout the module.

The next thing I want you to notice about the equation is that the subscripts on one side of the equation add up to the sum of the subscripts on the other side of the equation. This should make sense to you. After all, the subscripts represent the number of protons in each nucleus. On the left side of the equation, then, there are 95 protons. Since protons are not destroyed in this process, there should be 95 protons on the right side of the equation as well. In the same way, the mass numbers (the superscripts) represent the total nucleons in each nucleus. Since nucleons are not being destroyed in the process, the sum of all nucleons on the left side of the equation must be equal to the sum of the nucleons on the right side of the equation. When these two conditions are met, the nuclear equation is said to be **balanced**.

Finally, notice how I have labeled the participants in the equation. The only reactant is called the **radioactive isotope**. Some nuclear chemists also call it the **parent isotope**. The nucleus that results from the process is called the **daughter product**. Finally, the ^{4}He that is emitted in the reaction is called an **alpha particle**. Why is it called an alpha particle rather than a helium nucleus? The reason is historical. Scientists had determined that radioactivity existed long before they understood it. All they knew was that there were three distinctly different radioactive processes which resulted in three distinctly different particles being emitted. Since scientists at that time did not know what those particles were, they simply called them "alpha particles," "beta particles," and "gamma particles" (alpha, beta, and gamma are the first three letters in the Greek alphabet). Despite the fact that we now know what all of these particles are, we still cling to the old terminology. Thus, the radioactive process which produces alpha particles is typically called **alpha decay**.

Now that you know what alpha decay is, I will continue by discussing **beta decay**. When a nucleus undergoes beta decay, an amazing thing happens: *a neutron turns into a proton*! How does this happen? Well, look at the mass of a neutron (1.0087 amu) as compared to a proton (1.0073 amu). Also, consider the fact that a neutron is neutral, whereas a proton is positive. Suppose a neutron were able to emit an electron. What would happen? Its mass would decrease, and it would turn positive. After all, if a neutral particle releases a negative charge, the particle left over must be positive. Thus, *a neutron turns into a proton by emitting an electron*. This process can be written as the following reaction:

$$_0^1 n \rightarrow {}_1^1 H + {}_{-1}^0 e \tag{16.2}$$

Now what in the world do those symbols mean? Well, the symbol on the reactant side represents a neutron. After all, how many protons are in a neutron? None, of course! Thus, the subscript for a neutron in a nuclear equation must be zero. What is the mass number of a neutron? It is the sum of all neutrons and protons. Thus, for a single neutron, the mass number is 1. That's why we use the symbol $_0^1 n$ to represent a neutron. In the same way, what is a proton? A proton is simply a hydrogen nucleus with a mass number of 1. Thus, the symbol $_1^1 H$ is used in a nuclear reaction to represent a proton. Finally, the symbol $_{-1}^0 e$ is used to symbolize an electron in a nuclear equation. After all, an electron has no protons and no neutrons in it, so its mass number is zero. Since it has the opposite charge of a proton, you can think of the atomic number of an electron as -1.

Notice that using these symbols, Equation (16.2) balances just like Equation (16.1). The total number of protons on the left side of the equation is 0. The sum total of subscripts on the right side of the equation is also zero. The total number of nucleons on the left side of the equation is 1, and the sum of all superscripts on the right side of the reaction is also 1. Because these kinds of symbols for protons, neutrons, and electrons allow us to balance nuclear equations, I will continue to use them throughout this module.

It is important for you to know that Equation (16.2) represents a spontaneous reaction that will occur with *all* neutrons that are not a part of the nucleus. The rate of this reaction is a bit slow (in a group of neutrons, roughly half of them will undergo the process within 10 minutes); nevertheless, it will eventually happen to any free neutron. Interestingly enough, this reaction is usually not spontaneous for a neutron that exists in a stable nucleus. It is theorized that the pion exchange which goes on in a nucleus stabilizes the neutrons so that they do not decay into protons and electrons. Without that pion exchange, the neutron is not stable, and it will eventually decay into a proton and an electron.

Even if a neutron is in a nucleus, it can still decay if the nucleus itself is not stable. For example, the nucleus ^{90}Sr lies just to the left of the valley of stable nuclei in Figure 16.2. In order to move to the valley of stable nuclei, one of its neutrons will release an electron to make a proton.

$$_{38}^{90} Sr \rightarrow {}_{39}^{90} Y + {}_{-1}^0 e \tag{16.3}$$

Radioactive isotope   Daughter product   Beta particle

Notice that this equation is balanced, because the superscripts on one side add up to the superscripts on the other, and the subscripts on one side add up to the subscripts on the other.

Also, even though the electron produced in this process is just an electron, we still call it a **beta particle**. As a result, this process is called beta decay.

The last type of radioactive decay that I want to discuss is **gamma decay**. It turns out that a gamma particle (also called a **gamma ray**) is really just a photon. Remember, photons are light "particles," so a gamma particle is really just a "piece" of light. The light has a very large energy (thus a short wavelength), but it is still just light. Since light has no protons and no neutrons in it, a gamma particle is symbolized as $_{0}^{0}\gamma$, where the symbol γ is the lower-case Greek letter gamma. Since a gamma particle has no neutrons or protons, the emission of a gamma particle does not affect the identity of the nucleus. However, it does remove energy from the nucleus. Thus, if a nucleus is stable but has too much energy, it will rid itself of the extra energy by emitting a gamma particle. For example, if a ^{90}Y nucleus has too much energy, it will emit a gamma particle.

$$_{39}^{90}Y \quad \rightarrow \quad _{39}^{90}Y \quad + \quad _{0}^{0}\gamma \tag{16.4}$$

This process, not surprisingly called **gamma decay**, simply rids the ^{90}Y nucleus of its excess energy. For historical reasons, gamma rays are also called **X-rays**. When you get an X-ray in order for a doctor to diagnose a condition, gamma rays are being shot at you.

Now that you have been introduced to the three forms of natural radioactivity, study the examples and solve the "on your own" problems that follow to be sure you understand how to deal with nuclear equations.

EXAMPLE 16.2

^{14}C is a radioactive isotope that goes through beta decay. What is the daughter product of this decay? Write a balanced equation for the decay process.

According to the periodic chart, carbon has an atomic number of 6. This tells us that a ^{14}C atom has 6 protons and 8 neutrons in its nucleus. When a radioactive isotope undergoes beta decay, one of its neutrons turns into a proton. Thus, it will end up with one more proton and one less neutron. The daughter product (the nucleus that results from the beta decay), then, will have 7 protons and 7 neutrons. According to the chart, all atoms with 7 protons are symbolized with an "N." The mass number of this nitrogen atom will be 7+7=14. Thus, the daughter product is ^{14}N.

Now that we know the daughter product, the balanced equation is rather simple. Using the notation for a beta particle that was discussed above, the equation is:

$$_{6}^{14}C \quad \rightarrow \quad _{7}^{14}N \quad + \quad _{-1}^{0}e$$

Note that this equation is balanced, because the subscripts on one side add up to the subscripts on the other, as do the superscripts.

^{232}Th is a radioactive isotope that goes through alpha decay. What is the resulting daughter product and balanced equation?

According to the chart, thorium (Th) atoms have 90 protons. Thus, this particular atom has 90 protons and 142 neutrons in it. When it goes through alpha decay, it actually spits out 2 protons and 2 neutrons in the form of a ^{4}He nucleus. The result will be only 88 protons and 140 neutrons in the daughter product. The chart tells us that Ra is the symbol for all atoms with 88 protons. The mass number of the resulting nucleus will be 88+140 = 228. Thus, the daughter product is $\underline{^{228}\text{Ra}}$.

Now that we know the daughter product, the balanced equation is rather simple. Using the notation for an alpha particle that was discussed above, the equation is:

$$\underline{^{232}_{90}\text{Th} \rightarrow \ ^{228}_{88}\text{Ra} \ + \ ^{4}_{2}\text{He}}$$

Note that this equation is balanced, because the subscripts on one side add up to the subscripts on the other, as do the superscripts.

Write a balanced reaction for the gamma decay of ^{22}Na.

Gamma decay simply takes energy away from the nucleus in the form of light. It does not change the identity of the nucleus. Thus, the daughter product is still ^{22}Na. The equation, then, is particularly easy to produce:

$$\underline{^{22}_{11}\text{Na} \ \rightarrow \ ^{22}_{11}\text{Na} \ + \ ^{0}_{0}\gamma}$$

A radioactive decay process starts with a ^{234}Th nucleus and produces a ^{234}Pa nucleus. What kind of radioactive decay is this?

In this case, we are asked to figure out the radioactive decay by examining the radioactive isotope (^{234}Th) and the daughter product (^{234}Pa). In ^{234}Th, there are 90 protons and 144 neutrons. In ^{234}Pa, there are 91 protons and 143 neutrons. Thus, this must be beta decay, because the daughter product has one more proton than the radioactive isotope and one less neutron. This can only happen if a neutron turns into a proton.

ON YOUR OWN

16.4 Write a balanced nuclear equation for the beta decay of ^{87}Rb.

16.5 The daughter product of an alpha decay process is ^{220}Rn. What was the radioactive isotope that went through alpha decay?

16.6 A nucleus goes through radioactive decay but does not change its number of neutrons or protons. What kind of decay process did the nucleus undergo?

Before I leave this section, I want to point out something. Radioactive decay reactions as discussed in this section of the module produce an enormous amount of energy. If you add up the masses of the products produced in radioactive decay, you will find that the sum is less than the mass of the radioactive isotope. The "missing mass" is converted into energy according to Equation (8.7). Most of that energy is released as heat. In fact, radioactive decay processes are so hot that geophysicists speculate they are partially responsible for keeping the earth's interior hot!

Artificial Radioactivity

The three kinds of radioactivity that I discussed so far make up the phenomenon known as "natural radioactivity." The reason for this term is simple. These three types of radioactive decay are the only ones that occur naturally here on earth. As technology has improved, however, scientists have become able to synthesize their own nuclei in a nuclear chemistry/nuclear physics lab. As a result, scientists have artificially produced nuclei that decay via other mechanisms. The two "artificial" forms of radioactive decay are **electron capture** and **positron emission**.

In electron capture, a proton in a nucleus captures an electron (typically from the electrons that surround the nucleus). What will be produced when a proton captures an electron? Well, when a neutron releases an electron, the result is a proton. Electron capture is the reverse of this process. Thus, when a proton captures an electron, the result is a neutron. The following is an example of an electron capture reaction:

$$^{14}_{8}O \; + \; ^{0}_{-1}e \; \rightarrow \; ^{14}_{7}N$$

In this reaction, ^{14}O has too many protons and not enough neutrons. To fix this problem, one of the protons captures an electron from the electron orbitals and the result is a stable ^{14}N nucleus.

In positron emission, a proton emits a positron to become a neutron. What is a positron? Well, it is a form of **antimatter**. A positron is, in fact, an anti-electron. Although this sounds a bit like Star Trek, it is reality. A positron has positive charge and behaves just the opposite of an electron. Not surprisingly, then, a positron is symbolized with a $^{0}_{+1}e$ in nuclear physics. Interestingly enough, when a positron and an electron encounter one another, they destroy each other, leaving nothing behind but a gamma ray (high energy light).

$$^{0}_{+1}e \; + \; ^{0}_{-1}e \; \rightarrow \; ^{0}_{0}\gamma$$

This process, called **annihilation**, is what makes a positron antimatter. Matter and antimatter destroy each other. Thus, a positron is an anti-electron because, when it encounters an electron, the two particles destroy each other, leaving only energy (no mass) behind. This reaction, then, is an example of matter being converted into energy.

In the radioactive process known as positron emission, a proton emits a positron to turn into a neutron:

$$^{8}_{5}B \rightarrow {}^{8}_{4}Be + {}^{0}_{+1}e$$

Notice that this process has the same effect as electron capture, because it transforms a proton into a neutron.

The Rate of Radioactive Decay

As I said before, the reason that unstable nuclei exist in Creation is that although all unstable nuclei *eventually* decay into stable nuclei, this can often take quite some time. How much time does it take? That depends on the parent isotope. All radioactive nuclei have their own specific rate at which they decay. However, all radioactive isotopes do follow the same basic equation:

$$N = N_o \cdot e^{-kt} \tag{16.5}$$

In this equation, N represents either the *number* or *mass* of radioactive isotopes at any given time, N_o is the initial number or mass of radioactive isotopes, and k is a constant that changes from radioactive isotope to radioactive isotope. Often, the rate of an isotope's radioactive decay is expressed in terms of **half-life**, which is given by the following equation:

$$t_{1/2} = \frac{0.693}{k} \tag{16.6}$$

The half-life tells you how long it will take for half of your sample to decay. For example, suppose the half-life of a radioactive isotope is 5 days, and you have 10.0 grams of the isotope. After 5 days, you would have only 5.00 grams, because half will have decayed away. What will you have after another 5 days? You might be tempted to say 0, but the answer is 2.50 grams. Remember, half of the sample decays during the half-life. After the first 5 days, your sample was 5.00 grams. Thus, after the next 5 days, *half of that sample* will decay. Radioactive isotopes, then, never really go away. They just keep decreasing in abundance by half. From a practical standpoint, however, the radioactivity of a sample has generally been reduced to near zero if it passes through a total of 10 half-lives.

Some radioactive decay reactions proceed quickly, and some do not. For example, the alpha decay of ^{214}Po into ^{210}Pb has a half-life of 0.00016 seconds. That's a pretty fast reaction. On the other hand, some radioactive processes are incredibly slow. For example, ^{238}U alpha decays via a reaction whose half-life is 4.41×10^9 *years*! Now *that's* a slow reaction! Thus, unstable nuclei abound in Creation because many of them take a long, long time to decay.

When we look at radioactive decay rates, there is an easy way to analyze the situation and a hard way. The easy way is when the time span you are considering is an integral multiple of the half-life. In that case, you can just keep splitting the sample in half to get the answer. If the time span given is not an integral multiple of the half-life, however, you must use Equation (16.5). See what I mean by studying the following example.

EXAMPLE 16.3

The alpha decay of ^{210}Bi proceeds with a half-life of 5.00 days. A chemist makes 100.0 grams of the isotope.
  a. How many grams will be left in 15.00 days?
  b. How many grams will be left in 18.00 days?

a. This part is not so bad. The amount of time elapsed is an integral multiple of the half-life. Thus, after 5.00 days, there are only 50.00 grams left, after the next 5.00 days there are only 25.00 grams left, and after a total of 15.00 days, there are only 12.50 grams.

b. This one is not so easy, because the elapsed time is not an integral multiple of the half-life. Thus, we need to use Equation (16.5). To use that equation, however, we need to know k. This comes from Equation (16.6):

$$5.00 \text{ days} = \frac{0.693}{k}$$

$$k = \frac{0.693}{5.00 \text{ days}} = 0.139 \frac{1}{\text{days}}$$

Now we can use Equation (16.6):

$$N = N_o \cdot e^{-kt}$$

$$N = (100.0 \text{ grams}) \cdot e^{-(0.139 \frac{1}{\text{days}}) \cdot (18.00 \text{ days})} = 8.19 \text{ g}$$

ON YOUR OWN

16.7 The half-life of ^{131}I is 8 days. How much of a 10.0 gram sample will be left after 10 days?

<u>The Dangers of Radioactivity</u>

Now that you know a little bit about radioactivity, you might be interested in knowing why everyone is so afraid of it. Well, part of the fear is based on ignorance, and part of the fear is based on fact. Radioactivity *can be* dangerous, but it is *not always* dangerous. That's a good thing, too, because we are *constantly* being exposed to radioactivity. If you have brick or mortar in the walls of your home, they are radioactive. By standing near them, you are exposed to beta particles. You are exposed to gamma rays when you are outside in the sun. If you have a smoke detector in your house, you are exposed to alpha particles, because the main detection component of a smoke detector undergoes alpha decay. In fact, you are exposed to beta particles each time you get close to someone, because people themselves are radioactive! It's a good thing, then, that radioactivity is not always dangerous.

The first thing you have to understand is why radioactivity can be dangerous. Radioactivity does not act like a poison. A poison is dangerous because it chemically reacts with your body, causing chemical processes to occur in your body which should not occur. This upsets your body's chemistry, causing sickness or even death. Some poisons actually build up in your body. As you take them in small doses, they do not cause you any problems. However, as they continue to build up in your body, they eventually start causing chemical reactions that shouldn't happen in your body, and that's when you are in trouble.

Unlike poisons, radioactivity is not dangerous because it can upset your body's chemistry. It also cannot build up in your body. Instead, radioactivity affects your body much like a tiny machine gun. You see, the danger in radiation comes from the particles that are emitted during the radioactive decay. Depending on the isotope involved, radioactive decay involves a nucleus "spitting out" something. In alpha decay, the nucleus spits out an alpha particle. In beta decay, it spits out a beta particle. In gamma decay, the nucleus spits out high energy light. There is nothing chemically poisonous about these things. They are dangerous, however, because they have a lot of energy.

When alpha, beta, or gamma particles collide with atoms or molecules in their way, the energy of the collision can ionize the atom or molecule with which the particle collides. Thus, alpha, beta, and gamma particles are referred to as **ionizing radiation**, because they ionize matter as they pass through it. If you happen to be unfortunate enough to be in the way of the emitted particle, it might collide with one of your cells. The vast majority of the time, when an alpha, beta, or gamma particle collides with a cell, it results in the cell's death, because it ionizes chemicals in the cells that should not be ionized. Every now and again, however, the cell will not die. If the particle hits the cell just right, the resulting ionization might mutate the cell's DNA rather than kill the cell.

Do you see why I say that radioactivity acts like a tiny machine gun? When you have a sample of radioactive material, each atom in that sample can "shoot" a "bullet" (an alpha particle, a beta particle, or a gamma ray). Since there are trillions and trillions of atoms in even a small sample of matter, that means that a sample of radioactive isotopes can shoot off trillions and trillions of these "bullets." If you happen to be in the path of these bullets, each bullet that hits you will most likely kill an individual cell. Thus, a radioactive sample is like a tiny machine gun that kills you one cell at a time. Every now and again, however, rather than killing a cell, the particle will cause a mutation in the cell's DNA.

Sounds dangerous, doesn't it? Well, it *can* be dangerous, but *not necessarily*. You see, your body *expects* cells to die. God therefore designed your body to reproduce cells. This helps you grow and mature, and it also replaces cells that die. When you scratch an itch, for example, you actually kill as many as several hundred cells. This is no problem, as your body quickly replaces them. Thus, as long as your cells do not die faster than they can be replaced by your body, there is no real problem.

When your cells are being destroyed by the little "bullets" that are being "shot" from a sample of radioactive isotopes, then, there is no problem as long as the "bullets" are not killing your cells faster than your body can replace them. If you are exposed to too much radiation too quickly, then your cells will be killed faster than your body can replace them, leading to radiation burns, organ damage, and the like.

What about the chance for mutating a cell's DNA? Isn't that bad? Well, yes, but once again, it depends on the amount of mutation that is going on. Everyone's body has a few mutant cells. Most of them simply die off. The bad thing about mutation is that a mutant cell can result in cancer or some other sickness. This happens only rarely, however, so once again, a few mutant cells in your body is not a bad thing. Everyone has them. The problem only occurs when you have too many mutant cells. Thus, as long as you are not exposed to too much radiation, the danger is minimal.

In the end, then, the important thing to remember about the dangers of radioactivity is that it depends on the level of radioactivity to which you are exposed. A small amount of radioactivity is reasonably safe, a large amount is not. How much radioactivity exposure is too much? Well, nuclear scientists have come up with ways of measuring how much ionizing radiation people are exposed to. They refer to this as the **dose** of radiation to which a person is exposed.

There are two units nuclear scientists use to measure radiation dosage. They are the **rad** (radiation absorbed dose) and the **rem** (roentgen equivalent in man). The rad is the amount of radiation that will deposit 100 Joules of energy into a kilogram of living tissue. This is a fine measure of radiation exposure, but it neglects the fact that certain types of radiation are more damaging to biological systems than others. Alpha particles, for example, do more damage to tissue per Joule they deposit because of the details of how alpha particles ionize matter. As a result, alpha particles are considered "more effective" at destroying living tissue.

To take this into account, nuclear scientists have come up with the **RBE** (relative biological effectiveness) factor. This factor is different for each type of ionizing radiation. Alpha particles, for example have an RBE factor of 4 while gamma and beta particles have an RBE factor of 1. When the number of rads are multiplied by the RBE factor, the result is the dosage in rems.

$$\text{rems} = (\text{RBE}) \times \text{rads} \qquad\qquad (16.7)$$

Thus, if you are exposed to 0.010 rads of beta particles, your radiation dose is $1 \times 0.010 = 0.010$ rems. If you are exposed to 0.010 rads of alpha particles, your radiation dose $4 \times 0.010 = 0.040$ rems.

Remember when I said that brick and mortar are radioactive, as well as smoke detectors and other people? If you add up all of the radiation you are exposed to from such sources, your average radiation dose each year would be about 0.2 rems. Since studies by radiation biologists indicate that a lethal dose of radiation is about 470 rems, the dose of radiation you get as a result of everyday activity is simply too minimal to be worried about.

Even if you are in a position in which you are exposed to large amounts of radioactivity, there are ways you can protect yourself. It is possible to stop the little "bullets" before they ever reach your body. For example, alpha particles are extremely weak in terms of how much matter they can travel through. If you put a piece of paper between you and the radioactive source emitting the alpha particles, the vast majority of those alpha particles will stop in the paper. As a result, they will never hit you. Beta particles can travel through obstacles a bit better. It typically takes a thin sheet of metal to stop most of the beta particles coming from a radioactive isotope that emits them. Finally, gamma rays are the strongest type of radiation, requiring several inches of lead to stop them.

Thus, one way you can protect yourself is to block the radiation before it hits you. This method is called "shielding." The other way you can protect yourself from an intensely radioactive source is to simply move away from it. The farther you move away, the fewer "bullets" can hit you. Of course, most people will never be exposed to a large amount of radiation in their lifetime, so they will never be faced with such a situation.

ON YOUR OWN

16.8 People who regularly work with large samples of radioactive isotopes sometimes wear special suits that are lined with a thin layer of lead or other heavy material. What kinds of radiation are these people protected from when wearing such a suit?

Radioactive Dating

The fact that radioactive isotopes decay at a measurable rate allows scientists to use radioactive decay as a means of dating objects whose age we do not know. This is known as **radioactive dating**. Although radioactive dating can be accurate under certain circumstances, it is important to note that it has some serious weaknesses as well. As a result, radioactive dating techniques must be viewed rather critically. Despite the fact that some scientists will try to convince you that radioactive dating is an accurate means of determining the age of an object, the scientific facts tell quite a different story.

The best way of examining the strengths and weaknesses of radioactive dating is to examine one of the radioactive dating methods in detail. Since ^{14}C is probably the best known radioactive dating technique, I might as well discuss that one. ^{14}C decays by beta decay with a half-life of 5,730 years. It turns out that all living organisms contain a certain amount of ^{14}C, which is part of the reason that all living organisms are radioactive.

Interestingly enough, living organisms continually exchange ^{14}C with their surroundings. Human beings, for example, exhale carbon dioxide, some of which contains ^{14}C. In addition, human beings eat other organisms (plants and animals), which contain ^{14}C as well. Finally, part of the air that we inhale is made up of carbon dioxide, some of which contains ^{14}C. Thus, organisms are continually exchanging ^{14}C with their environment. The practical result of all of this exchange is that, at any time when an organism is alive, it contains the same amount of ^{14}C as does the atmosphere around the organism.

This changes when the organism dies, however. At that point, the ^{14}C exchange ceases. Thus, the organism cannot replenish its supply of ^{14}C, and the amount of ^{14}C in the organism begins to decrease because of the beta decay of ^{14}C. The half-life of this process is 5730 years, so the decay happens slowly. Nevertheless, it is a measurable effect. In general, then, organisms that have been dead a long time tend to have less ^{14}C in them as compared to those that have been dead for only a short time.

Now if you think about it, this fact can be used to measure the length of time that an organism has been dead. After all, if we know how much ^{14}C was in an organism when it died, and if we measure the amount of ^{14}C in it now, the difference will be the amount of ^{14}C that has decayed away. With that information, Equation (16.5) will tell us how long the organism has been dead. Pretty simple, right?

Well, it *would* be simple, *if* we knew how much ^{14}C was in the organism when it died. The problem is, how do we figure that out? After all, no one was around to measure the amount of ^{14}C in the organism when it died; thus, we must make an *assumption* about how much ^{14}C would have been measured if someone had been there to measure it. Now there is nothing wrong with making assumptions in science. The trick is that you have to know your assumptions are accurate.

In the case of ^{14}C dating, scientists assume that, on average, the amount of ^{14}C in the atmosphere has never really changed that much. They assume that the amount of ^{14}C in the atmosphere today is essentially the same as it was 100 years ago, 1,000 years ago, etc. Thus, when the age of a dead organism is being measured with ^{14}C dating, we assume that the amount of ^{14}C it had when it died was the same as the amount of ^{14}C that is in the atmosphere now. That gives us a value for how much ^{14}C was initially in the dead organism. We can measure the amount of ^{14}C that is in the organism now and then determine how long the organism has been dead.

Notice, however, that the age we get from this process is completely dependent on the assumption that we made about how much ^{14}C was in the organism when it died. If that assumption is good, the age we calculate will be accurate. If that assumption is bad, the age we calculate will not be accurate. So the question becomes, "Is the assumption accurate?" In short, the answer is, "No."

Through a process involving tree rings, there is a way we can measure the amount of ^{14}C in the atmosphere in years past. When you cut down a tree, you can count the rings in the tree's trunk to determine how old it is. Each ring represents a year in the life of the tree. We know which ring corresponds to which year by simply counting the rings from the outside of the trunk to the inside. Well, it turns out that through a rather complicated process, you can actually measure the amount of ^{14}C in a tree ring and use it to determine how much ^{14}C was in the atmosphere during the year in which the tree ring was grown. As a result, scientists have determined the amount of ^{14}C in the atmosphere throughout a portion of the earth's past.

It turns out that scientists have studied the ^{14}C content in tree rings that are as many as 3,000 years old. From these measurements, scientists have determined the amount of ^{14}C in the atmosphere over the past 3,000 years. What they have seen is that the amount of ^{14}C has varied by as much as 70% over that time period. The variation is correlated to certain events that occur on the surface of the sun. As a result, *we know* that the amount of ^{14}C in the atmosphere has not stayed constant. Instead, it has varied greatly. Thus, *we know* that the initial assumption of ^{14}C dating is wrong. Thus, one must take most ^{14}C dates with a grain of salt. After all, we know that the assumption used in making those dates is wrong. Consequently, we cannot put too much trust in the results!

Notice that I said we must take "most" ^{14}C dates with a grain of salt. Why "most?" Why not "all?" Well, it turns out that since we can determine the amount of ^{14}C in the atmosphere during the past using tree rings, we can actually use that data to help us make our initial assumption. As a result, the assumption becomes much more accurate. The problem is, however, that we don't have ^{14}C measurements for tree rings that are older than 3,000 years. Thus, we can only make an accurate assumptions for organisms that have died within the last 3,000 years. As long as the organism died in that time range, we can use tree ring data to help us make an accurate assumption of how much ^{14}C was in the organism when it died. For organisms that have died longer than 3,000 years ago, we have no tree ring data, so we have no way to make an accurate assumption. As a result, we cannot really believe the ^{14}C date.

In the end, then, the ^{14}C dating method can be believed for organisms that have been dead for 3,000 years or less. Thus, it is a great tool for archaeology. If an archaeologist finds a manuscript or a piece of cloth (both cloth and paper are made from dead plants), the archaeologist can use ^{14}C dating to determine its age, provided all of the experimental techniques of ^{14}C dating have been followed accurately. As long as the result is about 3,000 years or younger, the date can be believed. If the date turns out to be older than 3,000 years, it is most likely wrong.

So you should see that radioactive dating involves a pretty important assumption. If the assumption is good, the date you get from radioactive dating is good. If the assumption is bad, the result you get from radioactive dating will be bad. Now there are a lot of other radioactive dating techniques besides ^{14}C dating. Unfortunately, they all suffer from a similar malady. In every radioactive dating technique, you must make assumptions about how much of a certain substance was in the object originally. Such assumptions are quite hard to make accurately.

The difficulty of making these assumptions can be seen in the fact that radioactive dates have been demonstrated to be wrong in many, many instances. John Woodmorappe, in his book *Studies in Flood Geology*, has compiled more than 350 radioactive dates that conflict with one another or with other generally accepted dates. These erroneous dates demonstrate that the assumptions used in radioactive dating cannot be trusted. As a result, the dates that one gets from radioactive dating cannot be trusted, either.

Unfortunately, many in the scientific community are unwilling to admit to the inadequacies of radioactive dating, because many scientists like its *results*. Because certain radioactive decay schemes have long, long half-lives, the dates that one calculates from these methods can be breathtakingly large. For example, there are rocks on the planet that radioactive dating techniques indicate are more than 4 *billion* years old. It turns out that many scientists *want* the earth to be that old because they believe in the discredited hypothesis of evolution. This hypothesis *requires* a very old earth, and radioactive dating techniques provide dates that indicate the earth is very old. As a result, they turn a blind eye to the inadequacies of radioactive dating, because it gives them an answer that they want! Hopefully, as time goes on, this unfortunate situation will change!

Other uses of Radioactivity and Ionizing Radiation

Radioactivity has far more reliable applications than the tenuous process of radioactive dating. For example, radiation has revolutionized medicine. When a doctor wants to look at your bones, the doctor gives you an X-ray. This is accomplished by placing the portion of your body that needs to be examined between a sheet of film and a high-intensity gamma ray source. As you are exposed to the gamma rays, some pass through your body and hit the film, while others collide with cells in your body and stop. Gamma rays collide more with the dense portions of your body (the bones) than with the fleshy parts of your body. As a result, the film gets hit by gamma rays more frequently when bone is not between the gamma ray source and the film. When the film is developed, this will result in the parts of the film behind your bones being much whiter than those parts of the film behind the rest of your body. As a result, the gamma rays form an image of your bones on the film.

Now when you get an X-ray, the gamma rays used to make the X-ray work are killing your cells and mutating some DNA. Nevertheless, as I have discussed before, that is not a problem as long as you do not get too many X-rays. Any risk caused by your exposure to gamma rays is far outweighed by the medical benefit of being able to see your bones without surgery. Of course, the person *giving* you the X-ray would be exposed to gamma rays all day if he or she were not shielded from them. That's why the person giving you the X-ray stands behind thick shielding during the X-ray process.

Radioactive isotopes are also used to track things like blood flow inside the body. If a gamma emitting isotope is injected into your bloodstream, doctors can analyze how the blood flows to different parts of your body by detecting where the gamma rays are coming from inside your body. Once again, although this exposes you to gamma rays, the risk is low as long as the amount of exposure is minimized. The diagnostic benefit to such a procedure outweighs the risk of the gamma ray exposure.

Ionizing radiation is even used to kill cancerous cells in tumors and the like. People with thyroid cancer often are given radioactive iodine (^{131}I) to drink. Since iodine collects in your thyroid, drinking radioactive iodine (usually called "the cocktail") will concentrate radiation in your thyroid, killing cancerous cells. The healthy cells will die as well, but your body is more likely to replace the healthy cells and not the cancerous cells, so this is a very popular treatment for thyroid cancer.

Finally, ionizing radiation is even used to keep you safe from fire. Most homes have a smoke detector. In a smoke detector, there are two metal plates hooked to a wire. One plate is hooked to the positive side of the battery and is thus positively-charged. The other is hooked to the negative end of the battery and is thus negatively-charged. An ^{241}Am source is placed under the plates, and it emits alpha particles through a small hole in the bottom plate. As the alpha particles collide with the molecules in the air between the plates, the molecules are ionized. The positive ions travel to the negative plate and the negative ions travel to the positive plate.

When there is no smoke in the air, the ^{241}Am source shoots a steady stream of alpha particles, resulting in a constant rate of ion production. The electronics in the smoke detector detect those ions when they hit their respective plates. When smoke gets between the plates, however, the smoke traps the ions, not allowing them to hit the plates. This causes a drop in the number of ions detected by the electronics, and that causes the alarm to go off.

As with all forms of ionizing radiation, there is a small amount of inherent risk in having a radioactive isotope (the ^{241}Am in the smoke detector) in your house. Nevertheless, the chance of you dying or being hurt in a fire is *millions of times* greater than any chance of your being hurt by one of the alpha particles in the smoke detector. As a result, they are used in homes despite the fact that they are radioactive.

Nuclear Reactions

Although radioactive decay is, by far, the most common nuclear process that occurs on earth, there are other types of nuclear reactions that occur over and over again in outer space as well as in nuclear power plants and nuclear research facilities. These nuclear reactions can usually be classified as one of two types:

Nuclear fusion - The process by which two or more small nuclei fuse to make a bigger nucleus

<u>Nuclear fission</u> - The process by which a large nucleus is split into two smaller nuclei

You have probably heard of both of these processes before, but I want to make sure that you understand them in a thorough way.

I will begin with nuclear fission, which is the basis for nuclear power plants and most nuclear bombs. Usually, nuclear fission begins with a neutron colliding with a large nucleus. For example, if a neutron were to collide with a ^{235}U nucleus, the nucleus would become very unstable. It would be so unstable that it would, in fact, break apart into two smaller nuclei. One possible reaction would be as follows:

$$\,^{1}_{0}n \; + \; \,^{235}_{92}U \; \rightarrow \; \,^{112}_{45}Rh \; + \; \,^{121}_{47}Ag \; + \; 3\,^{1}_{0}n$$

Notice what this equation says happened in the reaction. A neutron collided with a ^{235}U nucleus. The result is a ^{112}Rh nucleus, a ^{121}Ag nucleus, and 3 neutrons. Don't be alarmed about the coefficient of 3 next to the neutron on the right side of the equation. Like chemical equations, nuclear equations can also have coefficients. The meaning of these coefficients is the same in both cases. Thus, the 3 simply tells you that 3 neutrons are produced.

Notice also that the equation is balanced. On the left side, there are a total of 92 (92 + 0) protons (subscripts). On the right side, there are also 92 (45 + 47 + 3x0) protons. On the left side, the mass numbers total to 236 (235 + 1). On the right side, the mass numbers also total to 236 (112 + 121 + 3x1). Although this is the first nuclear equation that you have seen with a coefficient, it should not disturb you. You use it just as you would if it were in a chemical equation or an algebraic equation. Since there is a 3 in front of the neutron, you multiply the numbers associated with the neutron by 3.

Now it is very important for you to realize that although the equation above represents a valid reaction that occurs when a neutron collides with a ^{235}U nucleus, it is not the only possible reaction that occurs under those conditions. One of the very interesting aspects of nuclear reactions is that, unlike chemical reactions, the same reactants will not always produce the same products. When a neutron collides with a ^{235}U nucleus, sometimes the nucleus will split apart to give the products listed above. Many times, however, it will split so as to produce other products. For example, the following reaction is even slightly more likely to occur than the one listed above:

$$\,^{1}_{0}n \; + \; \,^{235}_{92}U \; \rightarrow \; 2\,^{117}_{46}Pd \; + \; 2\,^{1}_{0}n$$

Notice that this reaction is balanced. In this case, remember that you have to multiply the subscripts and superscripts for Pd by 2 because there is a coefficient in front of Pd as well. It turns out that there are a host of possible products for the neutron-induced fission of ^{235}U. The two equations I have shown you are just a couple of the possible reactions that will occur when a neutron collides with a ^{235}U nucleus. When a bunch of neutrons collide with a bunch of ^{235}U nuclei, many different kinds of products are produced.

Notice something else about both of the reactions I have listed. In each case, the reaction produces more than one neutron. Since a neutron is one of the reactants in the fission reaction, this sets up a very interesting situation. Imagine that you have a large sample of ^{235}U. Suppose one neutron collides with one nucleus in this sample and a fission reaction results. What will happen next? Well, the neutrons produced in this reaction can go out *and start more fission reactions, each of which will produce even more neutrons which can go out and start even more reactions*. Thus, a single neutron can start a series of events that will result in more and more fission reactions occurring.

What do we call this? We call it a **chain reaction**. Nuclear fission can result in chain reactions because the very process of nuclear fission forms one of the reactants. Thus, as long as there is enough ^{235}U around, the number of fission reactions occurring each second can grow and grow and grow.

What's the practical upshot of all of this? Well, if you sum up the masses of the products in a fission reaction, you will find that the sum is less than that of the reactants. This means that fission reactions produce energy, because the mass that is "missing" in the product gets converted directly to energy. Well, if the number of fission reactions grows each second, then the amount of energy being released grows each second. If the amount of energy released gets large enough, an explosion will occur.

This is, of course, the idea behind a nuclear bomb. In a nuclear bomb, the chain reaction goes out of control, producing an enormous amount of energy in a short period of time. This results in a devastating explosion. Remember, however, that you can only produce enough energy to make an explosion if there is *enough* ^{235}U. The amount of ^{235}U necessary to allow a fission chain reaction to sustain the process of fission indefinitely is called the **critical mass** of ^{235}U.

Critical mass - The amount of fissioning nucleus necessary for the chain reaction to be self-
    sustaining

If you have a critical mass of ^{235}U just "lying around" in the right geometry, a self-sustained reaction is inevitable. That's because the earth is constantly being bombarded by neutrons from the sun. Thus, eventually a single neutron will start a single fission reaction, and the chain reaction will keep the reaction going indefinitely. However, that in itself might not lead to an explosion. In order for an explosion to occur, the chain reaction must spin out of control. This will happen only if the critical mass of ^{235}U is highly concentrated.

Luckily, of course, the two nuclei that are used in nuclear bombs (^{235}U and ^{238}Pu) are very rare. The isotope ^{235}U, in fact, makes up only 0.7% of all uranium on the earth. In order to make a bomb, then, the amount of ^{235}U in a sample of uranium must be increased. This process, called **isotopic enrichment**, separates out the other isotopes of uranium, trying to leave behind only ^{235}U. This allows nuclear chemists to concentrate ^{235}U so as to get a critical mass of the isotope. The problem is, since ^{235}U is nearly identical to the other isotopes of uranium, this process is *very* difficult. In fact, the only thing that is secret about making a nuclear bomb is the means by which

^{235}U (or ^{238}Pu) is enriched from natural supplies. Anyone with even the most basic nuclear training can make a nuclear bomb. Making the *fuel* for the bomb is impossible, however, unless you know the secret technological steps necessary to enrich the ^{235}U (or ^{238}Pu) content in order to achieve a concentrated critical mass.

The other kind of nuclear reaction that I want to discuss is nuclear fusion. You can view nuclear fusion as the opposite of nuclear fission, because it takes small nuclei and makes them bigger. For example, ^{2}H nuclei can collide with each other and stick together, forming ^{3}He and a neutron:

$$2\,_{1}^{2}\text{H} \rightarrow \,_{2}^{3}\text{He} + \,_{0}^{1}\text{n}$$

This kind of reaction also produces energy, because there is less mass in the products than there is in the reactants.

You should notice a contrast between nuclear fusion and nuclear fission. Nuclear fusion has small nuclei as the reactants and nuclear fission has large nuclei as reactants. If you think about this in terms of nuclear binding energy, this should make some sense to you. Go back and take a look at Figure 16.1. According to this figure, the most stable nucleus in Creation is ^{56}Fe, because it has the most binding energy per nucleon. What does this mean? Well, it means that as long as nuclei are smaller than ^{56}Fe, they are "willing" to fuse with other nuclei so as to become more like ^{56}Fe. Nuclei heavier than ^{56}Fe, however, have no desire to fuse, because they would "like" to lose nucleons so as to become more like ^{56}Fe. Thus, nuclear fusion reactions between nuclei lighter than ^{56}Fe are spontaneous, whereas nuclear fusion reactions between ^{56}Fe nuclei and those that are heavier are not spontaneous. In the same way, nuclear fission reactions can be spontaneous for nuclei heavier than ^{56}Fe, but not for ^{56}Fe and those nuclei that are lighter.

Wait a minute. If fusion reactions between nuclei lighter than ^{56}Fe can be spontaneous, why don't all light nuclei fuse until they become ^{56}Fe? In the same way, why don't all heavy nuclei fission until they because ^{56}Fe? Although fusion reactions are spontaneous for light nuclei, they proceed so slowly as to be non-existent unless the nuclei can be forced close to one another. This is tough because, since nuclei are positively charged, they repel each other. Thus, unless there is enough activation energy to push the nuclei very close to one another, the nuclei will never fuse at any kind of appreciable rate.

Is there any place that such activation energy exists? Well, it exists in nuclear research labs where huge instruments called **particle accelerators** accelerate nuclei to such high speeds that they have enough energy to get close to and fuse with other nuclei. It also exists in stars, where the gravitational force is so strong and the temperature is so high that nuclei have enough energy to get close enough to fuse. In fact, most (if not all) of the sun's energy comes from the fusion of light nuclei into heavier nuclei.

Study the following examples so that you are sure you understand how to deal with fission and fusion reactions.

EXAMPLE 16.4

Fill in the blank for the nuclear fusion reaction below:

$$2\,^3_1\text{H} \;\rightarrow\; {}^4_2\text{He} \;+\; \underline{\hphantom{xx}}\,^1_0\text{n}$$

In order for this to be a valid reaction, it must balance. This means that the sum of the superscripts on both sides of the equation must equal each other as well as the sum of the subscripts. This is already the case for the subscripts. However, in order for the superscripts on the right side to equal 6, there must be 2 neutrons. Thus, the answer is:

$$\underline{2\,^3_1\text{H} \;\rightarrow\; {}^4_2\text{He} \;+\; 2\,^1_0\text{n}}$$

What is the missing reactant in the following equation? Is this fusion or fission?

$$^1_0\text{n} \;+\; \underline{\hphantom{xxx}} \;\rightarrow\; {}^{112}_{45}\text{Rh} \;+\; {}^{123}_{49}\text{In} \;+\; 3\,^1_0\text{n}$$

In order to get the subscripts to balance, the subscript in the blank must be 94. The chart tells us, then, that the symbol is Pu. To get the superscripts to balance, the superscript in the blank must be 237. That way the sum of the mass numbers on the left side (1 + 237) equals the sum of the mass numbers on the right side (112 + 123 + 3x1). Thus, the missing reactant is $\underline{{}^{237}_{94}\text{Pu}}$. This is <u>fission</u>, because a large nucleus is splitting into smaller nuclei.

ON YOUR OWN

16.9 What is the missing reactant in the following nuclear equation?

$$^{27}_{13}\text{Al} \;+\; {}^4_2\text{He} \;\rightarrow\; \underline{\hphantom{xxx}} \;+\; {}^1_0\text{n}$$

16.10 Is the reaction above a fusion or fission reaction?

<u>Using Nuclear Reactions to Make Energy</u>

As I have already noted, nuclear fission is used in today's nuclear power plants in order to make electricity. You should have learned in your first-year physics course that power plants turn the mechanical motion of magnets and loops of wire into electricity. To produce the motion, they use steam that comes from boiling water. The fuel in an electrical power plant, then, is simply used to boil water. Coal-burning power plants use the heat of combustion of coal to boil water. Nuclear power plants simply use the heat of a nuclear fission reaction to boil the water.

The wonderful thing about using nuclear fission to make electricity is that the fuel for nuclear fission is reasonably cheap and will last a long, long time. The downside is that nuclear fission can be quite dangerous. Now it is important to realize that the danger of nuclear fission is *not* that a nuclear power plant can create a nuclear explosion. That's physically impossible! In order to make a nuclear explosion, you must have a critical mass of the fissioning isotope and it must be highly concentrated. Since nuclear power plants *do not* have a concentrated critical mass of the fissioning isotope, they *cannot* explode.

Even though nuclear power plants cannot explode, other nasty things can happen. In a normally operating nuclear power plant, the rate at which the fission processes occur is heavily controlled. If the control operations fail, then the chain reaction starts producing too much energy. This will not lead to an explosion, but it can produce so much heat that everything in the vicinity, including the reactor itself, will begin to melt. When this happens, it is called a **meltdown**, and the results can be devastating.

This is what happened at the Chernobyl nuclear power plant in the former Soviet Union. This particular nuclear power plant did not have many safety protocols and, when the primary system which helps control the rate of the nuclear reaction failed, there was nothing that could keep the reaction from running out of control. As a result, the reactor began to melt. This caused widespread fire throughout the plant and resulted in the release of an enormous amount of radioactive isotopes. More than 30 people were killed as a result of the fires and structural damage in the power plant itself, and thousands were exposed to high levels of radiation. To this day, no one can live near where the plant was, because the radioactive contamination is so high.

Nuclear power in the form of nuclear fission, then, can be quite dangerous. You have to understand, however, that *all* forms of power production are dangerous. Since 1900, for example, more than 100,000 people have been killed in American coal mines due to mining accidents and black lung, a malady that is caused by exposure to too much coal dust. Coal is used primarily for the production of energy. Studies indicate that nuclear power is responsible for less death and fewer health maladies than any other form of power production that we have today.

Nuclear power in the form of fission also has another serious drawback: the by-products are radioactive. We have no safe way of disposing this radioactive waste. This can eventually lead to serious environmental problems. Of course, other forms of energy production also lead to serious environmental problems. Coal-burning power plants, for example, dump pollution into the air. The *amount* of pollution they dump into the atmosphere has been reduced considerably. Nevertheless, they still emit pollutants. They are, in fact, the principal contributors to the acid rain problem.

Although nuclear power in the form of nuclear fission can be dangerous and polluting, it is not clear that it is any more dangerous and polluting than other forms of energy production. There are those who think it is, in fact, one of the safest and cleanest forms of energy production. In France, for example, the scientific community is so convinced that nuclear power is (overall) the safest form of power production that more than 90% of the country runs on electricity produced by nuclear power plants.

In order to make energy production safer, better for the environment, and longer-lasting, scientists are trying to use nuclear fusion instead of nuclear fission to produce electricity. Nuclear fusion has no harmful by-products. Remember, when nuclear fusion occurs between two hydrogen atoms, the products are helium and a free neutron. Helium is not radioactive, and has no toxic chemical properties either. Thus, using nuclear fusion to produce electricity would completely eliminate the radioactivity problem caused by nuclear fission. It is also much safer than nuclear fission. Experiments indicate that nuclear fusion is much easier to halt, allowing for the nuclear fusion process to be stopped quickly. This would avert any meltdown possibilities. Finally, the fuel for nuclear fusion (^{2}H) is virtually unlimited and very inexpensive. Nuclear power from nuclear fusion, then, would be safe, cheap, and almost limitless.

Why don't we use nuclear fusion to make electricity, then? The answer is that from a *technological* viewpoint, we have not mastered the process yet. We *know* that nuclear fusion can be used to make energy. After all, it powers the sun. However, nuclear fusion can happen in the sun because of the intense heat and pressure in the sun's core. In order to get nuclear fusion to work, we have to essentially re-create that environment here on earth. That's a tough job! Right now, nuclear physicists can, indeed, cause nuclear fusion to occur in a variety of different ways. However, in each way used so far, there is an enormous amount of energy wasted in order to create the conditions necessary for the nuclear fusion. As a result, the total energy produced is rather small. In other words, right now we have to put an enormous amount of energy into a nuclear fusion reaction, and we don't get much more than that amount of energy back. As a result, nuclear fusion is not an economically viable process for the large-scale production of energy.

In the end, then, we know that there are some drawbacks to nuclear fission. Some consider those drawbacks to be quite serious, others consider them to be about the same or even a little less than what other forms of power production have. If scientists are ever able to overcome the technological problems associated with nuclear fusion, the result would be a much safer, cleaner, and cheaper form of power production. Whether that will ever happen, however, remains to be seen.

ANSWERS TO THE ON YOUR OWN PROBLEMS

16.1   Since iron's atomic number is 26, all Fe atoms have 26 protons. The mass number therefore indicates that a ^{56}Fe nucleus has 30 neutrons. The sum of the masses of 26 protons and 30 neutrons is:

$$26 \times (1.0073 \text{ amu}) + 30 \times (1.0087 \text{ amu}) = 56.4508 \text{ amu}$$

Since the mass of a ^{56}Fe nucleus is only 55.9349 amu, there is a mass deficit of 0.5159 amu. This mass deficit is converted to energy according to Equation (8.7). To use this equation, however, we must have consistent units. Since we have the speed of light in m/sec, then the energy will come out in Joules as long as the mass is in kilograms (remember, a Joule is a $(\text{kg} \cdot \text{m}^2)/\text{sec}^2)$. Thus, we must first convert the mass deficit to kg:

$$\frac{0.5159 \ \cancel{\text{amu}}}{1} \times \frac{1.6605 \times 10^{-27} \text{ kg}}{1 \ \cancel{\text{amu}}} = 8.567 \times 10^{-28} \text{ kg}$$

Now we can use Equation (8.7):

$$E = m \cdot c^2 = (8.567 \times 10^{-28} \text{ kg}) \cdot (2.998 \times 10^8 \ \frac{\text{m}}{\text{sec}})^2 = 7.70 \times 10^{-11} \text{ J}$$

This is not the answer. The question asks for the binding energy per nucleon, so we must divide this by the total number of nucleons in the nucleus, which is 56.

$$\frac{7.70 \times 10^{-11} \text{ J}}{56 \text{ nucleons}} = \underline{1.38 \times 10^{-12} \ \frac{\text{J}}{\text{nucleon}}}$$

16.2 Since we know that there are 4 protons and 3 neutrons in a ^{7}Be nucleus, we can figure out the mass of the nucleons:

$$4 \times (1.0073 \text{ amu}) + 3 \times (1.0087 \text{ amu}) = 7.0553 \text{ amu}$$

This isn't the mass of the nucleus, however, because the nucleons always lose some mass when they form a nucleus. How much mass do these nucleons lose? We can calculate it from the binding energy:

$$E = m \cdot c^2$$

$$5.739 \times 10^{-12} \text{ J} = m \cdot (2.998 \times 10^8)^2$$

$$m = 6.39 \times 10^{-29} \text{ kg}$$

We can convert that to amu:

$$\frac{6.39 \times 10^{-29} \text{ kg}}{1} \times \frac{1 \text{ amu}}{1.6605 \times 10^{-27} \text{ kg}} = 0.0385 \text{ amu}$$

Now remember, this is the mass that the nucleons *lose* when they make a nucleus. Thus, the mass of the nucleus is:

$$7.0553 \text{ amu} - 0.0385 \text{ amu} = \underline{7.0168 \text{ amu}}$$

16.3 a. <u>This is unstable</u>, because the chart tells us that uranium has 92 protons, and the figure tells us that all nuclei with more than 83 protons are unstable.

b. <u>This is stable</u>. There are 26 protons (look at the periodic chart) in an Fe. Thus, there are 30 neutrons in ^{56}Fe. If you find the spot on the graph where atomic number = 26 and neutron number equals 30, you are right in a group of dots.

c. <u>This is not stable</u>. The nucleus has an atomic number of 57, meaning that it has 43 neutrons. If you find that spot on the figure, you are far to the right of the band of dots.

d. <u>This is stable</u>. A nucleus with 6 protons and 6 neutrons is right on the line that indicates the number of protons equals number of neutrons, which for small nuclei is right in the band of dots.

16.4 A ^{87}Rb nucleus has 37 protons and 50 neutrons. In beta decay, a neutron turns into a proton. Thus, the daughter product will have 38 protons and 49 neutrons. This is ^{87}Sr. Thus, the reaction is:

$$^{87}_{37}\text{Rb} \rightarrow \ ^{87}_{38}\text{Sr} + \ ^{\ 0}_{-1}\text{e}$$

16.5 A ^{220}Rn nucleus has 86 protons and 134 neutrons. This nucleus is the result of the nucleus in question *losing* 2 protons and 2 neutrons. Thus, the original nucleus must have 88 protons and 136 neutrons, which is $\underline{^{224}\text{Ra}}$.

16.6 The only radioactive decay that does not change the type of nucleus is <u>gamma decay</u>.

16.7 This one is not so easy, because the elapsed time is not an integral multiple of the half-life. Thus, we need to use Equation (16.5). To use that equation, however, we need to know k. This comes from Equation (16.6):

$$8 \text{ days} = \frac{0.693}{k}$$

$$k = \frac{0.693}{8 \text{ days}} = 0.09 \, \frac{1}{\text{days}}$$

Now we can use Equation (16.6):

$$N = N_o \cdot e^{-kt}$$

$$N = (10.0 \text{ grams}) \cdot e^{-(0.09 \frac{1}{\text{days}}) \cdot (10 \text{ days})} = \underline{4 \text{ g}}$$

16.8 They will be protected from <u>alpha and beta particles</u>, but there is not enough matter to shield against gamma particles.

16.9 To get the sum of the subscripts to equal each other on each side of the equation, the missing product must have 15 protons. To get the sum of the superscripts equal to each other on both sides of the equation, it must have a mass number of 30 as well. Thus, the missing nucleus is ^{30}P.

16.10 This is two smaller nuclei forming a larger one. Thus, it is <u>fusion</u>.

Module 16: Nuclear Physics   611

REVIEW QUESTIONS FOR MODULE #16

1. What is binding energy? What is it used for?

2. What is the most stable nucleus in Creation?

3. What causes the strong nuclear force? Why does it act only over a short distance?

4. Using Figure 16.2, note which of the following nuclei are stable:

$$^{14}\text{N}, \ ^{88}\text{Ru}, \ ^{118}\text{Sn}, \ ^{50}\text{Ca}$$

5. What is an alpha particle? What about a gamma ray? What about a beta particle? Which can pass through the most matter? Which can pass through the least?

6. What are the two forms of artificial radioactivity?

7. What happens when a positron collides with an electron? What is the process called?

8. If ionizing radiation is dangerous, why do you get X-rays, and why do we use smoke detectors in our homes?

9. What is the difference between nuclear fission and nuclear fusion? Which nuclei tend to undergo fission? Which tend to undergo fusion?

10. Why don't we use fusion as a way of producing electricity?

PRACTICE PROBLEMS FOR MODULE #16

(The mass of a proton is 1.0073 amu, and the mass of a neutron is 1.0087 amu. The speed of light is 3.00×10^8 m/sec, and 1 amu = 1.6605×10^{-27} kg.)

1. The mass of a ^{19}F nucleus is 18.9984 amu. What is the binding energy per nucleon of the nucleus?

2. The binding energy of ^{59}Co is 8.326×10^{-11} J. What is its mass in amu?

3. The nucleus ^{131}I is radioactive and decays by beta emission. This is the nucleus most commonly used in the thyroid "cocktail" which is used to treat thyroid disease. Write a nuclear equation for the beta decay of this isotope.

4. The radioactive isotope ^{222}Rn decays into ^{218}Po. What kind of radioactive decay is this?

5. A ^{14}N nucleus is stable but has too much energy. What can it do to release the energy?

6. ^{218}At decays by alpha emission with a half-life of 2 seconds. If you have a 1.00×10^3 g sample of ^{218}At, how many grams will be left in half of a minute?

7. ^{206}Tl decays by beta emission with a half-life of 4.20 minutes. If a sample of this isotope has 1.2×10^{23} nuclei, how many nuclei will be left in 10.0 minutes?

8. A nuclear chemist studies an unknown radioactive isotope. The sample of isotope has a mass of 14.0 grams when the nuclear chemist begins the study. In 22.2 minutes, the mass is 13.6 grams. What is the half-life of the radioactive isotope?

9. Some nuclear power plants and most nuclear bombs use ^{239}Pu as their fuel. Write an equation for the neutron-induced fission of ^{239}Pu. Assume that 4 neutrons are produced and that the rest of the nucleus splits exactly in half.

10. ^{27}Al and ^{3}H fuse to make ^{27}Mg and one other product. What is that other product?

Glossary

The numbers in parentheses refer to the page number on which the definition is presented in the text. If there is no page number, then the definition should have been presented in your first-year physics course.

Acceleration - The time rate of change of an object's velocity

Accuracy - An indication of how close a measurement is to the true value.

Adiabatic process - A process in which no heat is transferred between the system and the surroundings (374)

Alternating current - Electrical current that changes direction back and forth in a circuit

Amplitude - The maximum distance away from equilibrium that an object in periodic motion will travel.

Angular velocity - The rate at which the position angle of an object changes in rotational motion.

Average velocity - The velocity of an object over an extended period of time

Binding energy - The energy formed from the mass deficit of a nucleus (582)

Capacitance - A measure of capacity for holding charge (452)

Capacitor - A device that stores charge

Centripetal Acceleration - The acceleration caused by centripetal force.

Centripetal Force - The force necessary to make an object move in a circle.

Charging by conduction - Charging an object by allowing it to come into contact with an object which already has an electrical charge

Charging by induction - Charging an object by forcing some of the charges to leave the object

Chemical energy - Energy associated with the chemical bonds of a molecule

Circuit breaker - A special switch made of a material that bends as it is heated. If too much electricity flows through a circuit, the material that makes up the switch bends. When the metal bends to a pre-determined point, it touches a lever flipping the switch open, so current can no longer flow. When this happens, we say that the circuit breaker has been "tripped."

Conductor - A substance through which charge flows easily

Conservation of angular momentum - In the absence of external torques, the angular momentum of a system cannot change. (195)

Conservation of momentum - In the absence of external forces, the momentum of a system cannot change.

Conservative force - A force in which the total work done is independent of the path taken (441)

Conventional current - Current that flows from the positive side of the battery to the negative side. This is the way current is drawn in circuit diagrams, even though it is wrong.

Converging lens - A lens that focuses light rays towards its focal point

Critical mass - The amount of fissioning nucleus necessary for the chain reaction to be self-sustaining (603)

Cycle time - The number of time per second that the current and voltage repeat themselves in an AC circuit. In the United States this is 60 times each second.

Density - An object's mass divided by the volume that the object occupies

Derived units - Units (like cm^3) derived from the basic units that make up the metric system

Diamagnetic substance - A substance that is made up of atoms with no net magnetic field

Dielectric - An insulating material (416)

Diffraction - The spreading of waves around an obstacle (264)

Direct current - Current that always flow in the same direction around a circuit

Dispersion - The variation in wave speed due to wavelength (268)

Displacement - The position of an object relative to a fixed point

Dynamic equilibrium - When an object moves with a constant velocity, it is said to be in dynamic equilibrium

Dynamic rotational equilibrium - The state in which an object has rotational motion with a constant rate

Eccentricity - The distance between the center of an ellipse and either focus divided by the length of the semimajor axis. (290)

Effective resistor - The single resistor that could replace many resistors in a circuit

Effective capacitor - The single capacitor that could replace many capacitors in a circuit

Einstein's General Theory of Relativity - The laws physics are the same in *all* reference frames, *regardless* of whether or not the reference frame is inertial. (314)

Einstein's Special Theory of Relativity - The laws of physics work the same in all inertial reference frames. (303)

Electric dipole - Two opposite electric charges separated by a certain distance in space (409)

Electric field lines - The arrows in a diagram describing the force exerted by a charged particle on other charged particles

Electrical current - The amount of charge that travels through an electrical circuit each second

Electrical energy - Energy associated with the motion (or potential motion) of charged particles

Electrodynamics - The study of charges in motion

Electrostatic force - The force that exists between two charges which are at rest

Electrostatics - The study of electrical charges at rest

Energy - The ability to do work (125)

Entropy - A measure of the disorder that exists in any system (364)

Equilibrium position - The position of an object when there are no net forces acting on it

Escape velocity - The minimum speed necessary for an object to escape the gravitational field of another object (299)

Faraday's Law of Electromagnetic Induction - The emf induced in a circuit is equal to the time rate of change of the magnetic flux through that circuit. (532)

Ferromagnetic substance - A substance whose magnetic atoms are aligned so that their magnetic fields add up

First Law of Thermodynamics - Energy cannot be created or destroyed. It can only change forms. (364)

Free fall - The motion of an object when it is falling without obstruction under the influence of gravity

Frequency (f) - The number of times per second an object in periodic motion returns to its point of origin

Friction - A force resulting from the contact of two surfaces. This force opposes motion.

Fuse - A thin conductor that is very sensitive to heat. The conductor is typically encased in glass and put at one end of the battery in a circuit If too much current runs through the fuse, the conductor will melt. Once this happens, the fuse acts like an open switch, because current can no longer pass through it, and the entire circuit ceases to function.

General Theory of Relativity - The laws of physics are the same in *all* reference frames, *regardless* of whether or not the reference frame is inertial. (314)

Graduated cylinder - This device looks a lot like a glass rain gauge. It is a hollow glass cylinder with markings on it. These markings, called graduations, measure the volume of liquid that is poured into the cylinder.

Gravity - The attractive force that exists between all objects which have mass

Harmonic wave - A wave that has a sinusoidal shape (230)

Heat - Energy that is transferred as a consequence of temperature differences (329)

Hooke's Law - The relationship between the force applied by a spring (**F**) and the distance that it stretches (**x**)

Impulse - The quantity $\mathbf{F} \cdot \Delta t$

Impulsive forces - Forces in contact with an object over a short time interval

Index of refraction - The ratio of the speed of light in a vacuum to its speed in another medium

Inertial mass - A measure of an object's resistance to a change in its state of motion (88)

Inertial reference frame - A frame of reference in which an object that is subject to no force travels at constant velocity (86)

Infrasonic waves - Waves with frequencies below 20 Hz

Instantaneous velocity - The velocity of an object at one moment in time

Insulator - A substance through which charge cannot flow

Intensity of a sound wave - The rate at which sound energy flows through a given area (251)

Isobaric process - A process which occurs at constant pressure (373)

Isochoric process - A process which occurs at constant volume (374)

Isothermal process - A process which occurs at constant temperature (373)

Kepler's First Law - The planets move in an elliptical orbit, with the sun at one focus. (290)

Kepler's Second Law - As a planet orbits the sun, a line drawn from the sun to the planet sweeps out the same area in a given time interval. (290)

Kepler's Third Law - The ratio of the period of the planet's orbit squared to the length of the semimajor axis cubed is the same for all planets. (291)

Kinematics – A study of an object's motion which determines its displacement, velocity, and acceleration

Kinetic energy - Energy in motion (125)

Kinetic friction - The force of friction that opposes motion once the motion has already started

Kirchhoff's First Rule (The Loop Rule) - The change in potential around a closed loop is always equal to zero. (484)

Kirchhoff's Second Rule (The Junction Rule) - The sum of the currents entering a junction must equal the sum of currents leaving a junction. (484)

Law of Charge Conservation - The total amount of electrical charge in the universe is constant

Law of Electromagnetic Induction - The emf induced in a circuit is equal to the time rate of change of the magnetic flux through that circuit. (532)

Law of Reflection - The angle of reflection equals the angle of incidence (267)

Lens's Law - The current produced by a change in magnetic flux will flow in the direction that will cause *its* magnetic field to oppose the change in flux. (533)

Lever arm - The length of an imaginary line drawn from the axis of rotation to the point at which the force is being applied

Longitudinal wave - A wave whose propagation is parallel to its oscillation (224)

Magnetic dipole - Two opposite magnetic poles separated by a certain distance in space. We assume that all magnets are dipoles.

Magnetic flux - The perpendicular component of a magnetic field through a given area (530)

Magnetic monopole - A theoretical magnetic pole isolated by itself

Magnetic poles - The two sides to a magnet, referred to as north and south poles

Mechanical energy - Energy associated with the movement (or potential movement) of objects

Moment of inertia - A measure of an object's resistance to a change in its state of rotational motion (182)

Motional emf - A potential difference established by the motion of a conductor in a magnetic field (527)

Newton's First Law (The Law of Inertia) - An object in motion (or at rest) will tend to stay in motion (or at rest) until it is acted upon by an outside force (84)

Newton's Second Law - When an object is acted on by one or more outside forces, the sum of those forces is equal to the mass of the object times the resulting acceleration.(84)

Newton's Third Law - For every action, there is an equal and opposite reaction (84)

Nonconservative force - A force in which the work done is dependent of the path taken (441)

Non-Ohmic substances - Materials that conduct electricity but do not follow Ohm's Law

Normal force - The force that a surface uses to counteract the force of gravity. It is always directed perpendicular to the surface that is applying the force

Nuclear fission - The process by which a large nucleus is split into two smaller nuclei (602)

Nuclear fusion - The process by which two or more small nuclei fuse to make a bigger nucleus (601)

Nucleon - A term used to refer to both protons and neutrons (581)

Ohm's Law - The relationship between the current in a conductor and that conductor's resistance

Opaque object - An object through which light cannot travel

Open circuit - A circuit that does not have a complete connection between the two sides of the battery. As a result, current does not flow.

Optics - The study of how light travels from one place to another and what happens when that light encounters obstacles

Parabolic motion - Motion that occurs on a curved path which can be described by a parabola

Parallel-plate capacitor - Two conductive plates that are parallel to one another, but separated by a small distance

Paramagnetic substance - A substance whose magnetic atoms are arranged so that their individual magnetic fields cancel out. Under the influence of an external magnetic field, however, these substances are weakly magnetic.

Particle/wave duality of light - The concept that light sometimes act like a wave and sometimes acts like a particle

Period (T) - The time it takes for an object in periodic motion to travel repeat its motion

Periodic motion - Motion that repeats itself regularly

Potential energy - Energy that is stored, ready to do work (125)

Power - The amount of energy expended per second

Precision - An indication of how good the measuring device was

Real Image - An image formed as the result of intersecting light beams

Recoil velocity - The velocity that an object develops in response to launching another object, which is a result of the Law of Momentum Conservation

Refraction - The process by which a light ray bends when it encounters a new medium (267)

Resistance - A measure of how much a conductor impedes the flow of electrons

Resistivity - A measure of a conductor's inherent resistance to the flow of electricity (470)

Resonance - Using an external wave or other force to set up standing waves in a medium (256)

Restoring force - A force applied in opposition to a displacement

Right hand rule - To determine the direction of the cross product **A** x **B**, take your right hand and point your fingers in the direction of **A**. Then, curl your fingers towards **B**, along the arc of the angle between the vectors. Your thumb will then point in the direction of the cross product. This is also used to determine the direction of magnetic field lines in a current-carrying wire. (21, 523)

Rotational equilibrium - The state in which the sum of the torques acting on an object is zero

Rotational motion - Motion around a central axis such that an object could repeatedly pass the same point in space relative to that axis

Scalar quantity - A physical measurement that does not contain directional information

Second Law of Thermodynamics - The entropy of the universe must always either increase or remain the same. It can never decrease. (365)

Semiconductor - A substance whose conductivity changes remarkably based on certain conditions (420)

Significant figure - A digit within a number is considered to be a significant figure if:
> i. It is non-zero   OR
> ii. It is a zero that is between two significant figures OR
> iii. It is a zero at the end of the number and to the right of the decimal point

Simple harmonic motion - Periodic motion whose period is independent of its amplitude

Sonic waves - Waves with frequencies between 20 Hz and 20,000 Hz. In general, human ears are sensitive to these waves

Special Theory of Relativity - The laws of physics work the same in all inertial reference frames. (303)

Specific heat capacity - The amount of heat necessary to raise the temperature of 1.0 gram of a substance by 1.0 $^\circ$C (332)

Speed - The time rate of change of the total distance traveled by an object

Static equilibrium - When an object is at rest, it is said to be in static equilibrium

Static friction - The force of friction that opposes the initiation of motion

Static rotational equilibrium - The state in which an object has no rotational motion

Superconductor - A substance that conducts electricity with virtually no energy loss (421)

Temperature - A measure of the concentration of thermal energy in a system (329)

Tension - The force from a tight string, rope, or chain. This force is directed away from the object to which that the string is anchored.

Terminal velocity - The maximum velocity an object achieves when falling

The First Law of Thermodynamics - Energy cannot be created or destroyed. It can only change forms. (364)

The Law of Angular Momentum Conservation - If the sum of the torques on a system is equal to zero, then angular momentum never changes.

The Law of Momentum Conservation - When the sum of the forces working on a system is zero, the total momentum in the system cannot change.

The Law of Reflection - The angle of reflection equals the angle of incidence.

The Second Law of Thermodynamics - The entropy of the universe must always either increase or remain the same. It can never decrease. (365)

The Third Law of Thermodynamics - It is impossible to reach a temperature of 0 K in a finite number of cooling steps (392)

The Zeroth Law of Thermodynamics - If object A is in thermal equilibrium with object C, and if object B is in thermal equilibrium with object C, objects A and B are in thermal equilibrium with each other. (363)

Thermal energy - The kinetic energy in the random motion of molecules or atoms in a system (329)

Third Law of Thermodynamics - It is impossible to reach a temperature of 0 K in a finite number of cooling steps (392)

Torque - The impetus that causes rotational acceleration. The magnitude of the torque is equal to the length of the lever arm times component of the force that is applied perpendicular to it.

Translational equilibrium - An object is said to be in translational equilibrium when the sum of the forces acting on it is equal to zero.

Translational motion - Motion from one point to another which does not involve repeatedly passing the same point in space

Transparent object - An object which allows light to pass through it

Transverse wave - A wave whose propagation is perpendicular to its oscillation (224)

Two-dimensional motion - Motion that occurs in a plane

Ultrasonic waves - Waves with frequencies higher than 20,000Hz

Vector Quantity - A physical measurement that contains directional information

Velocity - The time rate of change of an object's position

Virtual Image - An image formed as the result of extrapolating light beams

Work - The product of displacement and the component of the applied force perpendicular to that displacement

Work-energy Theorem - The work done on an object is equal to the change in its kinetic energy (130)

Zeroth Law of Thermodynamics - If object A is in thermal equilibrium with object C, and if object B is in thermal equilibrium with object C, objects A and B are in thermal equilibrium with each other. (363)

APPENDIX

Physical Constants

Acceleration due to gravity: $g = 9.81 \frac{m}{sec^2}, 32.2 \frac{ft}{sec^2}$

Atomic mass unit $u = 1.66 \times 10^{-27} \ kg$

Avogadro's number $N_A = 6.02 \times 10^{23}$

Boltzmann's constant $k = 1.38 \times 10^{-23} \frac{J}{K}$

Charge of an electron: $e = 1.602 \times 10^{-19} \ Coulombs$

Charge of a proton: $e = 1.602 \times 10^{-19} \ Coulombs$

Coulomb Constant: $k = 8.99 \times 10^9 \frac{Newtons \cdot m^2}{C^2}$

Electron Volt: $1 \ eV = 1.602 \times 10^{-19} \ J$

Gas Constant: $R = 0.0821 \frac{liter \cdot atm}{mole \cdot K}, 8.31 \frac{J}{mole \cdot K}$

Gravitational Constant: $G = 6.67 \times 10^{-11} \frac{Newton \cdot m^2}{kg^2}$

Mass of earth: $m = 5.98 \times 10^{24} \ kg$

Mass of an electron: $m_e = 9.11 \times 10^{-31} \ kg$

Mass of a proton: $m_p = 1.67 \times 10^{-27} \ kg$

Mass of the moon: $m_m = 7.36 \times 10^{22} \ kg$

Mass of a neutron: $m_n = 1.67 \times 10^{-27} \ kg$

Mass of the sun: $m_s = 1.99 \times 10^{30} \ kg$

Permeability of Free Space: $\mu_o = 4\pi \times 10^{-7} \dfrac{\text{Newton}}{A^2}$

Permittivity of Free Space: $\varepsilon_o = 8.85 \times 10^{-12} \dfrac{C^2}{\text{Newton} \cdot m^2}$

Plank's Constant: $h = 6.63 \times 10^{-34} \text{ J} \cdot \text{s}$

Radius of earth $r_e = 6.37 \times 10^6 \text{ m}$

Rydberg Constant $R_H = 2.18 \times 10^{-18} \text{ J, } 13.6 \text{ eV}$

Speed of light: $c = 2.998 \times 10^8 \text{ m/sec}$

Conversion Relationships

Common Prefixes Used in the Metric System

PREFIX	NUMERICAL MEANING
micro (μ)	0.000001
milli (m)	**0.001**
centi (c)	**0.01**
deci (d)	0.1
deca (D)	10
hecta (H)	100
kilo (k)	**1,000**
Mega (M)	1,000,000

Relationships Between English and Metric Units.

Measurement	English/Metric Relationship
Distance	1 inch = 2.54 cm
Mass	1 slug = 14.59 kg
Volume	1 gallon = 3.78 L

Units

Physical Quantities and Their Base Units

Physical Quantity	Base Metric Unit	Base English Unit
Mass	gram (g)	slug (sl)
Distance	meter (m)	foot (ft)
Volume	liter (L)	gallon (gal)
Time	second (sec)	second (sec)

Derived Units

$$\text{Newton} = \frac{\text{kg} \cdot \text{m}}{\text{sec}^2} \qquad\qquad \text{Joule} = \frac{\text{kg} \cdot \text{m}^2}{\text{sec}^2}$$

$$\text{Watt} = \frac{\text{J}}{\text{sec}} = \text{Amp} \cdot \text{Volt} = \text{Amp}^2 \cdot \Omega \qquad \text{Farad} = \frac{\text{C}}{\text{V}}$$

$$\text{Volt} = \frac{\text{J}}{\text{C}} \qquad\qquad\qquad \text{Amp} = \frac{\text{C}}{\text{sec}}$$

Converting reference angle to vector angle

+ 180	do nothing
+180	+360

Formulas

(Presented in the order that they appear in the course)

<u>Vector Relationships:</u>   For any two-dimensional vector $\mathbf{A}$, $\mathbf{A} = A_x \cdot \mathbf{i} + A_y \cdot \mathbf{j}$

$$\sin\theta = \frac{A_y}{A}$$

$$\cos\theta = \frac{A_x}{A}$$

$$A = \sqrt{A_x + A_y}$$

$$\tan\theta = \frac{A_y}{A_x}$$

<u>Dot Product:</u> $\mathbf{A} \bullet \mathbf{B} = A_x \cdot B_x + A_y \cdot B_y$

$\mathbf{A} \bullet \mathbf{B} = A \cdot B \cdot \cos\theta$

<u>Cross Product:</u> $\mathbf{A} \times \mathbf{B} = (A_y \cdot B_z - A_z \cdot B_y) \cdot \mathbf{i} + (A_z \cdot B_x - A_x \cdot B_z) \cdot \mathbf{j} + (A_x \cdot B_y - A_y \cdot B_x) \cdot \mathbf{k}$

$|\mathbf{A} \times \mathbf{B}| = A \cdot B \cdot \sin\theta$

<u>Torque:</u> $\tau = \mathbf{r} \times \mathbf{F}$

<u>Work:</u> $W = \mathbf{F} \bullet \mathbf{x}$

<u>One-Dimensional Motion:</u> $\mathbf{v} = \dfrac{\Delta \mathbf{x}}{\Delta t}$

$$\mathbf{a} = \frac{\Delta \mathbf{v}}{\Delta t}$$

$$\mathbf{v} = \mathbf{v}_0 + \mathbf{a}t$$

$$\mathbf{v}^2 = \mathbf{v}_o^2 + 2\mathbf{a}x$$

$$\mathbf{x} = \mathbf{v}_o t + \frac{1}{2}\mathbf{a}t^2$$

Air Resistance: $\quad F_{drag} = \dfrac{1}{2}C\rho Av^2$

Terminal Velocity: $\quad v_{terminal} = \sqrt{\dfrac{2mg}{C\rho A}}$

Range Equation: $\quad \text{Range} = \dfrac{v_o^{\ 2} \cdot \sin 2\theta}{g}$

Newton's Second Law : $\quad \mathbf{F} = m \cdot \mathbf{a}$

Weight: $\quad W = m \cdot g$

Friction: $\quad f = \mu \cdot F_n$

Objects on an Inclined Surface

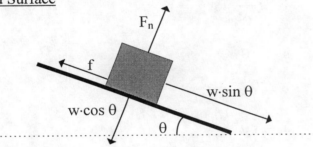

Kinetic Energy: $\quad KE = \dfrac{1}{2} \cdot m \cdot v^2$

Grav. Potential Energy: $\quad PE = m \cdot g \cdot h \quad$ (near the surface of the earth)

$$U_{grav} = -\dfrac{G \cdot m_1 \cdot m_2}{r} \quad \text{(in general)}$$

Electrical Potential Energy: $\quad PE = q \cdot V$

Electrical Potential: $\quad V = \dfrac{k \cdot Q}{r}$

Hooke's Law: $\quad F = -k \cdot \mathbf{x}$

Potential Energy of a Spring: $U_{spring} = \frac{1}{2} \cdot k \cdot x^2$

Power: $P = \dfrac{W}{t}$

Momentum: $\mathbf{p} = m \cdot \mathbf{v}$

Impulse: $\mathbf{J} = \mathbf{F} \cdot \Delta t = \Delta \mathbf{p}$

Center of Mass: $\mathbf{x}_{cm} = \dfrac{m_1 \cdot \mathbf{x}_1 + m_2 \cdot \mathbf{x}_2 + m_3 \cdot \mathbf{x}_3 \ldots m_n \cdot \mathbf{x}_n}{m_1 + m_2 + m_3 \ldots m_n}$

Angular Velocity: $\omega = \dfrac{\Delta \theta}{\Delta t}$

Angular Acceleration: $\alpha = \dfrac{\Delta \omega}{\Delta t}$

Angular Kinematics: $s = r \cdot \theta$

$v = r \cdot \omega$

$a = r \cdot \alpha$

"Rotational Second Law": $\tau_{net} = I \cdot \alpha$

Rotational Kinetic Energy: $KE_{rot} = \frac{1}{2} \cdot I \cdot \omega^2$

Angular Momentum: $\mathbf{L} = \mathbf{r} \times \mathbf{p} = I \cdot \omega$

Period (Mass/Spring): $T = 2 \cdot \pi \sqrt{\dfrac{m}{k}}$

Frequency: $f = \dfrac{1}{T} = \dfrac{v}{\lambda}$

Mass/Spring Kinematics: $\mathbf{x} = A \cdot \cos(\omega \cdot t + \delta)$

$\mathbf{v} = -\omega A \cdot \sin(\omega t + \delta)$

$\mathbf{a} = -\omega^2 A \cdot \cos(\omega t + \delta)$

Total Energy (Mass/Spring): $KE_{spring} + PE_{spring} = \dfrac{1}{2} \cdot k \cdot A^2$

Period (Simple Pendulum): $T = 2 \cdot \pi \cdot \sqrt{\dfrac{\ell}{g}}$

Period (Physical Pendulum): $T = 2\pi \cdot \sqrt{\dfrac{I}{m \cdot g \cdot d}}$

Wave Speed (string): $v = \sqrt{\dfrac{T}{\mu}}$

Harmonic Wave: $y = A \cdot \sin\left[\dfrac{2\pi}{\lambda} \cdot (vt \pm x)\right]$

Standing Waves on a String: $\lambda = \dfrac{2L}{n}$ where $n = 1, 2, 3 \ldots$

Speed of Sound in Air: $v = (331.5 + 0.606 \cdot T) \, \dfrac{m}{sec}$

Bel Scale: $B = 10 \cdot \log\left(\dfrac{I}{I_o}\right)$

Law of Gravitation: $F_g = \dfrac{G \cdot m_1 \cdot m_2}{r^2}$

Time Dilation: $t' = t \cdot \sqrt{1 - \left(\dfrac{v}{c}\right)^2}$

Mass/Energy Equivalence: $E = mc^2$

Celsius/Fahrenheit Scales: $^\circ C = \dfrac{5}{9}(^\circ F - 32.00)$

<u>Kelvin Scale</u>:	$K = {}^{o}C + 273.15$
<u>Heat</u>:	$q = m \cdot c \cdot \Delta T$
<u>Phase Changes</u>:	$q = m \cdot L$
<u>Length Increase from Heat</u>:	$\Delta L = \alpha \cdot L_o \cdot \Delta T$
<u>Volume Increase from Heat</u>:	$\Delta V = \beta \cdot V_o \cdot \Delta T$
<u>Pressure</u>:	$P = \dfrac{F}{A}$
<u>Ideal Gas Law</u>:	$PV = nRT$
<u>Kinetic Energy in Gases</u>:	$\overline{KE} = \dfrac{3}{2} \cdot kT$
<u>Molecular Speed in Gases</u>:	$\overline{v^2} = \dfrac{3kT}{m}$
<u>Heat in Gases</u>:	$q = n \cdot C_p \cdot \Delta T$
	$q = n \cdot C_v \cdot \Delta T$
	$C_p = C_v + R$
<u>Thermodynamics</u>:	$\Delta U = q - W$
	$W = P \cdot \Delta V$
	$\Delta S_{universe} \geq 0$
	$\Delta S_{rev} = \dfrac{q}{T}$
	$e_{Carnot} = 1 - \dfrac{T_c}{T_h}$
<u>Coulomb's Law</u>:	$F = \dfrac{k \cdot q_1 \cdot q_2}{r^2}$

Electric Field: $E = \dfrac{k \cdot Q}{r^2}$

Capacitance: $C = \dfrac{\varepsilon_o \cdot A}{d}$

Charge in a Capacitor: $\Delta V = \dfrac{Q}{C}$

Energy in a Capacitor: $U_{cap} = \dfrac{1}{2} \cdot \dfrac{Q^2}{C} = \dfrac{1}{2} \cdot C \cdot (\Delta V)^2 = \dfrac{1}{2} \cdot Q \cdot \Delta V$

Resistance: $R = \rho \cdot \dfrac{L}{A}$

Electrical Current: $I = \dfrac{\Delta Q}{\Delta t}$

Ohm's Law: $V = I \cdot R$

Electrical Power: $P = I \cdot V = I^2 \cdot R$

Snell's Law: $n_1 \cdot \sin\theta_1 = n_2 \cdot \sin\theta_2$

Series Resistors: $R_{effective} = R_1 + R_2 + R_3 + ...$

Parallel Resistors: $\dfrac{1}{R_{effective}} = \dfrac{1}{R_1} + \dfrac{1}{R_2} + \dfrac{1}{R_3} + ...$

Series Capacitors: $\dfrac{1}{C_{effective}} = \dfrac{1}{C_1} + \dfrac{1}{C_2} + \dfrac{1}{C_3} + ...$

Parallel Capacitors: $C_{effective} = C_1 + C_2 + C_3 + ...$

Magnetic Force: $\mathbf{F} = q \cdot (\mathbf{v} \times \mathbf{B})$

$\mathbf{F} = I \cdot (\ell \times \mathbf{B})$

Magnetic Field of a Wire: $B = \dfrac{\mu_0 \cdot I}{2\pi \cdot r}$

Motional Emf: $\Delta V = v \cdot B \cdot \ell$

Magnetic Flux: $\Phi = \mathbf{B \bullet A}$

Faraday's Law: $\dfrac{\Delta \Phi}{\Delta t} = \Delta V$

Photoelectric Effect: $E = h \cdot f$

de Broglie Wavelength: $\lambda = \dfrac{h}{p}$

Bohr Model: $E = -R_h \cdot Z^2 \cdot \left(\dfrac{1}{n}\right)^2$

$$\Delta E = (R_h) \cdot Z^2 \cdot \left[\left(\dfrac{1}{n_{final}}\right)^2 - \left(\dfrac{1}{n_{initial}}\right)^2\right]$$

$$r = (0.529 \text{ Å}) \cdot \dfrac{n^2}{Z}$$

Radioactive Decay: $N = N_o \cdot e^{-kt}$

$$t_{1/2} = \dfrac{0.693}{k}$$

The Periodic Table of Elements

1A	2A	3B	4B	5B	6B	7B	8B	8B	8B	1B	2B	3A	4A	5A	6A	7A	8A
1 **H** 1.01																	2 **He** 4.0
3 **Li** 6.94	4 **Be** 9.01											5 **B** 10.8	6 **C** 12.0	7 **N** 14.0	8 **O** 16.0	9 **F** 19.0	10 **Ne** 20.2
11 **Na** 23.0	12 **Mg** 24.3											13 **Al** 27.0	14 **Si** 28.1	15 **P** 31.0	16 **S** 32.1	17 **Cl** 35.5	18 **Ar** 39.9
19 **K** 39.1	20 **Ca** 40.1	21 **Sc** 45.0	22 **Ti** 47.9	23 **V** 50.9	24 **Cr** 52.0	25 **Mn** 54.9	26 **Fe** 55.8	27 **Co** 58.9	28 **Ni** 58.7	29 **Cu** 63.5	30 **Zn** 65.4	31 **Ga** 69.7	32 **Ge** 72.6	33 **As** 74.9	34 **Se** 79.0	35 **Br** 79.9	36 **Kr** 83.8
37 **Rb** 85.5	38 **Sr** 87.6	39 **Y** 88.9	40 **Zr** 91.2	41 **Nb** 92.9	42 **Mo** 95.9	43 **Tc** (98)	44 **Ru** 101.1	45 **Rh** 102.9	46 **Pd** 106.4	47 **Ag** 107.9	48 **Cd** 112.4	49 **In** 114.8	50 **Sn** 118.7	51 **Sb** 121.8	52 **Te** 127.6	53 **I** 126.9	54 **Xe** 131.3
55 **Cs** 132.9	56 **Ba** 137.3	57 **La** 138.9	72 **Hf** 178.5	73 **Ta** 180.9	74 **W** 183.9	75 **Re** 186.2	76 **Os** 190.2	77 **Ir** 192.2	78 **Pt** 195.1	79 **Au** 197.0	80 **Hg** 200.6	81 **Tl** 204.4	82 **Pb** 207.2	83 **Bi** 209.0	84 **Po** (209)	85 **At** (210)	86 **Rn** (222)
87 **Fr** (223)	88 **Ra** 226.0	89 **Ac** 227.0	104 **Unq** (261)	105 **Unp** (262)	106 **Unh** (263)	107 **Uns** (262)	108 **Uno** (265)	109 **Une** (266)									

Lanthanides

58 **Ce** 140.1	59 **Pr** 140.9	60 **Nd** 144.2	61 **Pm** (145)	62 **Sm** 150.4	63 **Eu** 152.0	64 **Gd** 157.3	65 **Tb** 158.9	66 **Dy** 162.5	67 **Ho** 164.9	68 **Er** 167.3	69 **Tm** 168.9	70 **Yb** 173.0	71 **Lu** 175.0

Actinides

90 **Th** 232.0	91 **Pa** 231.0	92 **U** 238.0	93 **Np** 237.0	94 **Pu** (244)	95 **Am** (243)	96 **Cm** (247)	97 **Bk** (247)	98 **Cf** (251)	99 **Es** (252)	100 **Fm** (257)	101 **Md** (258)	102 **No** (259)	103 **Lr** (260)

Index

E

E=mc^2, 312
eccentricity, 290
effective resistance, 481
Einstein, Albert, 550
Einstein's General Theory of Relativity, 314
Einstein's Special Theory of Relativity, 301, 303
elastic collision, 143
electric circuit power, 478
electric circuits, 476
electric circuits, AC, 498
electric circuits, DC, 498
electric circuits, parallel, 477
electric circuits, RC, 494
electric circuits, series, 477
electric current, 477
electric field, 408
electric field (of a capacitor), 455
electric field, quantitative, 410
electric potential, 444
electrical potential, 126
electrical potential energy, 126, 439
electricity, 401
electromagnet, 515
electromagnetic force, 265, 401, 513
electromagnetic induction, 532
electromagnetic spectrum, 266
electromagnetic waves, 211, 265
electromotive force, 492
electron capture, 592
electron drift speed, 470
electron volt, 551
electrostatics, 402
ellipse, 290
emf, 492
emf, motional, 527
emission spectra, 555
emission spectroscopy, 566
energy, 125
energy (of a capacitor), 456
Energy Conservation, 125
energy, binding, 312
energy/mass equivalence, 312
entropy, 364, 383
equation of a wave, 230
equations, kinematic, 49
equilibrium, 90
equilibrium, thermal, 333
equivalence, principle of, 314
escape velocity, 298, 299
ether, 265
eV, 551
event horizon, 300

evolution, 366
exhaust stroke (Otto cyle), 388
expansion of the universe, 261
exponents, units with, 2
extended bodies, gravity of, 293

F

Fahrenheit, 330
farad, 452
Faraday, Michael, 452
Faraday's Law, 532
ferromagnetic, 514
first harmonic, 226, 237
First Law of Thermodynamics, 125, 363, 367
fission, 602
flat mirrors, 270
flux, magnetic, 530
focal length, 271
focal point, 271
focus, virtual, 271
force, conservative, 441
force, dissipative, 441
force, electromagnetic, 513
force, nonconservative, 441
force, normal, 90
force, restoring, 135, 210
frame, reference, 85
free fall, 50
freezing point depression, 335
frequency of SHM, 210
frequency, angular, 214
frequency, fundamental, 226
frequency, resonant, 238
frequency, wave, 225
friction, 90
friction, coefficient of, 90
fundamental frequency, 226
fundamental harmonic, 237
fundamental unit of charge, 557
fusion, 604
fusion, latent heat of, 338

G

gamma decay, 590
gamma ray, 590
gas law, ideal, 344
gas, ideal, 343
general relativity laws of motion, 317
General Theory of Relativity, 314
geosynchronous orbit, 86, 293
glass, 332
God, 596
graphs, kinematics, 39